Investigating Physical Science

Christine Caputo

AMSCO

Amsco School Publications, Inc.
315 Hudson Street, New York, N.Y. 10013

The publisher wishes to acknowledge the helpful contributions of the
following reviewers and consultants:

Frank Coco
Physics Teacher
Warren Easton Charter High School
New Orleans, Louisiana

Ann Neufeld
Science Teacher
McAuliffe Middle School
Los Alamitos, California

The publisher also wishes to acknowledge the contributions of Jules J. Weisler.

Cover Design: Meghan J. Shupe
Text Design: Howard Petlack
Composition: Northeastern Graphic, Inc.
Artwork: Hadel Studio

Please visit our Web site at: **www.amscopub.com**

When ordering this book, please specify
either **R** 301 **W** *or* INVESTIGATING PHYSICAL SCIENCE

ISBN: 978-1-56765-950-4

Copyright ©2012 by Amsco School Publications, Inc.

Also available on CD or as an E-book.

Printed in the United States of America
1 2 3 4 5 6 7 8 9 10   17 16 15 14 13 12 11

Contents

Part 3: Properties of Matter

Part 4: Concepts of Energy

Part 5: Physics of Motion and Mechanics

To the Teacher

The content of *Investigating Physical Science* reflects the current knowledge and advances in the physical sciences. It is also aligned with the new Physical Science Core and Component Ideas of *A Framework for K–12 Science Education*. Where subject matter is taught as a physical science block, the book can be used in its entirety within a given grade. Where physical science units are alternated with life science and earth science units, a book can be used in segments for two or three grades.

▶ Outstanding Features of the Book

1. **Inquiry Investigations** Every chapter is introduced by an Inquiry Investigation that is closely integrated with one or more major ideas in the chapter. These investigations are well within the range of comprehension and manipulative ability of most students above the elementary grades and can be carried out at home or in classrooms. The laboratory investigations can readily be converted to classroom demonstrations. In addition to simple, clear instructions, each laboratory investigation includes questions that direct observation and evoke the independent formulation of conclusions. Where at all possible, we have made the labs, or sections of these labs, less guided and more student and inquiry oriented.

2. **Content** Every chapter begins with a set of focused reading questions that students should be able to answer after reading the chapter, and can also be used as a chapter review. The introduction of experimental material, including measurement, provides the laboratory base that is critical to the understanding of modern science. Both the English and metric systems of measurement are employed in the discussions and in the problems. Carefully selected practice problems guide the student through some difficult areas.

3. **Chapter Review** All **boldfaced** science terms are listed at the end of each chapter. Each Chapter Review section also contains a full set of questions of varying difficulty: matching, multiple-choice, modified true false, short answer and essay questions that require critical thinking skills, and "Take It Further" questions that require research on the Internet and include a career-oriented research project. The "Think Critically" questions stimulate the student to think, organize, and integrate the chapter topics.

4. **Investigating Issues in Science, Engineering, Technology, and Society features** These special, thought-provoking, end-of-chapter features explore current controversial issues in a nonjudgmental manner. "Think About It!" and "Extend It!" questions encourage students to evaluate the issues and make their own decisions.

▶ Suggestions for Using Investigating Physical Science

Investigating Physical Science is designed to be used in a variety of ways, one or more of which may suit the needs of individual teachers and students:

1. Overview
2. Pretesting
3. Remedial Teaching
4. Companion Book or Supplement
5. Adapting to Individual Needs

CHAPTER

1

Are You a Scientist?

Science goes far beyond laboratories and classrooms. It involves a way of approaching problems that you can use in everything you do.

After reading this chapter, you should be able to answer the following questions:

What is science?

How is science conducted?

How should you work in the laboratory?

How do scientists make measurements?

To a casual observer, an open bottle is of little interest. To a scientist, however, even an open bottle can yield interesting details if it is thoroughly explored.

Materials:
- ✔ two 4-ounce bottles
- ✔ fish tank or large pail
- ✔ water
- ✔ laboratory notebook

Part A Carefully examine the open bottle at your desk.

1. *What observations can you make about the bottle?*

2. *Form a hypothesis, or "educated guess," about what is in the bottle. Explain your reasoning.*

3. *Describe a procedure that will test your hypothesis.*

Part B After your teacher has approved your procedure, try it out in the laboratory.

4. *Describe your observations.*

5. *What do you conclude from your observations?*

Part C To test the conclusion you reached in Part B, try the following: Fill a large container, such as a fish tank or pail, about three-quarters full of water. Fill a bottle with water and hold the bottle under water. Turn it so that it rests mouth-down on the bottom of the tank. Call this Bottle A.

Lower an empty bottle, mouth-down, into the tank until it is completely under water. Call this Bottle B.

Raise Bottle A until it is directly over Bottle B. Slowly turn Bottle B over until its mouth is directly under the mouth of Bottle A. (See Figure 1-1.)

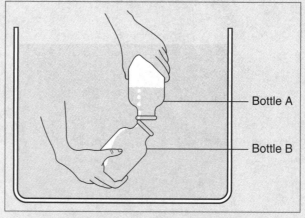

Figure 1-1. Note the arrangement of the bottles. Observe any changes that occur.

6. What do you observe?

7. What can you conclude about the contents of Bottle B?

8. Does your answer to question 7 support the hypothesis you formulated earlier? Explain.

9. What else might you do to verify your conclusion in question 7?

What Is Science?

When you think about science, what images come to mind? Do you imagine people in laboratories wearing white coats? Perhaps you picture glass flasks filled with colorful liquids. This might all be part of science, but there is much, much more. **Science** may be defined as a body of knowledge about the natural world. It is also the process through which that body of knowledge is obtained. Science, therefore, is a process of **scientific inquiry** through which scientists ask questions and seek answers to gain a better understanding of the natural world.

▶ What Are the Branches of Science?

Science generally is divided into four major branches:

Chemistry—the study of the composition, structure, and properties of matter
Physics—the study of the interactions of matter and energy
Biology—the study of living things
Earth science—the study of the earth and the universe

These branches are further divided into more specific sub-branches and, in many cases, branches overlap to form even more

sub-branches. For example, biochemistry, which is the chemistry of living things, combines biology and chemistry. Geophysics, which is the physics of Earth processes, combines earth science and physics. Table 1-1 on page 4 lists some branches and sub-branches of science.

▶ Who Conducts Science?

People who study science are known as **scientists**. You can look anywhere to find a scientist—perhaps even in the mirror. Scientists come from all over the globe and all cultures. The traits all scientists have in common are curiosity and imagination. Scientists must be curious about how things happen and must have the imagination to invent possible explanations and design ways to evaluate those explanations.

A scientist will not be satisfied with an explanation until all the available evidence has been examined. Even then, scientists cannot be certain that they are right. As new information becomes available, scientists review their explanations to decide if they still make sense. If not, the explanation needs to be modified or even replaced.

Scientific discoveries are seldom due to the work of a single individual. Rather, most scientific advances grow out of numerous

TABLE 1-1.
What Are Some Branches and Sub-Branches of Science?

Branch	Sub-branch	Description
Biology	Genetics	Study of heredity
	Botany	Study of plants
	Zoology	Study of animals
	Microbiology	Study of microscopic life-forms
	Biotechnology	Study of living things in engineering
Chemistry	Organic chemistry	Study of carbon compounds
	Polymer chemistry	Study of very large molecules such as those that make up plastics
	Nuclear chemistry	Study of the atom's nucleus
	Biochemistry	Study of the chemistry of living things
Physics	Astrophysics	Study of stars and other objects in space
	Mechanics	Study of forces
	Optics	Study of light
	Acoustics	Study of sound
Earth Science	Seismology	Study of earthquakes
	Meteorology	Study of weather
	Oceanography	Study of the oceans
	Petrology	Study of rocks

discoveries made by scientists often over long periods of time. Sir Isaac Newton, a great English scientist, once said that he was able to achieve what he did only because he was standing on the shoulders of giants. It was only through the work of the great scientists who preceded him that his own discoveries were made possible.

How Is Science Conducted?

Scientists, like most people, try to use a commonsense approach in solving problems. This approach is logical and systematic and is sometimes called the **scientific method**.

 What Is the Scientific Method?

The following steps have been found useful in working out the solution to problems (see Figure 1-2):

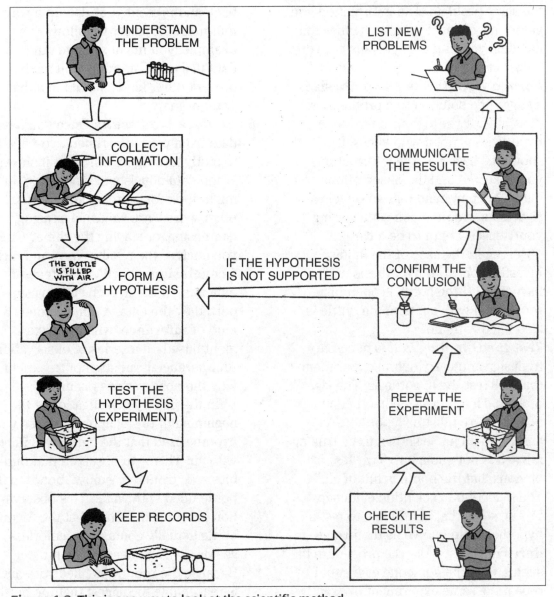

Figure 1-2. This is one way to look at the scientific method.

1. ***Understand the Problem*** After making observations, you realize that there is something you do not know or understand. As a result, you wonder why something happens as it does. You need to state the problem facing you clearly in the form of a question. Recall your inquiry investigation at the beginning of this chapter. You made observations about the bottle. Then you may have wondered if there was something inside the bottle. Observing the bottle

   and thinking about the situation might have led you to state the problem in the form of a question: Is the bottle "empty" or is it full of something?

2. ***Collect Information*** The first thing you need to do to answer your question is conduct research. Refer to books and other written materials that relate to your problem. Interview people with knowledge of your problem. It is possible that someone else may have information concerning

the same problem. The information you gather may provide you with clues that can help you find a way to answer your question.

3. ***Form a Hypothesis*** A **hypothesis** is a suggested solution to a problem or a possible answer to your question. A hypothesis is not a wild guess. It should be based on the information you collected and the observations you made. Keep in mind that an **observation** is information you gather using your senses. Learn to be a careful observer. In the case of the inquiry investigation, your hypothesis might have been: If the bottle is open in a room filled with air, then the bottle is also filled with air.

4. ***Test the Hypothesis*** It is necessary to design and carry out an experiment that will test the hypothesis. The sign of a good hypothesis is that it can be tested. There must be a possible answer that can be shown to be true or false. It is not enough to say, "It's obvious that the bottle is full of air." You must obtain scientific evidence.

   The steps that you follow to test a hypothesis are known as the **procedure**. You must write the procedure in such a way that someone else could repeat the same experiment in exactly the same way. You need to include the materials you used, the amount or size of each material, and what you did with the materials in the order you did it.

5. ***Keep a Record of Your Experiment*** As you carry out an experiment, observe carefully and record your observations, or **data**, in a laboratory notebook. Be sure to write the date and time of the observation and the conditions under which it was made. Do not try to remember what you observed and wait to write it down at a later time. You must record your data as you gather it. You can always go

back and present your data in a way that makes it easier to follow. For example, you might arrange numerical data in a table or graph. You might present other kinds of data in a diagram or map.

6. ***Analyze the Results*** Once you have data from your experiment, you need to study it to figure out what it shows. When data consists of numbers, you might look for patterns and trends. In other words, are values increasing, decreasing, or staying the same? Once you analyze the results, you can reach a **conclusion**, which is a statement indicating if the hypothesis was supported by the data. A conclusion is a kind of **inference**, which is a statement based on a series of observations. An inference is an attempt to explain why the observations occurred.

   In the inquiry investigation at the beginning of this chapter, suppose you hypothesized that the bottle was filled with air. Then you observed that bubbles rose from the "empty" bottle to the bottle filled with water. This observation provided evidence that the "empty" bottle actually contained a colorless gas that was lighter than water. Because the room was filled with air, it is reasonable to suggest that the bottle was also filled with air. You can conduct additional tests to confirm that the gas is indeed air.

   If the data does not support the hypothesis, the hypothesis must be rejected. Do not consider this a failure. Showing that the hypothesis is not correct provides new information. It guides you to develop and test a new hypothesis. That is part of the process of scientific inquiry. *Scientific inquiry* is the nature of scientific *thinking* and the process scientists use to solve problems.

7. ***Repeat the Experiment*** In any experiment, it is always possible that some

error was introduced. To avoid "jumping to conclusions," you should repeat your experiment as many times as possible. If you, or someone else, can duplicate the results of your experiment with little or no change, your conclusions are probably valid. Results that are valid are reasonable, logical, and can be achieved by repeated testing. This is another reason why your procedure needs to be well-written. Other people need to be able to repeat your experiment to confirm your results.

8. ***Confirm the Conclusion*** Repeating an experiment and getting the same results is one way to confirm the conclusion. Another important method of confirming a conclusion is to try to use the information revealed by the experiment to explain other related problems. If successful, you can be more certain that the conclusion is reasonable.

   If the conclusion to your inquiry investigation indicated that the "empty" bottle contained a gas, you should be able to confirm the conclusion by explaining the situation shown in Figure 1-3. When water is poured into the funnel, most of the water remains in the funnel, and it is impossible to fill the bottle. Can you explain why this is so?

9. ***Communicate the Results to Others*** It is important for others to know what you have learned so that they will be able to confirm your results and possibly use them to solve other problems. Scientists publicize their findings in several ways, such as writing reports in magazines known as scientific journals or giving lectures to other scientists at professional meetings.

10. ***Identify New Problems for Investigation*** Scientific knowledge has grown because the solution to one

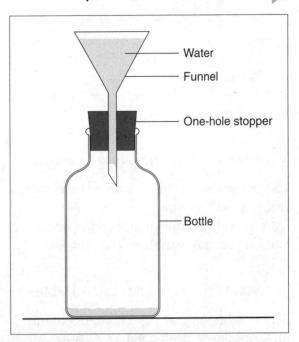

Figure 1-3. Water remains in the funnel because something is already in the bottle. The bottle is not empty. It is filled with air.

problem often leads to the investigation of new problems. For example, you showed that the "empty" bottle actually contained a gas. The next logical step would be to show that the gas is air. Can you suggest an experiment to do this?

▶ How Are Theories Developed?

After scientists have performed many experiments, made many observations, and tested several hypotheses, they may try to provide an explanation of their results that can be applied to related situations. They do this by formulating a theory. A **theory** is a detailed explanation of large bodies of information, represents the most logical explanation of the evidence, and is generally accepted as fact (unless shown to be otherwise). Theories are often revised as technology improves and new observations are made. Most theories are based on the work of many scientists over a long period of time and become stronger as more supporting evidence and experimental data are gathered.

No single experiment can prove that a theory is correct. The experimental results can support only the possibility that the theory is right. However, a single experiment can prove a theory wrong if the results do not support the theory.

What Are Variables and Controls?

Experiments must be conducted in an organized way so that you can reach valid results. Two important considerations for obtaining valid results are variables and controls.

What Are Experimental Variables?

Any conditions that can be changed during an experiment are called **variables**. In an experiment, you need to keep all but one of the variables *constant*, or unchanged. The one variable that you change is the **independent variable**. The variable that you observe to find out how it changes is the **dependent variable**. The hypothesis should relate these two variables. Suppose, for example, you want to find out how the height from which you drop a ball affects the height to which it bounces. Your hypothesis might be: If the height from which a ball is dropped increases, the height to which the ball bounces will increase. The starting height would be the independent variable and the height to which the ball bounces would be the dependent variable. (See Figure 1-4.)

Would it be a good experiment to drop a golf ball, a tennis ball, and a basketball from different heights in different places to observe how they bounce in order to test the hypothesis about height? No. All the balls bounce differently, so you will not know if it was the type of ball, the surface on which it bounced, or the height from which it was dropped that affected the height of the bounce. An experiment must have only one independent variable; otherwise, the results cannot be attributed to a single cause.

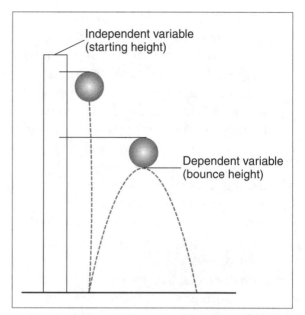

Figure 1-4. You change the independent variable and you measure the dependent variable. The dependent variable depends on, or is affected by, the changing independent variable.

What Are Controlled Experiments?

In order for the results of an experiment to be useful, they must be compared with some standard that does not change during the experiment. For example, suppose a teacher wants to find out if listening to classical music helps students perform better on exams. The teacher gathers a group of students for an exam. Should the teacher let all the students listen to music while taking the exam? If the teacher lets all the students listen to music and finds that most do well on the exam, the teacher cannot be sure that the change was because of the music. There might have been some other variable that affected all of the students. For example, the exam might have been easier than usual, or it might have been on a topic that students find interesting.

To establish something for comparison, the teacher needs to have only some of the students listen to music during the exam. Then, if all the students do well on the exam, the teacher knows it was not because of the music. If instead, the students who listened to music did substantially better on the exam than the other students, the teacher can conclude that it was because of the music. The group of students who were not allowed to listen to music is known as the **control** for this investigation.

How Can You Use the Scientific Method in Everyday Life?

You might be surprised to find out that you use the scientific method even when you are not in science class. The work of science requires a variety of abilities and qualities that are helpful in daily life. Suppose, for example, you have a cell phone that stops working. Perhaps you have been in that situation before, so you assume the battery needs to be charged. After plugging it into the charger, you find that the phone still does not work. What do you do next?

Before you give up on your cell phone, you would probably analyze the situation a little more closely. You might ask some friends who have similar cell phones if they have ever had the same problem. You might then go online to search for information at the manufacturer's Web site. There you might discover that other people have reported that their chargers stopped working, which might lead you to consider that your charger has stopped working as well. To check, you find a friend who has a working charger and use it to charge your cell phone. Your phone works fine! You buy a new charger and your problem is solved.

What does this example have to do with the scientific method? You will see if you think about the example in scientific terms. You made an observation that your phone did not work. Then you conducted research to investigate the problem. Based on your research, you made a hypothesis about the charger being the cause of the problem. Then you performed a test to evaluate your hypothesis. The test led you to reach a conclusion, which you explored by trying another charger.

This is just one of many examples you could consider to realize that you use the scientific method every day. Thinking scientifically is a useful way to solve problems and can be applied to common situations.

How Should You Work in the Laboratory?

Working safely in the laboratory is very important. Experiments often require the use of dangerous materials and tools. You should be concerned not only with your own safety, but also about the safety of others. Experiments are often performed in laboratories that are designed with safety in mind.

What Safety Precautions Should You Take in the Laboratory?

Students must be aware of safety in the laboratory, which involves taking certain precautions ahead of time. Before doing any lab work, tie back your long hair and wear protective clothing when necessary. Protective clothing includes aprons, lab coats, gloves, and safety goggles. Goggles must be worn when using any chemicals. You or your teacher should make sure that there is adequate ventilation and running water available. An eyewash or emergency shower should be available. When using a flame, make sure that a fire extinguisher and fire blanket are available. Never bring food or drink into the laboratory, and remove books and coats from the work area.

Listen carefully to all instructions. Read any labels completely and follow all directions. Be aware of the location of all safety

Figure 1-5. There is a right way and wrong way to test an odor.

Figure 1-6. A Bunsen burner is a tool used for heating materials in the laboratory.

equipment. When you have completed your experiment, make sure that you have put out any flame and turned off any gas, water, or electrical equipment that you were using. Be sure to clean up your workspace.

Special safety precautions must be observed in the laboratory when handling chemicals and laboratory glassware. There is always a danger of explosions, breakage, spills, and spattering. If you spill any chemical on your skin, clothing, or desk, immediately notify the teacher and follow your teacher's instructions carefully.

When testing any unknown substance, always assume that it may be dangerous. For example, to observe the odor of an unknown substance, fan the vapors toward your nose and sniff gently. Do not put your nose directly in the vapors or inhale deeply. (See Figure 1-5.) Also, you should never taste a chemical.

▶ How Do You Work Safely with Heat?

Many experiments require you to heat the materials. This can be done in various ways.

Two common ways to heat materials are to use a hot plate or a Bunsen burner. (See Figure 1-6.) Each piece of equipment presents its own special hazards. A hot plate, for example, looks exactly the same whether it is hot or cold. Therefore, it is always best to assume that it is too hot to touch.

A test-tube holder is designed so you can safely handle a test tube during and after heating. Special devices, called tongs, are designed for handling other hot objects. Tongs are available in different sizes and shapes. (See Figure 1-7.) You can get serious burns if you touch objects that were recently

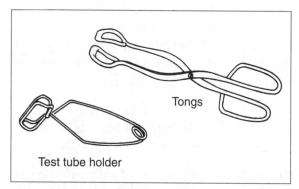

Tongs

Test tube holder

Figure 1-7. These tools are used to handle objects that need to be heated or that have been heated.

Right!   Wrong!

Figure 1-8. Wear goggles and be very careful when heating liquids. Heat liquids only in open containers.

heated. Report any burn, large or small, to the teacher immediately.

Even water becomes dangerous when heated. Like other liquids, hot water may splatter when it reaches its boiling point. For this reason, wear safety goggles whenever any liquids are heated—including water. When heating a liquid in a test tube, make sure that the mouth of the test tube does not point toward you or anyone else. Figure 1-8 illustrates the right and wrong ways to heat a test tube.

▶ How Do You Use Electricity Safely?

Electrical devices, such as hot plates and electric stirrers, are often used in a science laboratory. Electricity is dangerous and can injure or kill living things. Though it has become a common part of our lives, electricity should always be handled carefully. Observe commonsense safety rules whenever using electricity. Before working with any electrical device, check the wires for damage or breaks in the plastic or rubber insulating material. Electrical wires should not be used if they are broken or frayed, and plugs should be replaced if the wire is broken near the plug. If you find a wire that might be damaged, notify your teacher. Always unplug electrical devices before cleaning or moving them. When removing a plug from an electrical outlet, grip the plug itself, not the cord attached to it. Never touch the metal prongs of a plug!

Water can act as a conductor of electricity, so never handle electrical appliances, plugs, or outlets while you are in water or if you are wet. Keep all plugs, cords, and electrical appliances away from water. Also, do not attempt to remove an electrical plug if your hands are wet.

▶ How Do You Work Safely with Sharp Tools?

In a laboratory, students are sometimes asked to use sharp objects such as scalpels, probes, pins, and scissors. These tools are often called "sharps." They require their own special set of precautions when you handle them. Never touch the sharp edges of these tools. Even placing them on a table is a potential hazard. It is best to store sharps in drawers or cabinets when not in use.

If a sharp does cut you or any of your classmates, there are additional precautions you must take. Immediately report any cut, large or small, to the teacher. Do not attempt to clean up any blood spills yourself. Do not touch the sharp instrument that caused the cut. Your teacher will know the proper way to remove the dangerous materials. These materials include broken glass, which is one of the most common causes of injury in the laboratory.

Some types of hepatitis and some other contagious diseases are spread through contact with contaminated blood. A student may carry a disease and not show any symptoms. Therefore, the proper procedure is to assume that all blood is dangerous.

How Do Scientists Make Measurements?

Many observations in science involve measurements. The key to making an accurate measurement is understanding what quantity you are measuring and selecting the right tool and units of measurement. Some common measurements include length, mass, volume, and temperature. (See Figure 1-9.)

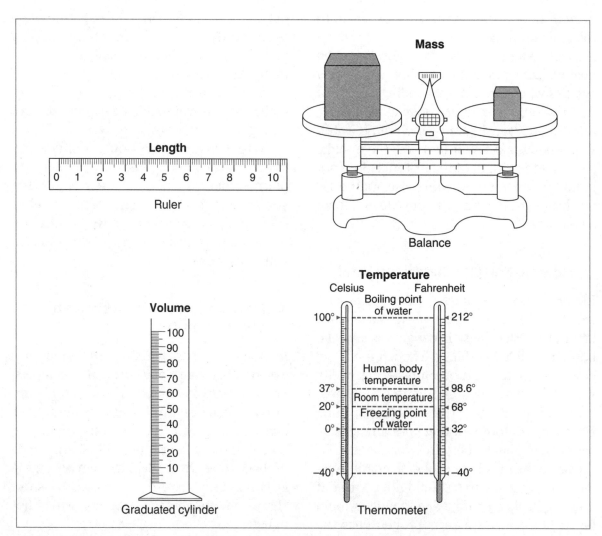

Figure 1-9. These are some of the tools you can use for making measurements.

What Are the Tools of Measurement?

Scientists use a variety of instruments to make measurements. You may have used some of these instruments.

Length When you measure **length**, you measure the distance between two points. Length is commonly measured with a ruler or tape measure.

Mass **Mass** is a quantity that measures the amount of material in an object. The tool used to measure mass is a balance.

Volume The **volume** of an object is the amount of space it takes up. You can measure the volume of a solid rectangular object by measuring its length, height, and width. You can use a graduated cylinder to measure the volume of a liquid or an irregularly shaped solid.

Temperature The **temperature** of a substance indicates how hot or cold it is. You measure temperature with a thermometer.

What Are the Units of Measurement?

All measurements must be described by a unit. For example, the number 2 does not give you much information about a measurement. If instead you say 2 feet, you know that it is a measurement of length. There are two general systems of measurement: the English system and the metric (SI) system.

The English System. The **English system** of measurement uses the foot as the unit of length, the pound as the unit of weight, and the gallon as the unit of volume. The English system has one major drawback: The large units cannot easily be subdivided into smaller units. For example, you must remember that in length units, 12 inches equals 1 foot; that 3 feet equals 1 yard; and that 5,280 feet equals 1 mile. In other words, you must know nonuniform equivalent measures before you can change from one unit to another.

For example, to change miles into inches, you must do the following calculations:

$$(5280 \text{ feet} \div 1 \text{ mile}) \times (12 \text{ inches} \div 1 \text{ foot})$$
$$= 63,360 \text{ inches in 1 mile}$$

or

$$5280 \frac{feet}{mile} \times 12 \frac{inches}{foot} = 63,360 \frac{inches}{mile}$$

The Metric System. A much simpler system of measurement, called the **metric system**, was adopted in France in 1837 as part of a larger system known as the International System of Units, or SI. This is the system used by scientists. It is so much easier to use than the English System that most of the nations of the world have adopted it for everyday use. The metric system (SI) uses the meter as the unit of length, the kilogram as the unit of mass, and the liter as the unit of volume. Table 1-2 shows you some units and their abbreviation.

This system is easy to use because the various units can be converted into other units by dividing or multiplying by 10, which is accomplished by moving the decimal point to the left or right. Thus, this is a decimal

Table 1-2.
What Are Some Commonly Used Metric (SI) Units?

Quantity	Unit	Abbreviation
length	meter	m
mass	kilogram	kg
volume	liter	L
time	second	s
temperature	degree Celsius	°C
energy	joule	J
power	watt	W
force	newton	N

Table 1-3.
What Are Some Prefixes of the Metric System (SI)?

Prefix	Meaning	Unit (length)	Equivalents
Kilo	One thousand times	Kilometer	1 kilometer = 1000 meters
		Meter	1 meter = 1.0 meter
Deci	One-tenth	Decimeter	1 decimeter = 0.1 meter
Centi	One-hundredth	Centimeter	1 centimeter = 0.01 meter
Milli	One-thousandth	Millimeter	1 millimeter = 0.001 meter
Micro	One-millionth	Micrometer	1 micrometer = 0.000001 meter
Nano	One-billionth	Nanometer	1 nanometer = 0.000000001 meter

system. Table 1-3 shows you some prefixes that are used in the metric (SI) system, as well as some equivalent values.

Suppose a sample of material has a mass of five thousandths of a gram (g). You could record this measurement as 0.005 gram. However, because there are 1,000 milligrams (mg) in 1 gram, you can rewrite the number by moving the decimal point three places to the left: 0.005 gram as 5 milligrams. Similarly, it is possible to write large numbers in a more compact manner. For example, a length of 10,000 meters can be written as 10 kilometers.

Although scientists prefer the metric system (SI), they sometimes find it necessary to use both the metric (SI) and English systems. It is therefore useful to know how to convert one system of measurement to the other (see Figure 1-10). Table 1-4 gives some common equivalents in the two systems.

To convert from one unit to another, you use a conversion factor, which is a fraction equal to 1. For example, suppose you want to write 4256 centimeters in meters. There are 100 centimeters in 1 meter so the conversion factor that relates centimeters to meters

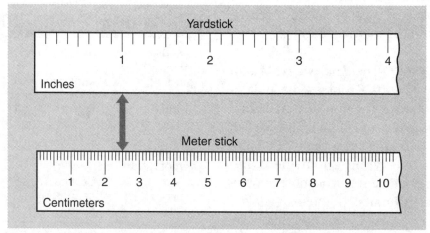

Figure 1-10. The drawing shows not only that 1 inch is equivalent to about 2.54 centimeters, but also that any measurement in inches can be converted to a measurement in centimeters by multiplying by 2.54.

Table 1-4.
Equivalents: English and Metric (SI) Systems

English Unit	Metric (SI) Equivalent
1 inch	2.54 centimeters
39.4 inches	1 meter
1 pound	454 grams
2.2 pounds	1 kilogram
1.06 quarts	1 liter

is $\frac{1 \text{ meter}}{100 \text{ centimeters}}$. Multiply the measurement by the conversion factor:

$$4256 \text{ cm} \times \frac{1 \text{ m}}{100 \text{ cm}} = 42.56 \text{ m}$$

Note that there are two different ways to write the same conversion factor. For example, you could have written the same conversion factors as $\frac{1 \text{ meter}}{100 \text{ centimeters}}$. Choose the form with the unit you desire in the numerator. That way the unit you start with will cancel out.

Chapter Review

Science Terms

The following list contains all of the boldfaced words found in this chapter and the page on which each appears.

conclusion (p. 6)
control (p. 9)
data (p. 6)
dependent variable (p. 8)
English system (p. 13)
hypothesis (p. 6)
independent variable (p. 8)

inference (p. 6)
length (p. 13)
mass (p. 13)
metric system (SI) (p. 13)
observation (p. 6)
procedure (p. 6)
science (p. 3)

scientific inquiry (p. 3)
scientific method (p. 4)
scientist (p. 3)
temperature (p. 13)
theory (p. 7)
variable (p. 8)
volume (p. 13)

Matching Questions

In your notebook, write the letter of the item in column B that is most closely related to the item in column A.

Column A
_____ 1. mass
_____ 2. control
_____ 3. 1 meter
_____ 4. hypothesis
_____ 5. metric system (SI)
_____ 6. scientific inquiry
_____ 7. volume
_____ 8. physics
_____ 9. dependent variable
_____ 10. 1 liter

Column B
a. suggested solution to a problem
b. the process of seeking answers to questions about the world
c. the amount of material in an object
d. 1.06 quarts
e. study of matter and energy
f. the part of an experiment that does not change
g. 39.4 inches
h. set of units based on multiples of 10
i. the amount of space a liquid or object takes up
j. quantity measured during an experiment

> **TEST-TAKING TIP** Be sure to read all the answer choices before making your selection. You may be able to eliminate choices that you know are incorrect.

Multiple-Choice Questions

In your notebook, write the letter preceding the word or expression that best completes the statement or answers the question.

1. To test a hypothesis, you
   a. draw a conclusion
   b. conduct an experiment
   c. ask a question
   d. communicate results

2. Alexis heated a gas in a sealed container. She measured the pressure of the gas at different temperatures. Which is the independent variable in this experiment?
   a. the size of the container
   b. the pressure of the gas
   c. the type of gas in the container
   d. the temperature of the gas

3. Which of the following might Juan develop after analyzing the data from his experiment?
   a. a conclusion
   b. a hypothesis
   c. a scientific theory
   d. a procedure

4. A scientist's "educated guess" about a problem is
   a. a conclusion   c. an observation
   b. a fact   d. a hypothesis

5. After a first attempt to solve a problem, a scientist most likely will
   a. report conclusions to other scientists
   b. repeat an experiment
   c. write articles for scientific journals
   d. proceed to find new and different problems

6. A scientist has developed a material that is extremely strong but very light. The scientist has completed several tests on the material. Why should the scientist share the results of the tests with other scientists?
   a. to prevent other scientists from conducting the same tests
   b. to become famous in scientific journals
   c. to allow other scientists to check the results
   d. to begin selling the material to manufacturers

7. A student has poured a liquid into a graduated cylinder. What characteristic of the liquid is the student measuring?
   a. volume   c. temperature
   b. mass   d. length

8. What is the purpose of having a control in an experiment?
   a. to get more data
   b. to make sure the hypothesis is correct
   c. to provide a basis for comparison
   d. to display data in a picture format

9. What is the basic unit of length in the SI system ?
   a. foot   c. centimeter
   b. inch   d. meter

10. A kilogram equals
    a. 10 grams   c. 100 grams
    b. 1,000 grams   d. 3 pounds

Modified True-False Questions

In some of the following statements, the italicized term makes the statement incorrect. For each incorrect statement, in your notebook, write the term that must be substituted for the italicized term to make the statement correct. For each correct statement, write the word "true."

1. *Chemistry* is the study of living things. _____

2. A *hypothesis* is a suggested solution to a problem. _____

3. Only the *independent* variable should be changed during an experiment. _____

4. In the SI system, the *meter* is the basic unit of mass. _____

5. One milligram = *0.01* gram. _____

6. *Conclusions* consist of information you gather through your senses. _____

7. The prefix "centi" means *one-thousandth*. _____

8. The *scientific method* is a logical and systematic approach to solving problems. _____

9. Mechanics is the study of *forces*. _____

10. A *procedure* is a detailed explanation of large bodies of information. _____

Check Your Knowledge

Write the answer to each question in your notebook.

1. What is scientific inquiry?

2. What is meant by Sir Isaac Newton's statement that he was standing on the shoulders of giants?

3. Describe the scientific method.

4. Why is it necessary to have a control in an experiment?

5. How is an independent variable different from a dependent variable?

6. What is the purpose of formulating a hypothesis?

7. What kind of information should you include in an experimental procedure?

8. Why can't a theory be formed after a single experiment?

9. Why is the English system of measurement difficult to use? In what way is the SI system of measurement a more convenient system to use?

10. Convert the following measurements in the metric system (SI) to the English system:
    a. 2 meters = _____ inches
    b. 1362 grams = _____ pounds
    c. 4 kilograms = _____ pounds
    d. 7 liters = _____ quarts
    e. 25.4 centimeters = _____ inches

11. Convert the following measurements in the English system to the metric system (SI):
    f. 44 pounds = _____ kilograms
    g. 197 inches = _____ meters
    h. 15 pounds = _____ grams
    i. 200 inches = _____ centimeters
    j. 106 quarts = _____ liters

Think Critically

Write the answer to each of the following questions in your notebook.

1. Design an experiment that would test the hypothesis that bees come from the buried horns of a bull.

2. Sharon wants to investigate whether a certain brand of fertilizer produces larger flowers. She grows petunias, pansies, and marigolds, adding the same amount of fertilizer to each plant at the same time. The plants are grown under the same conditions of soil, light, and temperature. Sharon measures the size of the flowers as soon as the plants blossom. She finds that the petunias are larger than the pansies or marigolds. What mistake did Sharon make in her experimental design? How can she correct the mistake?

3. Betty obtained three containers of Surefresh milk. She kept each one at a different temperature and checked on them each day. Her data is shown in the table.

Temperature	Time Until Milk Turned Sour
20°C	1 day
5°C	3 days
1°C	7 days

a. Identify the dependent and independent variables in the experiment.
b. Explain what conclusion Betty could reach based on her experiment.

c. Based on the data, what prediction can Betty make about how long it would take the milk to turn sour at 10°C?

Take It Further

1. Select one of the sub-branches of science. Research careers in this sub-branch. Describe one job this kind of scientist might do and one place he or she might work.

2. Create a poster showing how you use the scientific method to solve an everyday problem.

3. Measurements were once based on common objects, such as the length of a king's arms. Research the history of measurement systems. Choose a measurement you find particularly interesting and report on it to the class. Explain why a standard system of measurement is necessary in science. You may wish to visit the following sites in your research: *http://standards.nasa.gov/history_metric.pdf*, *http://www.ieeeghn.org/wiki/index.php/System_of_Measurement_Units*, and *http://ts.nist.gov/weightsandmeasures/metric/lc1136a.cfm*.

Investigating Issues in Science, Engineering, Technology, and Society

Are Hybrid Cars the Best of Both Worlds?

If you look at a conventional car and a hybrid side by side, chances are they don't look very different. To find what makes a hybrid unique, you need to take a peek under the hood. Modern hybrid cars generally have a traditional gasoline-burning engine along with one or more electric motors and a battery pack.

Very simply stated, a conventional gasoline-powered car has a fuel tank that supplies gasoline to the engine. The engine burns the fuel in order to power a transmission, which turns the wheels. This type of car can drive at high speeds for long distances. However, it uses gasoline, which not only can be expensive, but is also a limited resource. In addition, burning gasoline causes pollution.

An electric car has a set of batteries that provides electricity to an electric motor in order to power a transmission, which turns the wheels. This type of car does not contribute to air pollution as it moves because it releases almost no pollution-causing particles into the air and does not require gasoline. However, it cannot reach high speeds or go long distances without being recharged.

The hybrid car was developed to increase the fuel efficiency and reduce the pollutant emissions of a gasoline-powered car, while overcoming the shortcomings of an electric car. The key to making a hybrid car useful is a gasoline engine that is much smaller than the engine in a conventional car. Conventional cars have a large engine designed for "peak performance," which is attained when the driver presses the gas pedal to the floor. In reality, the engine works at peak performance less than 1 percent of the time the car is in use.

A small engine is more efficient because it can use smaller, lighter parts, and fewer cylinders. The engine in a hybrid car is determined to be closer to the average power requirement instead of what is needed for peak performance. What happens then,

Figure 1-11. Don't be fooled by sleek designs and flashy colors. Some of the most dramatic changes cars will undergo in the future may be under the hood.

when a driver wants to drive at peak performance? The gas engine gets some help from the electric motor and battery.

Aside from a smaller, more efficient engine, hybrid cars have some other features to improve fuel efficiency. In a conventional car, whenever a driver steps on the brake pedal, energy is removed from the car to slow it. This energy is usually wasted as heat. A hybrid car can capture some of this energy using a technology known as regenerative braking. With the saved energy, the electric motor charges the batteries while the car is slowing down.

Another technology that makes a hybrid more efficient is a start–stop feature. Conventional cars waste energy when they are idling, whether at a stop light or in a traffic jam. Because a hybrid has an alternate source of power, it can shut down the engine in these situations. It automatically restarts the engine when the driver releases the brake pedal.

Overall, hybrid cars have almost double the gas efficiency of conventional gasoline-powered cars and result in much lower pollution. In addition, many states offer tax breaks, rebates, and other perks for purchasing hybrid cars. The advantages are clear. So should your family rush out to buy a hybrid? As you might expect, there are two sides to every story, so the decision is not quite that simple.

The most immediate drawback of purchasing a hybrid car is price. Hybrids tend to be more costly than conventional cars because of the expense of the batteries and extra engine. Therefore, a high initial investment is required to become a hybrid owner. Another drawback is the resale value, or the price at which you can sell a car after you have used it for a while. Although newer batteries are designed to last for the lifetime of the car, replacement batteries are quite costly. This makes the car less desirable if you want to resell it.

Aside from the battery, other replacement parts can be very expensive and sometimes difficult to obtain. Until hybrids become more common, not all mechanics will have the parts readily available or the training to service the car.

Safety must also be considered when evaluating a car. Hybrid cars are generally lighter than conventional vehicles. The lighter frame can make them more prone to accidents during storms and more easily damaged in collisions. In addition, the batteries of some hybrids use very high voltages. In an accident, the high voltage wires may become exposed and pose a serious danger.

One last consideration is the overall pollution associated with a hybrid. Although using an individual hybrid car results in less air pollution than a conventional car, there is no reduction in pollution at the factory that manufactures the car. Some studies suggest that the pollution and energy consumption is even greater than for conventional cars because of the extra components required.

Like any product, hybrid cars have benefits and drawbacks. The key to making a decision that's right for you is to investigate fully and stay informed. Would you like to own a hybrid car? Why or why not?

Organize It!

Use a method that your instructor describes to organize the information in this article.

Think About It!

1. How is a hybrid car different from a conventional car?
   a. It does not require fossil fuels.
   b. It must be plugged into an electrical outlet.
   c. It has two or more sources of power.
   d. It is less expensive to purchase.

2. What keeps the batteries of a hybrid car working?
   a. They must be replaced each week.
   b. They are recharged when the brakes are used.
   c. They get power when gasoline is burned.
   d. They get energy from sunlight.

3. Why is the gasoline-powered engine smaller in hybrid cars than in conventional cars?
   a. It is not designed for peak performance.
   b. It uses unleaded fuel only.
   c. It shuts off when the car is not in motion.
   d. It is attached to a smaller gas tank.

4. Describe three features that make hybrid cars more fuel efficient than conventional cars.

5. Explain how scientists and engineers might use scientific methods to develop and improve hybrid cars.

Extend It!

6. Scientists and engineers continue to test hybrid designs in order to make improvements. Investigate future plans for hybrid vehicles. Report on one or two improvements planned in the future. You may wish to consult the following Web sites as you begin your research: *www.motortrend.com*, *http://www. hybridcars.com/*, and *http://www.hybrid center.org/hybrid-timeline.html*.

CHAPTER

2 What Are Elements?

These shiny wires are extremely useful because of the unique properties of copper. Like gold, silver, hydrogen, and carbon, copper is a chemical element.

After reading this chapter, you should be able to answer the following questions:

What is matter?

What are elements and how are they used?

How can the properties of elements be described?

What are elements made of?

What was John Dalton's view of the atom?

What is relative atomic mass?

How are the elements organized?

What Are Some Properties of Metals and Nonmetals?

You may not think about the materials you use every day. It is their unique properties, however, that make each material useful for a specific purpose. Analyzing the properties of materials can help you understand how they are alike and how they are different, and ways that you can use each material.

Materials:
- ✔ safety goggles
- ✔ samples of lead, tin, aluminum, copper, iron, sulfur, iodine, and carbon
- ✔ helium-filled balloon
- ✔ sandpaper or emery cloth
- ✔ hammer
- ✔ tongs

CAUTION: Wear safety goggles and use tongs when handling these substances. Iodine is toxic; avoid contact with skin and clothing.

Part A Carefully examine the materials at your desk.

1. *What observations can you make about the samples without changing them?*

2. *How are they alike? How are they different?*

Part B Use the sandpaper or hammer to investigate the properties of each of the materials.

3. *What did you do to affect the materials?*

4. *What properties did you discover?*

What Is Matter?

If someone asked you, "What's the matter?" what would you say? If you are in science class, you should define **matter** as anything that has mass and occupies space. Books, desks, backpacks, air, and even people are made up of matter.

Matter commonly exists in three states, or **phases**: solid, liquid, and gas.

1. Solids have a definite volume; that is, they take up a definite amount of space.

They also have a definite shape. The metals you observed in the inquiry investigation at the beginning of this chapter were solids. Lead, tin, aluminum, copper, and iron are examples of metals. Other common examples of solids are sugar, chalk, steel, and brick.

2. Like solids, liquids also have a definite volume. Unlike solids, however, liquids do not have a definite shape. They take

the shape of the container in which they are placed. For example, if you pour 50 mL of water into a beaker, the water will take the shape of the beaker. If you then pour the same water into a test tube, the water will take the shape of the test tube. The volume of water will not change. Other common examples of liquids are hydrogen peroxide, alcohol, gasoline, and oil.

3. Gases have neither a definite volume nor a definite shape. A gas, like a liquid, always takes the shape of the container in which it is placed; but, unlike a liquid, a gas fills all of the space in that container. The helium in the balloon in the inquiry investigation at the beginning of the chapter was a gas. Other common examples of gases are oxygen, carbon dioxide, nitrogen, and chlorine.

You are most familiar with solids, liquids, and gases. (See Figure 2-1.) There is actually a fourth state of matter, known as **plasma**, that is found more commonly throughout the universe. Matter in the plasma phase is similar to a gas. However, the matter breaks apart into charged particles due to its high energy. One obvious place to find plasma is in the sun and other stars. Closer to home, plasma is also found in fluorescent light bulbs and plasma televisions.

What Are Elements?

When you look at a glass of water, all you might see is a clear liquid. Water, however, is made of two simpler substances—hydrogen and oxygen. If you pass an electric current through water, bubbles of hydrogen gas and oxygen gas are released.

Like water, mercuric oxide is made up of simpler substances—mercury and oxygen. Mercuric oxide is a red-orange powder. If it is heated in a test tube, the test tube becomes filled with a colorless gas and the test tube walls become coated with a silvery film. The gas is oxygen and the film is mercury (see Figure 2-2 on page 24).(**CAUTION**: This experiment is **not** to be performed by students because mercury vapor, which is given off, is poisonous.)

The simpler substances of which water and mercuric oxide are made are elements. An **element** is a substance that cannot be decomposed, or broken down, by ordinary means to any simpler substances. A **substance** is any sample of matter that is homo-

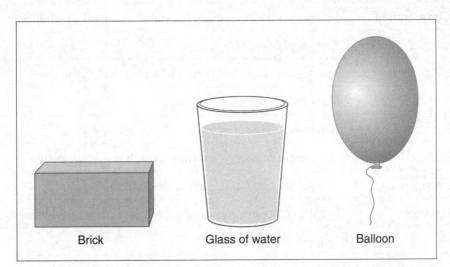

Figure 2-1. The three common states of matter are solid, liquid, and gas. Water is the only substance on Earth to exist in nature in all three states, as ice, liquid water, and water vapor.

Brick   Glass of water   Balloon

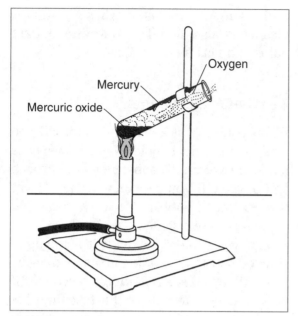

Figure 2-2. When mercuric oxide is heated, it breaks down into two elements—mercury and oxygen.

geneous, or uniform throughout, and has a unique set of properties. All the matter you see around you is composed of elements and combinations of elements.

How Are Some Elements Used?

Because of their special properties, elements are used in many ways in manufacturing and industry. For example, the silvery element chromium, which does not break down easily, is used to coat materials in water faucets and car parts in order to keep them from rusting. Cooking utensils are usually made of iron, silver, aluminum, or copper because these elements are good conductors of heat.

Perhaps the most important use of elements is in combining them in various ways

Table 2-1.
How Are Some Elements Commonly Used?

Element	Uses
Aluminum	Structural metal, kitchenware
Carbon	Fuels, graphite, electrodes, steel manufacture, plastics
Chlorine	Bleaches, water purification
Chromium	Forming protective covering on other metals, stainless steel
Copper	Electrical wire
Iodine	Antiseptics such as tincture of iodine and iodoform
Iron	Manufacture of steel, magnets
Mercury	Barometers, thermometers, silent light switches
Nickel	Forming protective coverings on other metals, coins
Nitrogen	Fertilizers, explosives, dyes, medicines
Oxygen	Breathing apparatus, welding, engines of space vehicles
Silicon	Computer chips
Sulfur	Manufacture of sulfuric acid, vulcanized rubber, matches
Uranium	Producing atomic energy

to make new or improved materials, such as nylon and steel. Such substances are important in everyday life as well as in industry. Table 2-1 gives some examples of the uses of elements.

▶ Where Are Elements Found?

Scientists have discovered 94 elements that occur naturally, even if they break down into other elements instantaneously. In addition to these, 23 elements are considered synthetic because they have been artificially produced in laboratories. Therefore, the total number of elements presently known is 117. Only eight of these elements make up about 98.6% of Earth's outer layer, its crust (see Table 2-2).

Table 2-2.
What Elements Compose Earth's Crust?

Element	Percentage (by Weight)
Oxygen	46.60
Silicon	27.72
Aluminum	8.13
Iron	5.00
Calcium	3.63
Sodium	2.83
Potassium	2.59
Magnesium	2.09
Total	98.59

How Can the Properties of Elements Be Described?

All matter possesses physical properties and chemical properties. Those characteristics of matter that can be observed without changing the composition of the matter are known as **physical properties**. Phase, mass, color, and odor are physical properties. The properties that concern the way in which a substance combines with other substances are known as **chemical properties**. The ability to burn, rust, or tarnish are examples of chemical properties. This section will focus on the physical properties of elements. Chemical properties and changes will be explored in Chapter 9.

Scientists use the properties of the elements to classify them into groups. Although no system of classification is perfect, elements are generally classified as metals, nonmetals, and metalloids.

▶ What Are Some Physical Properties of Metals?

Lead, copper, tin, aluminum, and iron are examples of **metals**. These elements are described as having *luster*, conducting heat and electricity, and being both *ductile* and *malleable*. The metals make up a large group of the natural elements. Except for mercury, which is a liquid, metals are solids at normal temperature and pressure. [*Note:* When you see conditions of temperature and pressure described as *normal*, you know that temperature is 20°C and pressure is 1 atmosphere.]

What Is Luster? When a sample of a metallic element, such as copper or iron, is rubbed with sandpaper, the metal appears shiny. Most metals are shiny because they reflect light. This property, called **luster**, makes some metals very useful. For example, the reflectors of automobile headlights are made of polished aluminum. These reflectors concentrate a beam of bright light, greatly intensifying the amount of light produced by the bulbs in the headlights.

What Is Meant by the Conduction of Heat and Electricity? Most cooking utensils are made of iron, copper, or aluminum because these metals are good **conductors** (carriers) of heat. A conductor does not oppose the flow of energy. You have probably experienced this firsthand if you have ever placed a metal spoon in a cup of hot cocoa and allowed the spoon to remain there for a few minutes. You soon felt the handle of the spoon becoming hot. If, instead of a metal spoon, you used a wooden spoon (a nonmetallic object), you would have found that the handle did not become hot. Wood is a poor conductor of heat.

In addition to being good conductors of heat, most metals are also good conductors of electricity. Wire made of copper is used in electrical appliances because copper is an excellent conductor of electricity. Silver is a much better conductor of electricity than copper, but its use is limited by its high cost.

What Is Ductility? Wires are made by drawing a heated metal rod through a tube that is wide at one end and narrow at the other. As the metal is pulled out of the narrow end of the tube, wire of the desired thickness is formed. The property of metals that enables them to be drawn into thin wires is known as **ductility**.

What Is Malleability? If you hammer a lump of lead, the lead becomes thinner and thinner, as you may have observed in the inquiry investigation at the beginning of this chapter. Continued hammering will eventually convert a lump of lead into a very thin sheet. Metals such as aluminum can be flattened by being passed between heavy rollers. The aluminum foil you use at home is manufactured this way. The property of metals that enables them to be flattened into thin sheets without shattering or crumbling is known as **malleability**.

What Are Some Physical Properties of Nonmetals?

Sulfur, iodine, and oxygen are examples of **nonmetals**. In general, nonmetals have prop-

erties that are opposite to those of metals. Nonmetals usually lack luster. They are generally poor conductors of heat and electricity, and are not ductile. If you hammer a piece of sulfur, as you may have in the inquiry investigation, you noticed that instead of becoming flattened, like lead, the sulfur crumbled into a powder. Sulfur, like all other nonmetals, lacks the property of malleability.

Unlike metals, which are mostly solids, nonmetals exist as solids, gases, and even one liquid at normal temperature and pressure. Nonmetals such as sulfur, iodine, and carbon are solids; nitrogen, oxygen, and chlorine are nonmetal gases; bromine is a liquid.

Some of the common nonmetals and their properties are:

Sulfur—a brittle, yellow solid that does not dissolve in water.

Iodine—a steel gray solid that dissolves only slightly in water. One of the interesting properties of iodine is that, when heated, it changes directly from a solid to a gas, without first becoming a liquid.

Carbon—a black solid that exists in several forms including charcoal, diamond, coal, and graphite, the writing material in a pencil.

Nitrogen—a colorless, odorless, and tasteless gas. About 78% of the air by weight consists of nitrogen.

Oxygen—a colorless, odorless, and tasteless gas. About 21% of the air by weight consists of oxygen.

Chlorine—a green-yellow poisonous gas with a pungent odor that smells like bleach.

Bromine—a red liquid with an extremely irritating odor.

Metals and nonmetals possess a variety of chemical properties that will be discussed in Chapter 10. Table 2-3 summarizes the physical properties of metals and nonmetals.

Table 2-3.
What Are Some Physical Properties of Metals and Nonmetals?

Metals	Nonmetals
Good conductors of heat	Poor conductors of heat
Good conductors of electricity	Poor conductors of electricity
Shiny in appearance (have luster)	Dull in appearance (lack luster)
Malleable	Shatter or crumble when struck
Ductile	Nonductile
All are solids except mercury (a liquid)	Exists in all three physical states

▶ What Are Metalloids and What Are Their Physical Properties?

The **metalloids** are elements with properties sometimes resembling metals and sometimes resembling nonmetals. They can be shiny or dull. They can conduct heat and electricity better than nonmetals, but not as well as metals. Some metalloids, such as silicon and germanium, can be made to carry an electric current. This makes them useful components in electrical devices, such as calculators and computers. All of the metalloids are solids under normal conditions. Boron, silicon, germanium, and arsenic are examples of metalloids.

▶ How Are Elements Named?

As scientists progressed in their study of matter, they learned more and more about the elements and how elements combine. In order to make the task of recording their observations easier, scientists developed a system of chemical shorthand.

▶ Who Developed the First Chemical Symbols?

The alchemists, who lived during the Middle Ages, are considered to be the first chemists. Although remembered chiefly for their attempts to convert metals such as lead into gold, the alchemists also designed a method of representing the elements. They used a series of picturelike symbols that changed over the years (see Figure 2-3), but the symbols varied from alchemist to alchemist, leading to much confusion.

What Chemical Symbols Are Used Today? In 1808, John Dalton, an Englishman, devised the first modern system of chemical notation. He suggested that the elements be represented as a series of circles with lines and dots. His symbols, however, were never widely adopted by chemists.

In 1814, Jöns Jakob Berzelius, a Swedish chemist, suggested a system of notation that is still being used today. In this system, the first letter of the name of an element is used as the **chemical symbol** for that element. Thus, the symbol for hydrogen is H; the symbol for iodine is I; the symbol for nitrogen is N. Note that each symbol is capitalized.

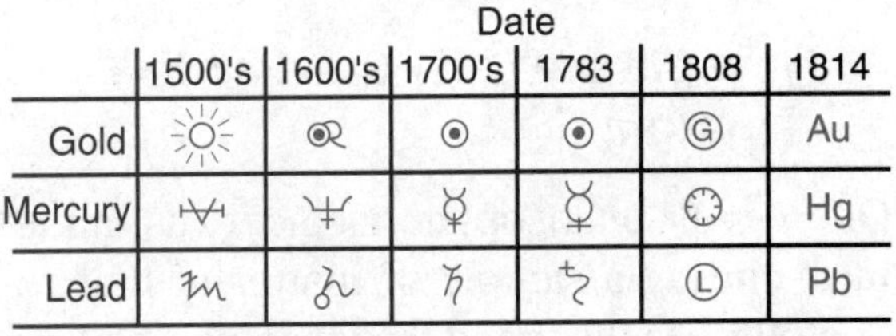

			Date			
	1500's	1600's	1700's	1783	1808	1814
Gold	☼	℞	☉	☉	Ⓖ	Au
Mercury	⩊	♉	☿	☿	☉	Hg
Lead	♏	♃	♄	♄	Ⓛ	Pb

Figure 2-3. During the past 500 years, the symbols for elements, such as gold, mercury, and lead have repeatedly changed. However, the system developed in 1814 has remained unchanged through today.

However, elements such as cadmium, calcium, carbon, chlorine, and cobalt all begin with the letter C. Therefore, Berzelius suggested that when the name of more than one element begins with the same first letter, a second important letter in the word should be added to the first. Thus, the symbol for calcium is Ca; for cadmium, Cd; for cobalt, Co; for chlorine, Cl. Note that the first letter is capitalized, but that the second is lowercase.

Berzelius found a few elements that would not fit into this pattern. The symbols for these elements would duplicate symbols for other elements and lead to confusion. He therefore suggested that the symbol for such an element be taken from the Latin or Greek name for that element. Some examples of symbols of elements taken from their Latin names can be found in Table 2-4.

What are Some Rules for Writing Symbols? In summary, the symbols for the elements generally follow these rules:

1. Select the first letter of the element's name and capitalize it.

Table 2-4.
What Are Some Chemical Symbols that Are Derived from Latin Words?

English Name	Latin Name	Chemical Symbol
Copper	Cuprum	Cu
Iron	Ferrum	Fe
Lead	Plumbum	Pb
Gold	Aurum	Au

2. Where a conflict occurs, select the first letter of the name plus one additional letter. Only the first letter is capitalized.
3. Where a conflict still occurs, select the symbol from the Latin name of the element.

Table 2-5 shows the elements and their symbols. Many of the newly developed elements have only temporary names until formal names are determined.

What Are Elements Made Of?

If you could break an element apart, what would you find? People have been asking that same question for thousands of years. Some philosophers in ancient Greece thought that all matter could be described in terms of four basic elements—earth, water, fire, and air.

How Did the Early Greeks View the Atom?

One Greek philosopher, Democritus, imagined cutting a sample of matter in half repeatedly. He theorized that at some point, he would reach a particle of matter that could not be divided any further. He called this particle an **atom**, from the Greek word *atomos*, meaning "indivisible."

Democritus believed that these atoms could not be destroyed and that atoms were unique to the substance from which they came, differing only in shape and size. He also believed that atoms were in constant motion and were able to join with one another to form different types of matter. The hypothesis that Democritus proposed was little more than a guess, without any real evidence to support it.

What Is Dalton's Atomic Theory?

It would be another 2,000 years before Democritus' idea would be revisited. Early in the nineteenth century, the English chemist John Dalton restated the view that matter

Table 2-5.
What Are the Chemical Elements and Their Symbols?

Element	Symbol	Element	Symbol	Element	Symbol
Actinium	Ac	Hafnium	Hf	Radium	Ra
Aluminum	Al	*Hassium	Hs	Radon	Rn
*Americium	Am	Helium	He	Rhenium	Re
Antimony	Sb	Holmium	Ho	Rhodium	Rh
Argon	Ar	Hydrogen	H	Rubidium	Rb
Arsenic	As	Indium	In	Ruthenium	Ru
*Astatine	At	Iodine	I	*Rutherfordium	Rf
Barium	Ba	Iridium	Ir	Samarium	Sm
*Berkelium	Bk	Iron	Fe	Scandium	Sc
Beryllium	Be	Krypton	Kr	*Seaborgium	Sg
Bismuth	Bi	Lanthanum	La	Selenium	Se
*Bohrium	Bh	*Lawrencium	Lr	Silicon	Si
Boron	B	Lead	Pb	Silver	Ag
Bromine	Br	Lithium	Li	Sodium	Na
Cadmium	Cd	Lutetium	Lu	Strontium	Sr
Calcium	Ca	Magnesium	Mg	Sulfur	S
*Californium	Cf	Manganese	Mn	Tantalum	Ta
Carbon	C	*Meitnerium	Mt	*Technetium	Tc
Cerium	Ce	*Mendelevium	Md	Tellurium	Te
Cesium	Cs	Mercury	Hg	Terbium	Tb
Chlorine	Cl	Molybdenum	Mo	Thallium	Tl
Chromium	Cr	Neodymium	Nd	Thorium	Th
Cobalt	Co	Neon	Ne	Thulium	Tm
*Copernicium	Cn	*Neptunium	Np	Tin	Sn
Copper	Cu	Nickel	Ni	Titanium	Ti
*Curium	Cm	Niobium	Nb	Tungsten	W
*Darmstadtium	Ds	Nitrogen	N	(Wolfram)	
*Dubnium	Db	*Nobelium	No	*Ununhexium	Uuh
Dysprosium	Dy	Osmium	Os	*Ununpentium	Uup
*Einsteinium	Es	Oxygen	O	*Ununquadium	Uuq
Erbium	Er	Palladium	Pd	*Ununseptium	Uus
Europium	Eu	Phosphorus	P	*Ununtrium	Uut
*Fermium	Fm	Platinum	Pt	Uranium	U
Fluorine	F	*Plutonium	Pu	Vanadium	V
Francium	Fr	Polonium	Po	Xenon	Xe
Gadolinium	Gd	Potassium	K	Ytterbium	Yb
Gallium	Ga	Praseodymium	Pr	Yttrium	Y
Germanium	Ge	Promethium	Pm	Zinc	Zn
Gold	Au	Protactinium	Pa	Zirconium	Zr

*Artificial element

was composed of tiny particles called atoms. Unlike Democritus, however, Dalton arrived at his conclusion after a long, detailed study of elements and the manner in which they combined. His idea, now known as **Dalton's atomic theory**, expressed a fairly good general view of the nature of matter. The atomic theory presents four major ideas, as follows:

1. Matter is composed of tiny particles called atoms.

2. The atoms of a particular element are alike in size, shape, and weight, but differ in these characteristics from the atoms of all other elements.
3. During chemical changes, the atoms of different elements unite, forming **molecules** of new substances (*compounds*). Molecules are the smallest particles of a compound that still retain the properties of the compound.
4. During chemical changes, the atoms themselves do not change.

Dalton's atomic theory, although further developed by other scientists, has remained essentially unchanged since 1803. The view that the atom is the smallest particle of matter, however, has undergone considerable change. In Chapter 4, we will consider a more modern concept of the atom.

▶ What Is Relative Atomic Mass?

The Dalton theory of the atom provided a basis for understanding how atoms of one element combine with atoms of another element to form molecules during chemical reactions. But chemists still did not understand why a certain amount of one element always seemed to combine with a certain amount of another element.

It was only through trial-and-error experiments in the laboratory that chemists began to learn how the weights of various elements were related in reactions. For example, scientists determined by experiment that 1 gram of hydrogen always combines with 8 grams of oxygen to form water. At first, chemists suspected that oxygen was probably 8 times more massive than hydrogen; that is, 1 atom of oxygen weighed as much as 8 atoms of hydrogen. Continued experiments, however, led to the conclusion that an oxygen atom weighs 16 times as much as a hydrogen atom.

Chemists did not know what the actual masses of the atoms were, but they could compare the masses of huge and equal numbers of hydrogen and oxygen atoms. As a result of years of experimentation, chemists determined the relative atomic masses of many elements. They found, for example, that a lithium atom is 7 times more massive than a hydrogen atom; that a carbon atom is 12 times more massive than a hydrogen atom; that a sulfur atom is 32 times more massive than a hydrogen atom. Recall that an oxygen atom is 16 times more massive than a hydrogen atom. Because there isn't any atom that has a mass that is less than that of the hydrogen atom, the relative atomic mass of oxygen was arbitrarily set at 16. Thus, a table of relative atomic masses was developed in which H = 1, Li = 7, O = 16, S = 32, and so on.

As you will see, this basic concept—the concept of relative atomic mass—led directly to perhaps the single most important discovery in all of chemistry: the Periodic Table of the Elements.

▶ How Are the Elements Organized?

Until you find out how books in the library are arranged, locating a particular book may be difficult. To help you find books, librarians arrange or organize books in several ways. Groups of books are organized according to the similarities in their subject matter. Then they are organized alphabetically according to the author's name.

Chemical elements are also organized in a logical manner. Although each element differs from all others, scientists have found a way to arrange them in a systematic way.

How Did Mendeleev Arrange Some of the Elements? One of the earliest contributions to organizing the elements came from Dmitri Mendeleev, a Russian chemist. In the late 1860s, Mendeleev knew from experiments that the properties of some elements, such as chlorine, bromine, and iodine, resembled each other. Using all available information, he prepared a separate card for each known element on which he listed the symbol, the relative atomic mass, and the chemical properties of the element. He arranged and rearranged the cards many times in an attempt to find a logical order. Mendeleev eventually placed the cards in order of increasing atomic mass. Some of the elements were arranged as follows:

first element: lithium

second element: beryllium

third element: boron

fourth element: carbon

fifth element: nitrogen

sixth element: oxygen

seventh element: fluorine

eighth element: sodium

ninth element: magnesium

tenth element: aluminum

eleventh element: silicon

twelfth element: phosphorus

thirteenth element: sulfur

fourteenth element: chlorine

Mendeleev noticed that, in his arrangement, the first element, lithium, had properties similar to that of the eighth element, sodium. Both sodium and lithium are very re-

active metals. Further, the fourth element, carbon, and the eleventh element, silicon, also had similar properties. In addition, the seventh element, fluorine, and the fourteenth element, chlorine, exhibited similar properties to each other, too. Both elements are gases, nonmetals, and are reactive. Thus, the properties of the elements seemed to repeat themselves.

Realizing that he had discovered an important relationship between properties of the elements and increasing atomic masses, Mendeleev arranged the elements in seven columns (see Table 2-6). In this way, the related elements fell in the same column. When the table is enlarged to include more elements, the repetition of properties continues in the same way. Today, chemists say that Mendeleev's arrangement indicates that the **periodicity** (repetition) of the properties of the elements is related to their atomic masses.

The Modern Periodic Table: An Introduction. After about one hundred years of research, scientists amended the Mendeleev table into what is now called the Modern Periodic Table of the Elements. (The complete Periodic Table of the Elements appears on page 58 in Chapter 5.)

Table 2-6.
How Did Mendeleev Arrange Some of the Elements?

I	II	III	IV	V	VI	VII
atomic mass: 7	atomic mass: 9	atomic mass: 11	atomic mass: 12	atomic mass: 14	atomic mass: 16	atomic mass: 19
Lithium	Beryllium	Boron	Carbon	Nitrogen	Oxygen	Fluorine
Li	Be	B	C	N	O	F
atomic mass: 23	atomic mass: 24	atomic mass: 27	atomic mass: 28	atomic mass: 31	atomic mass: 32	atomic mass: 35.5
Sodium	Magnesium	Aluminum	Silicon	Phosphorus	Sulfur	Chlorine
Na	Mg	Al	Si	P	S	Cl

TABLE 2-7. MODERN PERIODIC TABLE OF THE ELEMENTS
(abbreviated form)

Period	Group 1	Group 2	Group 13	Group 14	Group 15	Group 16	Group 17	Group 18
1	Hydrogen **H** 1.00797							Helium **He** 4.0026
2	Lithium **Li** 6.939	Beryllium **Be** 9.0122	Boron **B** 10.811	Carbon **C** 12.01115	Nitrogen **N** 14.0067	Oxygen **O** 15.9994	Fluorine **F** 18.9984	Neon **Ne** 20.183
3	Sodium **Na** 22.9898	Magnesium **Mg** 24.312	Aluminum **Al** 26.9815	Silicon **Si** 28.086	Phosphorus **P** 30.9738	Sulfur **S** 32.064	Chlorine **Cl** 35.453	Argon **Ar** 39.948

You will learn more about the Periodic Table in Chapter 5. However, as an introduction to this most important of all the chemical tables, take a look at a portion of a simplified form of the Periodic Table (see Table 2-7).

The table consists of horizontal rows called **periods** and vertical columns called **groups**, or families. Do you see any similarity between this table and the Mendeleev table? (**Hint**: Compare the period-2 elements and the period-3 elements with the Mendeleev arrangement in Table 2-6 on page 31.) What are some of the differences?

Chapter Review

Science Terms

The following list contains all of the boldfaced words found in this chapter and the page on which each appears.

atom (p. 28)

chemical property (p. 25)

chemical symbol (p. 27)

conductor (p. 26)

Dalton's atomic theory (p. 29)

ductility (p. 26)

element (p. 23)

group (p. 32)

luster (p. 25)

matter (p. 22)

malleability (p. 26)

metal (p. 25)

metalloids (p. 27)

molecule (p. 30)

nonmetal (p. 26)

period (p. 32)

periodicity (p. 31)

phase (p. 22)

physical property (p. 25)

plasma (p. 23)

substance (p. 23)

Matching Questions

*In your notebook, write the letter of the item in column B that is
most closely related to the item in column A.*

Column A

____ 1. an element found in water
____ 2. matter that has a definite shape and volume
____ 3. an element that is neither a metal nor a nonmetal
____ 4. a substance that cannot be decomposed into simpler substances
____ 5. an element that is malleable, ductile, and conducts heat and electricity
____ 6. the ability to be drawn into wires
____ 7. a shorthand notation for describing an element
____ 8. a philosopher who first described atoms as indivisible particles
____ 9. the repetition of properties among elements
____ 10. a vertical column of the period table

Column B

a. element
b. ductility
c. solid
d. group
e. periodicity
f. metal
g. hydrogen
h. chemical symbol
i. metalloid
j. Democritus

Multiple-Choice Questions

*In your notebook, write the letter preceding the word or expression
that best completes the statement or answers the question.*

1. In which physical state of matter is a sample that has a definite volume, but not a definite shape?
   a. solid
   b. liquid
   c. gas
   d. plasma

2. Substances that cannot be decomposed to any simpler substances are called
   a. elements
   b. compounds
   c. conductors
   d. plasmas

3. The element in Earth's crust with the greatest percentage by weight is
   a. aluminum
   b. silicon
   c. iron
   d. oxygen

4. Which element is found in the liquid state under normal conditions?
   a. nitrogen
   b. mercury
   c. iron
   d. sulfur

5. Which element is *not* found as a gas under normal conditions?
   a. fluorine
   b. hydrogen
   c. sulfur
   d. xenon

6. Iron, sodium, copper, and silver are examples of
   a. metals
   b. metalloids
   c. nonmetals
   d. compounds

7. Metals that reflect light are said to possess the property of
   a. malleability
   b. ductility
   c. conductivity
   d. luster

8. Metals can be hammered into thin sheets because they have the property of
   a. ductility
   b. malleability
   c. luster
   d. conductivity

9. Charcoal, diamond, coal, and graphite are all forms of the element
   a. silicon   c. carbon
   b. sulfur   d. oxygen

10. Who was the person who suggested the system of assigning chemical symbols to the elements that is used today?
   a. Berzelius
   b. Dalton
   c. Mendeleev
   d. Democritus

11. The Latin name for gold is
   a. ferrum   c. cuprum
   b. aurum   d. plumbum

12. Which is the chemical symbol for potassium?
   a. P   c. K
   b. Po   d. Pt

13. How did Dalton's theory of the atom differ from that of Democritus?
   a. Dalton based his theory on experimental data.
   b. Dalton was the first person to name particles atoms.
   c. Dalton believed that atoms were indivisible.
   d. Dalton arranged atoms into a periodic table.

14. Which property did Mendeleev use to arrange elements in his periodic table?
   a. color
   b. chemical symbol
   c. alphabetic name
   d. atomic mass

15. The horizontal rows in the Periodic Table of the Elements are known as
   a. families   c. lines
   b. periods   d. groups

Modified True-False Questions

In some of the following statements, the italicized term makes the statement incorrect. For each incorrect statement, in your notebook, write the term that must be substituted for the italicized term to make the statement correct. For each correct statement, write the word "true."

1. Matter is anything that has *color* and occupies space. _____

2. A *gas* is matter that has neither a definite volume nor a definite shape. _____

3. When an electric current is passed through water, bubbles of *nitrogen* and oxygen are released from the water. _____

4. Mass, color, and odor are *physical* properties of matter. _____

5. An element is *ductile* if it can be hammered into sheets. _____

6. *Metals* are good conductors of heat and electricity. _____

7. Elements that sometimes resemble metals and sometimes resemble nonmetals are called *metalloids*. _____

8. *Democritus* devised a system of chemical notation in which elements were represented by circles with lines and dots. _____

9. When two letters are used as a chemical symbol, only the *second* letter is capitalized. _____

10. *Carbon* is represented by the chemical symbol Ca. _____

11. The word *element* comes from the Greek word meaning "indivisible." _____

12. Dalton stated that all atoms of a particular *element* are alike in size, shape, and weight. _____

13. *Hydrogen* has a relative atomic mass of 1. _____

14. Mendeleev found that when he arranged the elements in order of increasing atomic mass, the *third* element repeated the properties of the first element. _____

15. Elements with similar properties are found in the Periodic Table of the Elements in vertical columns called *periods*. _____

Check Your Knowledge

Write the answer to each question in your notebook.

1. How are solids, liquids, and gases alike? How are they different?

2. How did heating mercuric oxide in a test tube help scientists recognize the existence of elements?

3. What is a physical property of matter? Give an example.

4. What is a chemical property of matter? Give an example.

5. State five general properties of nonmetals.

6. Name one nonmetal and describe its properties.

7. Write the name of the element described by each chemical symbol:

H	Fe
B	Pb
C	O
Cu	Na

8. Describe the main ideas of Dalton's atomic theory.

9. What contribution did Mendeleev make to the understanding of elements?

10. What is the structure of the Modern Periodic Table of the Elements?

TEST-TAKING TIP Be sure to go back and reread the question to make sure you have answered it correctly and have addressed all parts of the question.

Think Critically

Write the answer to each of the following questions in your notebook.

1. Why is air considered an example of matter, but music is not?

2. Democritus had difficulty convincing other philosophers about his model of the atom. Explain how Dalton's approach to developing an atomic model was more credible.

3. Chemical formulas describe compounds made up of elements. Mercuric oxide, which you read about at the beginning of

the chapter, has the chemical formula HgO. What elements are in table salt if its chemical formula is NaCl?

4. The graphs compare the abundances of elements by mass in Earth's crust and in the human body. What are the three most abundant elements in Earth's crust and in the human body?

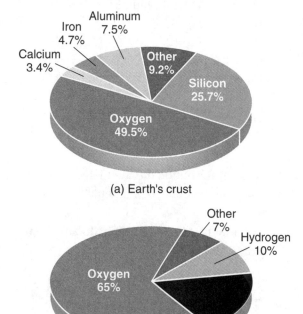

(a) Earth's crust

(b) Human body

Figure 2-4. Abundance of elements by mass in (a) Earth's crust and (b) the human body.

Take It Further

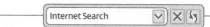

1. Minerals are resources formed in nature. Many minerals, such as copper, silver, and gold, are elements. Investigate mineral elements and the processes through which they are mined. You may wish to begin your research by reading the articles at the following sites: *http://www.greatmining.com/ minerals.html* and *http://www.nswmin.com.au/Mining-in- NSW/About-the-Industry/How-we- mine/Mining-Methods/How-We-Mine--- Mining-Methods/default.aspx*.

2. The scientists who discover a chemical element are often given the honor of naming the element. Some elements are named after scientists, such as Einsteinium or Mendelevium, others are named after the homes of their discoverers, such as polonium or californium. Either choose an element name that you find interesting and find out the reason the name was chosen, or investigate the naming process and the reason why some elements have only temporary names. Create an oral presentation to deliver to the class. You may wish to access the following sites in your research: *http:// www.ccmr.cornell.edu/education/ ask/index.html?quid=358*, *http://old. iupac.org/general/FAQs/elements.htm l#name*, and *http://periodic.lanl.gov/ index.shtml*.

Investigating Issues in Science, Engineering, Technology, and Society

Lighting the Way to the Future

The lightbulb has surely changed since its invention in the 1800s. Many lightbulbs have gone from clear and round to white and squiggly. The squiggly new bulbs are known as compact fluorescent lights, or CFLs.

Figure 2-5. More than just interesting to look at, this light bulb is far different from the one Thomas Edison invented many years ago.

A conventional lightbulb, or incandescent bulb, is made of a piece of wire inside a glass bulb. When electric current passes through the wire, the wire gets hot and glows. Over time with repeated use, the wire eventually becomes thin and breaks, at which point the bulb must be discarded and replaced.

A CFL is made of a long, sealed glass tube that is bent into a screw shape or zigzag to save space. A small amount of the element mercury is added to the tube. When the mercury in the tube is heated, it gives off ultraviolet light. This light is absorbed by a coating on the tube that fluoresces, or gives off visible light.

What's the big deal? CFLs are also more efficient. A conventional lightbulb emits less than 3 percent of the energy supplied to it as light. The rest of the energy is wasted, mostly as heat. This is why a conventional lightbulb feels hot after it has been on for a while. A CFL stays much cooler and is, on average, 75 percent more efficient than a conventional bulb. Electric power is measured in watts. Manufacturers suggest that a 20-watt CFL can produce the same amount of light as a 75-watt incandescent bulb. That is a huge savings in electric power!

You might be surprised to see how expensive they are compared to conventional bulbs. However, because they use less electricity, they can reduce a monthly electric bill by up to 7 percent. And because they last longer, they don't need to be replaced as often.

Why is this important to you? If your family decides to use CFLs its electricity bills will be lower. Using CFLs is also good for the environment because there is a savings in the natural resources used to produce the electricity. This results in a reduction in the amount of pollution released into the air by burning those resources. If every household, including yours, switched three incandescent bulbs for CFLs, it would be the equivalent of taking more than 3 million cars off the road! And that's not all. Because CFLs stay cooler your family—all families—won't have to use as much air-conditioning during the summer months, further lowering electricity bills. In addition, a CFL can last up to eight times longer than a conventional bulb and poses less of a fire risk.

Should you run right out and change all the lightbulbs in your house to CFLs? Well, CFLs have drawbacks, too. The most significant may be the mercury they depend on to operate. Mercury is a neurotoxin, which means it can adversely affect the functioning of the nervous system.

Supporters of CFLs argue that each bulb contains a mere 5 mg of mercury. However, opponents point out that the amount becomes substantial if you consider that millions of CFLs might wind up in landfills over time. The mercury can leak into air and water resources, and also endanger sanitation workers. Therefore, CFLs need to be properly recycled as hazardous waste. Unfortunately, recycling the mercury-laced bulbs is not nearly as convenient as purchasing them. Many consumers are unaware of proper disposal methods. Even consumers who do recognize the need to recycle may have to drive long distances to do so. In the process, they burn gasoline and produce pollution that possibly counters the savings to the environment earned by using the CFLs in the first place.

CFLs pose a danger when they break indoors, too. The Environmental Protection Agency (EPA) outlines a rigorous clean-up process that involves airing out the room, carefully disposing of the glass in sealed containers, and avoiding vacuuming to prevent the mercury from entering the air. The threat and clean-up process may seem too daunting for some potential CFL users.

Manufacturers are investigating the use of other materials instead of mercury and are working toward reducing the amount of mercury in each bulb. These efforts have so far been unsuccessful. Manufacturers also remind the public that the mercury released by CFLs would be minor when compared with the amount of mercury released each year from coal-burning power plants.

Mercury released by burning coal is emitted directly into the air where it cannot be contained. Supporters of CFLs explain that reduction in energy usage and burning of coal due to use of CFLs will result in an overall decrease in the amount of mercury released into the environment. This is still true even if the CFL were to break in a landfill.

Another problem you might have if you purchased a CFL is: Where would you use it? CFLs are not recommended for dimmer switches, which enable you to change the light from dim to bright. So you would have to choose a room that does not use a dimmer. Because CFLs have electronic parts in them, most should not be used in very hot or moist environments. That means you should not use them close to a stove or outside on the front porch where rain might reach them, or in your bathroom or near a shower. The best location to use a CFL is in a place where lights are used the most. Perhaps there is a light in your living room or bedroom that you leave on for hours at night, or a lamp used for hours of reading or homework in the evening.

As you might have concluded, there are two sides to this story. Do you think the drawbacks of a CFL are worth the advantages? Would you replace your incandescent bulbs with CFLs? What do you think?

Organize It!

Use a method that your instructor describes to organize the information in this article.

Think About It!

1. Why is most of the energy supplied to an incandescent bulb wasted?
   a. The wires break easily.
   b. The bulbs are small in size.
   c. Energy is lost as heat.
   d. The glass absorbs some of it.

2. What happens when mercury is heated in a glass tube?
   a. It absorbs visible light.
   b. It emits ultraviolet light.
   c. It becomes toxic.
   d. It changes into electricity.

3. What characteristic of light bulbs is measured in watts?
   a. electric power supplied to them
   b. length of time they last
   c. brightness of light produced
   d. size of lamp into which it fits

4. How can using CFLs reduce the amount of air pollution produced in a given year?

5. Suppose you have a light fixture that uses three 40-watt bulbs. You change to three 15-watt CFLs. What is the savings in energy?

Extend It!

CAREER

6. Environmental engineers apply science and engineering principles to protect and improve the quality of the environment. Research the education environmental engineers require, jobs they might perform, and agencies they might work for. You may wish to consult the following website to get started: *http://www.aaee.net/*.

3

Is It a Compound or a Mixture?

This collection of fruits and vegetables is a scrumptious example of a mixture. In science, some combinations are mixtures and others are compounds.

After reading this chapter, you should be able to answer the following questions:

What is a compound?

What is the law of definite proportions?

What are chemical formulas?

What is a mixture?

How do you separate the parts of a mixture?

How are compounds different from mixtures?

Separating the Parts of Compounds and Mixtures

You can separate some of the matter you deal with every day into parts. Other matter does not come apart so easily. Which kinds of matter come apart, and how can you separate them? Investigate to find out.

Materials:
- ✔ safety goggles
- ✔ sand
- ✔ salt
- ✔ iron filings
- ✔ magnet
- ✔ filter paper
- ✔ funnel
- ✔ water
- ✔ stirring rod
- ✔ 2 beakers (250-mL)
- ✔ hot plate
- ✔ hydrogen peroxide
- ✔ manganese dioxide
- ✔ 2 test tubes (150-mm)
- ✔ wooden splints
- ✔ matches

NOTE: Wear safety goggles while performing this activity.

Part A On a sheet of paper, mix approximately equal quantities of sand, salt, and iron filings.

1. *Describe possible ways you think you might be able to separate the parts of the mixture.*

2. *With your teacher's approval, try your methods for separating the mixture. Which methods were successful? Which methods were not?*

Part B Design a way to use a magnet to separate the parts of this mixture.

3. *After you have described how you can use the magnet to separate parts of the mixture, demonstrate your method.*

4. *Why was this method successful?*

Part C Place the remainder of the mixture in a beaker containing 50 mL of water. Stir the mixture vigorously.

5. *What do you observe?*

6. *What can you do now to separate the sand from the mixture?*

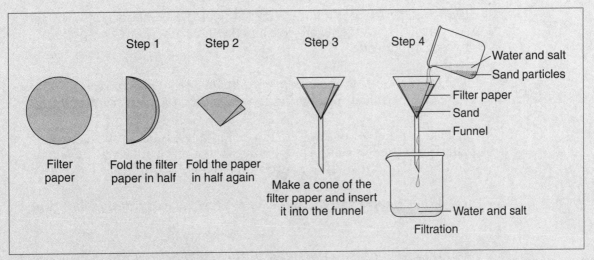

Figure 3-1.

Part D Prepare a piece of filter paper as shown in Figure 3-1 and place it in a funnel. Pour the mixture from the beaker into the funnel.

7. *What happens to the water? What happens to the sand?*

8. *Describe the substance remaining on the filter paper.*

9. *What happened to the salt? How might it be recovered?*

Part E Set up the apparatus shown in Figure 3-2. On the hotplate, heat the beaker and its contents until *almost* all the water has boiled away.

10. *What happens to the water as you heat the beaker?*

11. *What remains at the bottom of the beaker?*

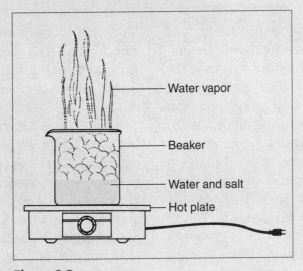

Figure 3-2.

Part F Hydrogen peroxide is a liquid consisting of the elements hydrogen and oxygen. These elements are combined chemically in the compound hydrogen peroxide.

12. *Do you think you can separate the hydrogen and oxygen using the same methods you used to separate the salt, sand, and iron?*

Place a pinch of manganese dioxide in a test tube. Thrust a glowing splint into the test tube. Then do the same thing with a test tube containing about one inch of hydrogen peroxide.

13. *What happens to the splint in the test tube containing manganese dioxide?*

14. *What happens to the splint in the test tube containing hydrogen peroxide?*

Part G Pour the hydrogen peroxide into the test tube containing the manganese dioxide. Thrust a glowing splint into the test tube.

15. *Describe what happens.*

16. *The element oxygen supports combustion. What can you conclude about the contents of the test tube now?*

17. *What substance do you observe at the bottom of the test tube?*

What Is a Compound?

More than a million words can be formed from the 26 letters of the alphabet. The letters *t*, *e*, and *n*, for example, can form the words *ten*, *net*, *tent*, and *teen* just to name a few. In much the same way, many more than a million different substances can be formed from the naturally occurring elements.

Combinations of elements are of two general types: compounds and mixtures. Substances composed of two or more elements, chemically united, are **compounds**. Water, table salt, carbon dioxide, sugar, and alcohol are examples of compounds. Water is composed of the elements hydrogen and oxygen.

Table salt is composed of sodium and chlorine. Carbon dioxide is composed of carbon and oxygen. Sugar and alcohol contain differing amounts of carbon, hydrogen, and oxygen.

Recall from Chapter 2 that substances have physical and chemical properties. Substances can undergo changes that affect their properties. A **physical change** involves a change in the form or appearance of a substance. Bending a metal paper clip or folding a sheet of paper is a physical change. A **chemical change** occurs when substances are changed into different substances with different properties. Burning a log or baking a cake are chemical changes. Another name for a chemical change is a **chemical reaction**.

Compounds are formed as a result of chemical reactions. The compound that is produced has different properties than the individual elements from which it is formed. The following examples demonstrate how the properties of compounds differ from those of their components.

1. The element hydrogen is a combustible gas, which means that it burns easily. The element oxygen, on the other hand, is a gas that supports combustion. That means that substances can burn in oxygen. When hydrogen and oxygen combine chemically, they form the compound water. Unlike the elements from which it is made, water is a liquid that neither burns nor supports combustion. In fact, water is commonly used to put out fires. (See Figure 3-3.)
2. The element iron is a gray metal that has magnetic properties. The element sulfur is a yellow nonmetal that lacks magnetic properties. When iron and sulfur are heated together, the compound iron sulfide is formed. This substance is not magnetic and is almost black in color.
3. When carbon reacts with oxygen, carbon dioxide forms. Carbon is a black solid that can burn, and oxygen is a gas that

does not burn but supports combustion. Carbon dioxide, however, is a gas that neither burns nor supports combustion.

Chemical reactions can be expressed as follows, where the plus symbol means "combines with" and the arrow means "forms." You will learn much more about chemical reactions in Chapter 9.

1. hydrogen + oxygen → dihydrogen oxide (water)
2. iron + sulfur → iron sulfide
3. carbon + oxygen → carbon dioxide

▶ **What Is the Law of Definite Proportions?**

When hydrogen reacts with oxygen to form water, 1 gram of hydrogen reacts completely with 8 grams of oxygen. That is, there is neither unreacted hydrogen nor oxygen remaining. Water is also formed with greater amounts of hydrogen and oxygen, for example, 1 kilogram of hydrogen reacts *completely* with 8 kilograms of oxygen to form water. When water is formed, the proportion by mass of hydrogen to oxygen is always 1 part of hydrogen to 8 parts of oxygen.

This 1 to 8 proportion is true only for the hydrogen and oxygen that actually react to form water. If, for example, 3 grams of hydrogen combine with 8 grams of oxygen,

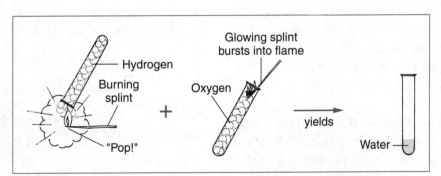

Figure 3-3. The elements hydrogen and oxygen can chemically combine to form the compound water. The properties of water differ from those of hydrogen, which is combustible, and oxygen, which supports combustion.

water is formed; but 2 grams of hydrogen remain unreacted. Why? Because the 8 grams of oxygen can combine with only 1 gram of hydrogen. The extra 2 grams of hydrogen do not take part in the reaction. Suppose 1 gram of hydrogen and 9 grams of oxygen combine to form water. Will all the oxygen be used in the reaction? Why?

Chemists find that when compounds are formed, elements always combine with one another in definite proportions by mass. This observation is called the **law of definite proportions**.

What Are Chemical Formulas?

Scientists use a shorthand notation called a **chemical formula** to represent a specific chemical compound. For example, the formula for one molecule of water is H_2O. The letters in a formula are chemical symbols describing the elements in the compound. Thus, the formula H_2O indicates that water is made up of the elements hydrogen (H) and oxygen (O). The numbers of atoms of each element in a molecule of the compound are indicated by numbers in small print that are written to the right and below the symbol. These numbers are called **subscripts**. When no subscript is written, one atom of the element is understood to be present. The formula H_2O indicates that 2 atoms of hydrogen (H_2) are combined with 1 atom of oxygen (O_1 or O).

The formula for carbon dioxide is written as CO_2 (see Figure 3-4). This means that a molecule of carbon dioxide contains 1 atom of carbon and 2 atoms of oxygen. Table 3-1 contains formulas for several common compounds.

Recall from Chapter 2 that relative atomic mass compares elements by mass. When determining the relative atomic masses of the elements, chemists originally gave an arbitrary value of 16 to oxygen (see page 30). However, scientists discovered that naturally occurring oxygen consisted of three different forms of oxygen. Each form of oxy-

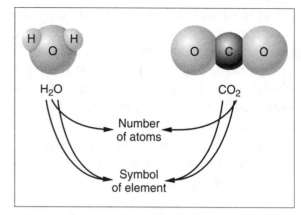

Figure 3-4. H_2O and CO_2 are formulas for the compounds water and carbon dioxide. The letters are symbols for the elements in each compound. The small numbers, or subscripts, tell how many atoms of each element are present in each molecule of the compound. If there is no subscript, only one atom of the element is present.

gen had a slightly different atomic mass. The existence of these different forms of oxygen led to disagreement between chemists and physicists as to which form to use for relative atomic masses. In 1961, the O = 16 standard was abandoned. In its place, all scientists agreed to use a scale based on the assumption that a single atom of the most common form of carbon, called carbon-12, has a relative atomic mass of exactly 12.

Table 3-1.
What Are the Formulas of Some Common Compounds?

Compound	Formula
Water	H_2O
Carbon dioxide	CO_2
Sodium chloride	NaCl
Hydrogen peroxide	H_2O_2
Sulfuric acid	H_2SO_4
Sodium hydroxide	NaOH
Alcohol (grain alcohol)	C_2H_5OH
Sugar or glucose	$C_6H_{12}O_6$

The relative atomic masses given in Table 2-7 (page 32) are based on the carbon-12 scale. With the exception of chlorine and copper, these values are rounded off to the nearest whole number. In the discussion to come, the values from the right-hand column in Table 3-2 will be used.

By referring to a table of atomic masses (Table 3-2) and the chemical formula for a compound, you can determine the proportions, by mass, of the elements in that compound. For example, the formula H_2O shows that a molecule of water is composed of 2 atoms of hydrogen and 1 atom of oxygen. Table 3-2 reveals that one atom of hydrogen has an atomic mass of 1, and one atom of oxygen has an atomic mass of 16. Thus,

$$\text{atomic mass of } H_2 = 2 \times \text{atomic mass of } H$$
$$= 2 \times 1 = 2$$

$$\text{atomic mass of } O = 1 \times \text{atomic mass of } O$$
$$= 1 \times 16 = 16$$

From this calculation, you know that the proportion of elements in water by mass is

$$(\text{mass of hydrogen}):(\text{mass of oxygen}) = 2:16$$

Thus, the composition of water by mass is $H:O = 1:8$

Similarly, the formula for carbon dioxide, CO_2, reveals that one molecule of carbon dioxide is composed of one atom of carbon and two atoms of oxygen. From the table of

Table 3-2.
What Are the Relative Atomic Masses of Some Common Elements?

Element	Symbol	Atomic Mass (carbon-12 = 12)	Atomic Mass (rounded off)
Hydrogen	H	1.00797	1
Helium	He	4.0026	4
Lithium	Li	6.939	7
Carbon	C	12.01115	12
Nitrogen	N	14.0067	14
Oxygen	O	15.9994	16
Fluorine	F	18.9984	19
Sodium	Na	22.9898	23
Magnesium	Mg	24.312	24
Aluminum	Al	26.9815	27
Phosphorus	P	30.9738	31
Sulfur	S	32.064	32
Chlorine	Cl	35.453	35.5
Potassium	K	39.102	39
Calcium	Ca	40.08	40
Copper	Cu	63.54	63.5

atomic masses (Table 3-2), you know that one atom of carbon has an atomic mass of 12 and one atom of oxygen has an atomic mass of 16. You can now indicate the composition of the compound by mass:

$$\text{atomic mass of C} = 1 \times \text{atomic mass of C}$$
$$= 1 \times 12 = 12$$

$$\text{atomic mass of } O_2 = 2 \times \text{atomic mass of O}$$
$$= 2 \times 16 = 32$$

The composition of CO_2 by mass is
$$\text{C:O} = 12{:}32, \text{ or } 3{:}8$$

This information is important because some elements form more than one compound. For example, carbon and oxygen form CO and CO_2.

What Is a Mixture?

The cereal you might have had for breakfast or the salad you munched for lunch are examples of mixtures. A **mixture** consists of two or more substances (elements, compounds, or both) that do not combine chemically. In other words, no chemical reaction occurs during the mixing. The substances in a mixture are not necessarily present in definite proportions by mass. They retain their individual properties and can be separated from one another by physical means.

How Do You Separate the Parts of a Mixture?

When the particles of a mixture of two substances are large in size and different in appearance, they may be easily separated from each other by picking them out by hand. If a bin of vegetables contains both potatoes and onions, it is easy to separate the two types of vegetables by removing one of them.

When the particles of a mixture are as small as grains of powder, however, other measures must be used to separate them. Recall the inquiry investigation at the beginning of the chapter. When you mixed salt into water, it mixed so well that you could not see the salt anymore. The salt dissolved in the water and mixed thoroughly with it. The fact that salt dissolves in water and sand does not

enabled you to separate one substance from the other by filtering.

You used the property of magnetism to separate iron filings from the sand and salt, and evaporation to separate the salt from the water. In each case, differences in physical properties were used to separate the parts of the mixtures.

How Are Compounds Different from Mixtures?

You were able to separate the parts of the mixture in the inquiry investigation because each of the components retained its own physical properties. However, when two or more elements combine chemically, the properties of the resulting compound are different from those of its component elements, as you saw in the experiment with hydrogen peroxide. To separate the parts of a compound, you generally must use chemical methods or large amounts of energy. For example, if you pass an electric current from a battery through water in a certain way, a chemical reaction takes place that separates the hydrogen from the oxygen. (**CAUTION**: Never try to do this except under the direction of a teacher.) Table 3-3 summarizes some of the differences between compounds and mixtures.

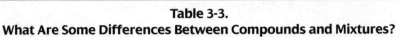

Table 3-3.
What Are Some Differences Between Compounds and Mixtures?

Compound	Mixture
Composed of elements	Composed either of elements or compounds or both
Components are chemically combined	Components are not chemically combined
Has a fixed proportion of elements by mass	Has variable proportions of elements and compounds
Properties are different from those of the component elements	Properties of each of the components remain the same
Components can be separated by chemical means	Components can be separated by physical means

Chapter Review

Science Terms

The following list contains all of the boldfaced words found in this chapter and the page on which each appears.

compound (p. 42)   chemical reaction (p. 43   mixture (p. 46)

chemical change (p. 42)   law of definite proportions   physical change (p. 42)

chemical formula (p. 44) (p. 44)   subscript (p. 44)

Matching Questions

In your notebook, write the letter of the item in column B that is most closely related to the item in column A.

Column A

_____ 1. compound

_____ 2. law of definite proportions

_____ 3. chemical formula

_____ 4. mixture

_____ 5. subscript

_____ 6. combines with

_____ 7. carbon-12

_____ 8. chemical reaction

_____ 9. evaporation

_____ 10. magnetism

Column B

a. number that indicates the quantity of atoms of an element in a compound

b. standard for atomic masses

c. property that can be used to separate iron from a mixture

d. two or more elements chemically united

e. substances put together but not chemically combined

f. process through which substances change into different substances

g. 1:8 expresses this phenomenon

h. what the + symbol represents

i. $C_6H_{12}O_6$ is an example of one

j. process through which a dissolved solid can be separated from a liquid

Multiple-Choice Questions

In your notebook, write the letter preceding the word or expression that best completes the statement or answers the question.

1. Which substance is a compound?
   a. mercury
   b. salt water
   c. carbon
   d. carbon dioxide

2. The elements in a compound are
   a. chemically united.
   b. always the same.
   c. combined in varying proportions.
   d. easily separated by physical means.

3. When a chemical reaction occurs
   a. all elements retain their original properties.
   b. some atoms are destroyed and new ones are created.
   c. new substances with different properties are formed.
   d. elements combine in unpredictable ways.

4. What does the law of definite proportions suggest about every water molecule?
   a. Each molecule consists of 1 atom of hydrogen and 8 atoms of oxygen.
   b. The mass of hydrogen to oxygen is always 1:8.
   c. The properties of hydrogen and oxygen are the same as the properties of water.
   d. Water can be made up of different elements as long as they combine in the same way.

5. What is a chemical formula?
   a. a recipe for mixing ingredients together
   b. a sentence that describes a chemical change
   c. a procedure for conducting an investigation
   d. a shorthand notation for describing a compound

6. The number of atoms of oxygen in the formula $C_6H_{12}O_6$ is
   a. 1
   b. 6
   c. 12
   d. 24

7. What is the composition of CO_2 by mass?
   a. C:O = 1:2
   b. C:O = 1:16
   c. C:O = 3:8
   d. C:O = 6:32

8. What happens when several substances are placed together but do not combine chemically?
   a. They form a compound.
   b. They form a mixture.
   c. They form an element.
   d. They form a molecule.

9. What process can be used to separate sand from a mixture of sand, salt, and water?
   a. condensation
   b. filtration
   c. boiling
   d. evaporation

10. How do you separate a mixture of iron filings and sulfur?
    a. by using a magnet
    b. by placing them in water
    c. by passing an electric current through them
    d. by heating them in a beaker

Modified True-False Questions

In some of the following statements, the italicized term makes the statement incorrect. For each incorrect statement, in your notebook, write the term that must be substituted for the italicized term to make the statement correct. For each correct statement, write the word "true."

1. Substances composed of two or more elements that are chemically combined are *compounds*. _____

2. A *physical* change occurs when substances are changed into different substances with different properties. _____

3. Elements combine with each other in definite proportions by *volume*. _____

4. The chemical formula for a water molecule is H_4O. _____

5. Numbers written below and to the right of a chemical symbol are called *exponents*. _____

6. In the formula, H_2SO_4, there are *four* different types of atoms. _____

7. The relative atomic scale is currently based on the mass of *carbon-12*. _____

8. The relative atomic mass of a hydrogen atom in a molecule of sugar, $C_6H_{12}O_6$, is *6*. _____

9. Unlike a compound, the substances in a *mixture* are not chemically combined. _____

10. A process that uses heat to separate mixtures is *filtration*. ___

TEST-TAKING TIP Study definitions in advance of an exam so you do not become confused between similar terms.

Check Your Knowledge

Write the answer to each question in your notebook.

1. What characteristics make sugar a compound?

2. How is a chemical change different from a physical change? Give an example of each.

3. Describe the law of definite proportions in your own words.

4. How are chemical formulas useful for describing compounds? Describe what the formula for sulfuric acid, H_2SO_4, indicates about the compound.

5. What is the composition of hydrogen peroxide, H_2O_2, by mass H:O?

6. What are the characteristics of a mixture? Give an example.

Think Critically

Write the answer to each of the following questions in your notebook.

1. What challenges would you face in trying to separate a mixture of salt and sugar?

2. You are given a clear solution in which two liquids have been mixed. You are told to separate the liquids. What information do you think you would need to accomplish this task?

3. The atoms in chemical compounds are often shown in drawings like these.

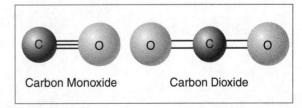

Carbon Monoxide   Carbon Dioxide

Figure 3-5.

Based on the drawings, what is the difference between carbon monoxide and carbon dioxide? What would be the chemical formula for each compound?

Take It Further

1. Select a chemical compound named in the chapter or that you have identified elsewhere. Create a poster that shows information about the compound, such as how the compound forms, the elements in the compound, the chemical formula for the compound, the properties of the compound, how it might be used, and what it might look like.

2. French chemist J. L. Proust developed the law of definite proportions in 1799. Research who he was and what experiments led him to this law. Present your findings in a report.

CAREER

3. Chemists work with compounds and mixtures regularly. A food or flavor chemist, for example, studies the chemistry of foods. Find out what a food or other type of chemist does, what education a chemist requires, and where a chemist might work. You may find the American Chemical Society's Web site helpful in your research at *http://portal.acs.org/ portal/acs/corg/content*.

4

What Is the Structure of Matter?

Believe it or not, this image of atoms has been magnified hundreds of thousands of times. Individual atoms are only about one ten-billionth of a meter, yet they combine in many different ways to form you and everything around you!

After reading this chapter, you should be able to answer the following questions:

How is matter electrical in nature?

How do electrical charges lead to static electricity?

How did the atomic model develop over time?

What subatomic particles exist within atoms?

What information is shown in each box of the Periodic Table?

Where are electrons located within atoms?

How are atomic diagrams constructed?

How do atoms combine to form compounds?

Have you ever rubbed a balloon against your hair and then placed it against a wall? If so, you know that the balloon will "stick" to the wall on a dry day. The explanation of why this happens has to do with electrical charges. In this investigation, you will explore the electrical nature of matter.

Materials:
✔ 2 glass rods
✔ silk cloth
✔ 2 rubber rods
✔ piece of fur
✔ pith ball suspended from a stand

Part A Briskly rub a glass rod with a piece of silk cloth for about 1 minute. Bring the rod close to (but not touching) a pith ball suspended from a stand with a piece of string. Use the setup shown in Figure 4-1 as a guide.

1. Describe your observations.

Part B Briskly rub a rubber rod with a piece of fur for about 1 minute. Bring one end of the rod close to the suspended ball.

2. Describe your observations.

Part C Briskly rub a glass rod with a piece of silk cloth. Suspend the rod from a stand by a piece of string.

Briskly rub another glass rod with a piece of silk cloth. Bring this rod close to the suspended rod.

3. Describe your observations.

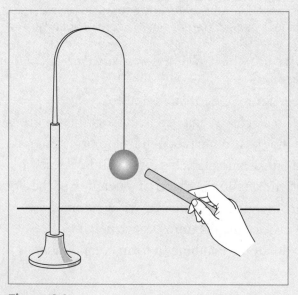

Figure 4-1.

Part D Predict what would happen if you rubbed both rods with fur. How would you conduct a test to prove if your prediction is correct?

Part E Predict what would happen if you bring a glass rod rubbed with silk near the suspended rubber rod after it has been rubbed with fur. How would you conduct a test to prove if your prediction is correct?

What Is the Electrical Nature of Matter?

Experiments performed during the latter part of the nineteenth century led scientists to reject Dalton's hypothesis that the atom was the smallest particle of matter. The experiments revealed that matter contains still smaller particles, each carrying an electric charge. It is this electric charge that is responsible for your observations in the inquiry investigation.

What Are Electrons and Protons?

In 1870, Sir William Crookes, a British scientist, observed that gases under low pressure conduct electricity. He set up a glass tube containing a very small quantity of gas. Metal electrodes were sealed into each end. (See Figure 4-2.) When Crookes passed a high voltage between the electrodes, he saw a green glow in the walls of the tube. To explain this observation, he suggested that something was given off from one of the electrodes, traveled in a straight line, and struck the glass walls of the tube.

The "something" that was given off by one of the electrodes was a stream of negatively charged particles, which came to be called **electrons**. They were given off by the negative electrode, also known as the **cathode**. In one experiment proving the existence of electrons, a metal cross was inserted into a gas tube as shown in Figure 4-3. The green

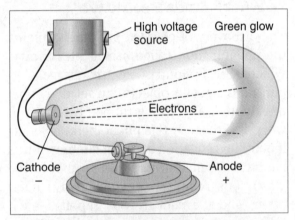

Figure 4-2. First invented by British scientist Sir William Crookes, vacuum tubes similar to this led to the discovery of negatively charged particles called electrons. In a Crookes tube, as the device came to be called, electrons are given off from the negative electrode (cathode), travel in a straight line, and produce a green glow at the end of the tube.

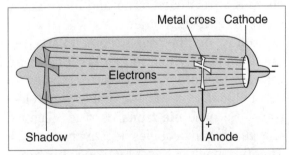

Figure 4-3. When Crookes placed a metal cross in the path of the electrons, the image of the cross appeared at the end of the tube. This result helped confirm that electrons were given off at the cathode and traveled in straight lines.

glow appeared as it did before, *except* in the region of the shadow cast by the cross. This suggested that particles did indeed travel across the tube and could be stopped by the metal.

Later, other experiments showed that positively charged particles, called **protons**, exist at the positive electrode, also known as the **anode**. Scientists therefore concluded that matter is electrical in nature. Because electrons and protons are particles within atoms, they are known as **subatomic** particles.

What Is Static Electricity?

The discovery of charged particles explains the phenomenon called **static electricity**, which is the buildup of electric charge. Certain nonmagnetic objects attract and repel one another after being rubbed briskly. You were able to study this phenomenon in your inquiry investigation at the beginning of this chapter. When the rods were rubbed, the glass rods repelled (pushed away) each other, and the rubber rods repelled each other. In other words, a glass rod repelled a glass rod, and a rubber rod repelled a rubber rod. On the other hand, the glass and rubber rods attracted each other, or pulled together. The glass rod attracted a rubber rod, and vice versa. These actions can be explained by the **law of electrical attraction and repulsion**, which states that opposite electric charges attract each other and like electric charges repel each other.

So how did the rods become charged in the first place? When rubber is rubbed with fur, electrons are transferred from the fur to the rubber. As a result, the rubber gains electrons. Because electrons carry a negative charge, the rod becomes negatively charged. The fur, having lost electrons, becomes positively charged. On the other hand, glass rubbed with silk gives up electrons and becomes positively charged, while the silk becomes negatively charged. When the pos-

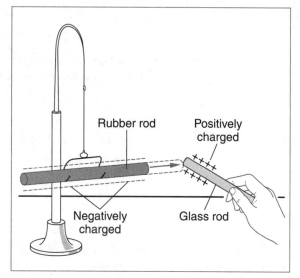

Figure 4-4. A rubber rod given a negative charge will move toward a glass rod given a positive charge. This experiment reveals that oppositely charged objects attract each other. Positive charges are represented by + signs and negative charges are represented by − signs.

itively charged glass rod is brought near the negatively charged rubber rod, the unlike charges attract each other. When two rubber rods or two glass rods are brought near each other, the like charges repel one another. (See Figure 4-4.)

How Did the Atomic Model Change Over Time?

Before the close of the nineteenth century, J. J. Thomson, a British physicist, suggested that the interior of an atom might be like an English dessert known as "plum pudding." He pictured the atom as a positively charged sphere with the negatively charged electrons spaced all through the sphere, just as raisins might be spread throughout a pudding (see Figure 4-5). As more was learned about the atom, scientists discovered that many properties of atoms could not be explained by using Thomson's model. Another view seemed necessary.

In 1911, Ernest Rutherford, a native of New Zealand, suggested another model of

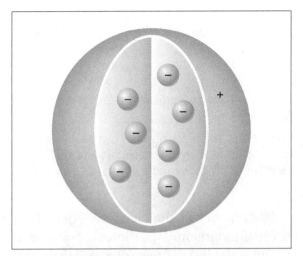

Figure 4-5. British physicist J. J. Thomson envisioned the atom as a positively charged sphere with negatively charged electrons scattered throughout.

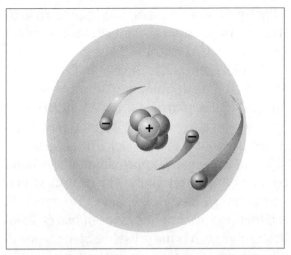

Figure 4-6. The atomic model proposed by Danish physicist Niels Bohr consisted of a central nucleus around which electrons orbit at various distances. The drawing shows how a lithium atom would be depicted today according to Bohr's concept.

the atom based on experiments he performed. In this model, the positive charges of the atom, or protons, are concentrated in a small region inside the atom, called the **nucleus**. Outside the nucleus, negatively charged particles, or electrons, are present. The number of electrons outside the nucleus is equal to the number of protons in the nucleus. Most of the atom consists of empty space.

Experiments have shown that the positive electrical charge of the proton is equal in strength to that of the negative charge of the electron. This accounts for the observation that individual atoms are electrically neutral. The positive charges exactly balance the negative charges. The mass of a proton, however, is about 1837 times greater than that of an electron. Therefore, the mass of an atom is concentrated in the nucleus.

Following Rutherford, the Danish scientist Niels Bohr suggested that an atom consists of electrons revolving around the central nucleus. Bohr believed that the electrons revolve around the nucleus in orbits very much like the orbits in which planets revolve around the sun (see Figure 4-6). Bohr also suggested that the negatively charged electrons are held in orbit by the attraction

of the positive charge of the nucleus. Unlike Thomson's model of the atom, the Rutherford and Bohr models contain large amounts of empty space between the electrons and the nucleus. Although the Bohr model of the atom does not explain all observations, it does provide a basis for a simple approach to atomic structure. With this understanding, the Bohr atom will be referenced throughout this textbook. Today, scientists employ a new model of the atom that is considerably more complex and addresses atomic particles as having both a particle and a wave nature, which is beyond the scope of this discussion.

▶ What Is a Neutron?

In the early twentieth century, the British chemist F. W. Aston conducted experiments to determine the atomic mass of the gaseous element neon. He discovered two different types of neon atoms. Although each type of neon had a slightly different atomic mass, he found that the numbers of protons and electrons in these neon atoms were the same. Atoms of the same element, which differ slightly in atomic mass, are known as **iso-topes**. Aston could not satisfactorily explain the presence of isotopes.

In 1932, James Chadwick, an English scientist, found another particle present in atoms. These particles, called **neutrons**, helped solve the mystery of isotopes. Neutrons are found in the nuclei of atoms. The mass of a neutron is approximately the same as that of a proton. Unlike the proton, which has a positive electrical charge, the neutron is neither positive nor negative—it has no electrical charge. It is the presence of neutrons in atomic nuclei that explains the existence of isotopes of many elements. Thus, all neon atoms have the same number of protons and electrons, but some neon atoms have more neutrons than others do (see Figure 4-7). Consequently, some neon atoms are more massive than others are. This knowledge has made it possible to account for the slight differences in the atomic masses of neon atoms, which were first noted by Aston.

The **mass number** of an atom is the sum of its protons and neutrons. The chemical symbol for an element can be written to show the number of protons and mass number. Because the number of protons is the same for all atoms of an element, an isotope is often written with its mass number only. The isotope of carbon shown in Figure 4-8 would be written as carbon-12.

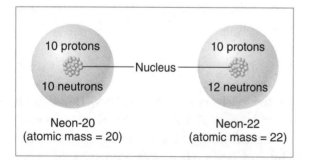

Figure 4-7. The drawing shows two isotopes of neon. Although each atom has 10 protons, making them both neon atoms, each contains a different number of neutrons. Therefore, each atom has a different mass. Atoms of the same element having different masses are called isotopes.

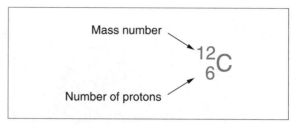

Figure 4-8. The mass number can be written as a superscript next to the chemical symbol. The number of protons can be written as a subscript.

A summary of the characteristics of the three fundamental particles of atoms is found in Table 4-1. These characteristics are based on the Bohr model of the atom.

What Other Atomic Particles Exist?

It turns out that protons, neutrons, and electrons are not the only subatomic particles. In fact, only electrons are actually fundamental particles, which are not made up of smaller particles. Scientists conducting research into the nuclei of atoms have developed a model, known as the Standard Model, which describes atoms in terms of 12 elementary particles. These particles can be divided into two groups: quarks and leptons. Protons and neutrons form from different combinations of quarks. Electrons are a type of lepton. According to this model, four additional particles transmit forces inside and outside the nucleus. These particles include bosons, gluons, and photons. Theories about the nature of such particles are discussed in more advanced physics courses. For now, you only need to consider protons, neutrons, and electrons as the basic subatomic particles.

How Are Elements Described by Atomic Number?

In Chapter 3, you learned that the properties of the elements repeat themselves regularly, and that this idea was used to develop the Periodic Table. A further study of the parti-

Table 4-1.
What Particles Make up an Atom?

Particle	Mass	Electric Charge	Location	Number
Proton	Mass is approximately equal to that of a neutron	Positive charge (+)	Nucleus	The same for all atoms of the same element; equal to the number of electrons in a neutral atom
Electron	Mass of an electron is approximately 1/1837 the mass of a proton	Negative charge (−)	Orbit around nucleus	Equal to the number of protons in a neutral atom
Neutron	Mass is approximately equal to that of a proton	No charge (neutral)	Nucleus	Number can vary among atoms of the same element

cles present in atoms helps explain why the properties of the elements repeat themselves in this manner.

Each atom of a particular element contains a specific number of protons. No two elements are alike in this respect. The specific number of protons in an atom is known as the **atomic number** of the element. The atomic number identifies an atom of an element.

In 1912, Henry Moseley, a British chemist, experimentally determined the atomic numbers of many elements. He then modified Mendeleev's table by arranging the elements in order of their atomic numbers rather than their relative atomic masses. In so doing, Moseley corrected some shortcomings of the Mendeleev table, in which some light elements had to follow heavier elements in order for the periodic nature to hold true. For example, in order to group iodine with other elements that have similar properties, Mendeleev had to place it after tellurium even though iodine has a lower relative atomic mass than tellurium. However, Moseley found that iodine has a higher atomic number than tellurium. Therefore, iodine actually belonged after tellurium when the elements were arranged in order of atomic number.

Moseley's arrangement is the periodic table of the elements that is used today. It shows that the properties of the elements repeat themselves when they are arranged according to increasing atomic number.

▶ **What Information Does the Periodic Table Show?**

Now that you know more about subatomic particles, you can appreciate the information about an element shown in its box on the Periodic Table. The first thing you see when you look in a specific box is the chemical symbol for the element. Above the chemical symbol is the atomic number, which tells you the number of protons in each atom of the element.

Below the chemical symbol, you see another number known as the **average atomic mass**. Recall that relative atomic mass compares each element by mass with carbon–12. However, different isotopes of the same element have different masses because they have different numbers of neutrons. The average atomic mass is a weighted average of the masses of all the isotopes of an element. That means that the atomic masses are averaged together, but the more common isotopes affect the average more than less common isotopes. (See Figure 4-9 on page 58.)

Key

- 6 — Atomic number
- C — Symbol
- 12.01 — Atomic mass

Group	1	2	3	4	5	6	7	8	9	10	11	12	13	14	15	16	17	18
	1 H 1.008																	2 He 4.003
	3 Li 6.941	4 Be 9.012											5 B 10.81	6 C 12.01	7 N 14.01	8 O 16.00	9 F 19.00	10 Ne 20.18
	11 Na 22.99	12 Mg 24.31											13 Al 26.98	14 Si 28.09	15 P 30.97	16 S 32.07	17 Cl 35.45	18 Ar 39.95
	19 K 39.10	20 Ca 40.08	21 Sc 44.96	22 Ti 47.88	23 V 50.94	24 Cr 52.00	25 Mn 54.94	26 Fe 55.85	27 Co 58.93	28 Ni 58.69	29 Cu 63.55	30 Zn 65.39	31 Ga 69.72	32 Ge 72.61	33 As 74.92	34 Se 78.96	35 Br 79.90	36 Kr 83.80
	37 Rb 85.47	38 Sr 87.62	39 Y 88.91	40 Zr 91.22	41 Nb 92.91	42 Mo 95.94	43 Tc (98)	44 Ru 101.1	45 Rh 102.9	46 Pd 106.4	47 Ag 107.9	48 Cd 112.4	49 In 114.8	50 Sn 118.7	51 Sb 121.8	52 Te 127.6	53 I 126.9	54 Xe 131.3
	55 Cs 132.9	56 Ba 137.3	57 La 138.9	72 Hf 178.5	73 Ta 181.0	74 W 183.8	75 Re 186.2	76 Os 190.2	77 Ir 192.2	78 Pt 195.1	79 Au 197.0	80 Hg 200.6	81 Tl 204.4	82 Pb 207.2	83 Bi 209.0	84 Po (209)	85 At (210)	86 Rn (222)
	87 Fr (223)	88 Ra 226.0	89 Ac 227.0	104 Rf (261)	105 Db (262)	106 Sg (263)	107 Bh (262)	108 Hs (265)	109 Mt (268)	110 Ds (281)	111 Rg (272)	112 Cn (285)	113 Uut (284)	114 Uuq (289)	115 Uup (288)	116 Uuh (292)	117 Uus	118 Uuo (294)

Lanthanides

58 Ce 140.1	59 Pr 140.9	60 Nd 144.2	61 Pm (145)	62 Sm 150.4	63 Eu 152.0	64 Gd 157.3	65 Tb 158.9	66 Dy 162.5	67 Ho 164.9	68 Er 167.3	69 Tm 168.9	70 Yb 173.0	71 Lu 175.0

Actinides

90 Th 232.0	91 Pa 231.0	92 U 238.0	93 Np 237.0	94 Pu (244)	95 Am (243)	96 Cm (247)	97 Bk (247)	98 Cf (251)	99 Es (252)	100 Fm (257)	101 Md (258)	102 No (259)	103 Lr (260)

Figure 4-9.

How Are Electrons Arranged in Atoms?

You know that in neutral atoms, the number of electrons is equal to the number of protons. Therefore, you can determine the number of electrons in an atom of an element by looking at the Periodic Table. Exactly where are the electrons located within each atom? According to Bohr, electrons in atoms are found in orbits, or **shells**. Each shell can hold a specific maximum number of electrons. This number of electrons generally depends upon the distance the shell is from the nucleus.

Electrons in a particular shell have a certain amount of energy that allows them to remain in that shell. Electrons are therefore said to move around in particular **principal energy levels**. If energy is added to an atom—for example, if the atom is heated—an electron jumps up to a higher energy level that is farther away from the nucleus. The atom is then said to be unstable, excited, or at a higher energy level than it is normally. When the electron returns to its original energy level, the energy that was previously added to it is given off, or emitted. This emitted energy is sometimes seen as colored light. Thus, when sodium metal is heated in a flame, electrons in the sodium atoms enter higher energy levels. When the electrons return to their original energy levels, they emit energy in the form of yellow light.

The energy levels of electrons are identified by numbers, as shown in Figure 4-10A. The energy level closest to the nucleus is known as the first principal energy level. This energy level can hold a maximum of 2 electrons. The next level is the second principal energy level, which can hold no more than 8 electrons. For elements from atomic numbers 1 through 20, the third energy level holds 8 electrons. However, it has the capacity to hold up to 18 electrons. As the atomic numbers of the elements increase beyond 20, each energy level is *not* filled to capacity before the next level is started.

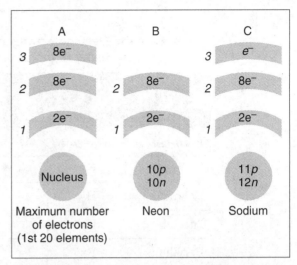

Figure 4-10. (A) Among the first 20 elements, the first energy level can hold a maximum of two electrons, the second can hold eight electrons, and the third can hold eight electrons. (B) Neon has a complete second energy level. (C) Sodium has only one electron in its third energy level.

Table 4-2 lists the first 21 elements in order of their increasing atomic numbers. In the first 20 elements, notice that each energy level is filled in turn. Thus, the second energy level of lithium contains 1 electron, the second energy level of beryllium contains 2 electrons, and so on, until neon, for which the second energy level is completely filled with 8 electrons (see Figure 4-10B).

Scandium, atomic number 21, is the first element that does not follow the rule for the orderly filling of energy levels. It would seem logical that, since calcium has 8 electrons in its third level and 2 electrons in its fourth level, scandium should have 8 electrons in its third level and 3 electrons in its fourth level. However, as Table 4-2 on page 60 reveals, scandium does not follow the rule. This book shall be concerned chiefly with elements of atomic numbers 1 to 20.

How Are Atomic Diagrams Constructed?

The atomic diagram in Figure 4-10 provides information about the electrons in each

Table 4-2.

What Are the Electron Arrangements of the First 21 Elements, in Order of Increasing Atomic Number?

Element	Symbol	Atomic Number	Number of Electrons in Energy Levels			
			1	2	3	4
Hydrogen	H	1	1			
Helium	He	2	2			
Lithium	Li	3	2	1		
Beryllium	Be	4	2	2		
Boron	B	5	2	3		
Carbon	C	6	2	4		
Nitrogen	N	7	2	5		
Oxygen	O	8	2	6		
Fluorine	F	9	2	7		
Neon	Ne	10	2	8		
Sodium	Na	11	2	8	1	
Magnesium	Mg	12	2	8	2	
Aluminum	Al	13	2	8	3	
Silicon	Si	14	2	8	4	
Phosphorus	P	15	2	8	5	
Sulfur	S	16	2	8	6	
Chlorine	Cl	17	2	8	7	
Argon	Ar	18	2	8	8	
Potassium	K	19	2	8	8	1
Calcium	Ca	20	2	8	8	2
Scandium	Sc	21	2	8	9	2

atom. You can use information about atoms of different elements to construct diagrams like these for other elements, too. Remember, these diagrams merely show the *relationships* between the atomic particles. Atomic diagrams are *not* pictures of atoms.

Consider the element sodium, $^{23}_{11}Na$, as an example. The atomic number of sodium is 11 and the mass number is 23.

The number of neutrons is $23 - 11 = 12$. In drawing the atom, protons are abbreviated by the letter p, neutrons by the letter n, and electrons by the letter e with a superscript minus sign, e^-. (The minus sign indicates that an electron has a negative charge.) Keep in mind that each energy level can hold only a specific maximum number of electrons. If it is necessary, you can refer to Table 4-2 to find the electron arrangement in a specific atom. Many students merely memorize the maximum number of electrons in each level for the first 20 elements. Thus:

1st	2nd	3rd
2	8	8

Follow these steps to draw a diagram of the sodium atom:

Step 1. List the necessary information:
number of protons = $11p$
number of neutrons = $12n$
number of electrons = $11e^-$

Step 2. Draw a circle to represent the nucleus of the sodium atom, showing the information obtained in Step 1.

Step 3. Indicate the electrons in their energy levels around the nucleus, filling each level to capacity as you move away from the nucleus.

(Figure 4-10C on page 59 shows an atomic diagram of a sodium atom.)

How Are Compounds Formed?

Recall from Chapter 3 that a compound forms when elements combine or separate during a chemical reaction. The diagram of the sodium atom can be used to help explain why elements react as they do.

Chemists have learned that certain elements are much *less reactive* than others are; that is, they are *more* **stable**. Further, energy levels in these stable elements are filled to capacity with electrons. Among the first 20 elements, helium, neon, and argon are examples of relatively stable elements. These stable elements are called the **noble gases**. An inspection of Table 4-2 shows that helium has 2 electrons in its outermost (first) level; neon has 8 electrons in its outermost (second) level; argon has 8 electrons in its outermost (third) level. Thus, each noble gas has its outermost energy level filled, which makes it relatively stable and less likely to react with other elements. Because nature favors changes that make for greater stability, elements react to acquire electron

arrangements that will complete (fill to capacity) their outermost energy levels.

Look again at the sodium atom. Each sodium atom contains only 1 electron in its third level. The sodium atom would be far more stable if its outermost level were complete. This could be accomplished in two ways. The sodium atom might give up its single electron in the third level, thus leaving the second level as the outermost filled energy level (the electron structure of neon). On the other hand, the sodium atom might gain 7 additional electrons, thus completing its third level, which would then have the maximum of 8 electrons (the electron structure of argon). Experiments have shown that it is easier (less energy is required) for a sodium atom to lose 1 electron than to gain 7 electrons. As a result, when the sodium atom combines with another atom, the sodium atom loses the electron from its third level, acquiring the electron structure of neon.

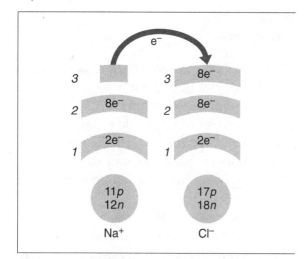

Figure 4-11. When atoms of sodium (Na) and chlorine (Cl) come close to each other, the electron from sodium's third level transfers to the third level of chlorine. The resulting compound is NaCl (table salt).

The chlorine atom in Figure 4-11 contains 7 electrons in its third level. This atom could become more stable either by accepting 1 electron in its outer energy level, or by giving away 7 electrons. Again, experiments have shown that it is easier for a chlorine atom to gain 1 electron than to lose 7 electrons.

If one atom of sodium and one atom of chlorine are sufficiently close to each other, they may combine. In this process, the single electron of the third level of the sodium atom is transferred to the third level of the chlorine atom, which already has 7 electrons. When this occurs, the sodium atom is left with an outer second level containing 8 electrons. The chlorine atom also now possesses 8 electrons in its third level. Each atom has a filled outermost energy level of electrons, as shown in Figure 4-11. As a result of the transfer of 1 electron, the sodium and chlorine atoms unite to form the compound sodium chloride.

As you can see, the tendency of one element to combine with another element depends to some extent on the number of electrons in the outermost energy level that can be transferred. The electrons in the out-

ermost energy level of an atom are known as **valence electrons**. The number of valence electrons, which represents the combining tendency of the atoms of an element, is known as the **valence number**. Valence number will be studied further in the next chapter.

Often, more than two atoms of an element combine to form a stable compound. An example of this occurs when atoms of calcium and chlorine unite. The calcium atom has 2 electrons in its fourth level. These electrons must be lost for the atom to become stable. Only *one* electron is required for a chlorine atom to become stable, Therefore, *one* atom of calcium combines with *two* atoms of chlorine to form calcium chloride, as shown in Figure 4-12. The calcium atom gives away two electrons, one electron to each chlorine atom. The formula for calcium chloride is $CaCl_2$, because 1 atom of calcium (Ca) combines with 2 atoms of chlorine (Cl).

Similarly, two sodium atoms and one oxygen atom combine to form sodium oxide (see Figure 4-13). The formula for sodium oxide is Na_2O, because 2 atoms of sodium (Na) combine with 1 atom of oxygen (O).

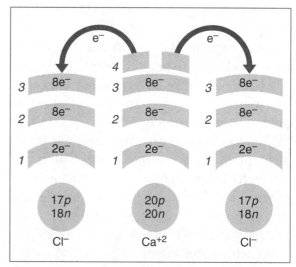

Figure 4-12. When calcium combines with chlorine, a calcium atom gives one of two valence electrons to each of two atoms of chlorine.

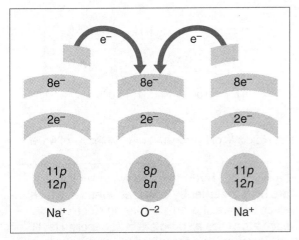

Figure 4-13. When sodium combines with oxygen, each of two sodium atoms donates one valence electron to an oxygen atom, which results in the formation of Na$_2$O.

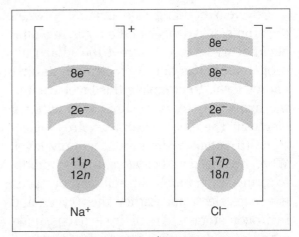

Figure 4-14. When sodium combines with chlorine, an electron is transferred from the sodium atom to the chlorine atom. The sodium atom now has one more proton than it has electrons, which gives it a net charge of 1+. By contrast, the chlorine atom now has one more electron than it has protons, giving it a net charge of 1−.

Recall that an element having a completed outermost energy level is called a noble gas. In addition to helium, neon, and argon, the noble gases include krypton, xenon, and radon. From their electron structures, you can predict that these elements should not react with other elements. An element that does not react with other elements is said to be **inert**. Under ordinary conditions, this prediction is found to be accurate for the noble gases. However, scientists discovered that xenon, radon, and krypton can be made to react and combine with active nonmetallic elements such as fluorine and oxygen. The explanation for this behavior is based on a more advanced atomic model.

▶ **How Do Atoms Bond?**

Understanding how atoms combine helps you to understand the forces that hold different atoms together. You know that a sodium atom combines with a chlorine atom by transferring one of its electrons to the chlorine atom. In doing so, the sodium atom is left with 10 electrons and 11 protons. In other words, the sodium atom now has 1 electron less than before and is thus posi-

tively charged. The chlorine atom, after accepting the electron from the sodium atom, has 18 electrons and 17 protons. It now has more electrons than protons and is thus negatively charged. (See Figure 4-14.) Atoms that become electrically charged after donating or receiving electrons are called **ions**. Electrical forces resulting from their opposite charges pull the sodium and chlorine ions together. This attraction between ions is known as **ionic bonding**, or **electrovalent bonding**.

A second type of bonding, called **covalent bonding**, results when electrons from two or more atoms are *shared*. For example, a molecule of hydrogen gas consists of 2 atoms of hydrogen. Its formula is H$_2$. Each hydrogen atom has 1 electron in the first energy level. By sharing a pair of electrons, each nucleus becomes "surrounded" by 2 electrons, as shown in Figure 4-15a on page 64. Hydrogen becomes stable when it has two electrons in the first energy level. The 2 electrons are shared rather than transferred as in ionic bonding. This makes the bond between the H atoms covalent.

Covalent bonding also occurs between the atoms of hydrogen and oxygen in a molecule of water (see Figure 4-15b). Each hydrogen atom has only 1 electron in its first energy level. To complete this level, each of the hydrogen atoms requires an additional electron. The oxygen atom requires 2 electrons to complete its second energy level. When hydrogen and oxygen atoms combine to form a water molecule, neither atom gains nor loses electrons. Rather, the oxygen and hydrogen atoms share their electrons, making it possible for the first energy levels of the hydrogen atoms and the second energy level of the oxygen atom to be filled to capacity. As with the H_2 molecule, the nucleus of each atom becomes "surrounded" by a completed outer energy level.

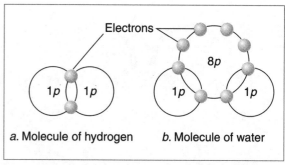

a. Molecule of hydrogen   b. Molecule of water

Figure 4-15. Hydrogen and water molecules are held together by covalent bonds in which electrons are shared. By sharing electrons, each atom has a complete outer energy level of electrons, two for hydrogen and eight for oxygen.

Chapter Review

Science Terms

The following list contains all of the boldfaced words found in this chapter and the page on which each appears.

anode (p. 54)

atomic number (p. 57)

average atomic mass (p. 57)

cathode (p. 53)

covalent bonding (p. 63)

electron (p. 53)

electrovalent bonding (p. 63)

inert (p. 63)

ionic bonding (p. 63)

ions (p. 63)

isotope (p. 56)

law of electrical attraction and repulsion (p. 54)

mass number (p. 56)

noble gases (p. 61)

nucleus (p. 55)

neutron (p. 56)

principal energy level (p. 59)

proton (p. 54)

shell (p. 59)

stable (p. 61)

static electricity (p. 54)

subatomic (p. 54)

valence electrons (p. 62)

valence number (p. 62)

Matching Questions

*In your notebook, write the letter of the item in column B that is
most closely related to the item in column A.*

Column A

_____ 1. atom that has gained or lost
   electrons

_____ 2. positive electrode

_____ 3. sum of protons and neutrons

_____ 4. subatomic particle with relatively
   negligible mass

_____ 5. stable element that does not react in
   nature

_____ 6. electrically neutral subatomic
   particle

_____ 7. scientist who proposed the "plum
   pudding" model of the atom

_____ 8. number of protons in an atom

_____ 9. type of bond in which atoms share
   electrons

_____ 10. atoms with the same atomic
   number but different atomic mass

Column B

a. atomic number
b. mass number
c. anode
d. neutron
e. electron
f. ion
g. noble gas
h. Thomson
i. isotopes
j. covalent

Multiple-Choice Questions

*In your notebook, write the letter preceding the word or expression
that best completes the statement or answers the question.*

1. The tiny, negatively charged particles first
described by Crookes are the
a. nuclei   c. electrons
b. protons   d. neutrons

2. The attraction of a rubbed comb for bits
of tissue paper gives evidence to the fact
that
a. matter is electrical in nature
b. matter is magnetic
c. matter contains subatomic particles
d. matter has mass

3. When two similarly charged objects are
brought close together, they
a. attract each other
b. have no effect on each other

c. stick to each other
d. repel each other

4. An object becomes positively charged
when it
a. has an excess of electrons
b. has a deficiency of electrons
c. has an equal number of protons and
   neutrons
d. has an equal number of protons and
   electrons

5. Which scientists proposed the "plum pudding" model of the atom ?
a. Rutherford   c. Thomson
b. Democritus   d. Bohr

6. The central portion of an atom in which most of the mass of the atom is concentrated is called the
   a. nucleus   c. electron
   b. shell   d. ring

7. In a neutral atom, the number of electrons is
   a. equal to the number of neutrons
   b. greater than the number of protons
   c. less than the number of protons
   d. equal to the number of protons

8. Atoms of the same element that differ slightly in mass are called
   a. neutrons   c. isotopes
   b. ions   d. positrons

9. The differences in the masses of atoms of the same element are attributed to different numbers of
   a. protons
   b. neutrons
   c. electrons
   d. positrons

10. Which atomic particle has a mass that is approximately 1/1837 that of a proton?
    a. a lepton
    b. a neutron
    c. a quark
    d. an electron

11. What does the atomic number of an element indicate?
    a. the number of protons
    b. the number of electrons
    c. the number of nucleons
    d. the number of neutrons

12. What scientist arranged the elements in the Periodic Table according to their atomic numbers?
    a. Moseley
    b. Mendeleev

c. Rutherford
d. Bohr

13. The atomic mass of an atom is equal to the mass of the
    a. protons
    b. protons and neutrons
    c. neutrons
    d. electrons

14. What are the electrons in the outermost energy level of an atom called?
    a. noble electrons
    b. ionic electrons
    c. energized electrons
    d. valence electrons

15. What is the maximum number of electrons found in the first level of any atom?
    a. 1   c. 8
    b. 2   d. 18

16. In the atom $^{40}_{18}\text{Ar}$, the number of protons is
    a. 18   c. 40
    b. 22   d. 58

17. Of the following, the element that has an outermost level that is complete is
    a. sodium
    b. neon
    c. chlorine
    d. oxygen

18. To achieve stability when it combines with chlorine, a sodium atom will
    a. accept 1 electron
    b. accept 7 electrons
    c. donate 1 electron
    d. donate 7 electrons

19. The element that has fewer than 2 electrons in its first energy level is
    a. neon
    b. hydrogen
    c. oxygen
    d. fluorine

20. The force of attraction between atoms that share electrons is called a
a. covalent bond
b. ionic bond
c. stable bond
d. partnering bond

___

TEST-TAKING TIP Make an outline of each chapter as you read through it. You can use the headings of the sections and include the boldface terms. Use the outline to review the content later on.

Modified True-False Questions

In some of the following statements, the italicized term makes the statement incorrect. For each incorrect statement, in your notebook, write the term that must be substituted for the italicized term to make the statement correct. For each correct statement, write the word "true."

1. An *ion* is an atom that has gained or lost electrons._____

2. Atoms of elements, held together by opposite electrical charges, are bonded by *covalent* bonds. _____

3. Atoms of different elements unite during chemical changes to produce new *elements*. _____

4. *Positively* charged subatomic particles are known as protons. _____

5. Like electrical charges *attract* one another. _____

6. *Neutrons* are found moving in the space around the nucleus. _____

7. The particles that travel in a Crookes tube and strike the walls of the tube are *anodes*._____

8. A neutral atom containing 13 protons contains *13* electrons. _____

9. The element $^{27}_{13}$Al contains 14 *protons*. _____

10. Among the first 20 elements, the first energy level holds up to *8* electrons. _____

11. Isotopes of an element have the same number of protons but different numbers of *electrons*. _____

12. The modern periodic table is arranged in order of *atomic number*. _____

13. Protons and neutrons are found in the *nucleus*. _____

14. The level in which an electron is located depends on its *energy*. _____

15. Ionic bonding occurs when electrons are *shared*. _____

Check Your Knowledge

Write the answer to each question in your notebook.

1. Describe the differences between the terms in each of the following pairs:
a. proton and neutron
b. ion and isotope
c. ionic bond and covalent bond
d. atomic number and atomic mass

2. How did the atomic model change due to the research of Thomson, Rutherford, and Bohr?

3. Complete the table.

Particle	Mass	Electric Charge	Location
Proton			
Electron			
Neutron			

4. What change did Henry Moseley make to Mendeleev's periodic table?

5. According to the Bohr model, what can cause an atom to emit light?

6. Why do some atoms form chemical bonds while others do not?

Think Critically

Write the answer to each of the following questions in your notebook.

1. Construct atomic diagrams for each of the following elements:
   a. $^{4}_{2}He$ d. $^{40}_{20}Ca$
   b. $^{25}_{12}Mg$ e. $^{20}_{10}Ne$
   c. $^{35}_{17}Cl$

2. Explain how calcium ($^{40}_{20}Ca$) and fluorine ($^{19}_{9}F$) become stable when they form calcium fluoride.

3. You are given a chemical whose identity is unknown. You are told, however, that the chemical is a pure element and is one of the first 20 elements (see Table 4-2 on page 60). You perform various experiments and observe the following:
   a. One atom of the element combines with two atoms of oxygen.
   b. The mass of the molecule of this new compound is 44.
   Determine the identity of the unknown element and the formula for its compound with oxygen. Explain how you reached your conclusions.

4. Figure 4-16 below show three different atoms. What conclusion can you reach about the relationship among the atoms?

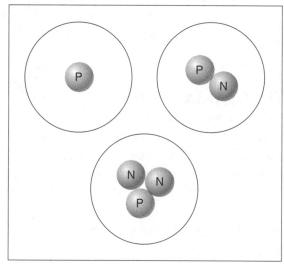

Figure 4-16.

Take It Further

1. Create a timeline that shows the evolution of the modern atomic model. Include each scientist who contributed to the model and describe the contribution.

2. Make a model of one of the first 20 elements of the Periodic Table. Choose items to represent each subatomic particle. Present your model to the class.

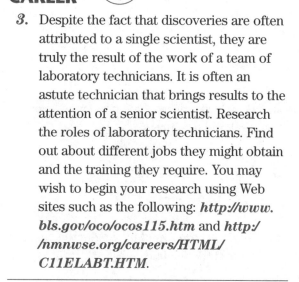

CAREER

3. Despite the fact that discoveries are often attributed to a single scientist, they are truly the result of the work of a team of laboratory technicians. It is often an astute technician that brings results to the attention of a senior scientist. Research the roles of laboratory technicians. Find out about different jobs they might obtain and the training they require. You may wish to begin your research using Web sites such as the following: ***http://www.bls.gov/oco/ocos115.htm*** and ***http://nmnwse.org/careers/HTML/C11ELABT.HTM***.

5 Why Do Elements React?

The beautiful colors and loud sounds of fireworks are all thanks to changes in matter. Elements react with each other in different ways according to their chemical properties, which result from their atomic structure.

After reading this chapter, you should be able to answer the following questions:

What is chemical reactivity and how does it depend on electrons?

How does reactivity vary within a given period or group of the Periodic Table?

What information does the valence number indicate?

What can you predict about elements that have more than one valence number?

What are polyatomic ions and how are they involved in chemical reactions?

What are replacement reactions and how are they related to the reactivity series?

An awesome firework celebration depends on the reactivity of several different kinds of metals. In this inquiry investigation, you will learn about and compare reactivity of different metals.

Materials:
✔ safety goggles
✔ metal strips of magnesium, zinc, iron, and copper
✔ graduated cylinder (25mL)
✔ dilute hydrochloric acid
✔ dilute copper(II) nitrate
✔ dilute iron(II) nitrate
✔ dilute silver nitrate
✔ dilute zinc nitrate
✔ 9 test tubes (150-mm)
✔ test-tube rack
✔ mossy zinc

NOTE: Observe the cautions indicated throughout.

Part A Place three test tubes in a rack. Place a small sample of the metallic element magnesium (Mg) in the first tube, about the same quantity of zinc (Zn) in the second, and about the same quantity of iron (Fe) in the third. Sandpaper each metal to remove any oxides.

CAUTION: Wear safety goggles while performing this experiment. If hydrochloric acid gets on your skin or clothes, wash immediately with plenty of water.

Add about 10 milliliters of dilute hydrochloric acid (HCl) to each test tube. Observe the test tubes carefully to determine how rapidly each metal reacts with the acid. The more reactive the metal is, the more gas bubbles will be formed.

1. *List the three metals in their order of reactivity, listing the most reactive metal first.*

Part B There is another way of determining whether one metal is more reactive than another metal. For example, in a water solution that contains a compound of a metal, a more reactive metal can replace the metal in the compound. You can tell when a metal has been replaced, because the replaced metal appears on the surface of the metal that is replacing it.

CAUTION: If any of these solutions spill on your skin, immediately wash with plenty of water and be sure to tell your teacher. Wear goggles.

Try the following:
a. Use a grease pencil to mark the numbers 1, 2, and 3 on separate test tubes.
b. To test tube 1, add 10 milliliters of dilute copper(II) nitrate solution.

c. To test tube 2, add 10 milliliters of dilute iron(II) nitrate solution.
d. To test tube 3, add 10 milliliters of dilute silver nitrate solution.
e. Add a small piece of mossy zinc to each of the three test tubes.
f. After 5 minutes, observe each test tube and record your observations.

Part C Perform this part of this experiment as follows:

a. Use a grease pencil to mark the numbers 4, 5, and 6 on separate test tubes.
b. To test tube 4, add 10 milliliters of dilute zinc nitrate solution.
c. To test tube 5, add 10 milliliters of dilute iron(II) nitrate solution.
d. To test tube 6, add 10 milliliters of dilute silver nitrate solution.
e. Add a small piece of copper to each of the test tubes.
f. After 5 minutes, observe each test tube and record your observations.

2. *Which is the most reactive metal? Explain your answer.*

3. *How does copper compare with silver in reactivity?*

4. *In your laboratory notebook, develop a table to organize and present your data. Transfer your data into the table.*

5. *Use your observations to prepare a list in which the metals copper, zinc, iron, magnesium, and silver are arranged according to their reactivity. List the most reactive metal first.*

What Is Chemical Reactivity?

When a sample of magnesium comes into contact with hydrochloric acid, as you observed in the inquiry investigation, the metal reacts vigorously with the acid. When a sample of copper comes into contact with hydrochloric acid, no reaction seems to take place. To understand why some elements are more **reactive**, that is, why some elements more readily interact chemically than other elements, you must study the electron structures of their atoms.

▶ How Are Electrons Related to Chemical Reactivity?

You have learned that an atom of an element becomes stable when it completes its outermost electron energy level. In this way, the element attains the electron structure of a noble gas. (See Figure 5-1 on page 72.)

Recall that elements may be generally classified as metals, nonmetals, and metalloids. The electron structures of the atoms of

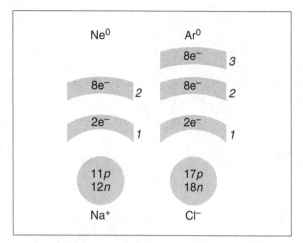

Figure 5-1. When sodium (Na) and chlorine (Cl) atoms become ions (Na$^+$) and (Cl?), their outermost electron energy levels assume the configuration of the nearest noble gases, neon (Ne) and argon (Ar).

metals show that these atoms generally have fewer than four electrons in their outermost levels. (See, for example, the electron structure of sodium, Figure 4-10, page 59, and of calcium, Figure 4-12, page 62.) In the previous chapter, you learned that a sodium atom loses its single electron when it reacts with a chlorine atom to form sodium chloride. Also, a calcium atom loses its two outer electrons when it reacts with two chlorine atoms to form calcium chloride. Similarly, the atoms of all metallic elements tend to lose electrons when they react.

The electron structures of the atoms of nonmetals show that these atoms, unlike the atoms of metals, generally have more than four outermost electrons. Consequently, two chlorine atoms, when reacting with calcium to form calcium chloride, each gain a single electron. In a similar manner, all nonmetallic atoms tend to gain electrons when they react.

The electron structures of the atoms of metalloids reveal that these atoms generally have four outermost electrons. Experiments show that the atoms of metalloids, such as silicon, may gain, lose, or share electrons when they react.

What Is the Significance of Valence Electrons?

Recall from Chapter 4 that the electrons in the outermost level, which an atom can transfer or share when reacting with other atoms, are called *valence electrons*. The reactivity and metallic properties of an element are related to the number of valence electrons it has. The elements in Period 2 (row 2) of the Periodic Table are lithium, beryllium, boron, carbon, nitrogen, oxygen, and fluorine. Table 5-1 shows how the number of outermost electrons is related to reactivity and metallic properties of these elements.

Notice that lithium has one valence electron, beryllium has two valence electrons, and boron has three valence electrons (Table 5-1). These electrons are given away when these elements react with nonmetals. Of these three elements, lithium is the most reactive, beryllium is the second most reactive, next, and boron is the least reactive.

What Accounts for Differences in Reactivity in a Given Period?

You can account for this difference in reactivity by assuming that less energy is needed to transfer the single valence electron of lithium than to transfer the two or three valence electrons of the other two metals. Remember that of these three elements, lithium has the smallest positive charge, and therefore shows the least tendency to attract electrons.

Notice that an atom of nitrogen has five valence electrons, oxygen has six valence electrons, and fluorine has seven valence electrons. These outermost levels gain electrons when the elements react with metals. Of these three elements, fluorine, having the largest positive charge, is the most reactive, oxygen is the second most reactive, and nitrogen is the least reactive. As you move toward the right across Period 2 from Group 1

Table 5-1.
How Many Electrons Are in the Outermost Energy Levels of Metals And Nonmetals (Period 2)?

	GROUPS						
	1 (IA)	*2* (IIA)	*13* (IIIA)	*14* (IVA)	*15* (VA)	*16* (VIA)	*17* (VIIA)
Symbol	$^{7}_{3}L$	$^{9}_{4}Be$	$^{11}_{5}B$	$^{12}_{6}C$	$^{14}_{7}N$	$^{16}_{8}O$	$^{19}_{9}F$
Name	lithium	beryllium	boron	carbon	nitrogen	oxygen	fluorine
Electrons in outermost energy level	1	2	3	4	5	6	7

decreasing metallic properties
→
increasing nonmetallic properties

reactive metals   reactive nonmetals

(IA) to Group 17 (VIIA), the number of outermost electrons increases by one in each successive group. This change in electron number appears to correspond to the differences in the reactivity of the elements in this period.

Thus, since the tendency to lose electrons is characteristic of metals, the elements on the far left side of the Periodic Table are more metallic than are those on the far right side. In going from left to right across a given row, metallic properties decrease and nonmetallic properties increase.

▶ How Is Atomic Radius Related to Chemical Reactivity?

Metals. In any group of metals in the Periodic Table, the *most reactive* metal in the group is found near the *bottom* of the column, whereas the *least reactive* member of the group is found near the *top*. Thus, in Group 1 (IA) shown in Table 5-2, cesium is more reactive than lithium. The reason for the differences in chemical reactivity within a group can also be understood by studying the electron structures of the atoms of these

Table 5-2.
How Are Electron Energy Levels Filled in Atoms of Elements in Group 1 (IA)?

Metal	*Symbol*	Electron Energy Levels					
		1	*2*	*3*	*4*	*5*	*6*
Lithium	Li	2	1				
Sodium	Na	2	8	1			
Potassium	K	2	8	8	1		
Rubidium	Rb	2	8	18	8	1	
Cesium	Cs	2	8	18	18	8	1

Group 1 (IA)

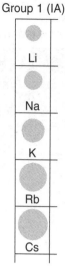

Figure 5-2. The atomic radius of Group 1 (IA) metals increases from top to bottom. The most reactive of these metals is that with the largest atomic radius, cesium.

easily lost, metals having distant electrons react readily with other elements and are, therefore, more reactive.

The distance of the outermost energy level from the nucleus of the atom generally describes the size of the atom and is known as the **atomic radius**. Thus, since rubidium has more occupied energy levels than lithium, the atomic radius of the element rubidium is greater than that of lithium. Therefore, the outermost electron of rubidium is more easily lost than the outermost electron of lithium. In Figure 5-2, you see a comparison of the number of occupied energy levels (atomic radius) of the elements in Group 1 (IA). Consequently, rubidium is more reactive chemically than lithium.

metals. In Table 5-2, note that the outermost level of the less reactive metal, lithium, is much closer to the nucleus of the atom than is the outermost level of the more reactive metal, rubidium. You already know that the negatively charged electrons are held in their energy levels by the attraction of the positively charged nucleus. This force of attraction *decreases* considerably as the *distance* from the nucleus *increases*. Therefore, electrons that are more distant from the nucleus are held less tightly and are more easily lost than are electrons closer to the nucleus. Since the more distant electrons are more

Nonmetals. In any group of nonmetals in the Periodic Table, the *most reactive* nonmetal in the group is found near the *top* of the column, whereas the *least reactive* nonmetal is found near the *bottom*. For example, in Group 17 (VIIA), shown in Table 5-3, fluorine is the most reactive nonmetal and iodine is the least reactive. Figure 5-3 shows that the atomic radius of the elements of Group 17 (VIIA) *increases* as you move from the top to the bottom of a group. Nonmetals combine chemically by attracting or gaining electrons. Since the attraction for electrons by the nucleus is greater when the atomic radius is small, the closer the outermost orbit is to the nucleus of a nonmetal, the more reactive the

Table 5-3.
How Are Electron Energy Levels Filled in Atoms of Elements in Group 17 (VIIa)?

Nonmetal	Symbol	Electron Energy Levels				
		1	2	3	4	5
Fluorine	F	2	7			
Chlorine	Cl	2	8	7		
Bromine	Br	2	8	18	7	
Iodine	I	2	8	18	18	7

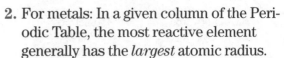

Group 17 (VIIA)

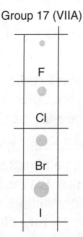

Figure 5-3. The atomic radius of Group 17 (VIIA) nonmetals increase from top to bottom. The most reactive element among these nonmetals is that with the smallest atomic radius, flourine.

element is. Accordingly, the elements at the *top* of nonmetallic groups are *more reactive* than those at the *bottom* of these groups.

Which Factors Determine Chemical Reactivity?

Chemical reactivity is therefore determined, to a large measure, by the number of electrons transferred between combining atoms and by the distance between these electrons and the nuclei of the atoms. To make meaningful predictions concerning reactivity, it is simpler (and safer) to compare elements in the same row or elements in the same column. In the same row on the Periodic Table, elements show small differences in atomic radius, and therefore it is the number of electrons that chiefly determines reactivity. In the same column, elements have the same number of outermost electrons and so it is the atomic radius that largely determines reactivity.

The factors determining chemical reactivity may be summarized as follows:

1. In a given row of the Periodic Table, the smaller the number of electrons transferred between reacting atoms, the more vigorous is the reaction.

2. For metals: In a given column of the Periodic Table, the most reactive element generally has the *largest* atomic radius.

3. For nonmetals: In a given column of the Periodic Table, the most reactive element generally has the *smallest* atomic radius.

What Information Is Indicated by Valence Number?

Recall from Chapter 4 that when two atoms combine, each atom tends to gain a complete outermost energy level of electrons. In a neutral atom, the outermost energy level is called the **valence shell**. The electrons in the valence shell, the valence electrons, are usually the only parts of atoms that are involved in chemical changes. Thus, the valence shell of an atom often reveals the number of electrons the atom may lose, gain, or share when the element reacts with other substances. This number is known as the *valence number.*

The valence number of an element is expressed by a sign (+ or −) and by a number. A positive sign (+) indicates that the atom tends to lose electrons; a negative sign (−) indicates that the atom tends to gain electrons. The number indicates how many valence electrons must be gained or lost to produce a valence shell that has the structure of a noble gas. For example, in Figure 5-4 on page 76, the valence number of aluminum is 3+. The positive sign indicates that, in a chemical change, atoms of aluminum tend to lose electrons. The number 3 represents the 3 electrons in the valence shell of the atom which, when lost, will leave a complete outermost level.

The valence number of oxygen is 2−, as shown in Figure 5-4. The negative sign indicates that atoms of oxygen tend to gain electrons in order to attain the structure of a noble gas. An oxygen atom normally has 6 electrons in its valence shell. The number 2 indicates that there is room in the valence shell of the atom for 2 more electrons. A gain of 2 electrons results in a complete outermost level of 8 electrons (the new particle

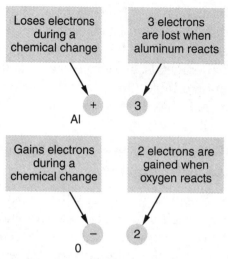

Figure 5-4. The valence number of an element indicates the number of electrons an atom of the element will lose (+) or gain (−) or share when it reacts to form compounds.

now has a total of 10 electrons, or has the structure of neon).

Table 5-4 lists the valence numbers for some common metals and nonmetals. Note that the valence numbers of the metals are

Table 5-4.
What Are the Valence Numbers of Some Common Elements?

Element	Symbol	Valence Number
Lithium	Li	1+
Sodium	Na	1+
Potassium	K	1+
Calcium	Ca	2+
Magnesium	Mg	2+
Aluminum	Al	3+
Carbon	C	4+
Fluorine	F	1−
Chlorine	Cl	1−
Oxygen	O	2−
Sulfur	S	2−

positive (+), and the valence numbers of the nonmetals are negative (−).

What Can You Predict About Elements That Have More Than One Valence Number?

Many experiments with different elements have shown that, under different conditions, some elements may have more than one valence number. For example, nonmetallic elements such as sulfur, phosphorus, and nitrogen may have either positive or negative valence numbers. This occurs because these nonmetals can either gain or lose (or sometimes share) electrons to complete their outermost shells. In the compound Na_2S (sodium sulfide), sulfur has a valence number of 2−, whereas in the compound SO_2 (sulfur dioxide), sulfur has a valence number of 4+.

Some metallic elements such as iron, copper, and lead may also have more than one valence number. Atoms of these elements, which have atomic numbers beyond 20, have more complex electron structures than atoms with atomic numbers below 20. For example, the element iron (atomic number 26) may form compounds in which the valence number of iron is either 2+ or 3+. This means that an atom of iron can lose either two or three electrons with relatively equal ease, depending on the specific reaction.

Chemists have devised a simple system for naming such compounds. The chemists incorporate Roman numerals into the names of the compounds. For example, iron oxide can form as FeO or Fe_2O_3. In FeO, iron has a valence number of 2+. In Fe_2O_3, iron has a valence number of 3+. Thus, chemists call the FeO iron(II) oxide and the Fe_2O_3 iron(III) oxide. Table 5-5 lists some metals that have more than one valence number and names the chlorine compounds of each.

What Are Polyatomic Ions?

In many reactions, groups of atoms behave as though they were one single atom. Such

Table 5-5.
Which Metals Have More than One Valence Number?

Metal	Symbol	Valence Numbers	Typical Compound	Formula
Iron	Fe	2+	iron(II) chloride	$FeCl_2$
		3+	iron(III) chloride	$FeCl_3$
Tin	Sn	2+	tin(II) chloride	$SnCl_2$
		4+	tin(IV) chloride	$SnCl_4$
Chromium	Cr	2+	chromium(II) chloride	$CrCl_2$
		3+	chromium(III) chloride	$CrCl_3$
Mercury	Hg	1+	mercury(I) chloride	Hg_2Cl_2
		2+	mercury(II) chloride	$HgCl_2$

groups of atoms are known as **polyatomic ions**, formerly called *radicals*. The atoms in most of these ions are bonded together by sharing the electrons in their valence shells. It is interesting to note that polyatomic ions, like atoms of elements, have a specific valence number. Table 5-6 summarizes the formulas, names, and valence numbers of some common polyatomic ions. These ions generally have a negative valence number, which means they behave as though they were non-

metals. The ammonium ion is an exception to this rule.

▶ What Is the Reactivity Series of Metals?

So far, you have seen how a study of atomic structure can help determine the relative reactivity of various elements. However, the discussion has been limited to elements that lie in the same period (row) or same family

Table 5-6.
What Are Some Common Polyatomic Ions?

Polyatomic Ion	Formula	Valence Number	Typical Compound	Formula
Ammonium	NH_4	1+	Ammonium chloride	NH_4Cl
Carbonate	CO_3	2−	Sodium carbonate	Na_2CO_3
Chlorate	ClO_3	1−	Potassium chlorate	$KClO_3$
Hydroxide	OH	1−	Magnesium hydroxide	$Mg(OH)_2$
Nitrate	NO_3	1−	Ammonium nitrate	NH_4NO_3
Sulfite	SO_3	2−	Sodium sulfite	Na_2SO_3
Sulfate	SO_4	2−	Copper sulfate	$CuSO_4$
Phosphate	PO_4	3−	Lithium phosphate	Li_3PO_4

(column) of the Periodic Table. Now consider three metals that do not lie in the same period or family: magnesium, zinc, and iron. As you observed in the inquiry investigation at the beginning of the chapter, the reactions of hydrochloric acid and these metals reveal that magnesium reacts more vigorously than zinc, and zinc reacts more vigorously than iron. Since the reactivity of a metal represents the tendency of the metal to lose electrons, magnesium loses electrons more readily than zinc, and zinc loses electrons more readily than iron. Since each of these metals has two electrons in its valence shell, the difference in reactivity is due largely to the differences in atomic radii. The atomic radius of magnesium is larger than the atomic radius of zinc, which, in turn, is larger than the atomic radius of iron. (See the Periodic Table in Chapter 4, page 58.)

What Are Replacement Reactions?

Experiments with solutions of compounds of magnesium, zinc, and iron reveal that the following reactions always take place:

$$(zinc) + (iron\ compound) \rightarrow$$
$$(iron) + (zinc\ compound)$$

$$(magnesium) + (zinc\ compound) \rightarrow$$
$$(zinc) + (magnesium\ compound)$$

In the first reaction, note that zinc (which is more reactive than iron) *replaces* iron; that is, the iron compound becomes a zinc compound. Similarly, in the second reaction, magnesium (which is more reactive than zinc) replaces zinc and becomes a magnesium compound.

Other experiments, such as your inquiry investigation with the nitrates, reveal that zinc replaces copper and silver from solutions of copper and silver compounds. Copper replaces silver from a solution of a silver compound, but copper does not replace zinc or iron from solutions of their compounds. In general, experiments reveal that the fol-

lowing reaction always takes place in a water solution:

$$\begin{pmatrix} more\ reactive \\ metal \end{pmatrix} + \begin{pmatrix} compound\ of\ less \\ reactive\ metal \end{pmatrix} \rightarrow$$
$$\begin{pmatrix} less\ reactive \\ metal \end{pmatrix} + \begin{pmatrix} compound\ of\ more \\ reactive\ metal \end{pmatrix}$$

This type of reaction is called a **replacement reaction**. Note that the more reactive metal, in becoming a compound, loses electrons.

What Is the Order of the Reactivity Series?

As a result of studying the preceding replacement reactions, we can arrange the metals in

Table 5-7.
What Are Some of the Metals in the Reactivity Series?
(At 20°C)

Order of Reactivity	Metal	Symbol
Most reactive	Lithium	Li
	Potassium	K
	Barium	Ba
	Calcium	Ca
	Sodium	Na
	Magnesium	Mg
decreasing activity	Aluminum	Al
	Zinc	Zn
	Iron	Fe
	Tin	Sn
	Lead	Pb
	Hydrogen	H
	Copper	Cu
	Mercury	Hg
	Silver	Ag
	Platinum	Pt
Least reactive	Gold	Au

decreasing order of reactivity: magnesium (most reactive), zinc, iron, copper, silver (least reactive). This list is known as the **Reactivity Series of the Metals** and is shown in part in Table 5-7.

Note the presence of hydrogen on this list. Although hydrogen is not a metal, it has been placed on the list because it behaves as though it were a metal in certain reactions. Metals found above hydrogen on this list will replace hydrogen in acids, while those metals below hydrogen on this list will *not* replace hydrogen in acids. Hydrogen is therefore used as a convenient reference point.

The reactivity series lists the different metals (and hydrogen) in order of their decreasing tendencies to lose electrons in water solution. Since reactivity also depends upon temperature, the series is usually stated at a given temperature, in this case 20°C.

As you learned, the tendency of a metal to lose electrons depends chiefly on the number of valence electrons and on the atomic radius of the atom. The reactivity series may be used to make reasonable predictions concerning the reactivity of different metals. According to this table, for example, aluminum will replace mercury in a solution of a mercury compound. Silver will not replace tin from a solution of a tin compound. Remember, however, that these conclusions are *predictions*. To be completely sure of any reaction, it is necessary to carry out the reaction in the laboratory. From time to time, you may note exceptions from what you predict. The reasons for these exceptions will become more and more apparent as you continue to gain more knowledge in your study of chemistry.

Chapter Review

Science Terms

The following list contains all of the boldfaced words found in this chapter and the page on which each appears.

atomic radius (p. 74)   reactive (p. 71)   replacement reaction (p. 78)

polyatomic ion (p. 77)   Reactivity Series of the Metals (p. 79)   valence shell (p. 75)

Matching Questions

In your notebook, write the letter of the item in column B that is most closely related to the item in column A.

Column A

_____ 1. valence electrons

_____ 2. atomic radius

_____ 3. polyatomic ion

_____ 4. replacement reaction

_____ 5. valence shell

_____ 6. reactive

_____ 7. valence number

_____ 8. hydrogen

_____ 9. iron(II) oxide

_____ 10. iron(III) oxide

Column B

a. compound in which iron has a valence number of 2+

b. process in which a more reactive metal takes the place of a less reactive metal

c. compound in which iron has a valence number of 3+

d. quantity of electrons in outermost shell

e. size of atom

f. only nonmetal on the Reactivity Series of the Metals

g. readily interacts chemically

h. involved in chemical reaction

i. outermost energy level

j. group of atoms that behave as a single atom

TEST-TAKING TIP Become familiar with the general structure of the Periodic Table. While you may not need to memorize it, knowing the locations of common elements as well as the relationships between groups of elements will help you make predictions and recall information.

Multiple-Choice Questions

In your notebook, write the letter preceding the word or expression that best completes the statement or answers the question.

1. What happens to metals when they react chemically?
   a. They gain electrons.
   b. They lose electrons.
   c. They gain protons.
   d. They lose protons.

2. Carbon has four electrons in its outermost level. When it reacts chemically, carbon
   a. always gains 4 electrons
   b. always loses 4 electrons
   c. may lose, gain, or share 4 electrons
   d. may lose or gain 4 electrons

3. How is metallic activity reflected in the Periodic Table?
   a. Metallic properties decrease from left to right across a period.
   b. Only elements in the top right are metallic.
   c. Elements along the zigzag line are metallic.
   d. Elements with metallic properties are highlighted along the bottom.

4. In the Periodic Table, where is the element that exhibits the strongest non-metallic properties ?
   a. on the upper left side
   b. on the lower left side
   c. on the upper right side
   d. on the lower right side

5. Which of the following is indicated by the fact that calcium has a valence number of 2+?
   a. Each atom of calcium has two protons in its nucleus.
   b. An atom will give up two electrons to become stable.
   c. Each atom of calcium has two electrons surrounding the nucleus.
   d. An atom will accept two electrons when it bonds with other atoms.

6. Rubidium and lithium are in the same group of the Periodic Table. Why is the outermost electron of rubidium more easily lost than the outermost electron of lithium?
   a. Rubidium has more electrons than lithium.
   b. Lithium has more protons to hold onto the electron.
   c. The outermost electron in rubidium is farther from the nucleus.
   d. Lithium has a lower atomic mass than rubidium.

7. Why does the atomic radius decrease from left to right across a row of the Periodic Table?
   a. As the number of protons increases, the electrons are pulled toward the nucleus more strongly.

b. As the number of electrons increases, they begin to exert an attractive force on one another.

c. As the number of protons increases, electrons are knocked out of the atom.

d. As the number of electrons increases, each electron becomes smaller in size.

8. Which nonmetal in Group 7 of the Periodic Table is most reactive?
   a. F
   b. Cl
   c. Br
   d. At

9. The valence number of aluminum is 3+. This means that, in a chemical reaction, aluminum is most likely to
   a. gain 5 electrons
   b. gain 3 electrons
   c. give away 5 electrons
   d. give away 3 electrons

10. As the atomic radius of an atom of a nonmetal decreases, electrons are
    a. lost more easily
    b. lost with greater difficulty
    c. attracted more easily
    d. attracted with greater difficulty

11. Which of the following metals exhibits more than one valence number?
    a. sodium
    b. potassium
    c. calcium
    d. iron

12. Of the following nonmetals, the element that does not exhibit more than one valence number is
    a. fluorine
    b. sulfur
    c. carbon
    d. nitrogen

13. What is the valence number of iron in the compound FeO?
    a. 2–
    b. 2+
    c. 3+
    d. 3+

14. What is the name of the compound $FeCl_3$?
    a. iron(I) chloride
    b. iron(II) chloride
    c. iron(III) chloride
    d. chloride(III) iron

15. When an iron nail is placed into a solution of copper sulfate, iron(II) sulfate is formed. Which of the following changes takes place during this reaction?
    a. Electrons are transferred from sulfur to iron.
    b. Sulfur atoms change into copper atoms.
    c. Copper atoms take the place of iron atoms.
    d. The iron replaces the copper.

Modified True-False Questions

In some of the following statements, the italicized term makes the statement incorrect. For each incorrect statement, in your notebook, write the term that must be substituted for the italicized term to make the statement correct. For each correct statement, write the word "true."

1. The most reactive metal in any group of the Periodic Table is found near the *top* of the column. _____

2. No reaction occurs when copper is placed into a solution of zinc nitrate because copper is *less* reactive than zinc. _____

3. An element that is *stable* will chemically interact more readily with other elements. _____

4. A list of metals arranged according to their activity is called the *Periodic Table of the Elements*. _____

5. Metals that are higher in the Reactivity Series have a *lesser* tendency to lose electrons. _____

6. Elements that have some properties of metals and some properties of nonmetals are called *mixtures*. _____

7. Metals that have fewer electrons in their valence shell require *less* energy when they react than metals with more valence electrons. _____

8. In nonmetals, as the distance of the valence electrons from the nucleus increases, the reactivity of the nonmetal *increases.* _____

9. The number of electrons lost, gained, or shared when an element reacts with other elements is given by the *atomic radius* of the element. _____

10. A *subscript* in the name of a compound that contains a metal indicates the valence number of that metal. _____

Check Your Knowledge

Write the answer to each question in your notebook.

1. Explain why each of the following statements is true:
    a. Potassium is a more reactive metal than sodium.
    b. Sodium is a more reactive metal than magnesium.
    c. Fluorine is a more reactive nonmetal than chlorine.
    d. Chlorine is a more reactive nonmetal than sulfur.
    e. When zinc is placed into a solution of copper sulfate, the zinc replaces the copper.

2. How does the valence number vary between metals, metalloids, and nonmetals? How does the valence number affect the reactivity of the elements?

3. Why are the valence electrons of cesium held less tightly than the valence electrons of lithium?

4. How does the size of the atomic radius affect reactivity in metals and nonmetals?

5. Why is magnesium more reactive than zinc, even though both atoms have two electrons in their valence shells?

Think Critically

Write the answer to each of the following questions in your notebook.

1. The following reactions were performed to test the activity of iron, hydrogen, copper, silver, and lead. From the information given by these reactions, arrange the five elements in order of increasing activity.
    a. copper + hydrochloric acid → no reaction
    b. lead + hydrochloric acid → hydrogen + lead chloride
    c. iron + lead nitrate → lead + iron nitrate
    d. copper + silver nitrate → silver + copper nitrate

2. Explain why there is danger of an explosion when potassium metal is placed in water. *Clue:* One product of this reaction is H_2.

3. For many years, chemists assumed that the noble gases (Group 18) would not react with other chemicals to form compounds. Then, about 30 years ago, chemists produced a compound of a noble gas and another element. Discuss which noble gas is likely to have been involved and which other element. Explain your reasoning.

4. According to Table 5-7 on page 78, what three metals can be replaced by mercury in a replacement reaction?

Take It Further

1. Find out why sodium and potassium are both stored in oil. Write a paragraph explaining your findings.

2. A blast furnace can be used to extract any metal that is listed lower than carbon in the Reactivity Series. Electrolysis must be used to extract metals listed higher than carbon in the Reactivity Series. Research each method. Find out what is involved and how each method is used. Present your findings to the class.

CAREER

3. Metallurgists need a thorough knowledge of the properties and reactivity of metals. Find out what a metallurgist or metallurgical engineer does, what education is required, and what kinds of jobs are available. You may wish to begin your research at *http://www.mmsa.net/* or *http:// www.aimeny.org/*.

6

How Are Chemical Compounds Described?

These sparkling crystals are actually different samples of sugar. They represent a special form of matter called a compound. Each crystal is made up of the basic elements carbon, hydrogen, and oxygen bound in specific ways.

After reading this chapter, you should be able to answer the following questions:

How are chemical formulas written?

How are compounds named?

What information do chemical formulas hold?

How is formula mass determined?

How is percentage composition by mass figured?

Finding the Percentage by Mass of Oxygen Released by the Decomposition of Hydrogen Peroxide

So far, you have learned a lot about chemical elements. The names and properties of chemical compounds depend on the elements from which they are formed. In this inquiry investigation, you will describe a compound by one of the elements from which it forms.

CAUTION: Wear safety goggles when completing this activity.

Materials:
✔ safety goggles
✔ 2 test tubes (150-mm)
✔ beaker (250-mL)
✔ manganese dioxide
✔ spatula
✔ triple-beam or electronic balance
✔ hydrogen peroxide (3%)
✔ wooden splints
✔ matches

Part A Place two test tubes into an empty beaker. Record the total mass of the beaker and test tubes.

Part B Add manganese dioxide (MnO_2) to a depth of about 1 cm to one of the test tubes. Record the total mass of the beaker, test tubes, and manganese dioxide.

Part C Add a 3% solution of hydrogen peroxide (H_2O_2) to a depth of about 2.5 cm to the empty test tube. Determine the total mass of the beaker, test tubes, manganese dioxide, and hydrogen peroxide.

Part D Pour the hydrogen peroxide into the test tube containing the manganese dioxide. Place the emptied test tube back in the beaker.

Part E After about 1 minute, hold a glowing splint near the mouth of the test tube containing the hydrogen peroxide and manganese dioxide.

   1. What happens to the glowing splint?

   2. What gas is at the mouth of the test tube? Explain.

Part F After the bubbling has stopped, wait 1 minute and then determine the total mass of the beaker, test tubes, and contents.

Part G Determine the change in mass that occurs during the reaction. This mass equals the mass of the oxygen released by the hydrogen peroxide.
   (In this reaction, oxygen is not released from the manganese dioxide. The manganese dioxide is a *catalyst;* it merely speeds up the release of the oxygen from the hydrogen peroxide.)

As you carried out your investigation, you were asked to find each of the following quantities:

Mass of beaker and test tubes
Mass of beaker, test tubes, and manganese dioxide
Mass of beaker, test tubes, manganese dioxide, and hydrogen peroxide
Calculate mass of hydrogen peroxide
Mass of beaker, test tubes, and contents after the reaction
Calculate mass of oxygen released during the reaction

Part H Find the percentage, by mass, of oxygen released from hydrogen peroxide as follows:

$$\text{percent oxygen released} = \frac{\text{mass of oxygen released}}{\text{mass of hydrogen peroxide}} \times 100\%$$

3. *Suppose you were to repeat this experiment several times. Would you expect to get exactly the same value for the percent oxygen released? Explain.*

How Are Chemical Formulas Written?

Recall from Chapter 3 that each element is represented by a chemical symbol. A compound is represented by the symbols of the elements of which it is made and by subscripts that indicate the number of atoms of each element. Such a representation, called a chemical formula, consists of a group of symbols and subscripts. Remember that a subscript, written below and to the right of the symbol, gives the number of atoms of an element in a molecule.

Each atom has a specific atomic mass. Therefore, the number of atoms also reveals the number of atomic masses of an element in a molecule. For example, the formula for hydrogen peroxide, H_2O_2, indicates that a molecule of this substance is composed of 2 atoms of hydrogen and 2 atoms of oxygen for a total of 4 atoms. The formula also reveals that the molecule is composed of 2 atomic masses of hydrogen and 2 atomic masses of oxygen.

The formula for manganese dioxide, MnO_2, indicates the presence of 1 atom (1 atomic mass) of manganese and 2 atoms (2 atomic masses) of oxygen in a molecule of manganese dioxide.

You have already learned that the number of atoms of each element in a compound is determined by the valence numbers, or the combining tendencies, of the atoms. Now use this knowledge to write the formula for the compound formed when aluminum and oxygen unite. This compound is called aluminum oxide.

As Figure 6-1 shows, each aluminum atom must lose 3 electrons to combine chemically, whereas each oxygen atom must gain 2 electrons. In order to form complete outermost levels (valence shells) for all the

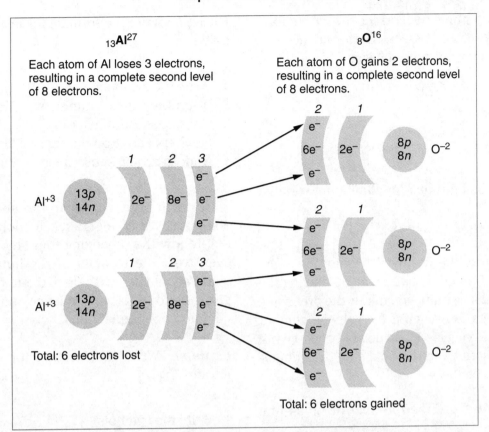

$_{13}Al^{27}$

Each atom of Al loses 3 electrons, resulting in a complete second level of 8 electrons.

$_{8}O^{16}$

Each atom of O gains 2 electrons, resulting in a complete second level of 8 electrons.

Total: 6 electrons lost

Total: 6 electrons gained

Figure 6-1. When aluminum reacts with oxygen to form aluminum oxide (Al_2O_3), each of the two aluminum atoms gives 3 electrons to the oxygen atoms.

atoms, 2 atoms of aluminum must combine with 3 atoms of oxygen. The 2 atoms of aluminum give up 6 electrons, which are accepted by the outermost levels of 3 atoms of oxygen. (Each atom attains the stable electron structure of neon.) Thus, the electron structure of the valence shells of the combining atoms determines their number in a compound. This knowledge allows you to figure out the formula for aluminum oxide, which is Al_2O_3.

Unfortunately, using electron structures for working out formulas is slow and cumbersome. However, if you know the valence number of each element, or can consult the Periodic Table, you can work out the correct formulas more quickly and easily. The Periodic Table (page 58) shows that aluminum has a valence number of 3+, whereas oxygen has a valence number of 2−. The 3+ valence number indicates that aluminum loses

3 electrons when it combines chemically. The 2− valence number of oxygen indicates that the oxygen atom gains 2 electrons when it combines chemically.

To write the chemical formula for a compound formed by two elements having different valence numbers, such as aluminum oxide, proceed as follows:

1. Write the symbols for the elements present in the compound, writing the element with the positive valence number first.

Al   O

2. Write the valence number of the element ABOVE and to the right of each chemical symbol, in other words as a superscript.

Al^{3+} O^{2-}

3. To determine the correct subscripts for the formula, "crisscross" the valence numbers, but drop the sign.

$$Al^{3+} \quad O^{2-}$$

$$Al_2 \quad O_3$$

4. The final formula for aluminum oxide is:

$$Al_2O_3$$

To write the chemical formula for compounds formed by two elements having the same valence numbers, follow the preceding four steps. However, if the valence number of each element is 1, you do not need to write the subscript 1 in the final step. It is understood to be there.

Example: Write the formula for potassium chloride.

1. Write the symbols: K Cl
2. Insert the valence numbers: $K^{1+} Cl^{1-}$
3. Crisscross the valence numbers and drop the signs: K_1Cl_1
4. Omit the subscript 1:   KCl

If the valence numbers of the elements are greater than 1 but still equal, the subscript 1 is also understood.

Example: Write the formula for magnesium oxide.

1. Write the symbols: Mg O
2. Insert the valence numbers: $Mg^{2+}O^{2-}$
3. Crisscross the valence numbers and drop the signs: Mg_2O_2
4. Omit the equal subscripts: MgO

To write the chemical formula for a compound that contains a polyatomic ion, follow the preceding four steps. However, treat the formula of the ion as if it were an element. Table 5-6 on page 77 gives the formulas and valence numbers of common polyatomic ions.

Example: Write the formula for calcium nitrate.

1. Write the symbols: Ca NO_3
2. Insert the valence numbers: $Ca^{2+} NO_3^{1-}$
3. Crisscross the valence numbers and drop the signs: $Ca_1(NO_3)_2$
   Note: If more than one unit of the polyatomic ion is required, place parentheses around the ion before writing the subscript.
4. Omit the subscript 1: $Ca(NO_3)_2$

Table 6-1 gives several more examples.

Table 6-1.
How Are Valence Numbers Used To Write Formulas?

Compound	Valence Numbers	Formula
Sodium phosphate	$Na^{1+} PO_4^{3-}$	Na_3PO_4
Zinc nitrate	$Zn^{2+} NO_3^{1-}$	$Zn(NO_3)_2$
Aluminum sulfide	$Al^{3+} S^{2-}$	Al_2S_3
Ammonium nitrate	$NH_4^{1+} NO_3^{1-}$	NH_4NO_3
Aluminum hydroxide	$Al^{3+} OH^{1-}$	$Al(OH)_3$

How Are Compounds Named?

You were introduced to some general rules for naming the metallic elements in compounds of metals in Chapter 5 (see page 76). The nonmetallic elements in compounds are named as follows:

1. For compounds that contain only two elements (**binary compounds**), name the metal first and then add the suffix -*ide* to the nonmetal.

   Examples: NaCl, sodium chlor*ide*
   CaO, calcium ox*ide*
   K_2S, potassium sulf*ide*

2. For compounds containing three elements (**ternary compounds**), such as a metal combined with a polyatomic ion that behaves as a nonmetal, write the name of the metal first and the name of the ion last. With the exception of hydroxides, which contain one or more (OH^-) ions, compounds of more than two elements often have last names ending in the suffix -*ite* or -*ate*. Both suffixes indicate the presence of oxygen in the compound. The

suffix -*ite* indicates a compound that generally has one oxygen atom less than the corresponding -*ate* compound.

Examples: $NaNO_3$, sodium nit*rate*
$NaNO_2$, sodium nit*rite*

3. For compounds containing two polyatomic ions, one of which acts as a metal and the other as a nonmetal, write the formulas for both ions, placing the one that has the positive valence number first. Then follow the same procedure as in rule 2.

   Examples: $(NH_4)_2SO_4$, ammonium sulf*ate*
   NH_4OH, ammonium hydrox*ide*

4. Use the prefixes *mono-*, *di-*, and *tri-* to represent 1, 2, and 3 atoms of an element in molecules composed of two nonmetals.

   Examples: CO, carbon *mono*xide
   CO_2, carbon *di*oxide
   P_2O_3, *di*phosphorus *tri*oxide

What Information Do Chemical Formulas Hold?

Now that you know how to write chemical formulas, you can learn how to use these formulas to find out additional information about elements and compounds. You can determine the formula mass of an element or compound. After you determine the formula mass, you can calculate the **percent composition** by mass.

How Is Formula Mass Determined?

A chemical formula shows the kinds of atoms in a molecule and the proportions of these atoms by mass. Thus, H_2O, the formula for water, indicates the presence of 2 atomic mass units (amu) of hydrogen and 1 atomic mass unit of oxygen. The sum of all the atomic masses in a molecule is the **formula mass**.

If you know the formula of a compound, you can compute its formula mass by referring to a table of atomic masses or to the Periodic Table. For example, there are 2 hydrogen atoms and 1 oxygen atom present in 1 molecule of H_2O. Table 3-2 (page 45) shows that the atomic mass of hydrogen is 1 amu

Table 6-2.
How Is Formula Mass Calculated?

Find the formula mass of calcium carbonate, $CaCO_3$.

Element	Number of Atoms	Atomic Mass	Total Mass of Element
Ca	1	× 40 amu =	40 amu
C	1	× 12 amu =	12 amu
O	3	× 16 amu =	48 amu
		formula mass =	100 amu

Find the formula mass of ammonium phosphate, $(NH_4)_3 PO_4$.

Element	Number of Atoms	Atomic Mass	Total Mass of Element
N	3	× 14 amu =	42 amu
H	12	× 1 amu =	12 amu
P	1	× 31 amu =	31 amu
O	4	× 16 amu =	64 amu
		formula mass =	149 amu

and oxygen is 16 amu. Multiply the number of atoms of each element by the atomic mass of the element. Thus, 2 atoms of hydrogen have a total atomic mass of 2 amu. One atom of oxygen has an atomic mass of 16 amu. Adding the total atomic masses of the elements gives the formula mass of the compound. Thus, the formula mass of H_2O is 2 amu + 16 amu, or 18 amu. Table 6-2 provides examples for finding the formula masses of more complex compounds.

▶ **How Is Percent Composition by Mass Figured?**

Knowledge of the formula mass of a compound is valuable to the chemist who is concerned with extracting elements from compounds. For example, a chemist might be interested in knowing how many kilograms of a useful metal can be extracted from some given mass of a compound containing the metal combined with other elements. This information could be determined by carrying out time-consuming reactions and keeping careful records. This same information can be obtained based on the percentage composition of the metal in the compound. For example, if a chemist wishes to know how many kilograms of copper can be obtained from 100 kilograms of copper(II) carbonate, the chemist could follow these steps:

1. Use the formula $CuCO_3$ to determine the formula mass of copper(II) carbonate.

	Number of Atoms	Atomic Mass	Total Mass of Element
Cu	1	× 63.5 amu =	63.5 amu
C	1	× 12 amu =	12 amu
O	3	× 16 amu =	48 amu
		formula mass =	123.5 amu

2. Determine the **percent composition** of copper in copper(II) carbonate according to the following equation:

$$\% \text{ composition} = \frac{\text{total atomic mass of element}}{\text{formula mass of compound}} \times 100$$

$$\% \text{ composition of Cu} = \frac{63.5 \text{ amu}}{123.5 \text{ amu}} \times 100 = 51.4\%$$

Using this information, the chemist knows that approximately 51% of any amount of pure copper(II) carbonate is copper. Accordingly, every 100 kilograms of copper(II) carbonate contains 100 kg × 51/100 = 51 kilograms of copper.

As another example, find the percentage composition by mass of each element in pure calcium sulfate. First, determine the formula mass of calcium sulfate, $CaSO_4$.

	Number of Atoms	Atomic Mass	Total Mass of Element
Ca	1	× 40 amu =	40 amu
S	1	× 32 amu =	32 amu
O	4	× 16 amu =	64 amu
		formula mass =	136 amu

Then, find the percentage of each element in the compound using the formula:

$$\% \text{ composition} = \frac{\text{total atomic mass of element}}{\text{formula mass of compound}} \times 100$$

$$\% \text{ Ca} = \frac{40 \text{ amu}}{136 \text{ amu}} \times 100 = 29.4\%$$

$$\% \text{ S} = \frac{32 \text{ amu}}{136 \text{ amu}} \times 100 = 23.5\%$$

$$\% \text{ O} = \frac{64 \text{ amu}}{136 \text{ amu}} \times 100 = 47.1\%$$

As a check, note that the total of the percents = 100%.

Chapter Review

Science Terms

The following list contains all of the boldfaced words found in this chapter and the page on which each appears.

binary compound (p. 89)

formula mass (p. 89)

percent composition (p. 89)

ternary compound (p. 89)

Matching Questions

In your notebook, write the letter of the item in column B that is most closely related to the item in column A.

Column A

_____ 1. ternary compound

_____ 2. binary compound

_____ 3. suffix for a single nonmetal atom

_____ 4. example of a chemical formula

_____ 5. prefix indicating one atom

_____ 6. -ite

_____ 7. -ate

_____ 8. formula mass

_____ 9. di-

_____ 10. tri-

Column B

a. mono-

b. -ide

c. water's is 18

d. indicating three atoms

e. $NaNO_2$'s suffix

f. made of three elements

g. $C_6H_{12}O_6$

h. indicating two atoms

i. $NaSO_4$'s suffix

j. made of two elements

Multiple-Choice Questions

In your notebook, write the letter preceding the word or expression that best completes the statement or answers the question.

1. What information about a chemical compound is given by a chemical formula?
   a. the relative atomic masses of each element
   b. the type of reaction in which a compound will take part
   c. the elements and numbers of atoms of each element
   d. the total number of electrons in each atom of the compound

2. Subscripts in a chemical formula indicate
   a. the number of atoms of each element
   b. the number of molecules present
   c. the atomic number of each element
   d. the valence number of each element

3. How many atoms of sulfur are present in one unit of $(NH_4)_2SO_4$?
   a. 1   c. 4
   b. 2   d. 8

4. When using the "crisscross" method for writing formulas, the valence number of the nonmetal
   a. precedes the symbol for the metal
   b. follows the symbol for the metal
   c. follows the symbol for the nonmetal
   d. neither precedes nor follows the symbol for the metal

5. How is the formula for a compound written when the valence numbers of both the metal and nonmetal are 1?
   a. No number is written.
   b. The numeral 1 is written after the metal only.
   c. The numeral 1 is written after the nonmetal only.
   d. The numeral 1 is written after the metal and nonmetal.

6. When writing a chemical formula, the symbol for the element with a positive valence number

a. is written last
b. needs no subscript
c. is written first
d. is placed in parentheses

7. The formula for the compound formed when Mg^{2+} combines with O^{2-} is
a. Mg_2O_4
b. Mg_2O
c. MgO_2
d. MgO

8. The compound whose formula is ZnS is named
a. zinc sulfate
b. zinc sulfite
c. zinc sulfide
d. zinc and sulfur

9. What is the name of the compound whose formula is $Al(OH)_3$?
a. aluminum oxygen hydride
b. aluminum hydroxide
c. aluminum hydrogen oxide
d. aluminum oxide

10. The compound $NaNO_2$ is best named
a. sodium nitrate
b. sodium nitrite
c. sodium nitrogen oxide
d. sodium nitrogen dioxide

11. Which information are you unable to learn directly from a chemical formula for a compound?
a. the elements in the compound
b. the formula mass of the compound
c. the chemical properties of the compound
d. the percent composition of elements in the compound

12. What is the total number of atoms present in one molecule of $(NH_4)_2CO_3$?
a. 9
b. 10
c. 12
d. 14

13. The total atomic mass of an element in a compound is 12. The formula mass of the compound is 100. The percentage composition of the element in the compound is
a. 88%
b. 12%
c. 1.2%
d. 0.12%

14. What is the percentage of sodium in NaCl?
a. 22.9%
b. 39.3%
c. 50.0%
d. 60.7%

15. When an atom of aluminum with a valence of 3+ unites to form a compound, it
a. donates 3 electrons
b. accepts 3 electrons
c. donates 5 electrons
d. accepts 5 electrons

TEST-TAKING TIP Consult any resources that are available during an exam, such as the Periodic Table of the Elements. Even if you think you know a valence number or atomic mass, double-check your answer to make sure you are correct.

Modified True-False Questions
In some of the following statements, the italicized term makes the statement incorrect. For each incorrect statement, in your notebook, write the term that must be substituted for the italicized term to make the statement correct. For each correct statement, write the word "true."

1. The *atomic mass* of an element describes the electrons in the outermost energy level. _____

2. The valence number of an element can be found in the *Periodic Table of the Elements*. _____

3. A positive valence number indicates that an element *accepts* electrons when it combines. _____

4. To determine the correct subscripts for the elements in a compound, you "*criss-cross*" the valence numbers. _____

5. In writing a chemical formula, if more than one unit of the polyatomic ion is required, you separate the radical from the subscript by using a *comma*.

_____

6. In general, compounds composed of only two elements have last names ending in -*ide*. _____

7. To name a compound composed of two nonmetals, use the prefix tri- to indicate *two* atoms. _____

8. The *ternary* mass of a molecule is the sum of the atomic masses. _____

9. The relative proportion by mass of an element in a compound can be found by determining the *percent composition*.

_____

10. To find the percent composition, you must first determine the *atomic number*.

_____

Check Your Knowledge

Write the answer to each question in your notebook.

1. How is a binary compound different from a ternary compound? How is each type of compound named?

2. Complete the table by writing the formulas for the compounds formed by each combination of elements.

	O^{-2}	Cl^{-1}	S^{-2}	I^{-1}	N^{-3}
Na^{1+}					
Ca^{2+}					
Al^{3+}					

3. Name the compounds represented by the following formulas:
   a. $AlCl_3$ d. $Ca(NO_3)_2$
   b. Na_2O e. KOH
   c. $(NH_4)_2SO_4$

4. Write chemical formulas for each of the following pairs. Then write the name of the compound formed when the elements or radicals combine.
   a. Na^{1+}, PO_4^{3-} d. Zn^{2+}, NO_3^{1-}
   b. Ca^{2+}, SO_4^{2-} e. K^{1+}, ClO_3^{1-}
   c. Al^{3+}, CO_3^{2-}

5. Find the formula mass for each of the following:
   a. Na_2S c. $C_6H_{12}O_6$
   b. $Al(OH)_3$ d. $Ca(OH)_2$

Think Critically

Write the answer to each of the following questions in your notebook.

1. How many kilograms of iron can be obtained from 100 kilograms of Fe_2O_3?

2. You are a prospector who has discovered an abandoned gold (Au) mine in Australia. The mine contains rock that is 2% $AuAgTe_4$. After making careful calculations you find that the cost of mining and purifying the gold would come to $6000.00 per 100 kilogram of the rock, which you could mine and purify each week. The price of pure gold is $14.00 per gram. Can you earn at least $1000 per week after expenses?

Explain your answer and show all calculations.

3. The graphs below compare the percent composition of two compounds each containing potassium, chromium, and oxygen. Which graph represents potassium dichromate ($K_2Cr_2O_7$) and which graph represents potassium chromate (K_2CrO_4)? Support your answer with calculations.

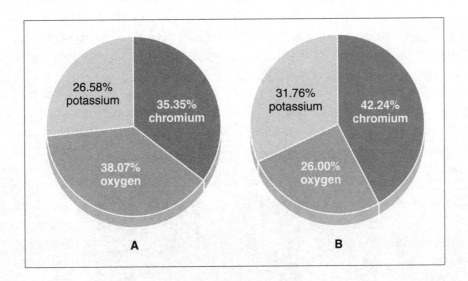

A   B

Take It Further

1. Mass spectrometry is a method of determining the elemental composition of a sample. Conduct research to find out how mass spectrometry works and situations in which it is used. Write a brief report or create an informational poster to present to the class.

2. You can use percents to compare the relative parts of mixtures. If a very small amount is part of a much larger amount, however, other comparisons may be more practical. Investigate the uses of parts per million and parts per billion. Find out situations in which these measurements are practical. Share some examples with your class.

3. The percent composition of copper in the penny has changed over time. Find out how and why it has changed. Use evidence from your research to create a timeline showing changes in the penny. You may wish to begin your research at the following site: *http://www.usmint. gov/about_the_mint/fun_facts/?flash= yes&action=fun_facts2*.

CAREER

4. The work of many types of chemists involves describing samples of chemical compounds. Find out about a career as a chemist. Investigate the type of education required, the job opportunities that exist, and the specific fields of chemistry available. You may find useful information at the following sites: *http://www.prince tonreview.com/Careers.aspx?cid=34* and *http://www.acs.org/careers*.

Chemicals on the Menu: Food for Thought?

"I'll have a serving of sodium nitrite, a side order of sulfites, maybe a little potassium sorbate, a scoop of BHA, and a sprinkling of calcium propionate. Oh, and don't forget the tricalcium phosphate and potassium bromate."

What you've just ordered are hot dogs, salad dressing, instant mashed potatoes, bread, iced tea, and dried apricots. Don't believe it? Read the labels!

Each of these chemicals has been added to your meal for a specific purpose. For example, sodium nitrite preserves meat. Sulfites maintain the color of certain dried fruits. Tricalcium phosphate keeps powdered iced tea from caking. And potassium bromate retards the spoilage of bread.

Figure 6-3. A worker adds an ingredient to a batch of food.

None of these chemicals add to the nutritional value of the food. Instead, they make food look better, last longer, or taste better. No one would likely argue with these benefits. Unfortunately, some of these chemicals, called *food additives,* may do more harm than good.

Consider sulfites, for example. Many people are allergic to this group of chemicals. Some people, especially those suffering from a condition called asthma, have died after eating foods treated with sulfites. Many more sulfite consumers have suffered from pounding headaches, dizziness, and stomach upsets.

Sulfites are just a few of the nearly 3000 chemicals that are added to processed foods. Why so many chemicals? As anyone who watches television commercials knows, the food industry is highly competitive. Anything that gives one product an edge over another becomes a valuable selling point.

A new group of chemicals has made its way into the food industry in recent years—artificial sweeteners. Aspartame and sucralose are just two varieties. They give foods the same sweet taste as sugar without the same calories, making them an attractive alternative for many people. However, some researchers argue that these chemicals, along with a chemical called monosodium glutamate (MSG), are directly related to health problems. Some studies suggest that their increased use is tied to the tremendous growth in cases of autism and attention deficit hyperactivity disorder (ADHD) over the past several decades.

So who decides what chemicals can go into foods? About 80 years ago, the United States Government established the Food and Drug Administration, or FDA. The FDA sets rules that food manufacturers must follow. For example, nothing can be added to a food that is known to cause cancer or birth defects. Despite such rules, critics say there are dangerous loopholes in FDA regulations. For example, chemicals that have been "generally recognized as safe" by "qualified experts" can be added to foods. One such group of chemicals is sulfites! "Safe for whom?" ask critics. They are certainly not safe for people allergic to sulfites, and the long-term effects are not conclusively known.

In addition, the FDA weighs out the risks and benefits in a manner with which everyone may not agree. For example, consider sodium nitrite. When cooked at high temperatures, sodium nitrite can form substances called nitrosamines. These substances are carcinogens and have been linked to cancers of the digestive tract and lungs in animals and possibly humans. Because sodium nitrite is effective in protecting against certain bacterial growth in foods, the FDA has allowed its use in limited amounts.

Another regulation loophole is that the FDA sometimes allows a food additive to be used for up to two and a half years or longer while its safety is being tested. Manufacturers should be given a fair chance to prove that their additives are safe, but at whose expense? Yours?

Should some food additives be banned? If so, which ones and under what conditions? What do you think?

Organize It!

Use a method that your teacher describes to organize the information in this article.

Explain It!

1. Sodium nitrite is used to
   a. preserve bread
   b. preserve meat
   c. preserve fruit
   d. preserve mashed potatoes

2. In some people, sulfites cause
   a. cancer
   b. birth defects
   c. allergic reactions
   d. colds

3. Aspartame and sucralose
   a. make foods taste sweeter
   b. cook foods faster
   c. make foods last longer
   d. lower the costs of foods

Extend It!

4. Investigate the responsibilities of the FDA. Choose one responsibility and write a paragraph describing what the FDA does and how it relates to the foods you eat. Share your findings with the class.

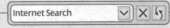

5. Critically evaluate the FDA rule that permits the use of food additives that have been "generally recognized as safe by qualified experts." Research specific examples. Find out what the additives are and who determined them to be safe, and through what processes. Try to find an example of an additive that was once considered to be safe, but then later identified as unsafe. Prepare a brief presentation of your findings.

CAREER

6. The FDA hires a variety of individuals to address its many responsibilities. Choose one FDA position and research what the position entails and the education that is required. You may wish to begin your research at the following site: *http://www.fda.gov/AboutFDA/WorkingatFDA/default.htm*.

7

What Is Organic Chemistry?

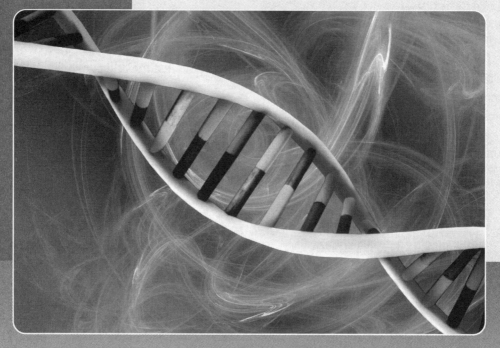

This twisted-looking ladder is the basis of all life. It is the organic compound known as DNA, which determines all the traits of a living thing. Organic compounds are so diverse and important that an entire branch of chemistry is devoted to their study.

After reading this chapter, you should be able to answer the following questions:

What are the properties of organic compounds?

How does carbon form compounds?

How do saturated and unsaturated carbon compounds differ?

What are isomers?

What are the classes of organic compounds?

What is the structure of a hydrocarbon?

What is the structure of an alcohol, organic acid, and amino acid?

You probably hear the term organic all the time. In chemistry, organic substances have specific properties and uses. In this inquiry investigation, you will compare some organic and inorganic substances.

Materials:
- ✔ safety goggles
- ✔ wooden splints
- ✔ matches
- ✔ watch glass
- ✔ pipe-stem triangle
- ✔ iodine solution
- ✔ cornstarch suspension
- ✔ bread
- ✔ candle
- ✔ candle stand
- ✔ tripod
- ✔ salt
- ✔ paraffin
- ✔ shortening or chicken fat
- ✔ sand (quartz)
- ✔ top of a metal can

CAUTION: Wear safety goggles while performing this experiment.

Part A Light a wooden splint with a match. As it burns, hold it directly under a watch glass as shown in Figure 7-1.

1. *Describe and explain the significance of what happens to the wooden splint.*

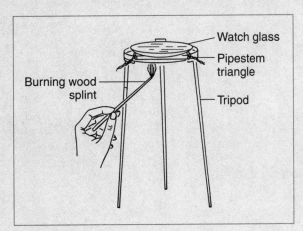

Figure 7-1.

2. **Describe what you observe on the bottom of the watch glass and interpret what you see.**

CAUTION: Iodine is a toxic substance; avoid contact with skin or clothing.

Part B Iodine solution causes starch, an organic food substance, to turn blue-black. Place a drop of iodine solution in a cornstarch suspension. Repeat this procedure by placing a drop of iodine solution on a piece of bread.

3. **Describe what you observe.**

4. **What can you conclude about the composition of bread?**

Part C Using the setup shown in Figure 7-2, describe what happens to each of the substances as it is heated.

5. **Salt (NaCl)**

6. **Paraffin (a complex hydrocarbon)**

7. **A small piece of shortening or chicken fat (consists mainly of organic substances)**

8. **Sand (SiO$_2$)**

9. **Based on your observations, what might you infer concerning the properties of inorganic versus organic substances?**

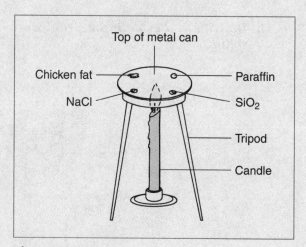

Figure 7-2.

What Are the Properties of Organic Compounds?

If you were asked what you, a giant redwood tree, a gallon of gasoline, a plastic raincoat, and a lump of sugar have in common, you might be stumped for an answer. To the unaided eye these objects seem totally unrelated. However, at the molecular level they have one very important similarity; they all consist primarily, if not exclusively, of carbon compounds.

Because carbon compounds were once considered to come only from living things, such substances became known as **organic compounds**. The word *organic* means "coming from living things." Today, many organic compounds, such as the wide variety of plastics, are made in laboratories and factories.

Do not confuse the organic compounds you will learn about in this chapter with organic products you might find in the grocery store. The term *organic* as used with the products you buy refers to how the products were formed or the produce was grown. Being described as organic generally means the products adhere to a set of regulations set by governments or other organizations. The organic compounds in this chapter are defined by their composition rather than a set of legal guidelines.

Organic compounds make up the largest family of chemical substances. There are thousands of them in your body alone and, perhaps, millions of them altogether. The study of this huge family of substances is called **organic chemistry**.

This large family is generally studied as a group of many mini-families. You will learn about some of the most important of these fascinating and useful mini-families in this chapter. First, you will discover what all of these mini-families of organic compounds have in common.

In general, organic compounds are more easily decomposed by heat than are inorganic substances. In the inquiry investigation at the beginning of the chapter, you saw that wood, which is largely composed of the organic substance **cellulose**, burned quite easily. This is certainly not the case with most inorganic substances. Moreover, when the wood burned, a black residue, or char, collected on the bottom of the watch glass. This char consists mostly of the main building block of organic compounds—carbon.

Organic compounds have relatively low melting and boiling points and, with some exceptions, are not very soluble in water. Those that do dissolve in water tend not to conduct an electric current very well. Unlike most inorganic substances, organic substances usually have an odor or aroma.

How Do Compounds of Carbon Form?

A carbon atom has four valence electrons. (See Figure 7-3.) This means that it can form four covalent bonds with other atoms. Moreover, these atoms may be either electropositive (can gain electrons), such as hydrogen, or electronegative (can lose electrons), such as oxygen, nitrogen, sulfur, chlorine, and fluorine. Carbon atoms can also form covalent

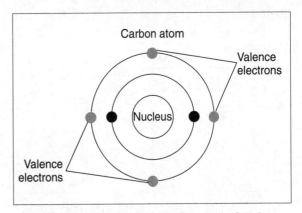

Figure 7-3. A carbon atom has a total of 6 electrons, 4 of which are valence electrons.

bonds with other carbon atoms to build chains and rings of various sizes and shapes. This means that there are an almost unlimited number of possible kinds of organic substances.

The number of bonds a carbon atom will form with another atom depends, of course, on the other atom's valence. For example, the valence of hydrogen is 1+. So a hydrogen atom can form only one bond by sharing one electron with an atom of carbon. On the other hand, the valence of oxygen is 2−, so an oxygen atom can form two bonds by sharing two electrons with a carbon atom.

You can represent the sharing of electrons, or the formation of covalent bonds, as dots or straight lines connecting the chemical symbols for elements. Figure 7-4 shows both ways to represent a molecule of methane, CH_4. Each straight line represents a shared pair of electrons.

This type of representation is called a **structural formula**. Structural formulas show the number of atoms in the molecule as well as the way they are arranged. The formula in Figure 7-5 shows the structural formula for the organic compound ethane, C_2H_6. Notice that there is a covalent bond between the two carbon atoms. This forms a chain with two carbon links. The ability to form chains like these is unique to carbon. In addition, each carbon atom in ethane forms covalent bonds with three hydrogen atoms.

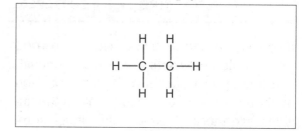

ETHANE (C_2H_6)

Figure 7-5. A structural formula, such as that of ethane, shows the number of atoms in the molecule and gives an idea of how they are arranged.

▶ How Do Saturated and Unsaturated Carbon Compounds Differ?

Ethane is an example of a **saturated compound**. In these compounds, carbon atoms form a single covalent bond with each other. Not all carbon compounds are saturated. Some carbon compounds are formed when carbon atoms share more than one pair of electrons. When two pairs of electrons are shared between two carbon atoms, a **double bond** is formed. When three pairs of electrons are shared, a **triple bond** is formed.

Organic compounds that contain carbon atoms linked by double or triple bonds are called **unsaturated compounds**. Figure 7-6 shows ethene, C_2H_4, which has a double bond between carbon atoms and ethyne, C_2H_2, which has a triple bond between carbon atoms.

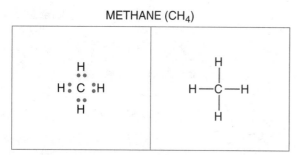

METHANE (CH_4)

Figure 7-4. A covalent bond, in which two electrons are shared, can be represented by two dots or a straight line. The structure shown is a molecule of methane.

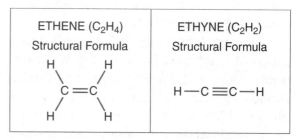

Figure 7-6. Unsaturated compounds come in two forms: those with double bonds between carbon atoms, such as ethane, and those with triple bonds between carbon atoms, such as ethyne.

What Are Isomers?

Up to this point in your study of chemistry, you have found that there is only one structural arrangement for each molecular formula. For example, you can draw only one structural formula for CH_4 or C_2H_6. As the chain of a carbon compound grows longer, however, substances with the same molecular formula may have different structures. Such substances are called **isomers**.

Butane, whose molecular formula is C_4H_{10}, is an example of a substance with more than one possible structure. Figure 7-7 shows two structures for butane. One structure has a straight chain and is called butane. The other has a branched chain of carbon atoms and is called 2-methyl propane, or *iso*butane. Despite the different structures, both isomers have the same molecular formula.

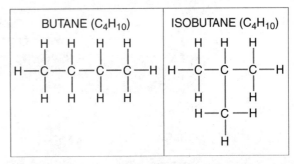

Figure 7-7. Butane has two isomers, or different structures. One structure (*left*) is a straight chain, whereas the other structure (*right*) is a branched chain. Both structures have the same molecular formula.

Notice that the butane isomers have only 4 carbon atoms. If the number of carbon atoms is greater than 4, more than 2 isomers are possible. The properties of isomers usually differ from one another.

What Are the Classes of Organic Compounds?

The mini-families of organic compounds mentioned previously are actually known as classes. The classes of organic compounds can be recognized by their structures and by the presence of certain groups of atoms known as function groups. A **functional group** is a specific arrangement of atoms that is capable of characteristic chemical reactions. Organic compounds are classified into classes according to their functional groups.

What Is the Structure of a Hydrocarbon?

Organic compounds that contain only atoms of hydrogen and carbon are called **hydrocarbons**. There is a very large variety of hydrocarbons because carbon atoms can form short or long chains, all sorts of branched chains, and many different kinds of ring shapes. What's more, chains and rings often combine to form completely new sub-

stances. In addition, these substances can be saturated or unsaturated.

Saturated hydrocarbons are called **alkanes**. The names of all of these compounds end in the suffix "-ane." You have already been introduced to meth*ane* and eth*ane*. Table 7-1 on page 104 gives some examples of the alkanes with some additional information. By the way, the prefixes of these compounds indicate the number of carbon atoms in the compound (*meth-*, one; *eth-*, two; *prop-*, three; and so on).

Saturated hydrocarbons have many technological applications including use as fuels. For example, methane and ethane are components of natural gas, propane is used in bottled gas, and octane is found in gasoline.

Unsaturated hydrocarbons are divided into three major types—alkenes, alkynes, and aromatic hydrocarbons. Those that contain at least one double bond between carbon atoms are called **alkenes**. All of the names of

Table 7-1.
What Are the Alkanes?

Name	Molecular Formula	Form	Possible Isomers
methane	CH_4	gas	0
ethane	C_2H_6	gas	0
propane	C_3H_8	gas	0
butane	C_4H_{10}	gas	2
pentane	C_5H_{12}	liquid	3
hexane	C_6H_{14}	liquid	5
heptane	C_7H_{16}	liquid	9
octane	C_8H_{18}	liquid	18
nonane	C_9H_{20}	liquid	35
decane	$C_{10}H_{22}$	liquid	75

these hydrocarbons end with the suffix "-ene." Examples of alkenes are eth*ene*, prop*ene*, and but*ene*. Propene is used to manufacture the plastic polypropylene.

Hydrocarbons that have at least one triple bond between carbon atoms are called **alkynes**. All of the names of these hydrocarbons end with the suffix "-yne." Examples of alkynes are eth*yne* and prop*yne*. Ethyne is commonly called acetylene and is used in welding torches as a fuel. In addition, it is used as a building block of vinyl plastics. Another group of unsaturated hydrocarbons consists of the **aromatic hydrocarbons**. As their name suggests, these compounds tend to have distinctive odors, or aromas, some of which are pleasant. Aromatic hydrocarbons have a ring structure, the simplest of which is that of benzene. Other examples of aromatic hydrocarbons are toluene and naphthalene. Many aromatic hydrocarbons are obtained from coal tar. Some are used to produce such products as explosives, dyes, and perfumes. Figure 7-8 shows an example of an alkane, alkene, alkyne, and aromatic hydrocarbon.

▶ **What Is the Structure of an Alcohol?**

Hydrocarbons in which a hydrogen atom bonded to a carbon atom is replaced by a hydroxyl group (—OH) are called **alcohols**. For example, you now know that methane is a hydrocarbon with the molecular formula of CH_4. The structural formula for methane is

$$
\begin{array}{c}
\mathrm{H} \\
| \\
\mathrm{H-C-H} \\
| \\
\mathrm{H}
\end{array}
$$

If one of the hydrogen atoms is replaced by a hydroxyl group, the formula becomes CH_3OH or

$$
\begin{array}{c}
\mathrm{H} \\
| \\
\mathrm{H-C-OH} \\
| \\
\mathrm{H}
\end{array}
$$

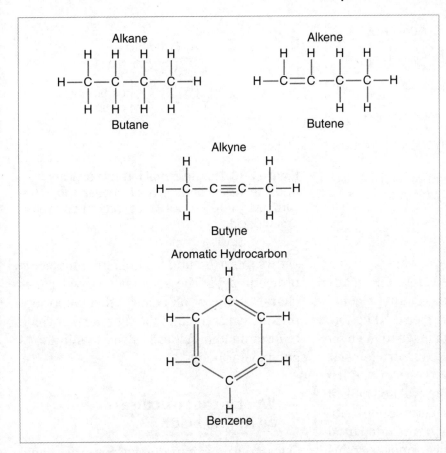

Figure 7-8. The structures of alkanes, alkenes, alkynes, and aromatic hydrocarbons differ with regard to bonding and whether the carbon atoms are linked in chains or rings. Alkanes contain single bonds between carbon atoms. Alkenes contain at least one double bond between carbon atoms, whereas alkynes have at least one triple bond between carbon atoms. Aromatic hydrocarbons contain at least one benzene ring in their structure.

This compound is called methyl alcohol, or methanol. Its common name is wood alcohol and it is poisonous. Alcohols can be named by adding the suffix "-ol" to the name of the hydrocarbon. Other examples of alcohols are ethanol, propanol, and isopropanol. See Table 7-2.

Although not as poisonous as methyl alcohol, ethyl alcohol has been placed on the list of narcotic substances. It can cause great

Table 7-2.
What Are Some Common Alcohols?

Name	Structure	Uses
Methyl alcohol / Methanol	H—C—OH	Solvent, fuel for some engines
Ethyl alcohol / Ethanol	H—C—C—OH	Solvent, fuel, alcoholic beverages
Isopropyl alcohol / Isopropanol	H—C—C—C—H	Rubbing alcohol

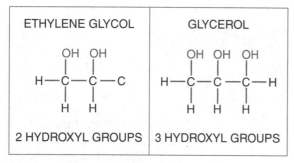

Figure 7-9. Ethylene glycol and glycerol are alcohols that contain, respectively, two and three hydroxyl groups.

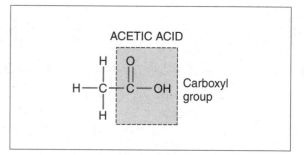

Figure 7-10. The structural formula of acetic acid, the major component of vinegar, shows the carboxyl group (—COOH) that is common to all organic acids.

harm to the human body over time or, in sufficiently high doses, immediately. Like many other drugs, prolonged use of ethyl alcohol in alcoholic beverages can cause addiction. It is also known to cause damage to the liver and brain and is a danger to unborn fetuses.

Alcohols can contain more than one hydroxyl group. Figure 7-9 shows a molecule of ethylene glycol, used as automobile antifreeze, and a molecule of glycerol, often used as a lubricant. Note that the former contains two hydroxyl groups while the latter contains three.

What Is the Structure of an Organic Acid?

When a **carboxyl group** (—COOH) replaces a hydrogen atom in a hydrocarbon molecule, an **organic acid** is formed. The carboxyl group gives the organic acid its characteristic properties. The general formula for organic acids is

$$R-\overset{\overset{\displaystyle O}{\displaystyle \|}}{C}-OH$$

where the R represents the hydrocarbon. Notice that in the carboxyl group, the carbon forms a double bond with an oxygen atom and a single bond with a hydroxyl group.

A very familiar organic acid, acetic acid, is the main ingredient of vinegar. Figure 7-10 shows the structural formula for a molecule of acetic acid. The sour taste of vinegar is characteristic of all acids. Other important organic acids include the fatty acids, which are the building blocks of the fats in foods and in your body.

What Is the Structure of an Amino Acid?

One of the most important groups of organic compounds is the **amino acids**. Just 20 amino acids make up the building blocks of **proteins**, which are among the most complex molecules found in living things. The molecule shown at the beginning of the chapter, DNA, determines the amino acids and therefore the proteins in an individual. There may be thousands of amino acids in a single molecule of a protein. The protein molecules are formed when long chains of amino acids are bonded together. The order in which the amino acids are linked distinguishes one protein from another. To get an idea of how this fact affects the variety of proteins found in nature, assume a protein is made up of only 10 amino acid links, rather than hundreds or thousands. How many different kinds of proteins could be made from the 20 different amino acids? Since the first link can be made by any of 20 amino acids and each subsequent link can be made by any of 20 amino acids, the answer is 20^{10}, or 10,240,000,000,000 different kinds of proteins!

Amino acids are organic acids in which an amino group ($-NH_2$) replaces an atom of hydrogen in the hydrocarbon molecule. The general formula for amino acids is

$$
\begin{array}{c}
\text{H} \\
| \\
\text{R}-\text{C}-\text{COOH} \\
| \\
\text{NH}_2
\end{array}
$$

Remember that the R represents the hydrocarbon. The—COOH radical is the carboxyl group that is characteristic of organic acids. The NH_2 is the amino group. Thus, amino acids contain both amino groups and carboxyl groups.

▶ **What Is the Structure of an Ester?**

Substances called **esters** are formed when an organic acid reacts chemically with an alcohol. For example, when acetic acid and ethyl alcohol react, the products are water and the ester, ethyl acetate.

$$CH_3COOH + C_2H_5OH \rightarrow$$
acetic acid + ethyl alcohol

$$CH_3COOC_2H_5 + H_2O$$
ethyl acetate + water

Generally speaking, most esters are liquids with a pleasant odor. The special scents of flowers and fruit are caused by the presence of esters. Some examples of esters are found in Table 7-3.

Table 7-3.
What Are Common Esters?

Name	Odor
Butyl acetate	Banana
Ethyl butyrate	Pineapple
Octyl acetate	Orange
Methyl salicylate	Oil of wintergreen
Methyl anthranilate	Grapes

Chapter Review

Science Terms

The following list contains all of the boldfaced words found in this chapter and the page on which each appears.

alcohol (p. 104)

alkane (p. 103)

alkene (p. 103)

alkyne (p. 104)

amino acid (p. 106)

aromatic hydrocarbon (p. 104)

carboxyl group (p. 106)

cellulose (p. 101)

double bond (p. 102)

ester (p. 107)

functional group (p. 103)

hydrocarbon (p. 103)

isomer (p. 103)

organic acid (p. 106)

organic chemistry (p. 101)

organic compound (p. 101)

protein (p. 106)

saturated compound (p. 102)

structural formula (p. 102)

triple bond (p. 102)

unsaturated compound (p. 102)

Matching Questions

In your notebook, write the letter of the item in column B that is most closely related to the item in column A.

Column A

_____ 1. shape of aromatic hydrocarbons

_____ 2. an alcohol with two hydroxyl groups

_____ 3. molecule formed when a carboxyl group replaces a hydrogen in a hydrocarbon

_____ 4. unsaturated hydrocarbon with at least one double bond

_____ 5. example of a saturated hydrocarbon

_____ 6. molecule in which the —NH_2 radical replaces a hydrogen in a hydrocarbon

_____ 7. substance that forms when an organic acid reacts with an alcohol

_____ 8. rubbing alcohol

_____ 9. an alcohol with three hydroxyl groups

_____ 10. hydrocarbon with at least one triple bond between carbon atoms

Column B

a. glycerol

b. propane

c. alkene

d. amino acid

e. isopropanol

f. ring structure

g. alkyne

h. ethylene glycol

i. ester

j. organic acid

Multiple-Choice Questions

In your notebook, write the letter preceding the word or expression that best completes the statement or answers the question.

1. The major component in organic compounds is

a. oxygen

b. carbon

c. hydrogen

d. chlorine

2. Wood is largely composed of which organic compound?

a. petroleum

b. cellulose

c. water

d. butane

3. Which of these substances would you expect to have the lowest melting point?

a. sodium chloride

b. silicon dioxide

c. sodium hydroxide

d. paraffin

4. How many covalent bonds can a carbon atom form?

a. 1

b. 2

c. 3

d. 4

5. Carbon can form two bonds with atoms that have a valence number of

a. 1

b. 2

c. 3

d. 4

6. An example of an unsaturated compound with a double bond is

a. ethane

b. ethyne

c. propane

d. ethene

7. The names of unsaturated compounds
    with a triple bond end in the suffix
    a. *-yne*
    b. *-ane*
    c. *-ene*
    d. *-ol*

8. How are isomers of a substance different
    from one another?
    a. They do not have the same structures.
    b. They do not have the same molecular
       formula.
    c. They do not have the same molecular
       mass.
    d. They are not made up of the same
       elements.

9. In alcohols, the group that replaces a
    hydrogen atom is
    a. $-Cl_3$
    b. $-COOH$
    c. $-OH$
    d. $-ClO_3$

10. Organic compounds that have pleasant,
    fruity odors are
    a. organic acids   c. alcohols
    b. esters   d. amines

11. Which group of atoms gives organic acids
    their characteristic properties?
    a. benzene group
    b. amino group
    c. hydroxyl group
    d. carboxyl group

12. The sour taste of vinegar is characteris-
    tic of
    a. acids
    b. alcohols
    c. esters
    d. alkenes

13. What is the other product formed in reac-
    tion below?

    acetic acid + ethyl alcohol → ethyl acetate + ?

    a. carbon dioxide   c. carbon
    b. oxygen   d. water

14. How is ethene, C_2H_4, different from
    ethyne, C_2H_2?
    a. Ethene is unsaturated whereas ethyne
       is saturated.
    b. Ethene has a double bond and ethyne
       has a triple bond.
    c. Ethene is organic and ethyne is
       inorganic.
    d. Ethene is one isomer and ethyne is
       another.

15. How can a small number of amino acids
    form a huge number of proteins?
    a. Amino acids form large rings.
    b. Each amino acid can change into
       another.
    c. The amino acids can be arranged in
       many different orders.
    d. Different numbers of bonds can form
       between each pair of amino acids.

Modified True-False Questions

*In some of the following statements, the itali-
cized term makes the statement incorrect. For
each incorrect statement, in your notebook,
write the term that must be substituted for the
italicized term to make the statement correct.
For each correct statement, write the word
"true."*

1. Organic compounds generally have *high*
    melting and boiling points._____

2. Most organic compounds are *nonelec-
    trolytes.* _____

3. When wood burns, it leaves a residue of
    oxygen. _____

4. An atom of carbon can form *4* covalent
    bonds. _____

5. A covalent bond can be represented by a
    straight line. _____

6. Compounds that contain double bonds between carbon atoms are *saturated*. _____

7. Ethyne is a hydrocarbon with at least one *double* bond. _____

8. Amino acids contain the radical —*COOH*. _____

9. Butane and isobutane are *ions*. _____

10. An example of an aromatic hydrocarbon is *benzene*. _____

Check Your Knowledge
Write the answer to each question in your notebook.

1. Why are organic compounds no longer defined as only those that come from living things?

2. Describe three general properties of organic compounds.

3. What property of carbon makes the possible kinds of organic substances almost limitless?

4. Draw the structural formula for each of the following substances.
   a. C_2H_6
   b. C_2H_2
   c. C_2H_5OH

5. What is the difference between saturated and unsaturated hydrocarbons?

6. Describe the aromatic hydrocarbons.

7. Compare the structure of alcohols and organic acids.

8. Describe how an ester is formed.

TEST-TAKING TIP Review any drawings that are provided in questions or that you make as part of a response. Read any labels or other information provided. Be sure to include labels on any drawings you provide.

Think Critically
Write the answer to each of the following questions in your notebook.

1. Benzene is toxic, yet many of the foods you eat contain benzene rings. For example, benzaldehyde gives some foods an artificial almond flavor. Why might some organic compounds with benzene rings be safe to eat?

2. You are a detective at a crime scene investigating a murder. You discover a white powder that may be lye (NaOH) or table sugar ($C_{12}H_{22}O_{11}$). You know that the victim was allergic to sugar but that lye might have been used by the killer. What might you do to determine whether the victim was poisoned by lye or sugar? NOTE: You have no laboratory equipment with you.

Take It Further

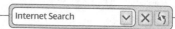

1. Organic substances have a variety of different names. They are all based on International Union of Pure and Applied Chemistry (IUPAC) naming conventions. Research IUPAC (*http://iupac-org.fiz-chemie.de*) to find out what it is and why naming conventions are useful. Share your findings along with some examples with your classmates.

2. Some of the earliest known anesthetics were used during the Civil War. They consisted of types of ethers. Conduct research

to find out what anesthetics are, why they are used, and what characteristics of ethers made them useful. Find out why they are no longer used today, and what kinds of substances have replaced them.

3. Investigate proteins in the human body and explain how of several such proteins are important. Identify the relationship between proteins and amino acids. Create a model to show how amino acids link in different ways to form a wide variety of proteins.

CAREER

4. You may think that a perfume maker is limited to style and fashion. Think again. The best perfume makers need many of the skills of an organic chemist. Find out what a perfume maker does, what skills are involved, what education is required, and what career opportunities exist. Share your findings with the class.

Investigating Issues in Science, Engineering, Technology, and Society

Should You Follow Your Carbon Footprint?

You may have made footprints in sand, wet footprints on a sidewalk, or even muddy footprints across a floor, but what on Earth is a carbon footprint? Perhaps you have seen articles about carbon footprints or heard people debating issues surrounding carbon footprints. A carbon footprint is not a visible mark like other types of footprints. Instead, a carbon footprint is basically a measure of the amount of greenhouse gases produced as a result of your daily living.

Greenhouse gases (GHG) are gases that absorb and hold heat in the atmosphere. To some extent, GHG emissions occur naturally, but human activities add significantly to the naturally occurring levels. For simplicity, GHG emissions are expressed in terms of the amount of carbon dioxide produced, which is the reason for the name *carbon* footprint.

Figure 7-11. Somewhat like footprints in the sand on a beach, your activities leave a carbon footprint on the environment.

At first glance, you might think you don't produce many greenhouse gases. After all, you're just a teenager. Think again. Did you ride in a bus or car to get to school today? The vehicles you ride in release greenhouse gases as they burn gasoline. Did you turn on a light, computer, or television? Fossil fuels are commonly burned to produce electricity. Did you use hot water, eat meat, or buy new clothes? You can trace the development of each product you use to determine the point at which carbon dioxide was released into the environment. You will find that most of the products you use and the activities you perform directly or indirectly release carbon dioxide into the environment.

Why should you care about your carbon footprint? As carbon dioxide and other greenhouse gases trap heat near Earth's surface, they have the potential to raise the air temperature in the lower atmosphere. The long-term consequences can be devastating to environments around the globe.

For example, climate change is linked to an increase in the spread of diseases carried by pests, such as malaria and West Nile virus. In addition, climate change will lead to the extinction of some species. The Golden Toad is believed to be the first species to become extinct because of climate change.

Is there anything you can do to reduce your carbon footprint? The answer is yes. Some approaches are quite simple. For example, electric appliances and electronic devices that stay plugged in all day draw power even if they are turned off. Simply unplugging them saves energy and therefore carbon. Raising your air conditioner's thermostat in the summer and lowering your heat setting in the winter, turning off lights and TV when you leave the room, and taking shorter showers also reduce your carbon footprint.

Buying local products or growing your own produce decreases the carbon released during long-distance shipping. Walking or riding a bicycle instead of using a motor vehicle similarly cuts down on the release of carbon. Some methods of reducing your carbon footprint involve some tough decisions. Some opponents of climate control measures argue that what is needed to reduce carbon footprints interferes with free trade (the ability to buy and sell products freely). Who should decide whether or not individuals or businesses should be forced to limit their carbon footprints? There are some tough decisions ahead. The answers depend on what really matters to you. What do you think?

Organize It!

Use a method that your teacher describes to organize the information in this article.

Think About It!

1. **Which is the primary greenhouse gas emitted by human activities?**
   a. nitrous oxide
   b. carbon dioxide
   c. methane
   d. radon

2. **What quantity does a carbon footprint measure?**
   a. the amount of carbon in the atmosphere each year
   b. the amount by which temperature rises due to daily activities
   c. the amount of fossil fuels consumed by an individual
   d. the amount of greenhouse gases released through daily processes

3. **Which change is linked to an increase in global temperatures?**
   a. an increase in diseases carried by mosquitoes and other pests
   b. an increase in international travel by people
   c. the introduction of new species of organisms
   d. a reduction in the amount of available natural resources

4. How does an increase in the release of greenhouse gases lead to climate change?

5. How might the use of electricity increase your carbon footprint?

6. Why does growing and eating vegetables from a home garden reduce your carbon footprint?

Extend It!

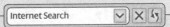

7. On average, each person in the United States is responsible for about 22 tons of carbon dioxide emissions each year. You can use several online tools to help calculate your individual or household carbon footprint. Try one of the following sites or find one of your own to calculate your carbon footprint: *http://www.nature.org/initiatives/climatechange/calculator/* or *http://www.epa.gov/climatechange/emissions/ind_calculator.html*.

8. Research additional ways to reduce your carbon footprint. Create a poster showing photographs or drawings of changes you can make as an individual to reduce the carbon you release into the environment. Present your ideas to the class.

CAREER

9. The U.S. Environmental Protection Agency (EPA) is the government organization that works to protect all aspects of the environment, including the air. Investigate careers within the EPA to find out what they involve and what education they require. Share your findings with the class. You may wish to begin your search at the following site: *http://www.epa.gov/*.

CHAPTER

8

What Is the Nature of Matter?

Drip, drip, drip. The melting icicle slowly changes from a solid mound of ice into a small puddle below. Melting is just one of the many changes that can occur to matter.

After reading this chapter, you should be able to answer the following questions:

What physical and chemical properties describe matter?

What happens when matter undergoes a physical or chemical change?

What is the kinetic-molecular theory of matter?

How does energy change the properties of matter?

How do chemical reactions depend on activation energy?

How can you stay safe while conducting chemical reactions?

How can you use what you know about chemical reactions to stay safe at home?

Solids, Liquids, and Gases

You are constantly surrounded by different forms of matter. In fact, you are made up of matter in different forms. Each form of matter can be described by its specific properties. In this inquiry investigation, you will explore three basic forms of matter.

Materials:
- ✔ safety goggles
- ✔ triple-beam or electronic balance
- ✔ beaker (250-mL)
- ✔ ice cube
- ✔ metric ruler
- ✔ Bunsen burner or electric hot plate
- ✔ graduated cylinder (100-mL)
- ✔ paper towels

Work through parts A–D of the experiment quickly so that as little of the ice melts as possible.

Part A Find and record the mass of a dry beaker.

Part B Place an ice cube in the beaker. Find and record the total mass of the ice and the beaker.

> *1. Calculate and record the mass of the ice alone. Show your calculation.*

Part C Carefully observe the ice cube in the beaker.

> *2. Describe the general characteristics of the ice.*

Part D Using a metric ruler, measure the length, width, and height of the ice cube. Return the ice cube to the beaker as quickly as possible.

> *3. Find the volume of the ice cube.*

> **CAUTION:** Be sure to wear safety goggles during this part of the activity.

Part E Gently warm the beaker over a flame (or electric hot plate) until all the ice has melted.

> *4. What change takes place?*

> *5. What determines the shape of the water in the beaker?*

Part F Find and record the mass of the beaker with the water in it.

> *6. Calculate and record the mass of the liquid water.*

Part G Find and record the volume of water in the beaker. (Note: One cubic centimeter is equal to one milliliter.)

7. *Compare the data for ice and water. Do the results agree with your expectations? Explain.*

Part H Heat the beaker of water over a flame (or hot plate) until the water boils. Allow the water to boil for 1 minute. Be sure to wear your safety goggles.

8. *If any water remains, determine its mass. Describe what happens to the water.*

What Physical Properties Describe Matter?

You learned in Chapter 2 that matter is anything that has mass and occupies space. You, your books, your desk, and the air you breathe are all examples of matter. You also learned that matter exists in different phases, or states, with different properties. Now that you know a little more about different types of matter, you can describe matter in more detail and explain the reasons for some of the properties of matter.

Recall that those characteristics of matter that can be observed without changing the chemical nature of the matter are known as physical properties. In addition to color, odor, and taste, other important physical properties of matter are reviewed below.

1. *Phase*, or state, indicates whether a substance is a solid, a liquid, or a gas under ordinary conditions of temperature and pressure. For example, table salt is a solid, olive oil is a liquid, and oxygen is a gas at standard temperature and pressure.
2. *Mass* is the amount of matter an object possesses. For example, the mass of an elephant is greater than that of a mouse because there is a greater quantity of matter in the elephant than there is in the mouse. The basic unit of mass is the kilogram (kg).

Mass must not be confused with weight. The gravitational attraction, or pull, on a given mass by another mass is called weight. The basic unit of weight is the newton (N). One newton is approximately the weight of an average apple with a mass of 100 g. Unlike mass, which is constant for a given object, weight can vary with location because the pull of gravity can vary.

3. *Volume* is the amount of space an object or substance occupies. For example, a bowling ball takes up more space than a golf ball and therefore has a greater volume.
4. *Density* is the mass of a given volume of a substance (mass per unit of volume). For example, the mass of 1 cubic centimeter (cc) of lead is greater than the same volume of aluminum. Therefore, the density of lead is greater than that of aluminum. You must be careful not to say that lead is heavier than aluminum. Obviously, a very large piece of aluminum may be heavier than a small piece of lead.

The density of water is used as the standard when comparing the densities of other substances. The density of water is 1 gram per cubic centimeter. In other words, every cubic centimeter of water has a mass of 1 gram.

5. *Boiling point* is the temperature at which a substance begins to boil. Under ordinary conditions, for example, pure water boils at 100°Celsius (100°C). Pure grain alcohol boils at 78.3°C. The boiling point is the same temperature at which a substance condenses.

6. *Melting point* is the temperature at which a solid begins to melt, forming a liquid. This is the same temperature at which the liquid begins to freeze, to re-form the solid. At sea level, for example, lead melts at 327°C. The molten lead also freezes at the same temperature of 327°C.

7. *Solubility* is the ability to be dissolved. For example, sugar readily dissolves in water; sand does not.

8. *Hardness* is the ability of one substance to scratch another substance. For example, diamond, the hardest natural substance, can scratch all other natural substances.

9. *Texture* is how the object feels to the touch. For example, the texture of sandpaper is rough; that of glass is smooth.

▶ What Happens When Matter Undergoes a Physical Change?

Under certain conditions, the physical properties of matter can change. The composition of the matter does not change, but the form or appearance of the matter is altered. A **physical change** is a change in matter in which the identity of a substance remains the same. You can observe a physical change without changing the makeup of matter.

A change in phase is an example of a physical change. For example, when ice melts into liquid water, its appearance changes. However, both ice and liquid water are made up of water molecules. Melting does not alter the composition of water. The same is true when liquid water becomes water vapor. Again, both liquid water and water vapor are composed of water molecules but they have a different form.

Physical changes occur all the time. When you fold a sheet of paper, break a piece of wood in half, or bend a paper clip, you are causing a physical change in matter. The key to determining if a change is physical is being able to identify the same substance before and after the change.

What Chemical Properties Describe Matter?

In addition to physical properties, which are easily observed, matter also possesses other properties, which are not usually visible. They influence how substances interact with one another. The properties that concern the way in which a substance reacts with other substances are known as **chemical properties**.

The ability to burn, also known as **combustibility**, is an example of a chemical property. During the process of burning, a substance changes into other substances. You cannot observe this property until a substance is burning, so observing chemical

properties involves changing the composition of matter.

Additional chemical properties include the ability to rust and the ability to tarnish. Iron, for example, combines with oxygen in the air to form a rust called iron oxide. Silver tarnishes when it combines with sulfur to form silver sulfide.

▶ What Happens When Matter Undergoes a Chemical Change?

When observing a chemical property of matter, you see substances change into other substances. For example, when a wooden splint is ignited, the materials in the wood combine with oxygen in the air. In the course of burning, the wood changes into carbon (a black substance), a gray ash (minerals), and gases such as carbon dioxide and water vapor. Changes that result in the formation of substances having properties that are both chemically and physically different from the original substances—changes in composition—are called **chemical changes**, or chemical reactions. The substances that enter into a chemical reaction are known as **reactants**, and the substances that result from a chemical reaction are known as **products**.

Another chemical change occurs when an electric current is passed through acidified water (see Figure 8-1). As a result, water is broken down into two gases—hydrogen and oxygen. Both gases are colorless and no longer have the properties of water. The hydrogen is combustible, whereas the oxygen can support combustion.

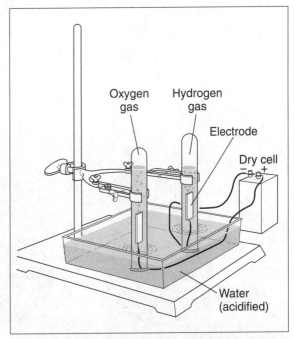

Figure 8-1. When an electric current is passed through acidified water, the water breaks down into two new substances—hydrogen and oxygen gases. This is an example of a chemical change.

What Is the Kinetic-Molecular Theory of Matter?

Properties and changes in matter depend on the particles from which the matter is made. Recall that matter is made up of tiny particles called atoms, and that atoms can bond to form molecules. A molecule is so small that it cannot be seen even with a powerful classroom microscope. It is only when a large number of molecules are held together (forming, for example, a drop of water) that you can observe any properties.

Although you cannot see them, the molecules of matter are in constant motion. The theory that molecules of matter are in motion is called the **kinetic-molecular theory**. This theory helps explain some differences in the properties and changes among samples of matter.

According to the kinetic-molecular theory, the constantly moving molecules of matter are held together by attractive forces. The weaker these attractive forces are, the more freely the molecules move.

In gases, for example, the attractive forces are comparatively weaker than in liquids and solids. As a result, the molecules of a gas can move about freely and the gas assumes the shape and volume of its container. In liquids, the attractive forces are somewhat stronger than in gases. Thus, the molecules of a liquid do not move as freely as the molecules of a gas, but they can flow past one another. The molecules of a liquid also assume the shape of their container, but they do not necessarily fill all of the space in a container. The attractive forces in solids are stronger than in liquids and gases. These forces prevent the molecules of a solid from moving far away from one

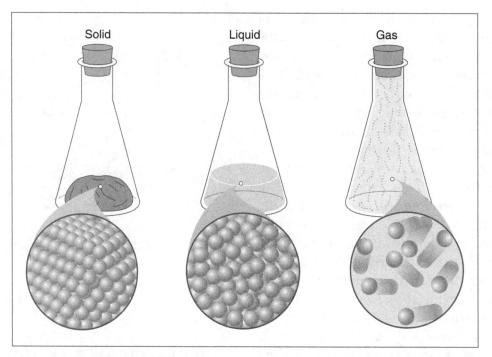

Figure 8-2. The forces attracting molecules to one another are strongest in solids, less strong in liquids, and least strong in gases.

another. As a result, a solid has a definite size and shape, regardless of the size and shape of its container. (See Figure 8-2.)

How Does Energy Affect the Properties of Matter?

The strength of the attractive forces between molecules depends partly on the energy supplied to them or removed from them. For example, adding energy to a sample of matter by heating it weakens the attractive forces between the molecules. This causes them to move faster and farther apart. Heating, therefore, can change solid ice into liquid water by breaking the molecules out of their relatively fixed positions. It can also change liquid water into water vapor in much the same way.

Removing energy by cooling has the opposite effect by strengthening the attractive forces between molecules. So, by cooling, gaseous water can be converted to liquid water by causing the molecules to move more slowly and stay closer together. Upon

further cooling, the liquid water turns into ice (solid water).

A process in which energy is released is called an **exothermic** process. The change through which fireworks release light and heat is an exothermic process. A process in which energy is absorbed is an **endothermic** process. Heating ice until it melts is an endothermic process.

How Do Chemical Reactions Depend on Activation Energy?

The movement of particles of matter also explains how substances undergo chemical reactions. Particles of matter must collide with one another in order to react. They must collide at a specific orientation so that bonds between atoms can be broken and new ones can form.

Merely colliding at the correct orientation, however, is not enough for a reaction to occur. The particles must also have a minimum amount of energy known as the **activation energy**. The activation energy is sometimes

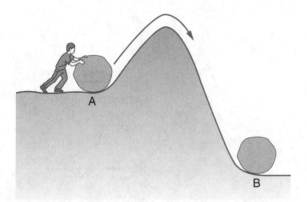

Figure 8-3. Like a hill over which a boulder is pushed, particles of matter must collide with enough energy for the reaction to proceed.

compared with pushing a boulder up a hill. Once the boulder reaches the top of the hill, it can roll down on its own. (See Figure 8-3.) Similarly, once particles collide with the appropriate amount of activation energy, the reaction can proceed on its own. If particles collide with less than the activation energy, they simply bounce apart.

You can represent the activation energy on a diagram (such as those shown in Figure 8-4) known as an energy profile. As you can see, both endothermic and exothermic reactions involve activation energy. The difference is that the energy of the products in an endothermic reaction is greater than that of the reactants. The opposite is true for an exothermic reaction: the energy of the reactants is greater than the energy of the products.

How Can You Change the Rate of a Reaction?

Some reactions progress very slowly. An example is the rusting of iron, which involves a reaction between iron and oxygen. Other reactions, such as those that involve the burning of wood, paper, coal, or gasoline, progress very rapidly. The speed at which a reaction occurs is known as the rate of reaction. The rate of reaction can be altered by changing the collisions between particles of matter. According to the collision theory, the more collisions there are between particles, the more likely they are to react. In other words, by increasing the number of collisions that occur, you increase the likelihood that particles will collide at the correct orientation with enough energy. Four factors can affect such collisions.

Concentration. Concentration describes how crowded the particles in a sample are. As the particles become more concentrated,

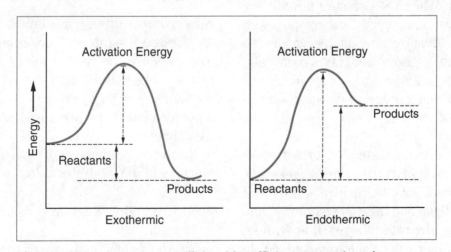

Figure 8-4. Reactants must collide with sufficient energy in order to react. If the reaction absorbs energy (endothermic), the products have more energy than the reactants. If the reaction releases energy (exothermic), the products have less energy than the reactants.

they have less space to spread apart. As a result, they collide more often. Increasing the concentration of the reactants, therefore, generally leads to an increase in reaction rate. Conversely, decreasing the concentration leads to a reduction in the reaction rate.

Temperature. Temperature describes the average motion of the particles. As temperature increases, particles move faster. As a result, they collide more often. Increasing temperature generally leads to an increase in reaction rate whereas lowering temperature leads to a reduction in reaction rate.

Particle Size. Particles of matter must be exposed in order to take part in a reaction. Consider a sugar cube placed in water. Only the particles on the outside of the cube are exposed to water. If, however, the cube is crushed into sugar granules, more sugar is exposed to water. The same is true for reactants in a chemical reaction. The smaller the particles of the reactants are, the more collisions that can occur and the faster the reaction will proceed.

Pressure. When the pressure on gaseous reactants is increased, the particles are pushed closer together. This causes them to collide more often. When the pressure is reduced, the particles can spread farther apart and collide less often. As a result, increasing the pressure on gaseous reactants generally causes the reaction to proceed faster whereas reducing pressure causes the reaction rate to decrease.

Catalysts. Certain substances, called **catalysts**, can also speed up the rate of a reaction. Although catalysts work in a number of ways, they have one thing in common: Catalysts change the rate of a reaction without themselves being permanently changed. In other words, they are the same at the end of a reaction as at the beginning. Many catalysts work by lowering the activation energy of the

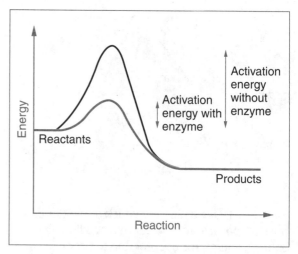

Figure 8-5. Many catalysts reduce the activation energy. As a result, more particles collide with sufficient energy for the reaction to proceed.

reaction. (See Figure 8-5.) The result is that more particles collide with enough energy for the reaction to proceed. Many catalysts make reactions possible that would otherwise not occur or would occur so slowly as to be of no practical value. The enzymes in your body perform such a function. Without digestive enzymes you would digest food too slowly to stay alive.

▶ How Can You Stay Safe While Conducting Chemical Reactions?

Although it is often important or necessary to increase the rate of a reaction, doing so may increase the risk of injury. For example, some reactions can proceed so rapidly as to become explosive, producing great amounts of heat and pressure that can injure experimenters.

To minimize these and other risks while working in the laboratory, do the following:

- Always follow directions exactly as written.
- Use only small amounts of reactants.
- Do not heat chemicals unless instructed to do so—and in a safe way—by your teacher.

- Never heat materials in a closed container.
- Never pour water into acids. Always pour acids into water.
- Never use an open flame to heat combustible substances. Use a water bath or hot plate. Follow your teacher's directions.
- Never taste or touch chemicals. Some chemicals are poisonous while others can harm your skin.
- Always wear safety goggles and a lab coat or apron when working with a flame or when handling chemicals or glassware.
- Never eat or drink in the lab.
- Always discard chemicals according to your teacher's instructions.
- If you get acid or any other chemical on your skin, in your eyes, or on your clothing, immediately flush the area with plenty of water.
- When heating a test tube, always point its mouth away from yourself and others.
- Keep your hands, equipment, and lab bench clean since small amounts of chemicals can react with one another with potentially dangerous results. Make sure any piece of equipment you use to transfer chemicals is free of other chemicals.
- Follow directions for pouring liquids so they do not spill on lab benches, clothing, or skin.
- If you wish to observe the odor of a substance, never place your nose directly over the substance. Fan your hand over the substance, moving the air toward your nose, which should be a few inches away from the substance.
- Become familiar with the kinds and locations of safety devices such as fire blankets, fire extinguishers, water fountains, eye-wash stations and first-aid equipment.
- Immediately report all accidents to your teacher.

How Can You Use What You Know About Chemical Reactions to Stay Safe at Home?

Many materials found in the home are poisonous when taken internally and some can cause severe injuries to your skin and eyes. Such materials include household cleaners, waxes, paints, polishes, hair sprays, and fluids used to start barbecues. In addition, all prescription and over-the-counter medicines should be considered dangerous if not taken as directed. To reduce the chances of household accidents caused by chemicals, do the following:

- Never take a prescription medicine not prescribed for you.
- When taking a prescription or over-the-counter medicine, always follow the directions on the label.
- Use any substance that gives off vapors, such as cleaning fluids and nail polish remover, in a well-ventilated place.
- Read labels to determine whether a fluid is flammable. If it is, never use it near an open flame. Note: *inflammable* means the same as *flammable*.
- Never mix household cleaners. Some mixtures can produce poisonous gases.
- Never heat an aerosol can such as those that contain paint or hair spray. Heat can make them explode.
- Always wear rubber or plastic gloves when using materials whose labels say anything like "may harm your skin."
- Always wear goggles when using materials whose labels say something like "Avoid contact with eyes."
- Read labels carefully to determine what you must do if the material is taken in by mouth or spilled on skin or clothes. Make sure you have in your home the first-aid materials called for on the labels.

- Keep all potentially dangerous materials out of the reach of small children.
- Keep all containers of household chemicals and medicines tightly closed.

- Dispose of outdated or leftover medicines and household chemicals in an appropriate manner that meets federal, state, and local guidelines.

Chapter Review

Science Terms

The following list contains all the boldfaced words found in this chapter and the page on which each appears.

activation energy (p. 120)

catalyst (p. 122)

chemical change (p. 119)

chemical property (p. 118)

collision theory (p. 121)

combustibility (p. 118)

endothermic (p. 120)

exothermic (p. 120)

kinetic-molecular theory (p. 119)

physical change (p. 118)

product (p. 119)

rate of reaction (p. 121)

reactant (p. 119)

Matching Questions

In your notebook, write the letter of the item in column B that is most closely related to the item in column A.

Column A

_____ 1. solid

_____ 2. hardness

_____ 3. density

_____ 4. catalyst

_____ 5. exothermic process

_____ 6. activation energy

_____ 7. weight

_____ 8. rate of reaction

_____ 9. combustibility

_____ 10. endothermic process

Column B

a. change that absorbs energy

b. speed at which a chemical change occurs

c. effect of gravity on mass

d. a measure of the ability to scratch another substance

e. change that releases energy

f. matter with definite shape and volume

g. ability to burn

h. substance that increases reaction rate

i. mass per unit volume

j. minimum energy required for chemical reaction

Multiple-Choice Questions

In your notebook, write the letter preceding the word or expression that best completes the statement or answers the question.

1. The amount of space a sample of matter occupies is its
   a. mass
   b. weight
   c. volume
   d. phase

2. In which state will matter expand to fill the space in its container?
   a. gas
   b. solid
   c. liquid
   d. plasma

3. In which state is a substance that has a definite volume but no definite shape?
   a. liquid
   b. solid
   c. gas
   d. plasma

4. Which of the following is a physical change in matter?
   a. a cake baking
   b. a nail rusting
   c. a candle burning
   d. an icicle melting

5. Which of the following is a chemical change in matter?
   a. tearing a newspaper in half
   b. exploding a firework
   c. sawing a log in pieces
   d. tying a string of yarn in a knot

6. An example of a chemical property is
   a. melting point
   b. boiling point
   c. combustibility
   d. solubility

7. How does the kinetic-molecular theory explain diffusion?
   a. Molecules stop moving once they escape their containers.
   b. Molecules lump together when forced into small volumes.
   c. Molecules become larger when they have room to expand.
   d. Molecules in motion collide and spread in all directions.

8. The attractive forces binding the molecules of a solid can be weakened by
   a. increasing the pressure
   b. decreasing the pressure
   c. heating the solid
   d. cooling the solid

9. The water in a glass evaporates over time. Why is this not considered a chemical change?
   a. The composition of the water does not change.
   b. Only the phase of the water changes.
   c. The volume of the water remains the same.
   d. Only the appearance of the water changes.

10. Processes in which energy is released are
    a. conservative
    b. exothermic
    c. radioactive
    d. absorptive

11. What does the activation energy indicate about a reaction?
    a. the minimum energy required for a reaction
    b. the difference between the reactant and product energies
    c. the energy released during the reaction
    d. the energy of reactant particles before colliding

12. Which change is most likely to increase the rate of a chemical reaction?
    a. decreasing the concentration of the reactants
    b. lowering the temperature of the reactants
    c. increasing the size of the reactant particles
    d. increasing the pressure of gaseous reactants

13. How might a catalyst change the reaction rate?
    a. It increases concentration by acting as a reactant.
    b. It increases the temperature of the reaction.
    c. It lowers the activation energy.
    d. It pulls reactant particles together.

14. Which of the following should you avoid when observing chemical reactions?
    a. Recording your observations in a journal.
    b. Tasting odorless chemicals to identify them.
    c. Wearing safety goggles and a lab coat.
    d. Pointing test tubes away from yourself and others.

15. Which is a good safety practice to follow at home?
    a. Sharing prescription medicine rather than wasting.
    b. Using a candle flame to read the labels on cleaning fluids clearly.
    c. Mixing household cleaners to try to make them stronger.
    d. Using cleaning fluids in well-ventilated places.

Modified True-False Questions

In some of the following statements, the italicized term makes the statement incorrect. For each incorrect statement, in your notebook, write the term that must be substituted for the italicized term to make the statement correct. For each correct statement, write the word "true."

1. A *liquid* has neither definite volume nor definite shape at room temperature. _____

2. In liquids, the attractive forces holding the molecules together are *weaker* than in gases. _____

3. The *texture* of an object describes how well it scratches other objects. _____

4. The amount of space a substance occupies is the *weight* of the substance. _____

5. Sugar dissolves in water. This describes the property of *solubility*. _____

6. The temperature at which a solid begins to melt is the same temperature as the *freezing* point of the solid. _____

7. The mass per unit volume of a substance is called *density*. _____

8. The burning of wood is an example of a *chemical* change. _____

9. A chemical reaction in which energy is absorbed is called an *exothermic* reaction. _____

10. Energy needed to get a reaction started is called *phase* energy. _____

TEST-TAKING TIP When performing mathematical calculations, begin by estimating the answer. Then compare your result with the estimate to decide if your answer is reasonable.

Check Your Knowledge
Write the answer to each question in your notebook.

1. How is a physical property different from a chemical property? Give an example of each.

2. How is a physical change different from a chemical change? Give an example of each.

3. How does the kinetic-molecular theory help explain how solids, liquids, and gases differ from one another?

4. List four factors other than catalysts that affect the rate of a reaction and explain the general principle underlying their action.

Think Critically
Write the answer to each of the following questions in your notebook.

1. a. Using a piece of wood, describe how you could cause the wood to undergo a physical change.
   b. Describe how you could cause the piece of wood to undergo a chemical change.

2. What is the density of a substance whose mass is 15 grams and whose volume is 5 cubic centimeters?

3. An object weighs 1800 N on Earth. What would this object weigh on the moon?

4. The energy profile for a chemical reaction is shown below. Is the reaction endothermic or exothermic? Justify your answer.

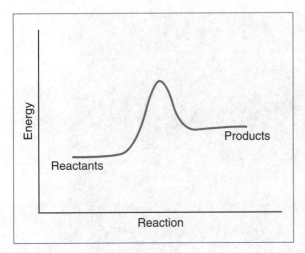

Take It Further

1. Plasma is a fourth state of matter. In fact, it is the most common state of matter in the universe. Research plasma and present your findings to the class. Include information about how this state of matter got is name, how it differs from solids, liquids, and gases, and where plasma is found on Earth and throughout the universe.

2. Water is found on Earth in three states of matter. Investigate why this is true and how this makes Earth unique in the solar system. Present your findings in a labeled diagram or poster.

3. A common endothermic reaction is photosynthesis. Conduct research to find out the changes that occur during photosynthesis. Prepare an oral report to describe this reaction, where it occurs, and why it is important on Earth.

CAREER

4. People who manufacture fireworks and present fireworks displays need a thorough understanding of chemical reactions. Investigate careers involving fireworks. Find out what they involve and what preparation is required. Present your findings to the class. You may wish to consult the following sites as you begin your research: *http://education-portal.com/ articles/Pyrotechnic_Technician_Job _Description_and_Requirements_for _Becoming_a_Pyrotechnic_ Technician.html* and *http://www. pyroinnovations.com/blog1/2007/02/ 07/a-pyrotechnic-career-2/.*

9

How Does Matter Take Part in Reactions?

Bright flames are just one clue that a chemical reaction has taken place. Flames of fire indicate that substances have changed into new substances with different properties. You can describe what happens during this and any type of chemical reaction.

After reading this chapter, you should be able to answer the following questions:

How can you describe a chemical reaction?

What is the law of conservation of mass?

How do you write chemical equations?

What are the different types of chemical reactions?

Conservation of Matter

During a chemical reaction, matter changes both its physical and chemical properties. The ways in which these changes occur do not affect the overall amount of matter involved in the reaction. In this inquiry investigation, you will explore the amount of matter involved in a chemical reaction.

Materials:
- ✔ safety goggles
- ✔ filter paper
- ✔ triple-beam or electronic balance
- ✔ barium chloride (solid)
- ✔ test tube (100-mm)
- ✔ distilled water
- ✔ sodium sulfate (solid)
- ✔ spatula
- ✔ Erlenmeyer flask (250-mL) with rubber stopper
- ✔ graduated cylinder (110 mL)

CAUTION: Be careful not to spill the solids or the solutions on yourself or clothes. Wear safety goggles. If spills occur, wash immediately with water.

Part A Cover the pan of a balance with a small sheet of clean filter paper. Determine the mass of the paper. Add about 1 gram of barium chloride ($BaCl_2$).
   Transfer the barium chloride to a 100-mm test tube half-filled with distilled water. Gently shake the test tube until all the barium chloride dissolves.

Part B Weigh out 1 gram of sodium sulfate (Na_2SO_4) as in Part A.
   Transfer the sodium sulfate to a 250-milliliter Erlenmeyer flask. Add 25 milliliters of water to the flask and shake the flask until the solid dissolves.

Part C Carefully lower the test tube containing the barium chloride solution into the Erlenmeyer flask, as shown in Figure 9-1. The solutions should not mix with each other. Stopper the flask.

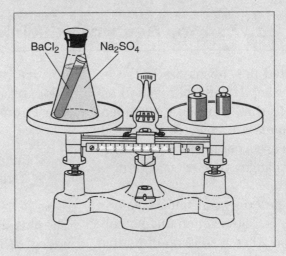

Figure 9-1.

1. *Describe the appearance of the solutions.*

Part D Place the apparatus prepared in Part C on the balance and determine its mass.

2. *What is the mass of the Erlenmeyer flask and its contents?*

Part E Carefully tip the Erlenmeyer flask until all of the barium chloride solution runs out of the test tube and mixes with the solution in the flask.

3. *What do you observe?*

4. *How do you account for what you see?*

Part F Again determine the mass of the Erlenmeyer flask and its contents on the balance.

5. *What is the mass of the Erlenmeyer flask and its contents?*

6. *How does this mass compare with the mass obtained in Part D?*

7. *From the data obtained in this experiment, what can you conclude about the mass of the products of a reaction compared to the mass of the reactants?*

8. *If you repeat this experiment using different quantities of barium chloride, sodium sulfate, and water, how would the results be affected?*

How Can You Describe a Chemical Reaction?

When you mixed the substances in the inquiry investigation, a chemical reaction occurred. Recall that during a chemical reaction, reactants are changed into products. Chemists use a **chemical equation** to describe the changes that occur during a chemical reaction.

One way to describe a chemical equation is by using words. The reaction that you observed occurred when a solution of barium chloride was added to a sodium sulfate solution to form barium sulfate and sodium chloride. You could write what happened as a **word equation**.

sodium sulfate + barium chloride →
= barium sulfate + sodium chloride

The plus sign indicates that one substance is added to the other. The horizontal arrow means "yields" or "forms."

However, writing out word equations can be time-consuming, especially when chemical reactions become more complex. To simplify the process, chemists use chemical formulas rather than words. By using chemical formulas, you can rewrite the word equation as shown below.

$$Na_2SO_4 + BaCl_2 \rightarrow BaSO_4 + 2NaCl$$

What Is the Law of Conservation of Mass?

If you look at the chemical equation long enough, you might notice something interesting—the atoms on the left side of the arrow are exactly the same as the atoms on the right side of the arrow.

$$Na_2SO_4 + BaCl_2 \rightarrow BaSO_4 + 2NaCl$$

2 Na	2 Na
1 S	1 S
4 O	4 O
1 Ba	1 Ba
2 Cl	2 Cl

During the reaction, bonds between the atoms of the reactants were broken. The atoms were rearranged to form the products, and new bonds were formed. No atoms were destroyed and no new atoms were created. This statement, called the **law of conservation of mass** (sometimes known as the law of conservation of matter), was first suggested by the French chemist *Anton Lavoisier* in the eighteenth century. Lavoisier heated mercury(II) oxide for several days in a sealed glass vessel. Although the compound changed color, indicating a chemical change, the sealed tube showed *no* change in mass.

Think back to the inquiry investigation at the beginning of the chapter. Remember that when barium chloride and sodium sulfate solutions were mixed, a chemical reaction oc-

curred that produced new substances. However, when you determined the masses of the substances before and after the reaction, you found that no change in total mass had occurred. Therefore, you demonstrated the law of conservation of mass.

Take another look at the equation for the reaction from the inquiry investigation:

$$Na_2SO_4 + BaCl_2 \rightarrow BaSO_4 + 2NaCl$$

As you already know, the formula mass of a compound is found by adding the atomic masses of the atoms in the compound. In this case, the formula mass of sodium sulfate (Na_2SO_4) is determined by adding the atomic masses of two atoms of sodium (2 × 23 amu = 46 amu), one atom of sulfur (32 amu), and four atoms of oxygen (4 × 16 amu = 64 amu). Thus the formula mass of Na_2SO_4 is found to be 142 amu. The formula masses of each of the other compounds in the equation are found in a similar manner. To simplify the calculations, use 35 amu as the atomic mass of chlorine.

formula mass of NaCl = 23 amu + 35 amu = 58 amu

formula mass of $BaCl_2$ = 137 amu + 70 amu = 207 amu

formula mass of $BaSO_4$ = 137 amu + 32 amu + (4 × 16 amu) = 233 amu

Now you can indicate the formula mass of each substance in the chemical equation and then determine the total formula masses of the reactants and the products.

	sodium sulfate	+	barium chloride	barium sulfate	+	barium chloride
formula masses:	142 amu		207 amu	233 amu		2 × 58 amu
total formula masses:		349 amu			349 amu	

Notice that the total mass of the reactants is, in fact, equal to the total mass of the products. This can only be possible if the numbers of atoms of each of the elements are the same on both sides of the equation. The law of conservation of matter governs all chemical reactions, so the following equation is a correct generalization:

$$\begin{pmatrix} \text{total formula} \\ \text{mass of reactants} \end{pmatrix} = \begin{pmatrix} \text{total formula} \\ \text{mass of products} \end{pmatrix}$$

▶ **How Do You Write Chemical Equations?**

The following rules will help you write chemical equations for some simple reactions:

1. First determine the reactants and products. Many times, you can use your knowledge of chemical reactions to do this, but sometimes it may require performing the experiment in the laboratory.
2. Write the word equation. That is, write the names of the reactants on the left side of the horizontal arrow, and those of the products on the right side of the arrow. For example, if you know that aluminum metal, when heated, reacts with oxygen gas to form aluminum oxide, you would write the word equation as follows:

$$\text{aluminum} + \text{oxygen} \xrightarrow{\Delta} \text{aluminum oxide}$$

[Note the small triangle (Δ) above the arrow indicates heating.]
3. Write the symbols and formulas for the products and the reactants under each substance. (Keep in mind that the formulas for compounds are determined by crisscrossing the valence numbers of the elements in them. See page 88. The formula for aluminum oxide is found by writing $Al^{3+}O^{2-}$, which, when the

valence numbers are crisscrossed, gives Al_2O_3.)

In the case of gaseous elements, scientists have found that one molecule of some gases may consist of more than one atom. For example, each molecule of oxygen, hydrogen, and nitrogen consists of 2 atoms. Accordingly, a molecule of oxygen is represented as O_2, of hydrogen as H_2, and of nitrogen as N_2. Now you can write proper symbols and formulas under the word equation:

$$\text{aluminum} + \text{oxygen} \xrightarrow{\Delta} \text{aluminum oxide}$$

$$Al + O_2 \xrightarrow{\Delta} Al_2O_3$$

4. Examining the equation reveals that there is 1 atom of aluminum on the left side of the equation and 2 atoms of aluminum on the right. Also, there are 2 atoms of oxygen on the left side, and 3 atoms of oxygen on the right. Remember that each atom represents a specific mass. Since there are more atoms on the right side of the equation than on the left, it appears as though matter has been created. Yet, according to the law of conservation of mass, this is impossible.

To satisfy the law of conservation of mass, and to write an equation that is correct, you must balance the equation. When this is completed, the same number of atoms of each element will appear on each side of the equation. To balance an equation, use the following steps as a guide:
   a. *Balance the nonmetallic elements.* In the equation

$$Al + O_2 \xrightarrow{\Delta} Al_2O_3$$

there are 2 atoms of oxygen on the left side of the arrow and 3 atoms of oxygen on the right side. To balance the atoms of oxygen, you must multiply the number of oxygen atoms on each side of the arrow by numbers that will make the number of oxygen atoms on each side equal. If you multiply the oxygen on the left side of the equation by 3 and the oxygen on the right side of the equation by 2, the result is 6 atoms of oxygen on each side. (Note: Mathematically, it is also possible to multiply the oxygen on the left by $1\frac{1}{2}$, resulting in 3 atoms of oxygen on each side of the equation.) These multipliers are called **coefficients**. Each coefficient refers only to the atoms in a particular molecule. Place each coefficient in front of the molecule that is being multiplied. In this case, write the number 3 in front of the O_2 and the number 2 in front of the Al_2O_3. The equation now becomes

$$Al + 3O_2 \xrightarrow{\Delta} 2Al_2O_3$$

When no coefficient is shown, it is understood that the coefficient is 1. Coefficients must never be placed within the formula of a compound, because doing so would change the composition of the compound itself. Thus, you write $2Al_2O_3$ and not $Al_2 2O_3$.

b. *Balance the metallic elements.* Now note that the left side of the equation shows 1 atom of aluminum whereas the right side now shows 2 Al_2, or 4 atoms of aluminum. Balance the metallic atoms by multiplying the aluminum on the left side by the coefficient 4:

$$4Al + 3O_2 \xrightarrow{\Delta} 2Al_2O_3$$

c. *Check the numbers of atoms on each side of the equation.* Count the number of atoms of each element on each side of the arrow. Begin with the first reactant on the left side of the

arrow. The 4 Al means 4 atoms (4 atomic masses) of aluminum. Notice that now there are also 4 atoms of aluminum on the right side of the arrow, since 2 Al_2 equals 4 atoms. Go on to the next reactant on the left side of the arrow. Note that there are 6 atoms (6 atomic masses) of oxygen, or 3 molecules of O_2, reacting with aluminum. Because 2 is the coefficient of the Al_2O_3 on the right side of the arrow, 6 atoms of oxygen are also present on this side. Checking this equation shows that it is now correctly balanced because atoms have been conserved.

d. *Never change the subscripts within a formula to balance an equation.* Changing the subscripts changes the formula, which, in effect, changes the composition of the substance. Thus, if you wrote the formula for aluminum oxide as AlO_2, the equation would not require coefficients to be balanced. However, according to the valence numbers, the correct formula for aluminum oxide is Al_2O_3.

e. *Confirm the conservation of matter.* Before the equation was balanced, you noted that the masses of the reactants were not equal to the masses of the products.

Unbalanced equation:

$$Al + O_2 \xrightarrow{\Delta} Al_2O_3$$

Atomic masses:

$$(1 \times 27 \text{ amu}) + (2 \times 16 \text{ amu}) = 1 \times 102 \text{ amu}$$

Formula masses:

$$27 \text{ amu} + 32 \text{ amu} = 102 \text{ amu}$$

Total formula masses:

$$59 \text{ amu} \neq 102 \text{ amu}$$

Now that the equation is balanced, you can see that this condition has been corrected.

Balanced equation:

$$4Al + 3\,O_2 \rightarrow 2Al_2O_3$$

Atomic masses:

$$(4 \times 27\ \text{amu}) + (6 \times 16\ \text{amu})$$
$$= 2 \times 102\ \text{amu}$$

Formula masses:

$$108\ \text{amu} + 96\ \text{amu} = 204\ \text{amu}$$

Total formula masses:

$$204\ \text{amu} = 204\ \text{amu}$$

To review, let us write and balance the chemical equation for the combination of hydrogen and oxygen to form water.

WORD EQUATION:

hydrogen + oxygen → water

FORMULAS: $\quad H_2 + O_2 \rightarrow H_2O$

1. Balance the nonmetallic elements.

$$H_2 + O_2 \rightarrow 2H_2O$$

Each side of the equation now contains 2 atoms of oxygen.

2. Balance the metallic elements.

$$2H_2 + O_2 \rightarrow 2H_2O$$

Each side of the equation now contains 4 atoms of hydrogen.

3. Check the number of atoms of each element on each side of the equation.

$$2H_2 + O_2 \rightarrow 2H_2O$$

Number of Atoms	Left Side	Right Side
Hydrogen	4	4
Oxygen	2	2

Note that the total formula mass on the left side of the equation is

$$(4 \times 1\ \text{amu}) + (2 \times 16\ \text{amu}) = 4 + 32\ \text{amu}$$
$$= 36\ \text{amu}$$

and the total formula mass on the right side is

$$(4 \times 1\ \text{amu}) + (2 \times 16\ \text{amu})$$
$$= 4\ \text{amu} + 32\ \text{amu}$$
$$= 36\ \text{amu}$$

You see that, in a balanced equation, the total formula masses of the reactants equal the total formula masses of the products. Although the substances in the reaction may have changed their form, the total amount of matter present is still the same.

▶ What Are the Different Types of Chemical Reactions?

In general, there are four types of chemical reactions: direct combination, decomposition, single replacement, and double replacement.

Direct Combination (Synthesis). A reaction in which two or more elements form a compound is called a **direct combination reaction** or **synthesis** (see Figure 9-2).

You have already encountered some examples of direct combination reactions. Now you can see from the chemical equations that two substances come together to form one.

$$\underset{\text{hydrogen}}{2H_2} + \underset{\text{oxygen}}{O_2} \rightarrow \underset{\text{water}}{2H_2O}$$

$$\underset{\text{aluminum}}{4Al} + \underset{\text{oxygen}}{3O_2} \rightarrow \underset{\text{aluminum oxide}}{2Al_2O_3}$$

Figure 9-2. In a direct combination reaction, two substances join to form a third substance—much like these dancers join, forming a couple.

$$Ca + Cl_2 \rightarrow CaCl_2$$
calcium   chlorine   calcium chloride

Notice that, in each of these reactions, a compound is formed from elements. Such a reaction may be represented by the following general equation:

$$A + B \rightarrow AB$$

where A and B are elements, and AB is a compound. When a metal combines in this manner with a nonmetal, which is the case in the last two examples, the product is a **salt**.

Decomposition (Analysis). A reaction in which a compound is broken down into two or more elements is called a **decomposition reaction** or **analysis** (see Figure 9-3). Such reactions are generally the opposite of synthesis reactions.

The equations below describe some examples of decomposition reactions.

$$2HgO \rightarrow 2Hg + O_2$$
mercury(II) oxide   mercury   oxygen

$$2H_2O \rightarrow 2H_2 + O_2$$
water   hydrogen   oxygen

$$2KClO_3 \rightarrow 2KCl + 3O_2$$
potassium chlorate   potassium chloride   oxygen

(The last example represents a more complicated type of decomposition—a complex compound breaking down into simpler substances.)

The general equation for a decomposition reaction is:

$$AB \rightarrow A + B$$

Note that the compound AB breaks down to form elements A and B. (In the last example shown, compound ABC breaks down to form compound AB and element C: ABC → AB + C.) Decomposition reactions usually require energy to make them proceed. The energy may be in the form of heat, light, or electricity.

Single Replacement. A reaction in which one element reacts with one compound to form another element and another compound is called a **single replacement reaction** (see Figure 9-4).

Figure 9-4. In a single replacement reaction, a free substance (A) replaces one substance (B) in a compound (BC). This produces a new compound (AC) and a new free substance (B). The diagram uses an analogy of one dancer replacing another in a dancing couple.

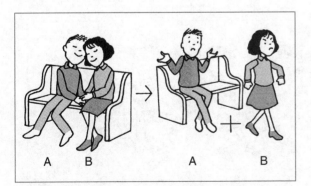

Figure 9-3. In a decomposition reaction, one substance breaks apart to form two or more substances—much like this couple separates.

Examples of single replacement reactions that have been mentioned earlier are:

$$Zn + Cu(NO_3)_2 \rightarrow Cu + Zn(NO_3)_2$$
zinc   copper(II) nitrate   copper   zinc nitrate

$$Cu + 2AgNO_3 \rightarrow 2Ag + Cu(NO_3)_2$$
copper   silver nitrate   silver   copper(II) nitrate

$$Mg + 2HCl \rightarrow H_2 + MgCl_2$$
magnesium   hydrochloric acid   hydrogen   magnesium chloride

Recall the Reactivity Series of the Metals on page 78. A single replacement reaction occurs when a free metal is more reactive than a metal combined in a compound. If the free metal is not more reactive, the reaction does not proceed.

In the examples cited, one metal replaced another in its compound. More reactive nonmetals may also replace less reactive nonmetals in compounds.

$$Cl_2 + 2KBr \rightarrow Br_2 + 2KCl$$
chlorine   potassium bromide   bromine   potassium chloride

A metal may replace the hydrogen in an acid.

$$Zn + 2HCl \rightarrow ZnCl_2 + H_2$$
zinc   hydrochloric acid   zinc chloride   hydrogen

The general equation for a single replacement reaction is:

$$A + BC \rightarrow AC + B$$
element₁   compound₁   compound₂   element₂

Observe that the elements A and B have merely changed places, so that B is now uncombined and A has combined with C to form the new compound AC.

Double Replacement (Ion Exchange). A reaction in which the metals present in two compounds change places to form two new compounds is called a **double replacement reaction**, or **ion exchange reaction** (see Figure 9-5). In such reactions, one of the products that forms removes ions from solution. This ion-removing product may be a precipitate (ppt), gas, or water. A **precipitate** is a solid that separates out of solution. You observed the formation of a precipitate in the inquiry investigation at the beginning of the chapter. The following are examples of double replacement reactions:

$$AgNO_3 + NaCl \rightarrow AgCl + NaNO_3$$
silver nitrate   sodium chloride   silver chloride (ppt)   sodium nitrate

Note that the elements silver and sodium have exchanged places to form the new compounds silver chloride and sodium nitrate. Also note that the silver chloride is a precipitate, removing Ag^+ and Cl^- ions. Other examples of double replacement reactions are:

$$NaOH + HCl \rightarrow NaCl + H_2O$$
sodium hydroxide   hydrochloric acid   sodium chloride   water

In this case, the formation of water removes the ions H^+ and OH^-.

Figure 9-5. In a double replacement reaction, two substances (A and C) exchange places to form new compounds (CB and AD). In the analogy shown in the diagram, partners from the dancing couples switch places.

$$NH_4Cl + NaOH \rightarrow NH_3 + H_2O + NaCl$$
ammonium   sodium   ammonia   water   sodium
chloride   hydroxide   (gas)   chloride

The general equation that represents a double replacement reaction is

$$AB + CD \rightarrow AD + CB$$

where the elements A and C exchange places to form the new compounds AD and CB. Although the last example shown above does not seem to follow this general equation, it actually does. That is because the reaction shown progresses in two stages, the second of which is shown above to illustrate how a gas removes ions. The first stage is:

$$NH_4Cl + NaOH \rightarrow NH_4OH + NaCl$$
ammonium   sodium   ammonia   sodium
chloride   hydroxide   hydroxide   chloride

The ammonium hydroxide then breaks down to form ammonia gas and water.

Chapter Review

Science Terms

The following list contains all the boldfaced words found in this chapter and the page on which each appears.

analysis (p. 135)

chemical equation (p. 130)

coefficient (p. 133)

decomposition reaction (p. 135)

direct combination reaction (p. 134)

double replacement reaction (p. 136)

ion exchange reaction (p. 136)

law of conservation of mass (p. 131)

precipitate (p. 136)

salt (p. 135)

single replacement reaction (p. 135)

synthesis (p. 134)

word equation (p. 130)

Matching Questions

In your notebook, write the letter of the item in column B that is most closely related to the item in column A.

Column A

_____ 1. example of a chemical equation

_____ 2. example of a word equation

_____ 3. reactants

_____ 4. products

_____ 5. general equation for single replacement reaction

_____ 6. general equation for double replacement reaction

_____ 7. general equation for synthesis reaction

_____ 8. general equation for decomposition reaction

_____ 9. example of a salt

_____ 10. precipitate

Column B

a. substances that interact

b. $A + BC \rightarrow B + AC$

c. $A + B \rightarrow AB$

d. substance that settles out of solution

e. $CaCl_2$

f. $4Al + 3O_2 \rightarrow 2Al_2O_3$

g. substances formed during a chemical reaction

h. $AB + CD \rightarrow CB + AD$

i. carbon plus oxygen yields carbon dioxide

j. $AB \rightarrow A + B$

Multiple-Choice Questions

In your notebook, write the letter preceding the word or expression
that best completes the statement or answers the question.

1. What does the arrow indicate in the following chemical equation?

   $$NaOH + HCl \rightarrow NaCl + H_2O$$

   a. and
   b. heat
   c. yields
   d. change of state

2. Which of the following occurs during a chemical reaction?
   a. Atoms of the reactants are rearranged to form products.
   b. Atoms of the reactants are destroyed.
   c. Atoms of the products are formed.
   d. Atoms are changed from one element to another.

3. Anton Lavoisier is credited with
   a. describing elements by chemical symbols
   b. defining matter as consisting of atoms
   c. recognizing that particles of matter have wave properties
   d. first suggesting that matter is conserved

4. Which of the following chemical equations is correctly balanced?
   a. $Cl_2 + KI \rightarrow 2KCl + I_2$
   b. $2Mg + O_2 \rightarrow 2MgO$
   c. $2Ag_2O \rightarrow 2Ag + O_2$
   d. $C_4H_8 + 6 O_2 \rightarrow 6CO_2 + 2H_2O$

5. The chemical equations for many decomposition reactions include a small triangle above the horizontal arrow. What does this triangle indicate?
   a. A gas is produced.
   b. A precipitate is produced.
   c. A liquid is formed.
   d. Heat is absorbed.

6. When silver nitrate and sodium chloride solutions are mixed together, a solid settles out of solution. The solid is known as
   a. an ion
   b. a reactant
   c. a precipitate
   d. a synthetic

7. Which type of chemical reaction is represented by the following general equation?

   $$AB \rightarrow A + B$$

   a. direct combination
   b. decomposition
   c. single replacement
   d. double replacement

8. In a chemical reaction, the total mass of the reactants
   a. is greater than the total mass of the products
   b. is equal to the total mass of the products
   c. is less than the total mass of the products
   d. cannot be determined

9. A student is writing a chemical equation that includes one molecule of hydrogen gas as a reactant. Which of the following should the student write to represent this reactant?
   a. H
   b. H_3
   c. 2H
   d. H_2

10. In a synthesis reaction,
    a. two metals change places
    b. two or more elements form a single compound
    c. a compound is broken down
    d. heat energy is created

TEST-TAKING TIP

Use scratch paper or space on your test paper to write out information you are trying to visualize. For example, you may wish to write the general form for a chemical equation or the formula for a compound.

Modified True-False Questions

In some of the following statements, the italicized term makes the statement incorrect. For each incorrect statement, in your notebook, write the term that must be substituted for the italicized term to make the statement correct. For each correct statement, write the word "true."

1. In a *decomposition* reaction, two simpler substances come together to form a compound. _____

2. In the reaction AB → A + B, AB represents *an element*. _____

3. In a single replacement reaction, one *metal* may replace another. _____

4. A single replacement reaction takes place when a free metal is *more* active than a metal combined in a compound. _____

5. In the reaction $AgNO_3$ + NaCl → AgCl + $NaNO_3$, AgCl is *a soluble* precipitate. _____

6. In a reaction, mass is always *conserved*. _____

7. A chemical *formula* is a shorthand notation for showing the reactants and products that form in a chemical reaction. _____

8. A *synthesis* reaction always forms a precipitate, a gas, or water. _____

9. The term $2AgNO_3$ represents 2 *atoms* of silver nitrate. _____

10. The reaction in which calcium carbonate is heated to form carbon dioxide and calcium oxide is a *decomposition* reaction. _____

Check Your Knowledge

Write the answer to each question in your notebook.

1. Explain the differences between each of the following:
   a. formula and equation
   b. synthesis and decomposition reactions
   c. single replacement and double replacement reactions
   d. chemical reaction and chemical equation
   e. subscript and coefficient

2. Identify the type of chemical reaction shown in each of the following:
   a. $AgNO_3$ + NaCl → AgCl + $NaNO_3$
   b. Zn + 2HCl → H_2 + $ZnCl_2$
   c. 2HgO → 2Hg + O_2
   d. $2H_2$ + O_2 → $2H_2O$
   e. Fe + $CuSO_4$ → Cu + $FeSO_4$

3. If they are not already balanced, balance the following equations:
   a. H_2O_2 → H_2 + O_2
   b. Al + HCl → H_2 + $AlCl_3$
   c. $BaCl_2$ + Na_3PO_4 → $Ba_3(PO_4)_2$ + NaCl
   d. Fe + O_2 → Fe_2O_3
   e. Mg + HCl → H_2 + $MgCl_2$

Think Critically

Write the answer to each of the following questions in your notebook.

1. Complete each of the following word equations. Then write a balanced equation for each.
   a. barium nitrate + sodium sulfate →
   b. magnesium + hydrochloric acid →
   c. zinc + copper nitrate →
   d. magnesium + oxygen →
   e. sodium hydroxide + hydrochloric acid →

2. Prove mathematically that each of the following equations satisfies the law of conservation of matter:
   a. Cu + $2AgNO_3$ → 2Ag + $Cu(NO_3)_2$
   b. $2KClO_3$ → 2KCl + 3 O_2

3. A student performs the following experiment:
    a. Carefully measures out 5 grams of pure carbon.
    b. Places the carbon in a fireproof dish.
    c. Determines that the mass of the dish and the carbon equals 20 grams.
    d. Ignites the carbon and allows it to completely burn.
    e. Determines the mass of the dish and contents and finds it to be 15 grams.
    f. Concludes that matter can be destroyed by fire.

    Explain why the student's conclusion does or does not make scientific sense. If necessary, use chemical equations to support your analysis.

4. The diagram below represents a chemical reaction. Write a word equation and a balanced chemical equation describing the reaction. Then explain how the diagram supports the law of conservation of matter.

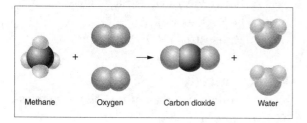

Methane   Oxygen   Carbon dioxide   Water

Take It Further

1. Some chemical reactions are classified as combustion reactions. Research the general description of a combustion reaction and several examples. Find out how they are similar to and/or different from the reactions you explored in this chapter.

2. The Ostwald Method is an industrial process for making nitric acid. Research this method and find chemical equations to describe the reactions that occur in the three basic steps of the method. Present your findings and an explanation of why the method is important and how it got its name.

CAREER

3. Many careers depend on products that utilize chemical reactions. Welders, for example, often use oxyacetylene torches and firefighters use carbon dioxide extinguishers. Choose one of these careers and research job opportunities and required training. Present your findings to the class.

10 What Are Metallic Resources?

This intimidating bull will not actually chase after you because it is made out of bronze. Like other metals, bronze gives this statue the properties it needs to stand up to different kinds of weather conditions.

After reading this chapter, you should be able to answer the following questions:

What are metal ores?

What are different types of ores?

How are metals separated from their ores?

How are iron and steel obtained?

What happens during corrosion?

You use metals all the time. Perhaps you eat with metal utensils, cook in metal pots, wear metal jewelry, or dig a garden with a metal shovel. Where exactly do metals come from? In this inquiry investigation, you will find one way to obtain metal.

Materials:
✔ safety goggles
✔ copper(II) carbonate
✔ crucible
✔ wire gauze
✔ ring stand
✔ iron ring
✔ Bunsen burner
✔ triple-beam or electronic balance
✔ powdered charcoal
✔ glass rod
✔ tongs
✔ beaker (100 mL)
✔ water

CAUTION: Wear safety goggles; do not touch the hot crucible.

Part A Place a small quantity of copper(II) carbonate in a clean crucible. Place the crucible on a wire gauze mounted on a ring stand as shown in Figure 10-1.

Part B Heat the crucible over the hot flame of a Bunsen burner for about 10 minutes. Turn off the flame. *Carefully* examine the crucible.

1. *What changes in the copper(II) carbonate do you observe?*

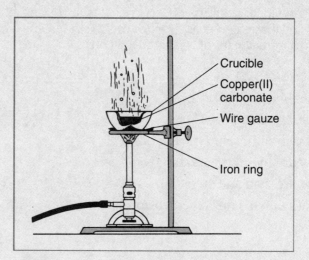

Figure 10-1.

2. *How might you account for your observations?*

Part C *Allow the crucible to cool.* Weigh out 5 grams of powdered charcoal on a balance. (Charcoal consists mainly of the element carbon.) Add the charcoal to the crucible. Using a glass rod, thoroughly stir the substances in the crucible.

Part D Heat the crucible over the strong flame of the Bunsen burner for about 10 minutes as you did in Part B. Use the same safety precautions. *Allow the crucible to cool.* Using crucible tongs, carefully pour the substance from the crucible into a beaker of water.

3. *What has happened to the mixture of the copper compound and charcoal?*

4. *Give a reason for pouring the mixture into the water.*

5. *What is the color of the substance close to the surface of the water?*

6. *What is this substance?*

Part E Carefully pour the water out of the beaker, taking care not to lose the solid at the bottom of the beaker.

7. *From its appearance, what is the solid at the bottom of the beaker? Explain.*

8. *Write the word equation for the reaction that took place in Part B of this experiment.*

9. *Write the word equation for the reaction that took place in Part D of this experiment.*

What Are Metal Ores?

Look around at the many kinds of metals you use every day. All the metals that you use were once part of the rocks inside Earth. Metals occur naturally as free elements or combined with other elements in compounds. Only those metals that are not very reactive are usually found free in nature. Examples of such metals are gold, silver, and platinum. Oc-casionally, even these metals are found combined in nature. Metals that are reactive are generally found combined in compounds in rocks. Such compounds are **minerals**.

When a mineral contains a quantity of metal sufficient to be extracted profitably, the mineral is an **ore**. Mining is the process by which ores are taken from Earth.

What Are Different Types of Ores?

Most everyday metals are obtained from three types of ores. These ores are oxide, sulfide, and carbonate compounds.

The oxide ores are sources of metals such as iron, aluminum, copper, and zinc. Some common oxide ores are: *hematite*, iron oxide; *magnetite*, magnetic iron oxide; *bauxite*, aluminum oxide; *cuprite*, copper(I) oxide; and *zincite*, zinc oxide.

The sulfide ores are sources of metals such as copper, zinc, lead, and mercury. Some common sulfide ores are: *iron pyrite*, iron sulfide (also known as "fool's gold" because its gold color often led prospectors to think they had found real gold); *chalcocite*, copper(I) sulfide; *sphalerite*, zinc sulfide; *galena*, lead sulfide; and *cinnabar*, mercury(II) sulfide.

The carbonate ores are sources of metals such as iron and zinc. Some common carbonate ores are *siderite*, iron carbonate, and *smithsonite*, zinc carbonate. Table 10-1 summarizes the important ores of metals.

Table 10-1.
Important Ores

Type of Ore	Chemical Formula	Name
Oxide	Fe_2O_3	Hematite
	Fe_3O_4	Magnetite
	Al_2O_3	Bauxite
	Cu_2O	Cuprite
	ZnO	Zincite
Sulfide	FeS_2	Iron pyrite
	Cu_2S	Chalcocite
	ZnS	Sphlerite
	PbS	Galena
	HgS	Cinnabar
Carbonate	$FeCO_3$	Siderite
	$ZnCO_3$	Smithsonite

How Are Metals Separated from Their Ores?

Ores are not useful unless the metals in them can be extracted. The science that deals with the extraction of metals from their ores is known as **metallurgy**. The techniques used to extract a specific metal depend on the composition of the ore, the kinds and quantities of impurities present in the ore, and how the metal will be used. Before the actual separation of the metal from the ore, some of the impurities are removed—a process called **ore concentration**.

Extraction of Metals From Oxide Ores

If a useful metal is found in an oxide ore, it is relatively easy to extract the metal because the process involves only a single step. Con-

sider the ore cuprite, which is an oxide of copper (Cu_2O). According to the Reactivity Series of Metals (see page 78), zinc is more reactive than copper. Therefore, under suitable conditions, zinc can replace the copper from copper(I) oxide in a single replacement reaction:

$$Cu_2O + Zn \xrightarrow{\Delta} 2Cu + ZnO$$
copper(I) oxide · zinc · copper · zinc oxide

This replacement reaction can be considered in another way: The zinc removes the oxygen from the oxide, unites with the oxygen, and forms zinc oxide. The type of reaction in which oxygen is removed from a compound is known as a **reduction reaction**. In this case, scientists would say that the copper in the compound was reduced to free copper by using zinc. Substances such as zinc that can reduce oxides are called **reducing agents**.

When ores are reduced commercially, the least expensive reducing agents are selected. Carbon (coke or powdered charcoal) is a commonly used commercial reducing agent (see Figure 10-2). Other commercial reducing agents include hydrogen gas (see Figure 10-3) and carbon monoxide gas. The following reactions show how these reducing agents can be used to extract copper from copper(II) oxide (all the reactions require heat):

$$2\,\underset{\substack{\text{copper(II)}\\\text{oxide}}}{CuO} + \underset{\text{coke}}{C} \xrightarrow{\Delta} 2\,\underset{\text{copper}}{Cu} + \underset{\substack{\text{carbon}\\\text{dioxide}}}{CO_2}$$

$$\underset{\substack{\text{copper(II)}\\\text{oxide}}}{CuO} + \underset{\text{hydrogen}}{H_2} \xrightarrow{\Delta} \underset{\text{copper}}{Cu} + \underset{\text{water}}{H_2O}$$

$$\underset{\substack{\text{copper(II)}\\\text{oxide}}}{CuO} + \underset{\substack{\text{carbon}\\\text{monoxide}}}{CO} \xrightarrow{\Delta} \underset{\text{copper}}{Cu} + \underset{\substack{\text{carbon}\\\text{dioxide}}}{CO_2}$$

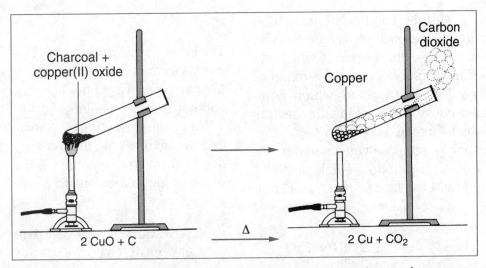

Figure 10-2. This laboratory setup illustrates a reduction reaction used to separate copper from copper(II) oxide.

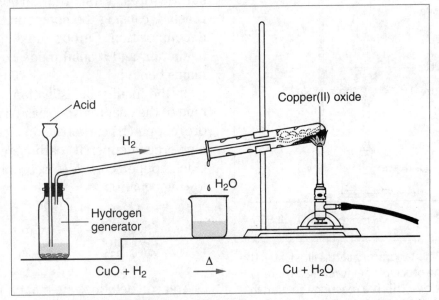

Figure 10-3. This laboratory setup illustrates a reduction reaction in which the reducing agent is hydrogen.

Extraction of Metals From Sulfide Ores

The extraction of metals from sulfide ores is a somewhat more difficult task than the extraction from oxide ores because the sulfur in sulfide ores is not easily removed. At least two main steps are usually involved in extracting metals from sulfide ores. First, the sulfide compounds are converted to oxide compounds. Then, the oxides are reduced.

When a sulfide compound is heated strongly in the presence of oxygen (in air), a chemical change takes place in which the sulfide of the metal becomes the oxide of the metal. This process, in which compounds are converted to oxides by heating them in air, is known as **roasting**.

For example, suppose you wanted to obtain lead from the sulfide ore galena (PbS). You would roast the lead sulfide (see Figure 10-4):

$$2PbS + 3O_2 \xrightarrow{\Delta} 2PbO + 2SO_2$$

lead(II) sulfide   oxygen   lead(II) oxide   sulfur dioxide

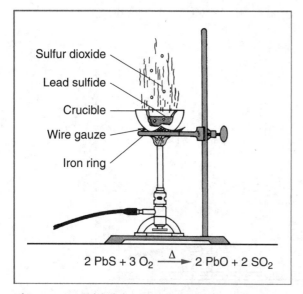

$$2\,PbS + 3\,O_2 \xrightarrow{\Delta} 2\,PbO + 2\,SO_2$$

Figure 10-4. This laboratory setup illustrates the first step in the process of extracting a metal from a sulfide ore. This is a roasting reaction in which the sulfide is converted to an oxide.

NOTE: You should not perform this experiment because lead sulfide and lead fumes are poisonous. Also note that, in addition to the formation of lead oxide, sulfur dioxide gas is produced. This gas escapes from the container, leaving the lead oxide behind. The lead oxide is mixed with powdered charcoal and heated. This reaction reduces the lead oxide and yields lead and carbon dioxide gas:

$$2PbO + C \xrightarrow{\Delta} 2Pb + CO_2$$

lead(II) oxide   charcoal   lead   carbon dioxide

The carbon dioxide gas, like the sulfur dioxide gas formed during roasting, escapes from the container. When the lead becomes cool enough, it forms a solid.

Thus, the extraction of a metal from a sulfide ore involves (1) the *roasting* of the sulfide to form an oxide and (2) the *reduction* of the oxide to form the free metal.

Extraction of Metals From Carbonate Ores

The separation of metals from their carbonate ores is accomplished by a method similar to the one used to separate metals from sulfide ores. First, the carbonate ore is roasted, causing the compound to undergo decomposition. Carbon dioxide is released to the air, and a solid oxide compound remains behind.

In the inquiry investigation at the beginning of the chapter, you roasted a carbonate ore, copper(II) carbonate, in a crucible. The blue-green copper(II) carbonate changes to black copper(II) oxide according to the following equation:

$$CuCO_3 \xrightarrow{\Delta} CuO + CO_2$$

copper(II) carbonate   copper(II) oxide   carbon dioxide

You can demonstrate that carbon dioxide is released by arranging an apparatus as shown in Figure 10-5 and allowing the gas that is formed to enter a container of lime-water. Whenever limewater comes in contact with carbon dioxide, the limewater turns milky. This is a commonly used test for carbon dioxide.

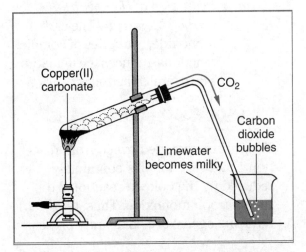

Figure 10-5. This setup illustrates a common test for carbon dioxide, which turns a clear solution of limewater to a milky suspension.

Once an oxide has been obtained from a carbonate, any reducing agent such as carbon, hydrogen, or carbon monoxide can be used to release the free metal. In the inquiry investigation, you carried out such a reduction by adding charcoal to the crucible of copper(II) carbonate that had been roasted. After further heating, red-brown copper separates from the black copper oxide. The equation for the reduction of the copper oxide is:

$$2CuO + C \xrightarrow{\Delta} 2Cu + CO_2$$

copper(II) oxide (black)   charcoal   copper (red-brown)   carbon dioxide

Thus, metals are extracted from carbonate ores (1) by *roasting* the carbonate to decompose it to the oxide and (2) by *reduction* of the oxide to the free metal.

How Are Iron and Steel Obtained?

Iron and steel are two very important industrial materials. Let us consider them separately. First we will discuss iron.

The Metallurgy of Iron

Iron, one of the most useful metals, is the fourth most abundant element in Earth's crust (see Table 2-2, page 25). Iron is a moderately reactive metal, so it is generally found combined in compounds. Iron is found in the form of oxides in ores such as hematite (Fe_2O_3) and magnetite (Fe_3O_4). Iron is also commonly found in the carbonate ore siderite ($FeCO_3$). Impurities, such as sand, are always found with these compounds of iron. Industrial chemists have designed a process in which both steps, the extraction of iron and the removal of impurities, are ac-

complished within one chamber called a **blast furnace**.

The Construction of a Blast Furnace. A blast furnace, shown in Figure 10-6 on page 148, is about 30 meters (98 feet) high and 8 meters (26 feet) in diameter. The furnace is lined with special bricks that can withstand extremely high temperatures. At the top of the furnace, an opening admits a mixture of hematite (Fe_2O_3), coke (C), and limestone ($CaCO_3$). Near the bottom of the furnace is a series of pipes through which large quantities of heated air are blown. It is this heated air that starts the reaction.

The coke burns to form carbon monoxide, which then reduces the hematite. The limestone combines with the impurities in the ore to form a *slag*, which floats on top

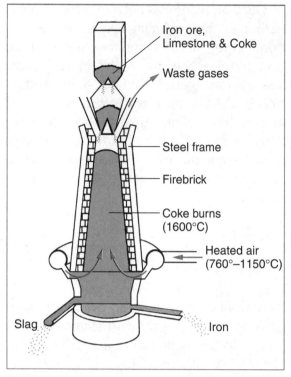

Figure 10-6. A blast furnace is used to separate iron from iron ore in a series of chemical reactions. Iron is removed at the bottom of the blast furnace while less dense waste gases and slag are piped off at higher levels.

of the iron. Waste gases escape through a pipe near the top of the furnace. Tap holes to drain the molten iron and the liquid slag are located under the air pipes, at the bottom of the furnace.

The Reactions in the Blast Furnace

Five chemical reactions take place in the blast furnace: oxidation of carbon, reduction of carbon dioxide, reduction of hematite, the formation of calcium oxide, and the formation of slag.

Reaction 1. Oxidation of Carbon. As the coke is heated, it combines with oxygen to form carbon dioxide:

$$C + O_2 \rightarrow CO_2$$

Reaction 2. Reduction of Carbon Dioxide. As carbon dioxide is formed, it reacts with the hot coke and is reduced to form carbon monoxide gas:

$$CO_2 + C \rightarrow + 2CO$$

Reaction 3. Reduction of Hematite by Carbon Monoxide. The carbon monoxide, in a series of complex reactions, reduces the hematite. The overall reaction is:

$$Fe_2O_3 + 3CO \rightarrow 2\ Fe + 3\ CO_2$$

The carbon dioxide formed from reaction 1 and reaction 3 is continually reduced by the coke in reaction 2 to form carbon monoxide. Thus, two reducing agents are constantly present.

Reaction 4. Formation of Calcium Oxide. The limestone that is mixed with the ore and coke is roasted by the intense heat of the furnace. On heating, the limestone decomposes to calcium oxide and carbon dioxide:

$$CaCO_3 \rightarrow CaO + CO_2$$

Reaction 5. Formation of Slag. The calcium oxide formed in reaction 4 reacts with the impurities, mainly sand (SiO_2), to form slag, which is largely calcium silicate ($CaSiO_3$):

$$\underset{\substack{\text{calcium} \\ \text{oxide}}}{CaO} + \underset{\text{sand}}{SiO_2} \rightarrow \underset{\substack{\text{calcium} \\ \text{silicate} \\ \text{(slag)}}}{CaSiO_3}$$

At the temperature of the furnace, the slag is liquid. Since the slag is less dense than the molten iron, it floats on top of the iron, protecting the iron from reoxidation. The slag is drained off from time to time. The iron is also drained from the furnace and allowed to run into rectangular forms called *pigs*, in which the iron cools and solidifies.

The iron obtained from the blast furnace is known as **pig iron**. When pig iron is melted and recooled, it is called **cast iron**. Cast iron is an impure iron that contains 3% to 5% carbon, 1% manganese, and small amounts of silicon, sulfur, and phosphorus. This type of iron is hard, extremely brittle, and cannot withstand sudden shock.

Cast iron is refined by means of a process of controlled oxidation, which eliminates the carbon and sulfur impurities in the form of the gases carbon dioxide and sulfur dioxide. The iron refined in this way is called **wrought iron**. Wrought iron is the purest form of iron. Wrought iron is comparatively soft, malleable, and ductile. It can be worked into almost any shape. Since it is not brittle, it is used for bolts, nails, and chains to which great stress or shock is applied. Today, most wrought iron has been replaced by special steels.

▶ Production of Steel

Steel is prepared from cast iron and contains a fixed amount of carbon, usually between 0.2% and 2%. In addition, steel contains other elements to give it desired properties. Steel can be prepared in several ways. Much of the steel prepared in this country is manufactured by using the **open-hearth process** and, more recently, the **oxygen top-blowing process**.

In these processes, molten cast iron is poured into special furnaces. The carbon and sulfur impurities burn in the presence of oxygen to form gaseous products that leave the furnace. Other impurities such as phosphorus and silicon are removed by the furnace lining to form a slag. Controlled amounts of carbon, manganese, chromium, and other elements are added to the purified molten iron. The addition of these substances produces steels with different properties suitable for different uses.

Steel can be cast into molds, formed into beams, hammered into sheets, and drawn into wire. Steel represents the backbone of industrial nations. It is the primary metal used for construction such as bridges, buildings, ships, armor plate, railroad tracks, and automobile bodies.

What Happens During Corrosion?

When iron objects are exposed to air and moisture for some time, reddish brown spots often form. These spots are called **rust**. The chemical analysis of rust reveals that it is composed of the compound iron(III) oxide (Fe_2O_3).

Rusting is an example of a general weathering process called **corrosion**. This process may weaken or even destroy metals. During corrosion, metals combine slowly with such chemical agents as oxygen, water, carbon dioxide, and sulfur dioxide. The new compounds formed are brittle and usually crumble. They lack the strength of the original metals.

▶ How Is Corrosion Prevented?

If chemists had not developed methods to prevent the corrosion of metals, many of the metallic objects you depend upon would wear away in a relatively short time. The methods used to protect metals against corrosion involve adding a surface coating to the metal. This coating is resistant to the agents of corrosion.

Galvanizing. Iron coated with zinc is called **galvanized iron**. Zinc is more reactive than iron and, on standing, forms a coating of zinc oxide. This coating protects the iron underneath from corrosion. In this coating process, the iron is dipped into molten zinc. When the molten zinc cools, it solidifies, forming a layer over the iron or steel.

Electroplating. In this process, less reactive metals such as nickel or chromium are deposited on the surface of more reactive metals such as iron by electrical means. The less reactive metal (nickel) corrodes less rapidly than the more reactive metal (iron). Tin and zinc may also be coated on iron or steel by such processes. The deposited metals are more corrosion-resistant than the metals they cover, so the deposited metals protect the metals beneath them from corrosion.

Coating With Nonmetallic Substances. Corrosion can also be prevented by applying coverings such as oil, grease, paint, plastics, and lacquers to metallic surfaces. By clinging to the surface of a metal, these substances keep agents of corrosion from coming in contact with the metal. This tends to preserve the metal.

Chapter Review

Science Terms

The following list contains all of the boldfaced words found in this chapter and the page on which each appears.

blast furnace (p. 147)

cast iron (p. 149)

corrosion (p. 149)

galvanized iron (p. 149)

metallurgy (p. 144)

minerals (p. 143)

open-hearth process (p. 149)

ore (p. 143)

ore concentration (p. 144)

oxygen top-blowing process (p. 149)

pig iron (p. 149)

reduction reaction (p. 144)

reducing agent (p. 145)

roasting (p. 146)

rust (p. 149)

wrought iron (p. 149)

Matching Questions

In your notebook, write the letter of the item in column B that is most closely related to the item in column A.

Column A

_____ 1. a sulfide ore of copper

_____ 2. a reducing agent

_____ 3. a use of zinc

_____ 4. a sulfide ore of lead

_____ 5. a gas formed as coke is heated

_____ 6. an oxide ore of aluminum

_____ 7. pig iron

_____ 8. wrought iron

_____ 9. a carbonate ore of iron

_____ 10. a carbonate ore of zinc

Column B

a. chalcocite

b. reducing agent

c. siderite

d. bauxite

e. Smithsonite

f. hydrogen

g. galena

h. iron formed through controlled oxidation

i. iron used to form cast iron

j. carbon dioxide

k. cinnabar

Multiple-Choice Questions

*In your notebook, write the letter preceding the word or expression
that best completes the statement or answers the question.*

1. Which best describes an ore?
   a. mineral material that can burn in the presence of oxygen
   b. any rock from which metals can be extracted profitably
   c. a natural substance that can reduce a metal
   d. a substance that breaks down into another substance by emitting energy

2. An important oxide ore of iron is
   a. hematite   c. siderite
   b. iron pyrite   d. bauxite

3. The science that deals with the extraction of metals from their ores is
   a. electroplating
   b. ore concentration
   c. roasting
   d. metallurgy

4. The removal of impurities from ores is accomplished through the process of
   a. roasting   c. ore concentration
   b. reduction   d. electroplating

5. Which type of reaction can be used to obtain a metal from a compound?
   a. synthesis
   b. precipitate
   c. single replacement
   d. double replacement

6. The removal of oxygen from a compound can be accomplished by the process of
   a. roasting   c. synthesis
   b. electroplating d. reduction

7. Among the following, the commercially used reducing agent is
   a. gold   c. lead
   b. carbon   d. iron

8. Metals are extracted from sulfide ores by
   a. first roasting, then reduction
   b. first reduction, then roasting
   c. reduction alone
   d. roasting alone

9. An example of an ore of lead is
   a. bauxite   c. galena
   b. cinnabar   d. magnetite

10. The reducing agent formed when carbon dioxide passes over hot coke is
    a. carbon
    b. carbon monoxide
    c. hydrogen
    d. calcium silicate

11. Slag is
    a. less dense than molten iron
    b. drained from the top of the blast furnace
    c. more dense than molten iron
    d. a gaseous substance

12. Through which process is cast iron refined?
    a. controlled reduction
    b. controlled oxidation
    c. electroplating
    d. coating processes

13. Steel is prepared from
    a. pig iron   c. cast iron
    b. wrought iron   d. slag

14. Of the following, the one that is not an agent of corrosion is
    a. water   c. oxygen
    b. chromium   d. sulfur dioxide

15. In the process of galvanizing, iron is coated with
    a. tin   c. copper
    b. lead   d. zinc

Modified True-False Questions

In some of the following statements, the italicized term makes the statement incorrect. For each incorrect statement, in your notebook, write the term that must be substituted for the italicized term to make the statement correct. For each correct statement, write the word "true."

1. Reactive metals found combined as compounds in Earth's rocks are called *ores*.

   _____

2. Hematite, coke, and *iron* are admitted into the top of a blast furnace. _____

3. In the blast furnace, coke burns to form *carbon monoxide*.

4. The first reaction in a blast furnace involves the oxidation of *iron*. _____

5. Iron obtained directly from the blast furnace is called *wrought iron*. _____

6. When cast iron is refined to eliminate the carbon and sulfur impurities, *wrought iron* is formed. _____

7. Most of the steel prepared in this country is manufactured by using the *open-hearth process*. _____

8. During the process of *top-blowing*, iron is dipped in molten zinc. _____

9. A general weathering process that may destroy metals is called *corrosion*.

   _____

10. A process in which some metals are electrically deposited on the surface of other generally more active metals for protection is known as *rusting*. _____

TEST-TAKING TIP Review definitions of key terms before exams. It may help to write them on index cards that you can use as flashcards for studying.

Check Your Knowledge

Write the answer to each question in your notebook.

1. Differentiate between the terms in each of the following:
   a. mineral and ore
   b. hematite and iron pyrite
   c. reduction and roasting
   d. cast iron and wrought iron

2. Complete and balance the following equations:
   a. $ZnO + H_2 \rightarrow$
   b. $Fe_2O_3 + C \rightarrow$
   c. $CuS + O_2 \rightarrow$
   d. $ZnS + O_2 \rightarrow$
   e. $CuCO_3 \rightarrow$

3. Describe the process through which most steel in the United States is produced.

Think Critically

Write the answer to each of the following questions in your notebook.

1. Using chemical equations, describe the steps you would use to obtain lead from galena (PbS).

2. Complete the table.

Ore	Formula	Metal Obtained
Zincite		
	Al_2O_3	
Magnetite		
	FeS_2	
Cinnabar		
	$FeCO_3$	

3. Discuss three methods to protect metals from corrosion. Evaluate each method in terms of cost and practicality.

Take It Further

1. At one time, aluminum was more valuable than gold because of the difficulty extracting it from its ore. Investigate examples from history that indicate its value. Find out what change occurred that decreased the value of aluminum. Present your findings to the class.

2. Major gold rushes took place in the nineteenth century. Find out what the gold rushes were, and investigate the California Gold Rush in particular. Report on the events that occurred, focusing on the process of mining gold at that time. Take a look at the following site as you begin your research: *http://www.eyewitnesstohistory.com/californiagoldrush.htm*.

CAREER

3. Metallurgists are employed by a wide variety of companies and government organizations. Research a career in this field to find out what it involves and what education is required. Present your findings to the class. You may wish to begin your research at the following site: *http://www.mmsa.net/* .

Mining Earth's Resources: At What Cost?

Does your home have copper wires or pots? Do you drink from aluminum cans? Do you enjoy gold or diamonds? If you answered *yes* to any of these questions, you can begin to see how much people depend on metals and minerals every day. Where do they all come from? They are obtained through mining, which is the extraction of minerals and metals from Earth.

Figure 10-7. The bald patch is a gold mining scar in the forests of Venezuela. It is a constant reminder of the environmental costs of obtaining precious metals.

There are generally two types of mining. In large-scale mining operations, miners use large pieces of equipment, such as bulldozers and excavators, to extract the metals and minerals from the soil. In the process, they use toxic chemicals such as cyanide, mercury, or methylmercury, to amalgamate (combine) the extractions.

In small-scale mining, a few workers move from one mining site to another. In one form of small scale mining, known as land dredging, miners dig a large hole in the ground. They then use a high pressure hose to expose the metals or minerals. This process produces a wet slurry that is pumped into a device known as a sluice box, which collects metal or mineral particles. The rest of the material flows into either an abandoned mining pit or nearby forest. The other form of small-scale mining, known as river dredging, involves moving along a river on a platform or boat. Miners use a suction hose to essentially vacuum gravel and mud as they move along the river. The vacuumed material goes through pipes, and any metal or mineral fragments are collected. The remaining material is returned to the river at a different location from where it was suctioned.

Mining is a very profitable business for the companies involved in it. It also creates job opportunities for many people. Even governments benefit from the revenue produced through mining operations. As you might expect, though, reaping the benefits of Earth's metals comes at a cost. Large-scale mining operations require that large areas of land must be cleared. Additional land is cleared to build roads leading to and from the mine, as well as to construct buildings for mine workers. As a result, these changes lead to tremendous deforestation.

Clearing vegetation for large-scale mining purposes not only endangers species of trees and other plants, it also eliminates habitats for a wide variety of organisms. Many organisms cannot adapt to the change and die. Numerous species are in danger of extinction because of such drastic environmental changes.

In addition to deforestation, mining generally involves the production of waste materials, many of which are poisonous. They enter land and waterways, threatening the organisms that live there. Ultimately, people who depend on fish for their food and livelihood are also affected. Workers and nearby residents can be directly exposed to the chemicals, causing serious health problems.

The pits dug during land dredging are often filled with water used in the process. They become stagnant pools of water that serve as breeding grounds for mosquitoes and other water-born insects. This increases the threat of disease to both workers and nearby residents.

Dumping gravel, mud, and rocks randomly during river dredging disrupts the natural flow of a river. Fish and other organisms can die because they are no longer able to find food and breeding grounds in obstructed rivers.

Is the cost of obtaining minerals and metals worth the risk of endangering species of living things? Is providing mining jobs more important than protecting the environment? What do you think? Would you be willing to reduce your use of metals and minerals? Do you think other compromises should be made?

Organize It!

Use a method that your instructor describes to organize the information in this article.

Think About It!

1. Which statement BEST describes mining?
   a. digging a deep hole to obtain water from inside Earth
   b. extracting minerals and metals from Earth
   c. using heat from inside Earth to produce electricity
   d. changing the route of a river inside a watershed

2. Which process involves the use of bulldozers and excavators?
   a. small-scale mining
   b. river dredging
   c. large-scale mining
   d. land dredging

3. What is the purpose of a sluice box?
   a. to clear land to expose minerals and metals
   b. to convert mined materials into useful products
   c. to vacuum gravel and soil at the bottom of a river
   d. to separate metals or minerals from waste materials

4. Describe ways that mining can lead to deforestation.

5. How might people who live far from waterways be harmed by mining?

6. In what way can mining lead to an increase in diseases carried by insects?

Extend It!

7. The Guyana spill of 1995 was an accident at a mine that poured toxic cyanide into the environment. Unfortunately, this was only one of many deadly mining spills. Research a mining spill to find out how it happened, what material was being mined, and how the environment and people were affected. Find out if any changes were made to prevent such spills thereafter. Share your findings with the class.

8. Some researchers are considering the idea of mining on the moon. Investigate the possibility of such mining plans, and identify the concerns associated with these plans. You may wish to begin your research at the following site: *http://www.space.com/news/moon-mining-rare-elements-security-101004.html*.

CAREER

9. Some miners are working toward sustainable mining that does not harm the environment in the same way as conventional mining. Research opportunities in sustainable mining. Find out where they are, what they involve, and what preparation is required. You may wish to begin your research at the following sites: *http://www.responsiblemining.net/pubs/ActualizingSustainableMining.pdf* and *http://www.smenet.org/*.

11

What Are the Characteristics of Solutions?

Imagine touring these amazing underground caves. They formed over time from solutions that seep slowly through the ground, dissolving rock known as limestone.

After reading this chapter, you should be able to answer the following questions:

How are compounds different from mixtures?

What are the characteristics of solutions?

Which factors affect the rate of dissolving?

How can solutions be described in terms of amount of solute?

How are solutions described by solubility curves?

What are supersaturated solutions?

How can the components of a solution be separated?

Many of the materials you use or see every day are not pure substances. Instead, they are mixtures. In this inquiry investigation, you will explore one special type of mixture known as a solution.

Materials:
- ✔ safety goggles
- ✔ potassium permanganate (solid)
- ✔ spatula
- ✔ 2 test tubes (150-mm)
- ✔ water
- ✔ glass rod
- ✔ microscope slide
- ✔ magnifying glass
- ✔ triple-beam or electronic balance
- ✔ copper(II) sulfate (solid)
- ✔ mortar and pestle
- ✔ grease pencil
- ✔ 4 beakers (250-mL)
- ✔ wristwatch or stopwatch
- ✔ Bunsen burner
- ✔ ring stand
- ✔ iron ring
- ✔ wire gauze
- ✔ graduated cylinder

CAUTION: Be careful not to spill the potassium permanganate solution; it is toxic and may stain your clothes permanently. Avoid contact with skin. Wear safety goggles.

Part A Using a spatula or a spoon, place a very tiny crystal of potassium permanganate ($KMnO_4$) in a 150-mm test tube containing 5 cm of water. Stopper the tube and shake carefully. Hold it up to the light.

1. *What happens to the crystal?*

2. *What is the color of the mixture of potassium permanganate and water?*

3. *How does the color of the mixture compare with the color of the crystal?*

Part B Using a glass rod, place a drop of the potassium permanganate solution on a clean microscope slide. Examine the drop with a magnifying glass.

4. *Do you see any crystals? Explain.*

5. *What do you conclude regarding the size of solid particles in this mixture?*

Part C Divide the contents of the test tube into two roughly *equal* parts. Compare the colors of each part.

6. *What do the colors of each of the parts of the mixture suggest to you?*

7. *State the characteristics of a mixture of potassium permanganate and water.*

8. *What is such a mixture called?*

CAUTION: Avoid contact with skin.

Part D Weigh out four samples of copper(II) sulfate crystals. Each sample should weigh about 2 grams.

Grind *three* of the samples with a mortar and pestle. Keep all the samples separate.

Number four 250-mL beakers from 1 through 4 with a grease pencil. Place the unground crystals in beaker 1. Place the ground crystals in beakers 2, 3, and 4. In the following experiment, record in a table, similar to the one below, the length of time it takes each sample to dissolve. (Use stopwatch or the second hand of a wristwatch to measure the time.)

Beaker 1: Add 100 mL of water. Allow the mixture to stand undisturbed.

Beaker 2: Add 100 mL of water. Allow the mixture to stand undisturbed.

Beaker 3: Add 100 mL of water. Stir the mixture with a glass rod.

Beaker 4: Add 100 mL of water. Heat the mixture over a Bunsen burner, stirring the mixture as it heats.

Beaker	Treatment of Copper Sulfate	Starting Time	Ending Time	Time Necessary to Dissolve Completely
1	None			
2	Ground			
3	Ground and stirred			
4	Ground, stirred, heated			

9. *Comparing beakers 1 and 2, how does grinding the crystals affect the rate at which the copper(II) sulfate dissolves?*

10. *Comparing beakers 2 and 3, how does stirring affect the rate at which the copper(II) sulfate dissolves?*

11. *Comparing beakers 3 and 4, how does heating affect the rate at which the copper(II) sulfate dissolves?*

12. *Based on your observations above, make a generalization about the factors that influence the rate at which a substance will dissolve.*

How Are Compounds Different from Mixtures?

You know that compounds are composed of elements chemically combined in definite proportions by mass. For example, in the compound iron(II) sulfide the ratio by mass of iron to sulfur is 56:32. If you were to attempt to form this compound by combining any other ratio of iron to sulfur, some iron or some sulfur would remain uncombined. Figure 11-1 shows a mixture of 9 grams of iron and 4 grams of sulfur being heated. **CAUTION: Do not perform this experiment. SO_2, which is poisonous, is given off.** After heating, a magnet removes 2 grams of uncombined iron. Thus, iron combines with sulfur in the ratio of 7 grams to 4 grams, or 56:32.

You may recall that when a compound forms, each element loses its own characteristics and the compound has a new set of characteristics. Thus, iron is magnetic and sulfur is yellow. However, the compound iron(II) sulfide is nonmagnetic and black.

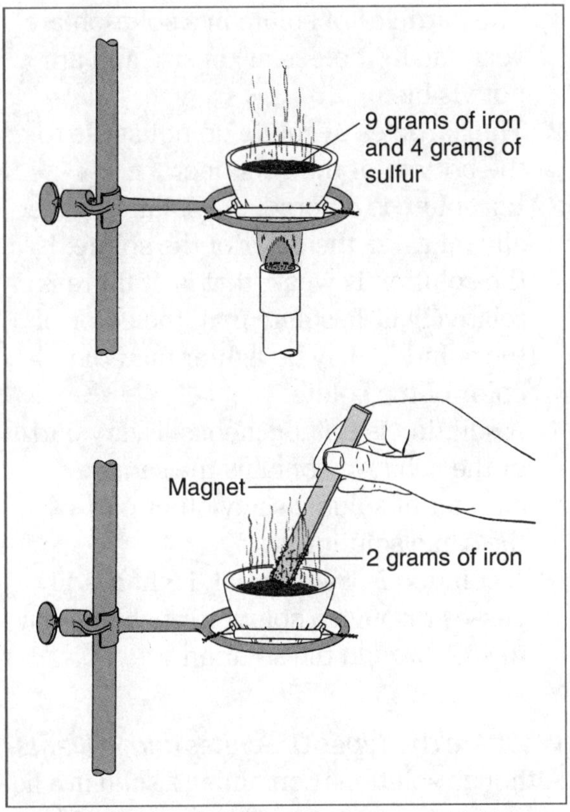

Compounds have a definite composition whereas mixtures have a variable composition. Using iron filings and powdered sulfur, you can make mixtures of any proportion by varying the amounts of the two elements. In any such mixture, you can distinguish between the iron and the sulfur by simple means, such as color or the magnetic property of iron. If you were to divide a mixture into equal smaller portions, each portion would not necessarily have the same proportion of iron to sulfur.

▶ Which Properties Make a Mixture a Type of Solution?

When you mix table salt (a solid) and water (a liquid), the salt seems to disappear in the water. The salt has *dissolved* in the water. Such a combination is quite different from a mixture of iron filings and sulfur, in which equal portions of the mixture may have different amounts of iron and sulfur. Equal portions of the salt-water mixture, however, have the same quantities of solid and liquid, and the mixture is said to be **uniform**, or **homogeneous**. Mixtures in which one ingredient dissolves in another to form a uniform mixture are **solutions**.

In a solution, the substance that is dissolved is called the **solute**, and the substance that does the dissolving is called the **solvent**. Thus, in a solution of salt in water, the salt is the solute and the water is the solvent. Similarly, when copper(II) sulfate is dissolved in water, the copper(II) sulfate is the solute and the water is the solvent.

In all the solutions discussed so far, water was used as the solvent. Water dissolves so

Figure 11-1. Iron combines with sulfur to form iron(II) sulfide in a ratio of 7:4 by mass. This is confirmed by the above experiment in which 2 grams of iron remain unreacted.

many substances that it is often called the **universal solvent**. Water, however, is not the only useful solvent. Many substances can be dissolved in alcohol, and the resulting solutions are known as **tinctures**. Thus, iodine crystals dissolve in alcohol to form tincture of iodine.

In some solutions, it is not clear which substance is the solvent and which is the solute, as in the case of an alcohol-water mixture. In liquid-liquid solutions, the solute is the substance present in the smaller amount. It usually is not necessary to make this distinction.

What Are the Characteristics of Liquid Solutions?

As shown in Figure 11-2a, if you were to blow chalk dust into an empty beaker and shine a bright light through the dust, you would see some of the particles of dust floating in the air. (This happens because you can see very tiny particles, such as dust, when the particles reflect light.) When you shine a light through a solution, however, you see no such particles (see Figure 11-2b). The solution appears to be clear and transparent. Even with a powerful microscope, you cannot see particles of the solute. Evidence of this kind indicates that the particles making up a solution are very small.

When you examine a colored solution, you see that the color is uniform throughout. Solutions of copper(II) sulfate are blue. Solutions of potassium permanganate, as you observed in the inquiry investigation, are purple. The solids have the same color as the solutions, although the solids appear darker. This similarity in color indicates that, although the particles of a solution are very small in size, the particles are still present in the solution and still retain physical properties such as color.

To summarize the characteristics of solutions:

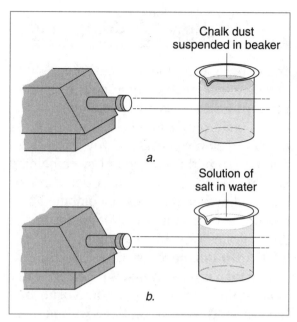

Figure 11-2. Light can be used to identify a solution. Particles in a true solution are so small that a beam of light passes through without revealing them.

1. The particles of solute in a solution are very small (molecular) in size and are not visible.
2. The particles of solute do not settle to the bottom of the container.
3. If a solute is colored, the solution generally takes on the color of the solute. If the solution is weak, that is, if there is relatively little solute in it, the color of the solution may be lighter than the color of the solute.
4. A solution is homogeneous. Every part of the solution contains the same amount of solute as any other part of the same solution.
5. A solution is transparent. Light readily passes through a solution, enabling you to see through the solution.

What Are the Types Of Solutes and Solvents?
Although solutions containing a solid in a liquid are very common, solutions involving other physical states of matter also exist. Table 11-1 gives examples of solutions containing other types of solutes and solvents.

Table 11-1.
What Are the Types of Solutes and Solvents?

Solvent	Solute	Example
Solid	Solid	Gold jewelry (copper in gold)
Solid	Liquid	Dental fillings (mercury in silver)
Solid	Gas	Charcoal gas mask (poisonous gases on carbon)
Liquid	Solid	Seawater (salt in water)
Liquid	Liquid	Rubbing alcohol (alcohol in water)
Liquid	Gas	Carbonated beverages (carbon dioxide in water)
Gas	Gas	Air (oxygen and other gases in nitrogen)
Gas	Gas	Natural gas (methane and other hydrocarbon gases)

Which Factors Affect the Rate of Dissolving?

You may know from experience that sugar dissolves faster in a cup of hot tea than in a glass of iced tea. From this example, you can infer that the rate of dissolving depends on factors related to the solute and solvent.

Temperature. As you observed in the inquiry investigation, temperature affects the rate at which a solid dissolves in a liquid. Why does an increase in temperature generally increase the rate of dissolving? According to the kinetic-molecular theory, heating causes the solvent molecules to move faster and farther apart. Consequently, the solute particles come in contact more easily with solvent molecules. Thus, heating a mixture of a solute and a solvent generally increases the rate of dissolving.

Particle Size. If you add 5 grams of granulated sugar to a cup of tea, the sugar dissolves more rapidly than if you add a 5-gram lump of sugar. This shows that a mass of small particles dissolves more rapidly than the same mass in the form of a single large lump. The rate of dissolving is greater because the larger surface area of the many small particles exposes more solute molecules to the solvent than does the surface area of a single large lump.

Stirring. The stirring of solute in a solvent tends to bring the solute particles into contact with all particles of the solvent. As a result, every part of the solvent dissolves some of the solute, increasing the rate of dissolving. This explains why you can increase the rate at which sugar dissolves by stirring a cup of tea after adding sugar to it.

Heating, grinding, and stirring increase the rate of dissolving. You can use all of these methods together to provide the quickest possible means for preparing a solution of a solid in a liquid (see Figure 11-3). To quickly dissolve copper sulfate crystals in water, a chemist would (1) grind the crystals to a fine

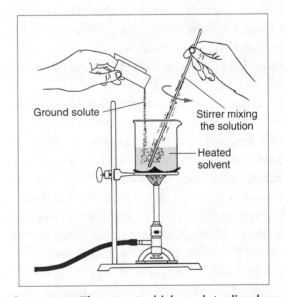

Figure 11-3. The rate at which a solute dissolves can be increased by reducing the size of solute particles (grinding), by heating, and by stirring the mixture.

powder, (2) heat the water; and (3) stir the mixture constantly as he or she adds the powdered crystals to the heated water.

How Can Solutions Be Described in Terms of Amount of Solute?

Not all solutions of the same substances contain the same amounts of solute and solvent. You can use the relationship between solute and solvent to describe the characteristics of a solution.

Dilute and Concentrated Solutions. Some people prefer to dissolve one teaspoonful of sugar in their tea. Others prefer two or more teaspoonfuls. In general, solutions vary in the amount of solute that dissolves in the solvent. The amount of solute in a given quantity of solvent determines the **concentration**, *or strength*, of the solution. A solution that contains relatively little solute in a given amount of solvent is generally said to be **dilute**, or *weak*. A solution that contains a relatively large amount of solute in a given amount of solvent is generally said to be **concentrated**, or *strong*.

Expressing the concentration of a solution using the terms *concentrated* or *dilute* is only an approximate measure of the strength of the solution. Chemists generally tend to express the concentration of a solution in more precise terms such as grams per liter.

Unsaturated and Saturated Solutions. All solutions may be considered either unsaturated or saturated. An **unsaturated solution** is one in which the solvent can dissolve more solute at the same temperature. As you continue to add more solute to such a solution, a point is reached where no more solute can dissolve. Any additional solute that is now added to the solution settles to the bottom of the container. Such a solution, in which the solvent has dissolved as much solute as it can hold at a given temperature, is called a **saturated solution**.

The effect of different temperatures on the ability of a solution to hold solute may be illustrated with a cup of tea. In Figure 11-4a the hot tea readily dissolves 3 teaspoonfuls of sugar and can dissolve even more sugar. The resulting solution is therefore *unsaturated*. But when the same cup of tea (containing three teaspoonfuls of dissolved sugar) is cooled, some sugar crystallizes out of the solution and settles to the bottom of the cup (see Figure 11-4b). The cold tea cannot hold three teaspoonfuls of sugar; only part of the sugar remains dissolved in cold tea. Since the excess sugar settles to the bottom of the cup, this solution of tea and sugar is now a *saturated* solution.

How Are Solutions Described by Solubility Curves?

The effect of varying temperatures on the quantity of sugar that can dissolve in tea is been shown in Figure 11-4. By carefully noting how much solute dissolves at different temperatures, chemists prepare graphs called **solubility curves**.

Figure 11-5 shows a group of solubility curves for several solid solutes in water. For

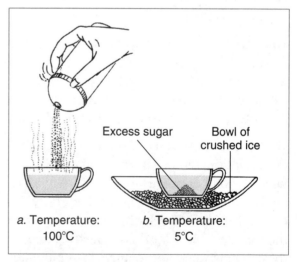

a. Temperature: 100°C   b. Temperature: 5°C

Figure 11-4. Heat increases the amount of solute that will dissolve in a given amount of solvent. When the same amounts of sugar are added to hot and cold tea, the cold tea becomes saturated while the hot tea does not.

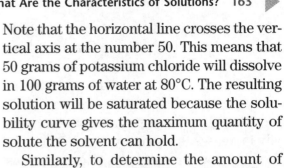

Figure 11-5. The graph shows the solubility curves of six substances. Solubility curves reveal the amount of a solute that will produce a saturated solution at various temperatures.

each solute, the solubility curve shows how many grams of solute dissolve in 100 grams of the solvent (water) at different temperatures. Thus, each curve reveals the amount of solute to use to prepare a saturated solution at a particular temperature.

Try using the graph to determine how much solute is needed to prepare a saturated solution of potassium chloride at a temperature of 80°C. To do so, proceed as follows:

1. Move across the horizontal axis of the graph until you find the 80°C line.
2. Move upward along this line to the point where the curve for potassium chloride crosses this line.
3. From this point, extend a horizontal line to the vertical axis.
4. Read the value on the vertical axis.

Note that the horizontal line crosses the vertical axis at the number 50. This means that 50 grams of potassium chloride will dissolve in 100 grams of water at 80°C. The resulting solution will be saturated because the solubility curve gives the maximum quantity of solute the solvent can hold.

Similarly, to determine the amount of potassium nitrate needed to saturate 100 grams of water at 70°C, first find the 70°C line on the horizontal axis. Then, move upward along this line to the point where the curve for potassium nitrate crosses this line. From this point, extend a horizontal line to reach the vertical axis. Note that this line crosses the vertical axis at the number 140. This means that 140 grams of potassium nitrate will dissolve in 100 grams of water at 70°C to form a saturated solution.

▶ **Which Factors Determine How Much Solute Can Dissolve?**

You already read about the factors that determine the *rate* of dissolving: temperature, particle size, and stirring. Now you will find out about the factors that determine the *quantity* (how much) of solute that can dissolve in a given quantity of solvent.

Temperature. When the temperature of a liquid solvent is increased, the solvent is able to dissolve more solid solute than at the lower temperature. Thus, when the temperature of water is increased by several degrees, the water can dissolve more solute at the new temperature than before. In other words, the quantity of solute required to saturate the water increases as the temperature rises.

If the temperature is lowered, the quantity of solute required to saturate the water decreases. For example, at a temperature of 50°C, a saturated solution of potassium nitrate (KNO_3) can be prepared by adding 85 grams of KNO_3 to 100 milliliters (100 grams) of water. When the temperature of the water is increased to 60°C, 110 grams of potassium nitrate can be dissolved in the same volume of water. When the solution is cooled back to 50°C and is stirred, the excess 25 grams of KNO_3 crystallize out of the solution and settle to the bottom of the container.

Although an increase in temperature usually increases the quantity of solid that can dissolve in water, there are some exceptions. Sodium chloride (table salt) is about equally soluble in cold or hot water. Calcium sulfate, on the other hand, is more soluble in cold water than in hot water.

Increases in temperature affect the dissolving of gases in liquids in a manner *opposite* to the dissolving of most solids in liquids. Ordinary tap water has some air dissolved in it. When the water is warmed, bubbles of air gather and rise to the surface of the water, as shown in Figure 11-6. The increase in temperature decreases the ability of the water to dissolve the air. Thus, heating the solution causes the air to bubble out of the solution even if the solution is not boiling.

Pressure. An increase or decrease in pressure has little effect on the solubility of solid solutes in liquid solvents. This is be-cause solids and liquids are virtually incompressible.

Gases, however, can be compressed. This means that differences in pressure greatly affect the solubility of gases in liquids. When the pressure of a gas is increased, the solubility of the gas also increases. When the pressure of a gas decreases, the gas becomes less soluble and leaves the solution. You see this effect when you open a bottle of soda water. When bottled and capped, the soda is under greater pressure than normal atmospheric pressure. Under this condition, more carbon dioxide gas dissolves in water and remains dissolved. When the bottle cap is removed, the pressure inside the bottle is reduced and you can see bubbles of carbon dioxide gas leave the solution and come to the surface of the liquid.

What Are Supersaturated Solutions?

Saturated solutions at one temperature can generally dissolve more solute at higher temperatures. Thus, 85 grams of potassium nitrate dissolve in 100 mL of water at 50°C, whereas 110 grams dissolve in the same volume of water at 60°C. When these hot saturated solutions are cooled, the excess solute usually crystallizes out.

However, when a hot saturated solution of photographer's hypo (sodium thiosulfate) is slowly cooled, the hypo remains in the solution (see Figure 11-7). Such a solution, in which the solvent holds more solute than it normally can at a given temperature, is called a **supersaturated** solution. Such solutions are unstable. If a single additional crystal of hypo is added to the supersaturated solution, or if the solution is shaken or stirred, all the excess hypo crystallizes out of the solution and settles to the bottom. When this occurs, the solute that remains dissolved is all the solute that the solvent can hold at the lower temperature. Thus, the solution of hypo remains saturated.

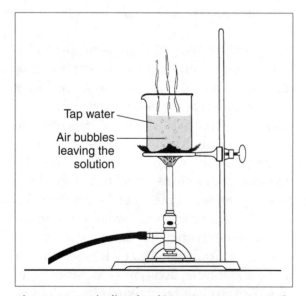

Tap water

Air bubbles leaving the solution

Figure 11-6. Air dissolved in water comes out of solution with heating. This demonstrates that gases are less soluble at higher temperatures than at lower ones.

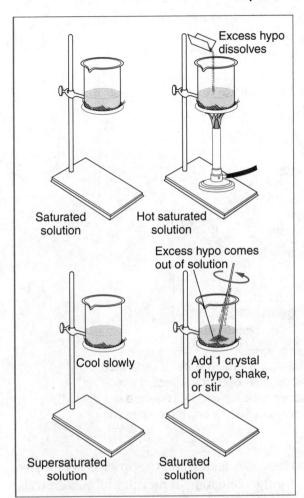

Figure 11-7. A supersaturated solution can be made by heating a saturated solution, adding additional solute, and slowly cooling the mixture. Supersaturated solutions, however, are very unstable and excess solute can be forced out by stirring, shaking, or adding as little as one crystal of the solute.

Labels in figure:
- Excess hypo dissolves
- Saturated solution
- Hot saturated solution
- Excess hypo comes out of solution
- Cool slowly
- Add 1 crystal of hypo, shake, or stir
- Supersaturated solution
- Saturated solution

▶ How Can the Components of a Solution Be Separated?

The components of liquid solutions can be separated by a variety of special methods. Among these methods are evaporation, distillation, fractional distillation, and chromatography.

Evaporation. When a solvent evaporates from a solution, the solute is left behind. **Evaporation** is the process whereby molecules of a liquid escape into the gas phase. When a drop of salt solution is placed in a teaspoon and heated, the water of the solution evaporates and tiny, white salt crystals remain in the spoon. This method is used when the purpose of the separation is to recover only the solute from the solution. The rate of evaporation of the liquid is usually increased by heating the solution in an open container and/or by increasing the surface area of the liquid.

Distillation. One of the methods used to separate and recover both the solute and the solvent of a liquid solution is known as **distillation**. In this process, the solution is heated in a distilling flask. As the liquid evaporates, the vapor is collected and then cooled. The solid remains behind. Figure 11-8 on page 166 shows a laboratory apparatus for this process.

To separate the components of a solution of potassium permanganate dissolved in water, for example, the solution is placed in a flask, as shown in the figure. As the solution is heated, the water evaporates. As the water evaporates, the vapor enters the inner condenser tube. This tube is cooled by a constant flow of cold water in the outer tube. As the water vapor is cooled by the flowing water in the outer tube, the vapor condenses to a liquid. The liquid water drains into the collecting beaker. The collected water is clear and free of all solid substances that had been dissolved in it. This water, called **distilled water**, is chemically pure. The solute remains in the flask. By this means, the components of the solution can be separated and both the solute and solvent can be recovered.

The demand for fresh water has increased enormously. The federal government continues to spend huge sums of money to develop methods of removing salt from seawater (**desalinization**), to provide an almost unlimited source of fresh water. Distillation of seawater is impractical for such large-scale usage and therefore other desalinization techniques are being developed.

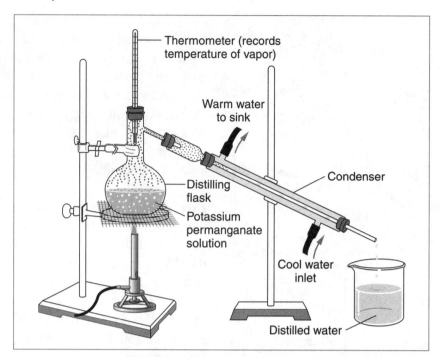

Figure 11-8. A laboratory distilling apparatus in which water is separated from potassium permanganate. The water boils off but is directed into a water-cooled condenser where the vapor condenses and is collected in a beaker. When all the water vaporizes, only potassium permanganate will remain in the flask.

Fractional Distillation. The separation of the components of liquid mixtures can be accomplished by **fractional distillation**. This process is used commercially to separate the components of petroleum, or crude oil, which is a liquid mixture of hydrocarbons—substances composed mainly of hydrogen and carbon. Gasoline, kerosene, and lubricating oils are examples of such mixtures of hydrocarbons. In this process, the crude oil is heated and piped into a fractionating tower. (See Figure 11-9.) The gasoline portion, or fraction, in the crude oil boils off before any of the other components in the oil because the hydrocarbons in gasoline have a low boiling point. After all of the gasoline has been evaporated, it is collected from the top of the fractionating tower. The temperature of the crude oil then rises and the kerosene fraction boils off. The kerosene vapors condense and are then collected from a level of the tower lower than that of the gasoline level. The temperature of the crude oil

then rises again, and the process is repeated for the collection of fuel oils, lubricating oils, and the other heavy residues.

Chromatography. To separate a mixture of solutes from a small quantity of solution, a process called **chromatography** is used. **Paper chromatography** is based on the ability of some solutes to stick to the molecules on the surface of a piece of porous paper. The process by which solute molecules stick to a solid surface is called **adsorption**. Since some molecules of solute are adsorbed on paper more readily than others, a mixture of solutes can be separated by this method.

A simple method for chromatography is shown in Figure 11-10. A drop of the solution containing one or more solutes is placed at the center of the filter paper and allowed to dry. The filter paper is cut and folded so that a part of it extends downward into a solvent, acting as a wick. When a solvent, such as

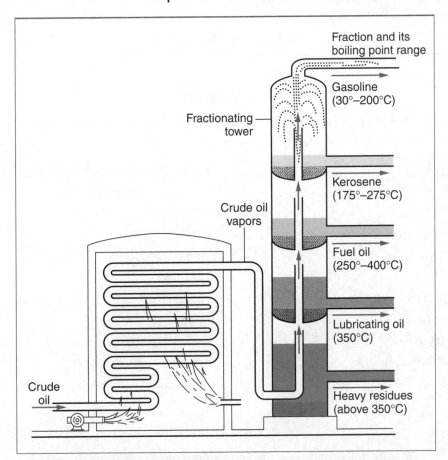

Figure 11-9. During fractional distillation, vaporized crude oil passes upward through a fractionating tower. Parts of the crude oil (fractions) cool as they rise in the tower. The fractions with the highest boiling points condense and are piped off at the lowest levels. Lower boiling point fractions condense and are piped off at progressively higher levels.

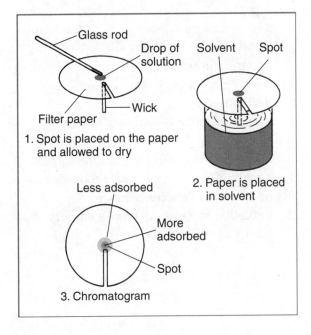

water or alcohol, wets the paper, the solvent and solutes in it travel outward on the paper. The solute that tends to be less strongly adsorbed on the paper moves outward faster than the others and is thus separated from them. For example, when a drop of blue ink is allowed to dry on a piece of filter paper and water is used as the traveling solvent, bands of different colors appear at different places on the paper. Each band is a solute of different color that was used in preparing the ink.

Figure 11-10. When an appropriate solvent passes through a mixture of two or more solutes on a piece of filter paper, the solutes will separate. This process is called paper chromatography.

Chapter Review

Science Terms

The following list contains all the boldfaced words found in this chapter and the page on which each appears.

adsorption (p. 166)

chromatography (p. 166)

concentrated (p. 162)

concentration (p. 162)

desalinization (p. 165)

dilute (p. 162)

distillation (p. 165)

distilled water (p. 165)

evaporation (p. 165)

fractional distillation (p. 166)

homogeneous (p. 159)

paper chromatography (p. 166)

saturated solution (p. 162)

solubility curve (p. 162)

solute (p. 159)

solution (p. 159)

solvent (p. 159)

supersaturated (p. 164)

tincture (p. 160)

uniform (p. 159)

universal solvent (p. 160)

unsaturated solution (p. 162)

Matching Questions

In your notebook, write the letter of the item in column B that is most closely related to the item in column A.

Column A

_____ 1. evaporation

_____ 2. solvent

_____ 3. saturated

_____ 4. concentrated

_____ 5. unsaturated

_____ 6. dilute

_____ 7. supersaturated

_____ 8. homogeneous

_____ 9. solute

_____ 10. tincture

Column B

a. description of a strong solution

b. a solution in which more solute dissolved than normally possible at a given temperature

c. a substance that dissolves in another substance

d. uniform throughout

e. the process through which a liquid becomes a gas

f. a substance that dissolves another substance

g. a solution in which alcohol is the solvent

h. a solution in which more solute can dissolve

i. description of a weak solution

j. a solution in which no more solute can dissolve at a given temperature

Multiple-Choice Questions

*In your notebook, write the letter preceding the word or expression
that best completes the statement or answers the question.*

1. When salt dissolves in water, equal portions of this mixture contain the same quantities of solid and liquid. Such a mixture is said to be
   a. unstable
   b. saturated
   c. uniform
   d. tincture

2. Which term describes the substance that is dissolved in a solution?
   a. solute
   b. solvent
   c. tincture
   d. distilled

3. How are tinctures different from other types of solutions?
   a. Precipitates form easily.
   b. They are not homogeneous.
   c. They are solids at room temperature.
   d. The solvent is alcohol.

4. Which of the following will reflect a beam of light?
   a. water molecules
   b. dust in the air
   c. the particles of a sodium chloride solution
   d. the particles of a copper sulfate solution

5. An example of a solution that is affected by changes in pressure is
   a. sodium chloride in water
   b. mercury in silver
   c. alcohol in water
   d. carbon dioxide in water

6. What are the characteristics of dilute solutions?
   a. They have a very small overall volume.
   b. They consist of a relatively small amount of solute in a given amount of solvent.

   c. They reflect a beam of light passed through them.
   d. They form solids that drop out of solution.

7. A solution to which more solute can be added at the same temperature is said to be
   a. saturated
   b. unsaturated
   c. supersaturated
   d. unstable

8. In general, what happens when a hot saturated solution to which excess solute is added, cools?
   a. The excess solute remains in solution.
   b. The solution becomes dilute.
   c. The solution becomes concentrated.
   d. The excess solute settles to the bottom of the container.

9. When the temperature of a liquid is raised, its ability to dissolve a solid solute
   a. decreases
   b. increases
   c. increases, then decreases
   d. decreases, then increases

10. What can happen to the carbon dioxide in the oceans if global warming causes oceans to become warmer?
    a. No change will be observed.
    b. More carbon dioxide will dissolve.
    c. Carbon dioxide bubbles will disappear.
    d. Carbon dioxide will escape from the water.

11. What will happen if the pressure on a sodium chloride solution increases?
    a. The change will have no effect.
    b. The increase will cause more solute to dissolve.
    c. The change will cause less solute to dissolve.
    d. The increase will produce a supersaturated solution.

12. The "pop" you hear when you open a can of soda results because
    a. particles escape supersaturated solutions
    b. the solubility of a gas decreases with decreasing pressure
    c. heating generally increases the amount of solute in solution
    d. evaporation separates the components of a liquid solution

13. Which method is best for recovering *both* the solute and solvent of a liquid solution?
    a. evaporation
    b. chromatography
    c. distillation
    d. filtration

14. Fractional distillation can be used to obtain
    a. water   c. petroleum
    b. crude oil   d. gasoline

15. The process of chromatography is based on the principle of
    a. adsorption   c. filtration
    b. absorption   d. desalinization

Modified True-False Questions

In some of the following statements, the italicized term makes the statement incorrect. For each incorrect statement, in your notebook, write the term that must be substituted for the italicized term to make the statement correct. For each correct statement, write the word "true."

1. Mixtures in which one ingredient dissolves in another to form a uniform system are known as *suspensions.* _____

2. The substance that dissolves in another substance is called the *solute.* _____

3. Solutions in which *air* is the solvent are called tinctures. _____

4. A solution in which each drop of the solution contains the same amount of solute is said to be *transparent.* _____

5. The amount of solute in a given amount of solvent determines the *saturation* of the solution. _____

6. Solutions that contain little solute are said to be *concentrated.* _____

7. The process through which salt is removed from seawater is known as *distillation.* _____

8. A solution in which the addition of an additional crystal of solute causes solute to leave the solution is said to be *concentrated.* _____

9. Graphs showing the amount of solute that dissolves in a given amount of solvent at a given temperature are called *solubility curves.* _____

10. A method used to recover only the solute from a solution is *distillation.* _____

Check Your Knowledge
Write the answer to each question in your notebook.

1. Describe the difference between the terms in each of the following pairs:
   a. solute and solvent
   b. concentrated and dilute
   c. saturated and unsaturated
   d. evaporation and distillation
   e. mixture and solution

2. Describe the process of paper chromatography and the conditions under which it might be used.

3. How does an increase in pressure affect the solubility of solid solutes in solids, liquids, and gases?

4. Describe the steps that you would perform to prepare a copper sulfate solution in the fastest possible way.

Think Critically

Write the answer to each of the following questions in your notebook.

1. Give a scientific explanation for each of the following:
   a. Hot tea can dissolve more sugar than iced tea.
   b. As water is warmed, bubbles of air in the water gather and rise to the surface of the water.
   c. As the pressure on a sodium chloride solution is increased, the solution is not affected.
   d. As a soda bottle cap is removed, a gas bubbles to the surface of the soda.
   e. Ground copper sulfate dissolves faster than a large crystal of copper sulfate.

2. Refer to the solubility curves (Figure 11-5 on page 163). For each of the following situations, write the number of grams of solute that will dissolve in 100 mL of water at the given temperature.
   a. potassium chlorate at 30°C
   b. potassium nitrate at 60°C
   c. sodium chloride at 100°C
   d. sodium chlorate at 50°C
   e. sodium nitrate at 10°C

TEST-TAKING TIP Whenever you encounter a graph, begin by reading the title and the labels on the *x* and *y* axis. Make sure you know the increments represented by each tick on the graph before you try to interpret the data presented.

Take It Further

1. Rock candy is a sweet treat formed through knowledge of solutions. Investigate the procedure for making rock candy. Present the process to your class, and explain how it involves solutions.

2. Solid solutions might not come right to mind when you think about solutions, but they are more common than you might realize. In fact, you might have one in your pocket right now—a penny. Research an example of solid solution. Explain what substances are in the solution and how it is made. Share your findings with the class.

3. Investigate how a change in the pressure of a gas in solution is related to a disease of deep-sea divers called "the bends." Write a brief report to present your findings.

CAREER

4. Many scientists are at work at this moment investigating alternatives to gasoline. One type of scientist is a geoengineering scientist. Research the role of a geoengineer, the education required, and the kinds of projects involved in this career. Present your findings. You may wish to consult the following site: *http://www.geoengineer.org/*.

12

What Are the Characteristics of Suspensions and Emulsions?

Sunlight glistens on a crisp morning in the forest. The beautiful rays of sunlight are visible thanks to the properties of the air and the substances in it. They form a mixture known as a suspension that reflects light.

After reading this chapter, you should be able to answer the following questions:

What is a suspension?

What are the different types of suspensions?

How are the components of a suspension separated?

How is water purified?

What are emulsions?

What are colloidal suspensions?

You don't have to look far to find an example of the type of mixture known as a suspension. The blood that circulates through your body is a suspension. In this inquiry investigation, you will explore the properties of other examples of suspensions.

Materials:
- ✔ safety goggles
- ✔ 3 test tubes (150-mm) with stoppers
- ✔ test-tube rack
- ✔ water
- ✔ graduated cylinder (25 mL)
- ✔ clay
- ✔ sand
- ✔ powdered chalk
- ✔ magnifying glass
- ✔ wristwatch or stopwatch
- ✔ filter paper
- ✔ funnel
- ✔ beaker (250-mL)
- ✔ alum
- ✔ dilute ammonium hydroxide solution
- ✔ spatula

Part A Pour 10 mL of water into each of three 150-mm test tubes. Add a pinch of clay to one test tube, a pinch of sand to the second test tube, and a pinch of powdered chalk to the third. Stopper the tubes and place them in a rack.

Part B Carefully examine the solid particles in each test tube with a magnifying glass.

    1. Describe the substances in terms of the sizes of their particles.

Part C Shake each test tube vigorously for a few seconds and then return it to the rack. Note how long it takes for most of the solid matter in each test tube to settle to the bottom of the tube.

    2. Describe the substances in terms of how quickly the solid matter in each test tube settles.

    3. Which substance fails to settle completely?

    4. What is the relation between the size of the particles and the rate at which the particles settle to the bottom of the test tubes?

Part D Pour 10 mL of water and add a pinch of clay to each of three 150-mm test tubes. Place the test tubes in a rack.

Part E Take one of the test tubes and shake it thoroughly. Pour the contents of the test tube onto a sheet of filter paper properly set up in a funnel (see Figure 3-1, page 41). Collect in a beaker the liquid that passes through the funnel. When the liquid stops dripping from the end of the funnel, carefully observe both the filter paper and the liquid in the beaker.

5. *What happened to the solid substance that was in the test tube?*

6. *Describe the appearance of the* **filtrate** *(the liquid that has passed through the filter paper).*

CAUTION: Ammonium hydroxide vapor is a strong irritant. Do not inhale.

Part F Add a pinch of alum and a little dilute ammonium hydroxide solution to the second test tube. Shake both the second and third test tubes vigorously for a few seconds and then return them to the rack. Observe both test tubes for about 5 minutes. Record how long it takes for any solid substances to settle to the bottom of the test tubes.

7. *How does the addition of alum and ammonium hydroxide to the test tube affect the length of time it takes for the solid substance to settle?*

8. *What is the purpose of the third test tube?*

What Is a Suspension?

You have learned that a liquid solution is a clear, homogeneous mixture. Because the particles of solute are molecular or smaller in size, they are not visible. The solute particles are evenly distributed throughout the solvent. Other types of mixtures can be prepared in which the particles remain visible and give the mixture a cloudy appearance. In some of these mixtures, the particles are not evenly distributed throughout the liquid. Such a **heterogeneous** (**nonuniform**) mixture of solid particles in a liquid is known as a **suspension**. Some common examples of suspensions are milk, milk of magnesia, and any medicine that requires shaking before using. Table 12-1 compares suspensions and solutions.

The inquiry investigation at the beginning of the chapter allowed you to observe some of the characteristics of suspensions. Sand quickly settled out of suspension and fell to the bottom of the tube. Some of the clay in the suspension also settled to the bottom of the tube. In the clay suspension, however, it took longer for the clay to separate from the water than it took for the sand. Some particles of clay may even have remained suspended in the water indefinitely. Finally, you observed that nearly all the particles of chalk dust remained in suspension.

The differences you observed can be understood in terms of the sizes of the particles in the mixtures. One way to compare the sizes of the particles in suspensions and in solutions is by passing a beam of light through each mixture. In a solution, the particles of the solute are molecular or smaller in size and do not interfere with the beam of light. The beam, therefore, passes through the solution unaffected. This effect was observed in Figure 11-2b, page 160. In a suspension, however, the solid particles have a wide range in sizes but are all larger than molecules. The light is reflected by those particles that are *just slightly larger* than molecules, and the light beam becomes visible in the liquid.

Figure 12-1. The Tyndall effect is seen when a beam of light passes through a suspension. As the light is reflected by particles that are just slightly larger than molecules, the light beam becomes visible.

Table 12-1.
What Are the Differences Between Liquid Suspensions and Liquid Solutions?

Suspensions	Solutions
Are cloudy	Are clear
Contain particles that generally settle out on standing; they do not dissolve	Contain particles that do not settle out on standing; they dissolve
Contain particles that vary in size but are larger than molecules	Contain particles that are molecular or smaller in size
May reflect light	Permit light to pass through
Are heterogeneous mixtures	Are homogeneous mixtures

This type of light reflection by the particles in a mixture is known as the **Tyndall effect**, as shown in Figure 12-1. Particles of chalk dust suspended in water reflect a light beam in the same manner as the particles of chalk dust suspended in air in Figure 11-2a on page 160. The Tyndall effect can be used to determine whether a liquid mixture is a solution or a fine suspension.

The Tyndall effect is characteristic of certain types of suspensions called **colloidal suspensions**. These include suspensions in liquids of very finely divided solids, which generally do not settle on standing.

Suspensions containing fairly large particles in liquids do not exhibit the Tyndall effect. In fact, such suspensions block the passage of a beam of light.

What Are the Different Types of Suspensions?

Suspensions can have different characteristics depending on the substances from which they are made. The components of a suspension, like those of a solution, may consist of gases, liquids, or solids.

When chalk dust floats in air and a light beam is sent through it, the dust particles reflect the light. This means that the dust particles and the light ray both become visible. Chalk dust in air is an example of a suspension in which very fine solid particles are scattered, or dispersed, in a gas.

You often see suspensions of a liquid in a gas. For example, you may have noticed that the room fills with a fine mist when you take a hot shower. The mist is composed of small droplets of water dispersed in air. Clouds and fog are other examples of this type of suspension.

The particles in gases are molecular in size. This means that gas particles tend to mix uniformly with one another and thus suspensions of a gas in a gas do not exist. Mixtures of gases in gases are therefore considered to be solutions rather than suspensions.

How Can You Separate the Components of a Suspension?

The particles in a suspension are larger than molecules. Therefore, the effect of gravity on such particles may be used to separate the component parts of a suspension. Among such methods of separating the suspended material are sedimentation, filtration, centrifugation, and coagulation.

Sedimentation. The settling of solid particles, such as clay or sand, from suspensions is known as **sedimentation**. The rate at which sedimentation occurs depends on the size of the suspended solid particles. The gravitational force between two objects at a certain distance apart, such as Earth and the particles in a mixture, depends on the masses of the objects. The particles of sand are more massive than those of clay. Therefore, Earth pulls more strongly on the sand than on the clay. This explains why the particles of sand in the inquiry investigation at the beginning of the chapter settled much faster than the particles of clay.

You can use what you have learned about particle size to predict how particles will settle when a mixture of gravel, sand, clay, and water is placed in a container, shaken, and allowed to stand. As shown in Figure 12-2, the gravel (the largest and heaviest particle) is found at the bottom of the container. The sand (the next largest particle) is found immediately above the gravel. The clay (the smallest and lightest particle) is found at the top of the sediment because clay settles at the slowest rate.

Filtration. The components of a suspension of solids in liquids can be separated by passing the suspension through a porous solid if the openings in the solid are smaller than the suspended particles. Filter paper and cheesecloth are typical porous solids that may be used to separate suspended particles from a liquid. This process is called **filtration** (see

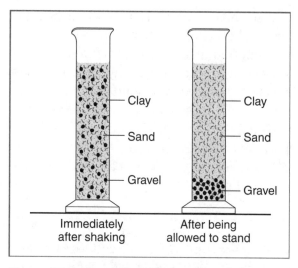

Figure 12-2. The sedimentation of particles in a suspension is proportional to their size and weight. Large, heavy particles settle faster than smaller, lighter ones.

page 177). You observe filtration when a cook prepares spaghetti. After the spaghetti is cooked, the suspension of spaghetti in water is poured through a strainer. The water passes through the holes in the strainer, but the spaghetti remains behind.

In the laboratory, filtration is normally used as a means of separating the liquid from the solid in a suspension (see Figure 12-3). The liquid that passes through the filter is called the **filtrate**.

Dissolved solid particles in a solution cannot be removed by filtration because the dissolved particles are molecular in size—much smaller than the pore openings of any ordinary filter.

Centrifugation. Particles settle out of suspension because of the attractive force of gravity. When a force stronger than gravity acts on a suspension, the rate of sedimentation increases. To understand this process, imagine that you are riding on a spinning ride at an amusement park. When the ride spins rapidly, you are thrown outward. This is due to the force created by the spinning ride. In the laboratory, a machine that can produce

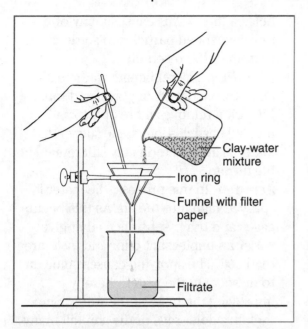

Figure 12-3. Unlike solids in solutions, solids in a suspension can be trapped and separated by using a filter. Solid particles of clay suspended in water are trapped by filter paper. Clear water, the filtrate, passes through the paper into the beaker.

such a force is the **centrifuge**, and the process is called **centrifugation**.

When a clay-water suspension is placed in a test tube in a centrifuge and spun, the sediment moves to the farthest end of the tube. The water, free of solid particles, is clear, and stays above the solid. When the centrifuge stops spinning, most of the clear water can be poured off and is thus separated from the clay.

Coagulation. Another method of increasing the rate of the sedimentation of suspensions is **coagulation**. In the inquiry investigation, you added alum and ammonium hydroxide to the suspension. These compounds react and form a jellylike mass to which the suspended particles stick. Since the particles and jelly are heavy, the mass settles rapidly. Figure 12-4 shows how a clay-water suspension may be separated by coagulation. The mass produced by adding alum and ammonium hydroxide quickly causes the clay to settle to the bottom of the container. Adding alum and lime will also cause coagulation.

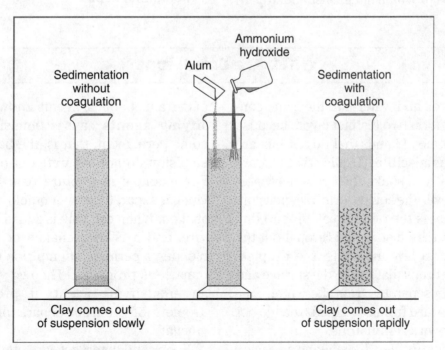

Figure 12-4. When alum and ammonium hydroxide are added to a suspension of clay, they form a jellylike mass with the clay. This process, called coagulation, adds weight to the clay, causing it to settle faster.

How Is Water Purified?

Supplying pure water for drinking purposes is perhaps one of the most important problems facing modern societies. Some of the water people use comes from wells fed by underground water sources. The remainder of the water supply is obtained by collecting water in reservoirs from direct rainfall and from runoff of rain and melted snow. Water runoff often carries into the reservoir certain undesirable materials such as sewage, fertilizers, chemical wastes from industrial plants, distasteful dissolved gases, and suspended material. Before the water from a reservoir reaches homes and businesses, the water is usually purified by several of the following processes:

1. *Sedimentation.* In a reservoir, large suspended particles, such as sand, settle to the bottom. Small suspended particles, such as clay, still remain in the water and must be removed by other means.
2. *Coagulation.* The addition of chemicals such as alum and lime produces a jelly-like mass to which small suspended particles adhere. This causes many of the tiny suspended particles to settle to the bottom of the reservoir.
3. *Filtration.* The remaining water is filtered through beds of gravel and sand. Filtration removes more of the suspended particles, but some suspended material and bacteria may still remain in the filtrate.
4. *Aeration.* In this process, the water is sprayed high into the air. As this occurs, gases and other substances that give water an unpleasant odor and taste are oxidized. The spraying causes some air to dissolve in the water, thereby improving the taste of the water. Since the ultraviolet rays of the sun kill many bacteria, the aeration of water is generally carried out on sunny days.
5. *Chlorination.* To destroy the bacteria still remaining after aeration, chlorine is added in the proportion of about 4 kilograms of chlorine to about one million kilograms of water. In this proportion, chlorine destroys the bacteria, but does not harm people.

What Are Emulsions?

If you pour oil and water into the same container, they form two distinct layers because they do not mix. Liquids that do not mix are said to be **immiscible**. (Liquids that mix are *miscible*.) If you shake the container vigorously, however, the liquids form a suspension. Shaking causes the oil to break up into tiny droplets that are distributed throughout the water. After a few moments, the droplets form larger drops that rise to the surface and the oil again separates from the water. Suspensions formed from two liquids that do not mix are known as **emulsions**.

Emulsions formed by shaking immiscible liquids are only temporary. The addition of certain chemical agents known as **emulsifying agents** causes emulsions to become permanent; that is, the liquids in the emulsion do not separate out on standing. For example, a mixture of salad oil and vinegar separates rather quickly after being shaken. When egg yolk is added to this mixture, and it is then shaken or mixed in a blender, a permanent emulsion called mayonnaise is produced. The egg yolk acts as an emulsifying agent; it prevents the droplets of oil from separating from the vinegar.

Soaps and detergents are other examples of emulsifying agents. When added to water

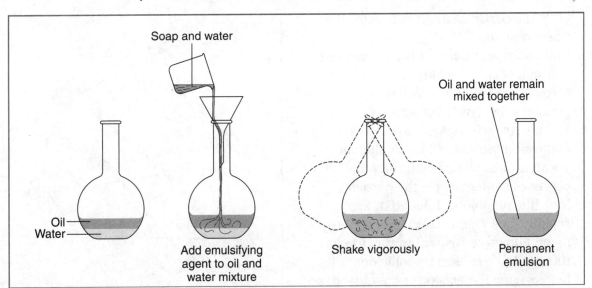

Figure 12-5. Normally, two immiscible liquids such as oil and water will form separate layers when mixed. The less dense substance floats on the more dense substance. However, if an emulsifying substance such as soap is added and the liquids shaken, a permanent emulsion will form and no separate layers will exist.

and brought into contact with dirt, these agents form an emulsion composed of the dirt or grease, the emulsifying agent, and water. The dirt is trapped in the emulsion, which can then be rinsed away easily. Figure 12-5 shows how soap is used in preparing a permanent emulsion.

What Are Colloidal Suspensions?

You have learned that a *colloidal suspension*, or a *colloid*, may be a suspension of finely divided solids in liquids that shows the Tyndall effect. Fog, shaving cream, and jelly are examples of colloids. The basic difference between solutions, suspensions, and colloids is the size of the particles in them. Solutions contain tiny particles. Suspensions contain relatively large, or coarse, particles. Colloids contain particles that are intermediate between those of solutions and suspensions.

The properties of colloidal suspensions, due to their finely divided particles, are as follows:

1. *The particles in colloids have a large surface area.* If a large rock were ground into a fine powder, the total area of the fine powder would be enormous when compared to the area of the rock. This large surface area permits the colloidal particles to attract other kinds of matter in contact with them. The accumulation of different substances on the surface of the particles of a colloid is called *adsorption*.

2. *The particles in colloids have an electrical charge.* Because of their large surface area, colloidal particles adsorb charged particles when they are present in the liquid in which the colloidal particles are suspended. The colloidal particles themselves attain a positive or negative electrical charge, depending on the medium in which they are suspended. When a wire from the positive pole of a battery and another from the negative pole are placed in a colloid, positively charged colloidal particles migrate toward the negative wire, and negatively charged

colloidal particles migrate toward the positive wire.

3. *Colloids reflect light.* Colloidal particles reflect a beam of light that is sent through the liquid in which they are suspended—the Tyndall effect.

4. *The particles in colloids exhibit Brownian motion.* When a colloidal suspension is observed through the high power of a microscope, the particles look like pinpoints of light that zigzag rapidly. (See Figure 12-6.) This movement, known as **Brownian motion**, is thought to be caused by collisions between the larger, slower colloidal particles and the smaller, more rapidly moving molecules of the liquid. These collisions keep the particles bouncing around, preventing them from settling to the bottom of the container.

Colloids are extremely important systems. They are, perhaps, as important as life itself because the contents of the cells that make up our bodies are colloidal systems.

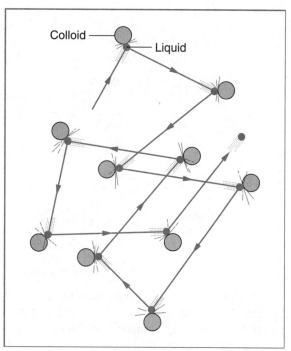

Figure 12-6. Colloids, which contain particles whose size falls between those in solutions and those in suspensions, exhibit Brownian motion—the appearance under the lens of a microscope of tiny moving points of light. These points of light are thought to be produced when colloid particles collide with molecules of the liquid.

Chapter Review

Science Terms

The following list contains all the boldfaced words found in this chapter and the page on which each appears.

Brownian motion (p. 180)
centrifugation (p. 177)
centrifuge (p. 177)
coagulation (p. 177)
colloidal suspension (p. 175)
emulsifying agent (p. 178)
emulsion (p. 178)
filtrate (p. 176)

filtration (p. 176)
heterogeneous (p. 174)
immiscible (p. 178)
nonuniform (p. 174)
sedimentation (p. 176)
suspension (p. 174)
Tyndall effect (p. 175)

Matching Questions

*On the blank line, write the letter of the item in column B that is
most closely related to the item in column A. [Note that the letters in
Column B can be used more than once.]*

Column A

_____ 1. a mixture in which the solute particles are not visible

_____ 2. a mixture that exhibits the Tyndall effect

_____ 3. a suspension formed by two immiscible liquids

_____ 4. a mixture made up of particles of large size

_____ 5. a mixture made up of particles of molecular or smaller size

_____ 6. a mixture in which particles exhibit Brownian motion

_____ 7. a mixture of a gas in a gas

_____ 8. a mixture that can be made permanent by adding another substance

_____ 9. a mixture in which the particles have an electric charge

_____ 10. a mixture in which no components may be separated by filtration

Column B

a. solution

b. suspension

c. emulsion

d. colloid

TEST-TAKING TIP The importance of getting adequate rest before a major exam cannot be overlooked. Plan your study schedule so that you are not cramming at the last minute. Instead, simply review the material the night before and get a full night's sleep.

Multiple-Choice Questions

*In your notebook, write the letter preceding the word or expression
that best completes the statement or answers the question.*

1. A type of mixture that always has a cloudy appearance is
a. a solution   c. a suspension
b. a tincture   d. a colloid

2. Which of the following is *not* an example of a suspension?
a. sugar water   c. milk of magnesia
b. milk   d. sand in water

3. What happens when sand is shaken in water and allowed to stand?
a. The sand dissolves.
b. The sand settles to the bottom.

c. The sand remains suspended.
d. The sand changes into a different substance.

4. When clay and sand are mixed with water and allowed to stand,
a. the sand dissolves, but the clay settles to the bottom
b. the clay dissolves, but the sand settles to the bottom
c. both the clay and sand settle to the bottom, but the clay settles faster
d. both the clay and sand settle to the bottom, but the sand settles faster

5. Which best describes the Tyndall effect?
   a. the hastening of the sedimentation of a suspension
   b. the separating of components of a suspension
   c. the reflection of light from particles slightly larger than molecules
   d. the aeration of water by spraying it into air

6. Which of the following is an example of a suspension?
   a. oxygen in air
   b. salt in water
   c. dust in air
   d. sugar in water

7. Which of the following methods of separation relies on high-speed spinning motion?
   a. sedimentation   c. centrifugation
   b. filtration   d. coagulation

8. The speed at which sedimentation occurs depends on the
   a. amount of liquid present
   b. size of the particles
   c. pressure on the particles
   d. temperature of the surroundings

9. The process in which a suspension is poured through a porous solid is called
   a. filtration   c. coagulation
   b. centrifugation   d. sedimentation

10. The process of separating a suspension in which a jellylike mass is formed is called
    a. sedimentation   c. coagulation
    b. distillation   d. filtration

11. In the purification of drinking water, large suspended particles are generally removed by
    a. aeration   c. chlorination
    b. sedimentation   d. filtration

12. To remove unpleasant odors and tastes from drinking water, the water is subjected to
    a. chlorination   c. aeration
    b. coagulation   d. filtration

13. What is the role of chlorine in the process of water purification?
    a. It destroys any bacteria remaining in the water.
    b. It gives water a pleasant taste.
    c. It attracts solid particles out of the water.
    d. It causes clay and other substances to clump together.

14. Which substance can be used to prepare a permanent emulsion of oil and vinegar?
    a. egg white   c. mayonnaise
    b. alcohol   d. egg yolk

15. The particles of colloids are
    a. molecular in size
    b. smaller than those of a solution
    c. larger than those of a suspension
    d. intermediate between the particles of a solution and those of a suspension

16. Colloidal particles
    a. have a small surface area
    b. have an electric charge
    c. do not reflect light
    d. settle out on standing

17. How is adsorption related to colloid particles?
    a. Different substances accumulate on the surface of the particles of a colloid.
    b. Colloid particles reflect a beam of light that is sent through the liquid.
    c. Colloid particles flow through narrow openings easily.
    d. Colloid particles settle to the bottom of their container when left undisturbed.

18. What does it mean to say that the particles of a colloid exhibit Brownian motion?
    a. They flow like falling water.
    b. They bob up and down like waves.
    c. They zigzag rapidly.
    d. They spin in small circles.

19. Of the following, the substance with the smallest particles is
    a. clay   c. gravel
    b. sand   d. pebbles

20. The particles of a solution
    a. absorb all light
    b. do not affect light
    c. reflect light
    d. are opaque to light

Modified True-False Questions

In some of the following statements, the italicized term makes the statement incorrect. For each incorrect statement, in your notebook, write the term that must be substituted for the italicized term to make the statement correct. For each correct statement, write the word "true."

1. A suspension is a *homogeneous* mixture. _____

2. The reflection of light by the particles in a suspension is called the *colloidal* effect. _____

3. The settling of solid particles from suspensions is known as *sedimentation*. _____

4. Cheesecloth can be used to separate suspended solid particles from a liquid in the process of *centrifugation*. _____

5. A device that produces a force that is used to separate the components of a suspension is a *centrifuge*. _____

6. *Alum* is a chemical used to coagulate suspended particles. _____

7. The formation of a jellylike mass takes place in the process of *chlorination*. _____

8. Two liquids that do not mix are said to be *unstable*. _____

9. Chemicals that produce permanent emulsions are called *emulsifying agents*. _____

10. The zigzagging motion of the particles in a colloid suspension is called the *Tyndall effect*. _____

Check Your Knowledge

Write the answer to each question in your notebook.

1. Define each of the following terms:
   a. suspension
   b. emulsion
   c. colloid
   d. emulsifying agent
   e. Brownian motion

2. State and describe the processes used to purify drinking water.

3. Describe how you could determine whether an unknown mixture is a colloid.

4. A suspension of gravel, sand, and clay in water is shaken together and is allowed to settle. Explain why the gravel is always found at the bottom and the clay is always found at the top.

Think Critically

Write the answer to each of the following questions in your notebook.

1. A student is using the balls shown to model heterogeneous aqueous mixtures. Which type of solution is most likely represented by each type of ball? Explain.

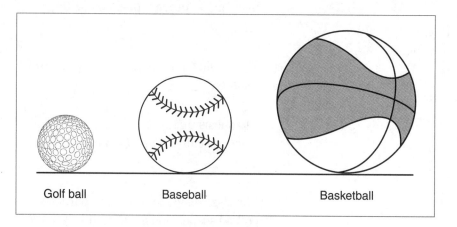

| Golf ball | Baseball | Basketball |

2. Blood consists of solid matter (mostly blood cells) and a liquid (plasma). Plasma consists of a wide variety of molecules, including proteins and minerals. If you were a doctor who needed to give a patient a transfusion consisting *only* of blood cells, what method would you use to obtain them rapidly from a sample of whole blood? Explain your answer.

Take It Further

1. Particle size is often measured in nanometers. Investigate the size of one nanometer, and compare solutions, suspensions, and colloids in terms of particle size as described in nanometers. Share your findings.

2. Many of the foods you eat are suspensions and colloids. Make a poster showing several examples. Describe the substances in the mixture as well as the properties of the mixture. With your teacher's permission, bring in some examples to show the class.

| Internet Search |

3. In 1974, the Safe Drinking Water Act was passed. Conduct research to find out what this act does, why it is important, and what updates have been made to it. Write a brief summary to present your findings.

CAREER

4. Maintaining the water supply for people to use is an essential job in this society. Explore job opportunities in wastewater management. Find out what the job entails, what training is required, and what types of organizations hire individuals in this field. Share your findings.

13

How Do Dissolved Particles Affect the Properties of Water?

This truck spraying salt during a snowstorm is a familiar sight in many cold climates. The salt prevents water on the road from turning into ice at the temperature at which water normally freezes.

After reading this chapter, you should be able to answer the following questions:

What are the properties of solutions?

What are the boiling point and freezing point of pure water?

What are the effects of solutes on the boiling point and freezing point of a pure solvent?

What is conductivity?

What is ionization?

How are ions related to electrical conductivity?

What is the effect of ions on boiling and freezing points?

The Boiling Temperatures of Solutions

Have you ever seen salt spread on roadways on a cold day? Or perhaps you have seen someone add salt to water being boiled in a pot? Adding salt to water changes its properties. In this inquiry investigation, you will learn a little about the boiling temperatures of solutions.

Materials:
✔ safety goggles
✔ distilled water
✔ beaker (100-mL)
✔ wire gauze
✔ ring stand
✔ ring
✔ thermometer
✔ cork stopper
✔ glass beads
✔ Bunsen burner
✔ test tube clamp
✔ sodium chloride (solid)
✔ triple-beam or electronic balance
✔ spatula
✔ wristwatch or stopwatch

CAUTION: Wear safety goggles while doing this activity.

Part A Pour 50 mL of distilled water into the 100-mL beaker. Place the beaker on a wire gauze pad supported by the ring on the ring stand. Suspend a thermometer in the water, as shown in Figure 13-1. (Your teacher will have inserted the thermometer in the cork.)

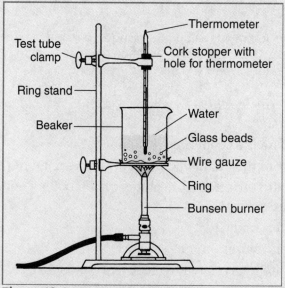

Figure 13-1.

Part B Add several glass beads to the water. Place a Bunsen burner under the beaker and heat the water until it begins to boil. (As the liquid begins to boil, the glass beads will begin to bounce on the bottom of the beaker. As they bounce, they burst the large bubbles of steam in the water. (This allows the water to boil safely.) Record the temperature of the water at one-minute intervals for 3 minutes. Turn off the burner.

1. *What happens to the temperature of the water as heat is applied?*

2. *What happens to the temperature of the water after it begins to boil and you continue to heat it?*

3. *How long did it take for the water to boil after heat was applied?*

4. *What is the temperature at which distilled water boils?*

Part C Using the same setup as above, weigh out 5 grams of sodium chloride (NaCl) and dissolve it in 50 mL of distilled water. Add several glass beads to the water, insert the thermometer, and heat the water until it boils. Record the temperature of the water at one-minute intervals for 3 minutes. Turn off the burner.

5. *How long did it take for the solution to boil after heat was applied?*

6. *What is the temperature at which the salt solution boils?*

7. *How does the boiling temperature of distilled water compare with the boiling temperature of an equal quantity of distilled water to which salt has been added?*

Part D Repeat the experiment in Part C. This time, however, add 10 grams of sodium chloride to the same quantity of distilled water. Record the temperature of the water at one-minute intervals for 3 minutes.

8. *How long did it take for the water to boil after heat was applied?*

9. *What is the temperature at which the salt solution boils?*

10. *What effect does adding 10 grams of sodium chloride to distilled water have on the boiling temperature of water?*

What Are the Properties of Solutions?

When two or more solid substances are mixed, the components of the mixture generally retain their own physical properties. When iron filings and sulfur are mixed, for example, the iron remains black and the sulfur remains yellow. Also, the iron filings can easily be separated from the sulfur with a magnet.

Unlike a mixture of iron filings and sulfur, many of the properties of solutions of solids in liquids differ from the properties of the pure liquid. As you will see, the boiling point, the freezing point, and the conductivity of a solution (ability to carry an electric current) all differ from those of the pure solvent.

What Is the Boiling Point of Pure Water?

The temperature at which a pure liquid begins to boil at sea level is known as its normal **boiling point**. The boiling point of a liquid is one of its characteristic properties, or *physical constants*. In the inquiry investigation, you determined the boiling point of pure water, which was approximately 100° Celsius (or 212° Fahrenheit). The temperature of the boiling water remained the same even though you continued to heat it. Depending on the volume of water and the amount of heat applied to it, a given volume of water will reach its boiling point in a given amount of time. The graph in Figure 13-2 shows one example of this process.

The behavior of water as it becomes warmer and then boils is explained by the kinetic-molecular theory. According to this theory, when heat energy is supplied to water, the water molecules move faster. As still more heat is supplied, the molecules increase their speed and the attractive forces between the water molecules decrease until the boiling point is reached. At this point, any additional heat energy that is supplied causes the water molecules to move fast enough to separate from one another in the liquid and to break away from the surface of the water, forming a gas. This is an example of a change of state, or phase change. The amount of heat needed to change 1 gram of a liquid to a gas at its boiling temperature is called the **heat of vaporization**.

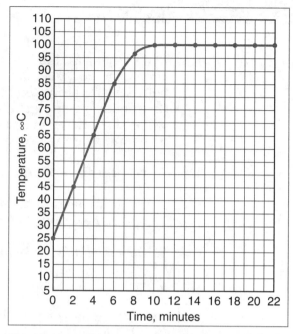

Figure 13-2. The graph shows how temperature varies with time as a given amount of heat is applied to a known volume of water. Note the plateau—the flat part of the curve—at 100°C. This is the boiling point of pure water.

When water boils and heat energy continues to be supplied to the boiling water, the extra energy is used up as liquid water changes into water vapor. As a result, the temperature of the water does not increase during boiling, but remains the same as long as any liquid water remains in the sample. This is the reason for the flat portion of the curve.

What Are the Effects of Solutes on the Boiling Point of a Pure Solvent?

In the inquiry investigation at the beginning of the chapter, you dissolved 5 grams of sodium chloride (NaCl) in the 50-milliliter sample of distilled water. When the temperature of the solution reached approximately 101°C, the solution began to boil. It appears, therefore, that adding the solute (5 grams of NaCl) *raises* the boiling point of water. When you dissolved 10 grams of sodium chloride in a 50-milliliter sample of distilled

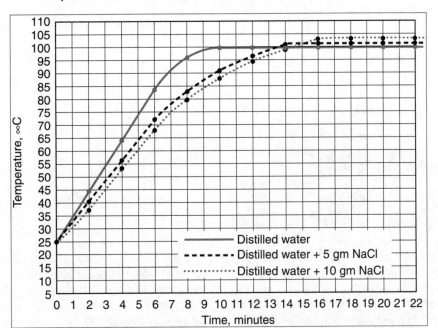

Figure 13-3. This graph reveals that the boiling point of water increases as the concentration of a solute, in this case NaCl, increases.

water, you found that the boiling point of the solution increased further to about 102°C. Adding still more solute raised the boiling point even more. The results can be expressed in a graph such as Figure 13-3.

As you study the two curves that represent the boiling of the salt solutions, keep in mind that the boiling points differ because of the different amounts of sodium chloride that are present and dispersed among molecules of water. Again, the kinetic-molecular theory describes what is happening. As heat is supplied to a mixture of water and sodium chloride, the water molecules move more rapidly than they did before they were heated. However, the molecules of water no longer have the complete freedom of motion they had before the sodium chloride was added. This occurs because the solute particles (NaCl) collide with the solvent molecules (H_2O) and interfere with their motion. This means that more heat energy must be supplied to boil the solution than was required to boil the water alone.

When you cook spaghetti or vegetables, salt is added to the water to improve the taste of the food. In addition, salt raises the boiling point of the water. This makes the water boil at a higher temperature and the food cook faster.

► What Is the Freezing Point of Water?

The temperature at which a liquid begins to solidify (becomes solid) is known as the **freezing point**. The freezing point of water is the temperature at which water changes to ice at sea level. It is also the same temperature at which the solid melts to re-form the liquid (the **melting point**). Like the boiling point, the freezing point is a characteristic property, or physical constant, of a substance.

If you wanted to determine the freezing point of pure water, you would pour 10 milliliters of distilled water into a small beaker and place a thermometer in the water. Then you would place this beaker in a larger beaker that contained a cooling bath whose temper-

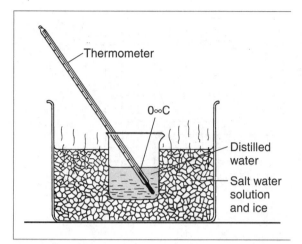

Figure 13-4. When a beaker of distilled water is placed in a cooling bath of salt water and ice, the temperature of the distilled water falls. When the temperature reaches 0°C, the freezing point of pure water, the distilled water will begin to freeze.

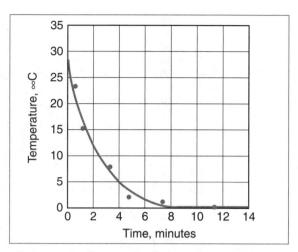

Figure 13-5. The graph relates temperature to time as pure water is cooled. Note that the curve becomes flat at 0°C, the freezing point of water. As long as any liquid water remains, the temperature will hold at 0°C.

ature was below 0°C. Such cooling baths usually contain mixtures of NaCl, chipped ice, and water or alcohol. See Figure 13-4.

In a few minutes, the thermometer would show a drop in the temperature of the water. As the temperature of the water continued to decrease and reached 0°C, particles of ice would form in the water. As more of the water continued to form ice, the temperature would remain the same. This temperature is the freezing point of water, which is 0°C. A typical graph of this process is shown in Figure 13-5.

Here, too, the kinetic-molecular theory helps you understand why the temperature of the water remains constant as it freezes. You know that molecules of the water in the liquid state are in constant motion. As heat energy is removed from the liquid, the water molecules slow and attract one another more strongly. As more heat is removed, these processes continue until the attractive forces between the water molecules are sufficiently great to change the water from a liquid to a solid. During freezing, as long as any liquid water remains, the temperature remains constant because continued withdrawal of heat energy results only in changing more of the liquid to solid.

The amount of heat that must be removed to change 1 gram of a liquid to a solid, at its freezing point, is known as the **heat of fusion**. Similarly, the heat of fusion is the quantity of heat required to melt 1 gram of solid at its melting point.

▷ **What Are the Effects of Solutes on the Freezing Point of a Pure Solvent?**

The freezing point of a liquid, as well as its boiling point, changes on the addition of a solute. If you add a solute to water and attempt to freeze this solution, you will find that the freezing point of the water is lower than 0°C. The more solute you add, the further the freezing point would be lowered. This occurs because the molecules of the solute prevent the molecules of water from coming together to form ice.

The fact that solutes lower the freezing point of water is used in many ways. For example, when enough salt is used, the freezing point of water can be lowered to about −2°C. If the temperature of, say, a sidewalk is −2°C or higher, any ice present will begin to melt, reducing the hazard to pedestrians.

For similar reasons, most automobile owners use antifreeze in their car radiators in the winter. Permanent antifreeze mixtures generally contain ethylene glycol. When this substance is dissolved in water, the freezing point of the mixture is reduced to a temperature below 0°C. As more ethylene glycol is added, the freezing point is lowered still further. Thus, the water in the radiator will not freeze at temperatures below those usually occurring in winter. Freezing would cause the water to expand and possibly crack the engine block.

What Is Conductivity?

You learned that metallic elements, such as silver and copper, are excellent conductors of electricity. Nonmetallic graphite (carbon) also conducts electricity. Is the property of electrical conductivity restricted to elements alone? To determine whether or not compounds conduct electricity, scientists use a conductivity apparatus. This consists of two graphite electrodes and an electric light bulb connected to a source of voltage (see Figure 13-6).

How Is Conductivity Related to Solutions?

When a metal is placed across the graphite electrodes and the conductivity apparatus is properly connected to a source of electricity, the bulb lights. This shows that the metal is a conductor of electricity.

If the two electrodes are now placed in a sample of sugar or in a sample of salt, the bulb does not light. When the sugar is dissolved in water and tested for conductivity, the sugar solution does not conduct electricity. However, when the salt is dissolved in water and the solution is tested for conductivity, this solution conducts electricity. A compound whose water solution conducts electricity is called an **electrolyte**. A compound whose water solution does not conduct electricity is called a **nonelectrolyte**.

The ability of compounds in water solutions to conduct electricity varies considerably. Chemists recognize three classes of these compounds:

1. Strong electrolytes—good conductors.
2. Weak electrolytes—poor conductors.
3. Nonelectrolytes—nonconductors.

You can distinguish strong electrolytes from weak electrolytes by observing the brightness of the bulb in the conductivity apparatus. Strong electrolytes cause the bulb to glow brightly; weak electrolytes cause the bulb to glow dimly; nonelectrolytes produce no glow at all. Chemists also employ more sensitive electrical measuring equipment to study conductivity. Such equipment may reveal that certain apparent nonelectrolytes, such as tap water, are, in reality, very weak electrolytes.

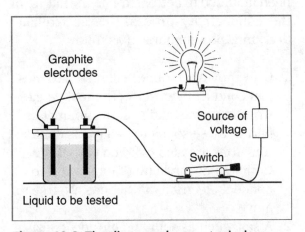

Figure 13-6. The diagram shows a typical conductivity apparatus used to determine whether a solid, liquid, or solution can conduct electricity. If the bulb lights, the substance being tested is a conductor.

Table 13-1.
What Is the Conductivity of Some Compounds?

Strong Electrolytes (bulb glows brightly)	Weak Electrolytes (bulb glows dimly)	Nonelectrolytes (bulb does not light)
Sulfuric acid (in H_2O)	Acetic acid in (in H_2O)	Alcohol (liquid)
Hydrochloric acid (in H_2O)	Carbonic acid (in H_2O)	Benzene (liquid)
Sodium hydroxide (in H_2O)	Ammonium hydroxide (in H_2O)	Concentrated acetic acid (liquid)
Calcium hydroxide (in H_2O)	Concentrated sulfuric acid (liquid)	Distilled water (liquid)
Copper(II) sulfate (in H_2O)		Glycerin (liquid)
Sodium chloride (in H_2O)		Sugar (in H_2O)
Sodium nitrate (in H_2O)		Turpentine (liquid)

Table 13-1 summarizes the results of conductivity experiments involving compounds that are solids, compounds that are liquids, and water solutions of compounds. The table reveals that substances conducting electricity are:

1. Aqueous (water) solutions of acids, such as hydrochloric acid.
2. Aqueous solutions of bases, such as sodium hydroxide.
3. Aqueous solutions of salts, such as sodium chloride.

(You will study acids, bases, and salts in the next chapter.) These same compounds, in the absence of water, do not conduct electricity. In addition, a number of pure liquids, such as alcohol and benzene, do not conduct electricity. Although water appears in the column for nonelectrolytes, water is a very weak electrolyte, as more sensitive equipment would reveal.

▶ **What Is Ionization?**

In 1887, *Svante Arrhenius*, a Swedish scientist, proposed **the theory of electrolytic**

dissociation. Simply put, this theory states that when certain compounds are dissolved in water, charged particles are formed. This means that the compound has become an electrolyte—a conductor of electricity. The Arrhenius theory is very limited because it is based on the concept that the atom is the smallest particle of matter. Because scientists now know that atoms consist of subatomic particles, such as electrons, protons, and neutrons, the views of Arrhenius have been modified to better explain the nature of the conductivity process. These explanations may be summarized as follows:

1. Only moving (mobile) charged particles can conduct electricity. The mobile electrons in metals and in some nonmetals permit these solids to behave as conductors. Ions are also charged particles. Compounds made up of ions will also conduct electricity if the ions are free to move.
2. A salt, such as sodium chloride, consists of positively charged sodium ions attracted to negatively charged chloride ions. Due to their opposite charges, these ions are bound together. In the

solid form, therefore, these ions cannot move and the solid compound is a non-conductor. In the presence of water (or some other solvent), the attractive forces between these ions are weakened and the ions become free to move.

An equation to show this change is:

$$Na^+Cl^- \xrightarrow{H_2O} Na^+ + Cl^-$$
salt (solid)

3. A base, such as sodium hydroxide, con-sists of positively charged sodium ions and negatively charged hydroxide ions bound together. The addition of water causes the sodium ions to separate from the hydroxide ions (the same effect that was produced when water was added to sodium chloride). As happened with the salt, freely moving ions are formed. An equation to show this change is:

$$Na^+OH^- \xrightarrow{H_2O} Na^+ + OH^-$$
(solid)

4. An acid, for example hydrochloric acid, is formed when molecules of gaseous hydrogen chloride, consisting of hydrogen atoms covalently bonded to chlorine atoms, is mixed with water. The hydrogen chloride molecules react with the water to form freely moving charged particles (hydrogen ions and chloride ions), as shown in the equation that follows:

$$HCl \xrightarrow{H_2O} H^+ + Cl^-$$
(gas)

5. Certain covalently bonded molecules, such as sugar or alcohol, do not react with water to produce ions. Hence, they cannot conduct electricity when pure, or in water solution.

6. Ions are electrically charged atoms or groups of atoms. Ions carry a charge that is generally equal to the valence number of the atom or the valence number of the polyatomic ion.
7. The formation of freely moving ions, usually in a water solution, from ions that are bound together, as in salt, is called **dissociation**.
8. The formation of freely moving ions under any circumstance is called **ionization**.

For the purposes of this discussion, the terms *dissociation* and *ionization* will be used interchangeably. It is the freely moving ions, or mobile ions, that carry an electric current. This is why solid salt, which con-tains *bound* ions, cannot conduct electricity. A salt solution, or melted salt, permits the ions to become mobile; conductivity then can take place.

Other examples of ions formed when cer-tain substances are dissolved in water are shown in the following equations:

$$Na_2SO_4 \xrightarrow{H_2O} 2\,Na^+ + SO_4^{-2}$$

$$HBr \xrightarrow{H_2O} H^+ + Br^-$$

$$H_2SO_4 \xrightarrow{H_2O} 2\,H^+ + SO_4^{-2}$$

$$KOH \xrightarrow{H_2O} K^+ + OH^-$$

$$KCl \xrightarrow{H_2O} K^+ + Cl^-$$

▶ **How Are Ions Related to Electrical Conductivity?**

The term **electricity** means a flow of elec-trons. (You will study electricity in more de-tail in Chapter 16.) The electric plug of a lamp or appliance has two terminals, or prongs, with wire running from each prong. The two prongs permit electrons to flow out

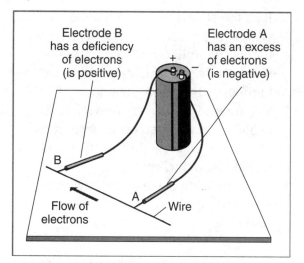

Figure 13-7. Electrons flow from an area that is relatively more negative (**A**) to an area that is relatively less negative, or positive (**B**).

they flow (electrode *B*). At electrode *A*, the electrons are in *excess*; at electrode *B*, the electrons are in *deficiency*.

The terminal or prong (in the plug) having the excess of electrons is labeled the **negative terminal**. The terminal having a deficiency of electrons (which means an excess of protons) is labeled the **positive terminal**.

When the electrodes of the conductivity apparatus (see Figure 13-8) are placed in an electrolyte and the apparatus is properly connected, the ions in the solution are attracted to the electrode that has a charge opposite to their own. Thus, in a hydrochloric acid solution, the positive hydrogen ions are attracted to the negative electrode, here called the **cathode**. At the cathode, the positive hydrogen ions gain electrons and become hydrogen gas. The negative chloride ions are attracted to the positive electrode, here called the **anode**. At the anode, the chloride ions lose their charge (electrons) and become chlorine gas. The gain and release of the electrons by the ions completes the circuit in the conductivity apparatus. The loss of hydrogen and chlorine gas causes

of a source, pass through one wire into the electrical appliance, and then return to the source through the other wire.

Electrons can flow from one point to another only under the following condition (see Figure 13-7): The point *from* which electrons flow (electrode *A*) must have more electrons present than the point to which

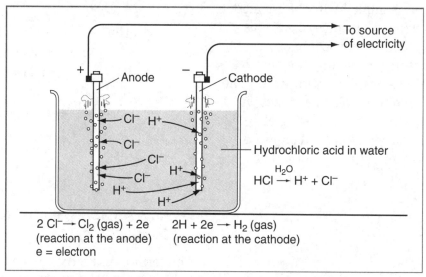

Figure 13-8. Ions of an electrolyte are attracted to electrodes of the opposite charge—negative chloride ions move to the positive electrode as positive hydrogen ions move to the negative electrode. Since chlorine ions lose electrons at the anode, the chlorine ions permit a flow of electrons to occur in solution.

more HCl to ionize (separate into H$^+$ and Cl$^-$ ions), which keeps electricity flowing.

As you discovered before, substances such as vinegar are weak electrolytes. In such acids, only a small number of ions are formed because weak electrolytes ionize only slightly. Most of the acetic acid molecules in vinegar do not react with water and few ions are formed. Since only a small number of mobile ions are present, vinegar is a poor conductor of electricity.

Solid nonelectrolytes, such as sugar, do not conduct an electric current because the sugar does not break down into ions. Furthermore, sugar molecules do not separate into ions in a water solution, and thus ionization does not occur in solution. In the absence of ions, electrons (or an electric current) cannot be transferred across the solution from one electrode to the other.

▶ **What Is the Effect of Ions on Boiling and Freezing Points?**

A comparison of the effects of electrolytes and nonelectrolytes on the boiling point and freezing point of water indicates that electrolytes have a greater effect than nonelectrolytes on these properties of water. Both of these properties are affected when solute particles interfere with the motion of water molecules as the temperature changes. How much interference depends on the number of solute particles present. When one million molecules of a nonelectrolyte such as sugar are dissolved in water, the molecules do not ionize. The solution still contains one million dissolved sugar particles and changes the boiling point to some extent. On the other hand, when one million particles of an electrolyte such as sodium chloride (NaCl) are dissolved in water, two million ions are formed. This occurs because each particle of sodium chloride forms two ions (one sodium ion and one chloride ion). The two million ions change the boiling and freezing points more than do the one million molecules of sugar.

Accordingly, you observe that electrolytes in solution form more solute particles than do nonelectrolytes of the same concentration or strength. Therefore, electrolytes have a greater effect on boiling and freezing points. Increasing the concentration of particles means increasing the numbers of particles in a given space. Thus, increasing the concentrations of electrolytes or nonelectrolytes also increases the effects on the boiling and freezing points.

Chapter Review

Science Terms

The following list contains all the boldfaced words found in this chapter and the page on which each appears.

anode (p. 194)

boiling point (p. 188)

cathode (p. 194)

dissociation (p. 193)

electricity (p. 193)

electrolyte (p. 191)

freezing point (p. 189)

heat of fusion (p. 190)

heat of vaporization (p. 188)

ionization (p. 193)

melting point (p. 189)

negative terminal (p. 194)

nonelectrolyte (p. 191)

positive terminal (p. 194)

theory of electrolytic dissociation (p. 192)

Matching Questions

*In your notebook, write the letter of the item in column B that is
most closely related to the item in column A.*

Column A

_____ 1. ionization

_____ 2. electricity

_____ 3. boiling point

_____ 4. melting point

_____ 5. heat of fusion

_____ 6. heat of vaporization

_____ 7. dissociation

_____ 8. anode

_____ 9. cathode

_____ 10. electrolyte

Column B

a. temperature at which a liquid turns to a gas

b. amount of heat removed to change a liquid to solid

c. the formation of ions under any circumstances

d. the formation of ions in a water solution

e. electrode at which negative ions lose electrons

f. compound whose water solution conducts electricity

g. amount of heat needed to change liquid to gas

h. electrode at which positive ions gain electrons

i. temperature at which a solid turns to a liquid

j. flow of electrons

Multiple-Choice Questions

*In your notebook, write the letter preceding the word or expression
that best completes the statement or answers the question.*

1. Which material is best separated from a mixture using a magnet?
a. sand   c. iron filings
b. sodium chloride   d. glycerin

2. In a graph of heat versus temperature, the shape of the graph at the melting point of a solid is
a. a steep downward slant
b. a flat horizontal line
c. a straight vertical line
d. a steep upward slope

3. When heat is supplied to water, molecular motion
a. increases, then decreases
b. increases
c. decreases
d. remains the same

4. When energy is added to boiling water, the energy is used to
a. raise the water temperature
b. lower the water temperature
c. break the water molecules into atoms
d. change the state of the water

5. When sodium chloride is added to water, the boiling temperature of water
a. decreases   c. stays the same
b. increases   d. none of these

6. What happens to water molecules as they lose heat energy?
a. They speed up and attract each other.
b. They slow down and repel each other.
c. They slow down and attract each other.
d. They speed up and repel each other.

7. How does adding salt affect the freezing point of water?
   a. It lowers it below 0°C.
   b. It keeps it steady at 0°C.
   c. It raises it above than 0°C.
   d. It raises it above more than 32°F.

8. Unlike the solutions that it forms, solid sodium chloride
   a. is not a conductor of electricity
   b. is a good conductor of electricity
   c. is a poor conductor of electricity
   d. is an electrolyte

9. Which of the following is an example of an electrolyte?
   a. dilute hydrochloric acid
   b. sugar solution
   c. alcohol
   d. distilled water

10. Benzene is an example of
    a. a weak electrolyte
    b. a nonelectrolyte
    c. a strong electrolyte
    d. an ionic compound

11. Sodium chloride is composed of
    a. positive sodium and positive chloride ions
    b. negative sodium and negative chloride ions
    c. negative sodium and positive chloride ions
    d. positive sodium and negative chloride ions

12. The chloride ion is represented as
    a. $Cl°$ c. Cl
    b. Cl^- d. Cl^+

13. In water solution, bases release
    a. hydrogen ions
    b. chloride ions
    c. hydroxide ions
    d. sulfide ions

14. In water solution, acids release
    a. hydrogen ions
    d. chloride ions
    c. hydroxide ions
    d. sulfide ions

15. In an electrolyte, the electric current is carried by
    a. electrons   c. atoms
    b. ions   d. molecules

16. A terminal having an excess of electrons is called the
    a. battery
    b. positive electrode
    c. negative electrode
    d. nonelectrolyte

17. In a hydrochloric acid solution,
    a. hydrogen ions migrate to the negative terminal
    b. chloride ions migrate to the negative terminal
    c. the ions are not mobile
    d. no ions are formed

18. In weak electrolytes
    a. no ions are formed
    b. few ions are formed
    c. many ions are formed

19. Nonelectrolytes do not conduct an electric current because
    a. no molecules are formed
    b. no ions are formed
    c. no atoms are formed
    d. no compounds are formed

20. When H_2SO_4 is dissolved in water, SO_4^{-2} ions are formed. Which other ions are formed?
    a. OH^- c. S^{-2}
    b. O^{-2} d. H^+

Modified True-False Questions

In some of the following statements, the italicized term makes the statement incorrect. For each incorrect statement, in your notebook, write the term that must be substituted for the italicized term to make the statement correct. For each correct statement, write the word "true."

1. The heat of *fusion* is the amount of heat needed to convert a liquid to a gas at its boiling point. _____

2. When salt is added to water, the boiling point of the water *increases.* _____

3. The temperature at which a liquid becomes a solid is known as the *boiling* point. _____

4. The amount of heat loss needed to change 1 gram of a liquid to a solid at its freezing point is known as the heat of *formation.* _____

5. In order to reduce the freezing point of water in car radiators, automobile owners add *antifreeze.* _____

6. Liquid solutions that can conduct an electric current are called *electrodes.* _____

7. Strong electrolytes are *poor* conductors of electricity. _____

8. According to the theory of electrolytic *dissociation,* certain compounds form charged particles when dissolved in water. _____

9. Acids release *hydroxide* ions into solution when mixed with water. _____

10. The formation of freely moving ions in a water solution from ions that are bound together is called *mobility.* _____

11. The formation of moving ions under any circumstances is called *ionization.* _____

12. The positive electrode is called the *cathode.* _____

13. As heat is supplied to water, the attractive forces between the water molecules *increase.* _____

14. The behavior of water molecules during boiling or freezing can be explained by the *chemical* theory. _____

15. When water begins to freeze, as long as some of it is liquid, its temperature *remains the same.* _____

TEST-TAKING TIP On a timed test, skip over any questions that you cannot answer quickly. You can return to them once you have answered the remaining questions.

Check Your Knowledge

Write the answer to each question in your notebook.

1. Compare each set of terms:
   a. boiling point and freezing point
   b. heat of vaporization and heat of fusion
   c. electrolyte and nonelectrolyte
   d. dissociation and ionization

2. Give a scientific explanation for each of the following:
   a. The addition of solutes increases the boiling point of water.
   b. The addition of solutes lowers the freezing point of water.

3. Explain why distilled water cannot conduct an electric current, but a sodium chloride solution can conduct a current.

4. Why do some melted solids conduct electricity while other melted solids do not?

Think Critically

Write the answer to each of the following questions in your notebook.

1. Write an equation to show the formation of ions for each of the following substances:
   a. NH_4OH _____
   b. HNO_3 _____
   c. K_2SO_4 _____
   d. $Ca(OH)_2$ _____
   e. HI _____

2. You are a chemist working for your local police department. The police have obtained a sample of what they think is an illegal drug—a white powder—during a search of a suspected drug dealer. The normal melting point of the drug is 125°C. You discover that the melting point of the white powder is 122°C. Explain why the police may have drawn the correct conclusion in spite of your findings.

Take It Further

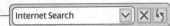

Internet Search

1. Calcium chloride is often added to roads. Find out what the calcium chloride does and why it is useful. In addition, find out what advantages it offers over sodium chloride.

2. People are commonly warned to get out of water during a lightning storm even though pure water does not conduct electricity. Create a pamphlet explaining why this warning is good advice in terms of solutions and conductivity.

CAREER

3. Testing for soil conductivity is important to farmers, gardeners, and others who rely on healthy soil. Investigate the role of a soil scientist. Find out what this career, involves, what training is required, and opportunities for employment. You may wish to begin your search at *http://soils.usda.gov/education/facts/careers.html*.

Should Chemical Dispersants Be Used to Clean Up an Oil Spill?

Each year, billions of barrels of oil are used around the world. To keep up with the ever-increasing demand, oil companies are having to drill deeper and in more remote locations. The oil must then be transported to refineries by ship, barge, or truck. Despite strict guidelines and preventative measures, accidents still happen during such transportation. In fact, there are 300 to 500 spills every year.

Oil spills do not only represent a loss of a limited natural resource. They lead to the destruction of delicate ecosystems and the loss of living things. Many animals become coated by the oil. For some animals, the oil interferes with their natural insulation. Unable to maintain normal body temperatures, the animals die from loss of body heat. The oil can also interfere with an animal's buoyancy, or ability to float. This can make it impossible for the animal to get the air or food it needs to survive. Still others swallow the toxic oil while attempting to clean themselves or their babies. Plants are not safe from the oil because they can take in oil through their roots. The oil interferes with the flow of water and nutrients in the plant, causing the plant to die and transferring the oil to any animal that might eat the plant.

With so much oil spilled, people should use every possible method of cleaning it up, right? Not so fast. Not all methods of cleaning up oil are the same. One method, for example, involves spraying compounds, known as chemical dispersants, onto the oil. The dispersants are intended to break the oil into tiny droplets that sink to the ocean floor. Dropping the oil to the ocean floor means that less oil reaches the coast where it can affect beaches, plants, and land animals. That's the good news.

The bad news is that the oil doesn't disappear. It stays on the sea floor or suspended in the water. It can move great distances with ocean currents. It can be consumed by microorganisms and move up the food chain in various forms. Many researchers argue that the toxic nature of the chemical dispersants in the water is worse than that of the oil. In fact, some of the compounds included in chemical dispersants currently being used are not identified to the public because companies have labeled them as proprietary. That means that environmentalists cannot even have the opportunity to evaluate the true impact of the compounds. No toxicity studies have even been performed on some of the compounds.

The use of chemical dispersants has been described as the lesser of two evils. What do you think about the use of chemicals to halt the spread of an oil spill? While not perfect, do you think it is better than the alternatives? In this case, "out of sight" should definitely not be "out of mind."

Figure 13-9. These workers are tirelessly cleaning oil from the Mississippi River. Is there an easier way?

Organize It!

Use a method that your instructor describes to organize the information in this article.

Explain It!

1. How is an animal harmed when oil interferes with its natural insulation?
   a. The animal cannot float on the water.
   b. The animal can no longer fly.
   c. The animal cannot maintain normal body temperature.
   d. The animal cannot produce eggs.

2. What does a chemical dispersant do to oil?
   a. It changes the oil into other substances.
   b. It breaks the oil into small drops.
   c. It clumps the oil into large balls.
   d. It makes the oil less toxic.

3. What does it mean to say that ingredients in chemical dispersants are proprietary?
   a. They belong to an individual company and do not have to be released.
   b. They are prepared to be sold to other companies at a financial profit.
   c. They are hazardous to living things and can get into food chains.
   d. They exist in only small quantities on Earth and need to be protected.

4. How does the world's dependence on oil affect methods used to obtain oil?

5. How might a bird or other animal ingest oil after a spill?

6. What does it mean for a substance to move up the food chain?

Extend It!

7. Controversial chemical dispersants were used to aid in the cleanup of the oil spill in the Gulf of Mexico in 2010. Investigate how the chemicals were used, what impact they had, and what lasting effects may have resulted. Identify arguments that were made for and against their use. Present your findings in a brief report.

8. Some oil spills, such as the one that resulted from the grounding of the *Exxon Valdez* in 1989, have been related to the design of ships' hulls. Find out how better design, such as double hulls, could prevent some types of oil spills. Write a report on what you discover.

CAREER

9. One concern of using chemical dispersants is that they can bioaccumulate, or build up, as they move along the food chain. Some biologists are scientists who study the impact of substances in food chains and other parts of ecosystems. Find out what an environmental biologist might do and what training is required. You may wish to begin your search at the following site: *http://www.aibs.org/careers/*. Share your findings with the class.

14

What Are Acids, Bases, and Salts?

Mono Lake in California contains almost 300 million tons of salt! The water is so alkaline, or basic, that no fish can live in it. The only species that thrives there is a species of tiny brine shrimp that live nowhere else on Earth.

After reading this chapter, you should be able to answer the following questions:

What are acids, and how are they prepared?

What are the properties and uses of acids?

What is acid rain?

What are bases, and how are they prepared?

What are the properties and uses of bases?

What are salts, and how are they prepared?

What are the properties of salts?

You are already familiar with many examples of acids and bases. Soft drinks, lemon juice, and vinegar contain acids. Soap, ammonia, and solutions of baking soda contain bases. What exactly are acids and bases? In this inquiry investigation, you'll find out one way to distinguish one from the other.

Materials:
- ✔ safety goggles
- ✔ red litmus paper
- ✔ blue litmus paper
- ✔ 4 dishes
- ✔ glass rod
- ✔ water
- ✔ dilute hydrochloric acid or lemon juice
- ✔ dilute sulfuric acid or clear soft drink
- ✔ dilute acetic acid or vinegar
- ✔ distilled water
- ✔ 4 test tubes (15-cm)
- ✔ test-tube rack
- ✔ graduated cylinder (25-mL)
- ✔ dilute hydrochloric acid
- ✔ dilute sodium hydroxide or soap solution
- ✔ dilute sulfuric acid
- ✔ dilute calcium hydroxide or baking soda solution
- ✔ dilute ammonium hydroxide or household ammonia
- ✔ mossy zinc
- ✔ wooden splints
- ✔ matches

CAUTION: Strong acids and strong bases can cause serious burns. Do not spill any solutions on your skin or clothing. If you do, rinse with water. Use safety goggles at all times. Report all spills to your teacher immediately.

Part A Place a strip of red litmus paper and a strip of blue litmus paper in each of four dishes. Using a clean glass rod, place a drop of dilute hydrochloric acid or lemon juice, which contains an acid, on each strip of litmus paper in one dish. Rinse the glass rod thoroughly under running water.

1. Describe what happens on each strip of litmus paper.

Part B Repeat the procedure in Part A, this time using dilute sulfuric acid or a clear soft drink, which contains an acid, and another dish. Again rinse the glass rod thoroughly after using it.

2. Describe what happens on each piece of litmus paper in the second dish.

Part C Repeat the procedure in Part A, this time using dilute acetic acid or vinegar, which contains acetic acid, and another dish. Again rinse the glass rod thoroughly after using it.

3. *Describe what happens on each strip of litmus paper in the third dish.*

Part D Repeat the procedure in part A, this time using distilled water in the fourth dish.

4. *Describe what happens to each piece of litmus paper in the fourth dish.*

5. *What is the purpose of using distilled water in the last part of this experiment?*

6. *What kind of litmus paper can be used as a test for acids?*

Explain.

Part E Place four 15-cm test tubes in a rack. Place a small piece of mossy zinc into each of the test tubes. To the first test tube, add 10 milliliters of dilute hydrochloric acid. To the second test tube, add 10 milliliters of dilute sulfuric acid. To the third test tube, add 10 milliliters of dilute acetic acid. To the fourth test tube, add 10 milliliters of distilled water.

7. *Describe what you observe in each of the test tubes.*

8. *Hold a burning splint to the mouth of each test tube. Describe what happens.*

9. *What gas is produced by all the acids you used? How do you know?*

Part F As you did in Part A, place a strip of red litmus paper and a strip of blue litmus paper into each of four dishes. Using a clean glass rod, place a drop of dilute sodium hydroxide or a solution of soap on each strip of litmus paper in one of the dishes. Rinse the glass rod thoroughly under running water.
Repeat the procedure, using a solution of calcium hydroxide or a solution of baking soda in the second dish, dilute ammonium hydroxide or household ammonia in the third dish, and distilled water in the fourth dish. All of these substances, except for water, are bases.

10. *In each case, describe what happens to the litmus paper in the dishes.*

11. *What kind of litmus paper can be used as a test for bases? Explain.*

12. *If you have an unknown liquid that does not respond to the litmus test, should you conclude that the liquid is distilled water? Explain.*

WHAT IS AN ACID?

In everyday life, you deal with many compounds that chemists classify as **acids**, which are substances whose water solutions contain hydrogen ions (H^+). In water solutions, hydrogen ions attach to water molecules, forming hydronium ions (H_3O^+). Orange juice and grapefruit juice contain citric acid. These juices, and others, also contain ascorbic acid, a substance more commonly known as vitamin C. Salads are often seasoned with vinegar, which contains dilute acetic acid.

In any chemistry laboratory, you find acids such as hydrochloric acid, sulfuric acid, and nitric acid. These acids are called **mineral acids** because they can be prepared from naturally occurring compounds called minerals. Mineral acids are generally stronger than household acids, and should be handled with great care because they can burn skin and clothing.

To test a substance for the presence of an acid, you use an **indicator** such as blue litmus paper. An indicator is a substance that changes color in response to acids or bases. In the presence of an acid, blue litmus paper turns red.

▶ How Are Acids Prepared?

In general, acids may be prepared by two methods: (1) certain gases, related to the acids, are dissolved in water; (2) certain compounds of metals and nonmetals known as *salts*, which are related to the acids, are allowed to react with sulfuric acid. A salt is generally an ionic compound composed of a metallic ion and a nonmetallic ion.

Preparing Acids From Gases. To prepare sulfurous acid (H_2SO_3), powdered sulfur is held in a deflagrating spoon, which is a stainless steel ladle used for burning substances over a flame. The sulfur is burned in air, forming sulfur dioxide gas (SO_2). The sulfur dioxide is then dissolved in water to form sulfurous acid. Figure 14-1 shows how small quantities of sulfurous acid may be prepared in the laboratory.

CAUTION: This should not be performed by students. The reactions take place according to the following equations:

$$\underset{\text{sulfur}}{S} + \underset{\text{oxygen}}{O_2} \rightarrow \underset{\substack{\text{sulfur} \\ \text{dioxide}}}{SO_2}$$

$$\underset{\substack{\text{sulfur} \\ \text{dioxide}}}{SO_2} + \underset{\text{water}}{H_2O} \rightarrow \underset{\substack{\text{sulfurous} \\ \text{acid}}}{H_2SO_3}$$

(Note that *sulfur* dioxide gas produces *sulfurous* acid.) When sulfurous acid is tested with blue litmus paper, the litmus turns red, indicating the presence of an acid.

When carbon dioxide gas dissolves in water, carbonic acid is formed according to the following equation:

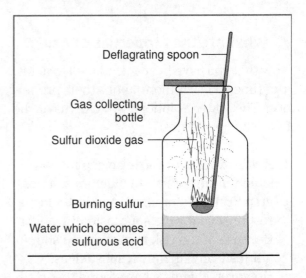

Figure 14-1. Sulfurous acid may be prepared in the laboratory by burning sulfur in the presence of water. The product of the burning, sulfur dioxide, combines with the water to form the acid.

$$CO_2 + H_2O \rightarrow H_2CO_3$$
carbon   water   carbonic
dioxide   acid

(Note that *carbon* dioxide gas produces *carbonic* acid.) When carbonic acid (soda water) is tested with blue litmus paper, the litmus turns red, indicating the presence of an acid.

Preparing Acids From Salts. Hydrochloric acid can be prepared from salts by heating a mixture of sodium chloride and sulfuric acid. The reaction is:

$$2NaCl + H_2SO_4 \rightarrow 2HCl + Na_2SO_4$$
sodium   sulfuric   hydrochloric   sodium
chloride   acid   acid   sulfate

Nitric acid can be prepared similarly by heating sodium nitrate (a salt) with sulfuric acid:

$$2NaNO_3 + H_2SO_4 \rightarrow 2HNO_3 + Na_2SO_4$$
sodium   sulfuric   nitric   sodium
nitrate   acid   acid   sulfate

In the preceding two equations, notice that hydrochloric acid (HCl) is made from chloride (Cl^-) salts, and that nitric acid (HNO_3) is made from nitrate (NO_3^-) salts.

▶ **What Are the Properties of Acids?**

Now that you have been introduced to acids, it is time to learn more about their properties. The water solutions of acids have the following properties:

1. *Acids taste sour.* Citric acid is responsible for the sour taste of lemons, limes, grapefruit, and oranges. Acetic acid is responsible for the sour taste of vinegar. Because of the risk involved, you should not taste any unknown substances. However, chemists have found that a sour taste is a characteristic of all acids.
2. *Acids turn litmus red.* Litmus is a vegetable dye that may be either red or blue, depending on its acidity. As you

observed in the inquiry investigation, acids turn litmus red, and bases turn litmus blue.

When a sample of an acid is placed on red litmus paper, the color of the litmus does not change. (Red litmus paper has been previously treated with acid. Adding more acid does not change the red color.) However, when the same acid is placed on *blue* litmus paper, the color turns from blue to red. (Blue litmus paper has been previously treated with a base. Adding acid causes the litmus to change color.) Citric acid, boric acid, and other acids have the same effect on litmus. Consequently, blue litmus is often used to test for acids.

3. *Acids contain replaceable hydrogen.* When a sample of zinc, a fairly reactive metal, is dropped into a test tube containing an acid such as hydrochloric acid, a reaction occurs; one of whose products is a gas. The bubbling in the tube confirms that a gas is released. When you test this gas by inserting a burning splint into the test tube, as you did in the inquiry investigation, the gas bursts into flame and perhaps produces a small popping sound (see Figure 14-2). This is a characteristic test for hydrogen gas. In general, when certain acids react with reactive metals, hydrogen gas is released, as shown in the following equations:

$$Zn + 2HCl \rightarrow H_2 + ZnCl_2$$
zinc   hydrochloric   hydrogen   zinc
          acid   chloride

$$Zn + H_2SO_4 \rightarrow H_2 + ZnSO_4$$
zinc   sulfuric   hydrogen   zinc
        acid   sulfate

$$Mg + 2HCl \rightarrow H_2 + MgCl_2$$
magnesium   hydrochloric   hydrogen   magnesium
              acid   chloride

From a study of many such reactions, chemists have concluded that hydrogen is an element common to all acids.

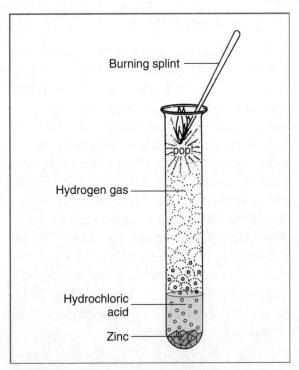

Figure 14-2. When zinc is mixed with hydrochloric or any other strong acid, a gas is given off. The gas "explodes" with an audible pop when exposed to a burning splint. This indicates the gas is hydrogen, a component of all acids.

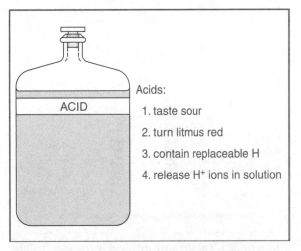

Figure 14-3. Like all substances, acids have various specific properties. The four properties listed above, however, are common to all acids.

Thus, acids are defined as substances that release hydrogen ions in solution. It is these H^+ ions that are responsible for the properties of acids. Because acids ionize, they are electrolytes. The properties of acids are summarized in Figure 14-3.

4. *Acids release hydrogen ions in water solutions.* When an acid is dissolved in water, the acid ionizes, releasing both hydrogen ions and ions of a nonmetal or nonmetallic polyatomic ion. Thus, when hydrochloric acid is dissolved in water, the acid ionizes, forming hydrogen ions and chloride ions, as shown in the following equation:

$$HCl \rightarrow H^+ + Cl^-$$

hydrochloric   hydrogen   chloride
acid   ion   ion

Other examples of the ionization of acids in water are:

$$H_2SO_4 \rightarrow 2H^+ + SO_4^{-2}$$

sulfuric   hydrogen   sulfate
acid   ion   ion

$$HNO_3 \rightarrow H^+ + NO_3^-$$

nitric   hydrogen   sulfate
acid   ion   ion

▶ What Are Some Uses of Acids?

Acids have a wide variety of uses in laboratories, at home, and in industry. Sulfuric acid, for example, is the chemical most widely used in industry. Sulfuric acid is used to make other acids, such as hydrochloric and nitric acids, because the boiling point of sulfuric acid is higher than that of other acids. This allows the acid being produced to be distilled and collected separately from the starting materials.

Sulfuric acid is also used to remove the surface oxide layers on metals (**pickling**) before the metals are coated with materials that prevent rusting. For example, before iron is coated with chromium (in chromium plating), the iron is dipped into dilute sulfuric acid to remove the iron oxide normally present on the surface of the iron. Another important use of sulfuric acid is in the storage cell that is part of a car battery. In a lead storage cell (see Figure 14-4 on page 208), dilute sulfuric acid serves as the electrolyte through which ions move be-

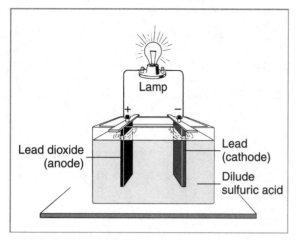

Figure 14-4. Dilute sulfuric acid is the electrolyte that makes the flow of current possible in a lead storage cell. The current flows from the cathode to the anode.

tween the lead plate, acting as the cathode, and the spongy lead dioxide, acting as the anode. When several such cells are connected together, they make up a storage battery.

Nitric acid, another important industrial acid, is used in the manufacture of fertilizers, plastics, photographic film, and dyes. Nitric acid is also used in the preparation of such explosives as dynamite and TNT and in the manufacture of rocket fuel.

Hydrochloric acid, like sulfuric acid, is used to clean metals. Hydrochloric acid is also used to clean brick and tile, and it is used in the manufacture of sugar and glue. The human body produces small quantities of hydrochloric acid in the stomach, where the acid aids digestion.

What Is Acid Rain?

Sulfur dioxide gas is one cause of **acid rain**, which is rain that is more acidic than normal. Acid rain pollutes lakes and streams, killing fish, and can destroy forests. Acid rain also can damage statues and may be a health hazard to human beings. It is largely a by-product of factories and power plants that burn coal for energy. If the coal contains sulfur, and almost all kinds of coal do to one extent or another, the sulfur forms sulfur dioxide when the coal is burned. The sulfur dioxide enters the atmosphere where it combines with oxygen and water to form sulfuric acid. This acid falls to Earth as rain or other forms of precipitation such as snow or sleet. The equation for this reaction is:

$$\underset{\substack{\text{sulfur}\\\text{dioxide}}}{2SO_2} + \underset{\text{oxygen}}{O_2} + \underset{\text{water}}{2H_2O} \rightarrow \underset{\substack{\text{sulfuric}\\\text{acid}}}{2H_2SO_4}$$

Various methods are used to "scrub" exhaust gases from such factories and power plants to reduce the amount of acid rain in the atmosphere. In addition, many companies have switched from high-sulfur coal to low-sulfur coal to produce energy. Unfortunately, low-sulfur coal is generally more expensive, which results in higher prices for products and electricity produced from this kind of coal.

What Is a Base?

Ammonium hydroxide, or ammonia water, is very irritating to the nose and to the eyes. This substance, called a **hydroxide**, or a **base**, is often used in the home for cleaning because bases generally dissolve grease. Milk of magnesia (magnesium hydroxide), which is used as an antacid, is a base; lye (sodium hydroxide), which is used in the manufacture of soap and in drain-clearing products, is another familiar example of a base.

How Are Bases Prepared?

Bases are ionic compounds containing metal ions and hydroxide ions. For example, sodium hydroxide contains sodium ions and hydroxide ions. In general, bases may be prepared by two methods: (1) by the reaction of water and very reactive metals, related to the bases; (2) by the reaction of water and certain oxides, related to the bases.

Preparing Bases From Water and Metals.
When sodium metal is placed in water, sodium hydroxide is formed, and hydrogen gas is released. Since the formula for water can be written as HOH instead of H_2O, you can see that the reaction involves single replacement and may be represented as follows:

$$2Na + 2HOH \rightarrow 2NaOH + H_2$$

sodium   water   sodium   hydrogen
hydroxide

Similar reactions occur with the metals potassium and calcium:

$$2K + 2HOH \rightarrow 2KOH + H_2$$

potassium   water   potassium   hydrogen
hydroxide

$$Ca + 2HOH \rightarrow Ca(OH)_2 + H_2$$

calcium   water   calcium   hydrogen
hydroxide

(In the preceding three equations, note that *sodium* forms *sodium* hydroxide; *potassium* forms *potassium* hydroxide; *calcium* forms *calcium* hydroxide.)

Care must be exercised in performing these reactions because the metals react strongly with water, which may produce splashing of strong hydroxides. Only very small quantities of metal should be used. Students must *not* handle these metals.

Preparing Bases From Water and Oxides.
When calcium oxide is mixed with water, calcium hydroxide is formed:

$$CaO + HOH \rightarrow Ca(OH)_2$$

calcium   water   calcium
oxide   hydroxide

(Note that *calcium* oxide forms *calcium* hydroxide.) Since considerable heat is released in this reaction, precautions must be taken.

What Are the Properties of Bases?

As you discovered with acids, bases can be described by specific properties. The water solutions of bases have the following properties:

1. *Bases taste bitter.* A bitter taste is characteristic of all bases. It is the presence of a base that gives unflavored milk of magnesia its bitter taste. Because of the risk involved, you should not taste any unknown substances.
2. *Bases feel slippery.* If you rub a drop or two of household ammonia between your fingers, you experience the slippery feeling of a base. Wet soap is also slippery because of the presence of a base.
3. *Bases turn litmus blue.* When you test bases with litmus paper, as you did in the inquiry investigation, you find that bases have no effect on *blue* litmus paper. However, bases cause *red* litmus paper to become blue. Thus, red litmus is often used to test for the presence of bases. Another common indicator, used to detect the presence of a base, is **phenolphthalein**, which, when mixed with a base, turns pink.
4. *Bases release hydroxide ions in water solution.* When dissolved in water, bases ionize, releasing metal ions (or metallic polyatomic ions) and hydroxide ions. For example, when sodium hydroxide is dissolved in water, the sodium hydroxide ionizes as follows:

$$NaOH \xrightarrow{H_2O} Na^+ \rightarrow OH^-$$

sodium   sodium   hydroxide
hydroxide   ion   ion

Other bases ionize as follows:

$$KOH \xrightarrow{H_2O} K^+ \rightarrow OH^-$$

potassium   potassium   hydroxide
hydroxide   ion   ion

$$NH_4OH \rightarrow NH_4^+ + OH^-$$

ammonium   ammonium   hydroxide
hydroxide   ion   ion

Thus, bases are defined as substances that release hydroxide ions in solution. It is these OH⁻ ions that are responsible for the properties of bases. Because bases ionize, they are electrolytes. The properties of bases are summarized in Figure 14-5.

What Are Some Uses of Bases?

Like acids, bases have many important uses. Ammonium hydroxide (NH_4OH), frequently called ammonia, is used in the preparation of important related compounds such as nitric acid and ammonium chloride. Ammonia is also used as a cleaning agent.

Sodium hydroxide is used in the manufacture of soap, rayon, and paper. Strong solutions of this base are very **caustic**; that is, they are extremely harmful to the skin.

Calcium hydroxide, commonly known as slaked lime, is used in the preparation of

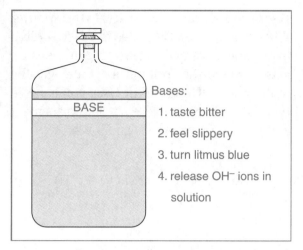

Figure 14-5. Bases may vary in composition, but they all possess the four properties listed.

plaster and mortar. Water solutions of calcium hydroxide, called **limewater**, can be used in the laboratory as a test for the presence of carbon dioxide.

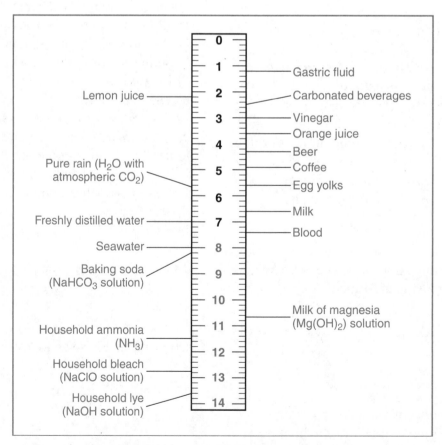

Figure 14-6. The pH scale can be used to identify substances as acidic, basic, or neutral.

How Are the Strengths of Acids and Bases Measured?

Throughout the chapter, you've learned that some acids and bases are stronger than others. How exactly are the strengths of acids and bases compared? The **pH scale** measures how acidic or basic a substance is. The measure of a substance on this scale is called its pH value. As you can see in Figure 14-6 on page 210, the scale ranges from 0 to 14. Substances with pH values lower than 7 are acids. Vinegar and lemon juice are acids. Substances with pH values above 7 are bases. Ammonia and lye are bases. Directly between acids and bases, a neutral substance has a pH value of exactly 7. Pure water is neutral.

What Is a Salt?

Some substances are neither acids nor bases, but instead may be classified as salts. The salt most familiar to you is probably table salt—sodium chloride. Baking soda is the salt sodium bicarbonate. Magnesium sulfate, also called Epsom salts, is a familiar salt used as a laxative.

How Are Salts Prepared?

In general, salts may be prepared by three methods: (1) the neutralization of acids and bases; (2) direct combination; (3) the reaction of a metal oxide with an acid.

Preparing Salts by Neutralization. When an acid and a base react, they counteract each other; that is, they neutralize each other. Such a reaction, known as a **neutralization reaction**, forms water and a salt. For example, when sodium hydroxide and hydrochloric acid react, water and the salt sodium chloride are formed. This occurs because the hydrochloric acid and the sodium hydroxide first ionize and then react:

1. The hydrochloric acid ionizes, releasing hydrogen ions and chloride ions. At the same time, the sodium hydroxide ionizes, releasing sodium ions and hydroxide ions.

$$HCl \rightarrow H^+ + Cl^-$$

$$NaOH \rightarrow Na^+ + OH^-$$

2. Since these four ions are mobile in the solution, hydrogen ions meet hydroxide ions and unite to form water. At the same time, sodium ions and chloride ions along with the water form a salt solution.

$$H^+ + Cl^- + Na^+ + OH^- \rightarrow HOH + NaCl$$

Other examples of neutralization reactions are:

$$\underset{\substack{\text{nitric} \\ \text{acid}}}{HNO_3} + \underset{\substack{\text{sodium} \\ \text{hydroxide}}}{NaOH} \rightarrow \underset{\text{water}}{HOH} \rightarrow \underset{\substack{\text{sodium} \\ \text{nitrate}}}{NaNO_3}$$

$$\underset{\substack{\text{hydrochloric} \\ \text{acid}}}{HCl} + \underset{\substack{\text{potassium} \\ \text{hydroxide}}}{KOH} \rightarrow \underset{\text{water}}{HOH} + \underset{\substack{\text{potassium} \\ \text{chloride}}}{KCl}$$

$$\underset{\substack{\text{sulfuric} \\ \text{acid}}}{H_2SO_4} + \underset{\substack{\text{ammonium} \\ \text{hydroxide}}}{2NH_4OH} \rightarrow \underset{\text{water}}{2HOH} + \underset{\substack{\text{ammonium} \\ \text{sulfate}}}{(NH_4)_2SO_4}$$

A study of many neutralization reactions reveals that neutralization reactions may be generalized as follows:

$$\text{an acid} + \text{a base} \rightarrow \text{water} + \text{a salt}$$

(Note that neutralization reactions are the reverse of hydrolysis reactions described on page 213.)

Table 14-1.
Percentage by Mass of Salts in Seawater

Salt	Formula	Percentage
Sodium chloride	$NaCl$	2.72
Magnesium chloride	$MgCl_2$	0.38
Magnesium sulfate	$MgSO_4$	0.17
Calcium sulfate	$CaSO_4$	0.13
Potassium chloride	KCl	0.09
Calcium carbonate	$CaCO_3$	0.01
Magnesium bromide	$MgBr_2$	0.01

Preparing Salts by Direct Combination.
When a metal reacts with a nonmetal, a salt is generally formed. For example, when the metal magnesium is burned in the nonmetal chlorine gas, the salt magnesium chloride is formed:

$$\underset{\text{metal}}{Mg} + \underset{\text{nonmetal}}{Cl_2} \rightarrow \underset{\text{salt}}{MgCl_2}$$

Preparing Salts From a Metal Oxide and an Acid. When a metal oxide reacts with an acid, a salt is formed. For example, when calcium oxide reacts with nitric acid, the salt calcium nitrate is formed:

$$\underset{\substack{\text{calcium} \\ \text{oxide}}}{\underset{\text{metal oxide}}{CaO}} + \underset{\text{nitric acid}}{\underset{\text{acid}}{2HNO_3}} \rightarrow \underset{\substack{\text{calcium} \\ \text{nitrate}}}{\underset{\text{salt}}{Ca(NO_3)_2}} + \underset{\text{water}}{HOH}$$

▶ What Are the Properties of Salts?

Salts are ionic compounds that have the following properties:

1. *Taste.* The salty taste of ocean water is due to the presence of such salts as sodium chloride and magnesium chloride. (Because of the risk involved, you should not taste any unknown substances.) Chemical analysis reveals that seawater contains many different kinds of salts. Table 14-1 lists these salts and their approximate percentages by mass in seawater.

2. *Salts dissociate in water.* You have already learned that salts consist of tightly bonded ions. In water, these bonds are weakened and the ions become mobile. This accounts for the fact that salt solutions are generally electrolytes. In water, for example, sodium chloride ionizes, or dissociates, according to the following equation:

$$\underset{\substack{\text{sodium} \\ \text{chloride}}}{NaCl} \rightarrow \underset{\substack{\text{sodium} \\ \text{ion}}}{Na^+} + \underset{\substack{\text{chloride} \\ \text{ion}}}{Cl^-}$$

Other examples of the ionization of salt solutions are as follows:

$$\underset{\substack{\text{potassium} \\ \text{sulfate}}}{K_2SO_4} \rightarrow \underset{\substack{\text{potassium} \\ \text{ion}}}{2\,K^+} + \underset{\substack{\text{sulfate} \\ \text{ion}}}{SO_4^{-2}}$$

$$\underset{\substack{\text{sodium} \\ \text{nitrate}}}{NaNO_3} \rightarrow \underset{\substack{\text{sodium} \\ \text{ion}}}{Na^+} + \underset{\substack{\text{nitrate} \\ \text{ion}}}{NO_3^-}$$

$$\underset{\substack{\text{calcium} \\ \text{sulfate}}}{CaSO_4} \rightarrow \underset{\substack{\text{calcium} \\ \text{ion}}}{Ca^{+2}} + \underset{\substack{\text{sulfate} \\ \text{ion}}}{SO_4^{-2}}$$

3. *Salts may react with water.* When solutions of salts are tested with litmus paper, some salts change blue litmus to red, indicating the presence of an acid. Other water solutions of salts cause red litmus to become blue, indicating the presence of a base. Still other salt solutions have no effect on litmus. To understand why this happens, examine what occurs when a salt such as sodium carbonate dissolves in water:

a. When sodium carbonate dissolves in water, the salt liberates sodium ions and carbonate ions. At the same time, the water itself ionizes slightly to form hydrogen and hydroxide ions (remember that water is a weak electrolyte):

$$Na_2CO_3 \rightarrow 2\,Na^+ + CO_3^{-2}$$

sodium   sodium   carbonate
carbonate   ion   ion

$$HOH \rightarrow H^+ + OH^-$$

b. Thus, the following particles may be present in a solution of sodium carbonate: water molecules, sodium ions, carbonate ions, hydrogen ions, and hydroxide ions. The ions of opposite charge attract one another and combine to form sodium hydroxide and carbonic acid:

$$2Na^+ + CO_3^{-2} + 2H^+ + 2OH^- \rightarrow 2NaOH + H_2CO_3$$

The reaction of a salt and water to form an acid and a base is called a **hydrolysis reaction**. The following general equation may be applied to all hydrolysis reactions:

$$salt + water \rightarrow acid + base$$

Because acids and bases react to form water and salt (you learned this in your study of neutralization reactions), hydrolysis reactions are the reverse of neutralization reactions. Thus, when sodium carbonate is dissolved in water, carbonic acid and sodium hydroxide are formed. Carbonic acid, H_2CO_3, is the acid present in soda water. Carbonic acid decomposes on standing to form CO_2 gas and H_2O. It is called a weak acid because it ionized only slightly in water. From conductivity experiments, we know that sodium hydroxide, NaOH, is a strong base; it ionizes almost completely in water.

When a solution of sodium carbonate is tested with blue litmus paper and red litmus paper, the red litmus becomes blue, indicating that the solution is basic. This is further proof that, in this case, the base formed during hydrolysis is stronger than the acid.

Thus, the equation in step 2 may be written as:

$$Na_2CO_3 + 2\,HOH \rightarrow H_2CO_3 + 2NaOH$$

weak   strong
acid   base

When the acid formed in a hydrolysis reaction is stronger than the base, the effect of such a solution on litmus is that of an acid. For example, a water solution of ammonium chloride results in the formation of the weak base, ammonium hydroxide, and the strong acid, hydrochloric acid:

$$NH_4Cl + HOH \rightarrow NH_4OH + HCl$$

weak   strong
base   acid

(Ammonium hydroxide ionizes only slightly, and on standing, decomposes to form gaseous ammonia, NH_3.)

Thus, when a solution of ammonium chloride is tested with blue litmus and red litmus, the blue litmus turns red, indicating that the solution is acidic.

Table 14-2. The Uses of Some Salts

Salt	Formula	Percentage
Ammonium chloride	NH_4Cl	In soldering; as electrolyte in dry cells
Sodium bicarbonate	$NaHCO_3$	In baking powder; in manufacture of glass
Sodium chloride	$NaCl$	For seasoning and preserving food; essential in life processes
Calcium chloride	$CaCl_2$	As a drying agent to absorb moisture; in freezing mixtures
Silver bromide	$AgBr$	In making photographic film
Potassium nitrate	KNO_3	In manufacture of explosives; fertilizer
Sodium nitrate	$NaNO_3$	Fertilizer; source of nitric acid

When both the acid and the base in a hydrolysis reaction are equally strong (or equally weak), the effect of such a solution on litmus paper is neither that of an acid nor of a base. For example, when sodium chloride is dissolved in water and the solution is tested with blue litmus and red litmus, neither color changes, indicating that the solution is neither acidic nor basic. Such a solution is said to be **neutral** and the sodium chloride has not undergone hydrolysis. The properties of salts are summarized in Figure 14-7. Table 14-2 lists the uses of some common salts.

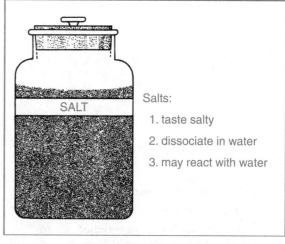

Figure 14-7. Although there are many different kinds of salts, all share the first two properties listed above, and some share the third.

Chapter Review

Science Terms

The following list contains all the boldfaced words found in this chapter and the page on which each appears.

acid (p. 205)
acid rain (p. 208)
base (p. 208)
caustic (p. 210)
hydrolysis reaction (p. 213)

hydroxide (p. 208)
indicator (p. 205)
limewater (p. 210)
mineral acid (p. 205)
neutral (p. 214)

neutralization reaction (p. 211)
pH scale (p. 211)
phenolphthalein (p. 209)
pickling (p. 207)

Matching Questions

*In your notebook, write the letter of the item in column B that is
most closely related to the item in column A.*

Column A

_____ 1. an example of a strong base

_____ 2. a substance that can be used to test
for carbon dioxide

_____ 3. a material that can be used to test
for acids

_____ 4. a material that can be used to test
for bases

_____ 5. a common acid produced in the
stomach

_____ 6. a property of bases

_____ 7. a property of acids

_____ 8. a measure of the strength of an acid
or base

_____ 9. an example of a weak acid

_____ 10. the opposite of hydrolysis

Column B

a. red litmus paper

b. milk

c. slippery to the touch

d. pH

e. lye

f. hydrochloric acid

g. limewater

h. blue litmus paper

i. neutralization

j. sour taste

k. ammonium hydroxide

Multiple-Choice Questions

*In your notebook, write the letter preceding the word or expression
that best completes the statement or answers the question.*

1. Acetic acid is commonly found in
a. vinegar   c. salad oil
b. ammonia water d. soap

2. Which of these properties most closely
relates to acids?
a. bitter taste   c. sour taste
b. sweet taste   d. salty taste

3. The sour taste of lemons and limes is due
to a substance called
a. acetic acid
b. citric acid
c. hydrochloric acid
d. carbonic acid

4. A dye used to test the acidity of a substance is
a. sodium chloride
b. litmus

c. sodium hydroxide
d. magnesium sulfate

5. Which of the following do all acids release
in solution?
a. nitrogen atoms
b. bubbles of oxygen
c. hydroxide ions
d. hydrogen ions

6. An acid used to prepare other acids
because of its higher boiling point is
a. HCl   c. HNO_3
b. H_2SO_4 d. H_2CO_3

7. The acid used in the storage battery is
a. nitric acid
b. hydrochloric acid
c. acetic acid
d. sulfuric acid

8. Milk of magnesia is an example of a base. What must be true about its pH?
   a. It is equal to 0.
   b. It is less than 7.
   c. It is equal to 7.
   d. It is greater than 7.

9. What happens to red and blue litmus paper when a water solution of a base is placed on it?
   a. No change is observed in either paper.
   b. The red litmus becomes blue and the blue is unchanged.
   c. The blue litmus becomes red and the red is unchanged.
   d. The red litmus becomes blue and the blue litmus becomes red.

10. When bases ionize, they release
    a. hydrogen ions   c. chloride ions
    b. sodium ions   d. hydroxide ions

11. A base used in the manufacture of soap is
    a. $Ca(OH)_2$ c. NH_4OH
    b. NaOH   d. $Zn(OH)_2$

12. A base can be prepared by the reaction between
    a. an active nonmetal with water
    b. a gas with water
    c. a sulfide with water
    d. an active metal with water

13. In general, salts
    a. are ionic compounds
    b. contain hydrogen ions
    c. contain hydroxide ions
    d. turn blue litmus red

14. When dissolved in water, salts
    a. are nonelectrolytes
    b. have a bitter taste
    c. are electrolytes
    d. release hydrogen ions

15. Testing salt solutions with litmus paper indicates that salt solutions
    a. are basic
    b. are acidic
    c. are sometimes basic and sometimes acidic
    d. can be basic, acidic, or neutral

16. In water solution, ammonium chloride produces
    a. a strong base
    b. a strong acid
    c. a weak acid
    d. a neutral solution

17. When a strong acid and a strong base are mixed together in equal amounts and tested with litmus paper,
    a. no change occurs in either litmus
    b. the red litmus becomes blue
    c. the blue litmus becomes red

18. Of the following, the salt that is used to make photographic film is
    a. NaCl   c. K_2SO_4
    b. $Ca(NO_3)_2$ d. AgBr

19. A salt used as the electrolyte in dry cells is
    a. ammonium carbonate
    b. ammonium chloride
    c. silver nitrate
    d. sodium sulfate

20. When water solutions of an acid and a base are mixed, a salt is formed. What other product is formed?
    a. hydrogen   c. water
    b. oxygen   d. carbon dioxide

Modified True-False Questions

In some of the following statements, the italicized term makes the statement incorrect. For each incorrect statement, in your notebook, write the term that must be substituted for the italicized term to make the statement correct. For each correct statement, write the word "true."

1. Oranges, grapefruits, lemons, and limes all contain *boric acid*. _____

2. Dyes used to determine whether a substance is an acid or a base are called *detectors*. _____

3. Substances that release hydrogen ions in solution are known as *acids*. _____

4. The pH value of a base is *less than* 7. _____

5. A water solution of calcium hydroxide is commonly called *litmus*. _____

6. Sodium bicarbonate is commonly used in *soldering*. _____

7. Chemical analysis of seawater reveals it contains many *salts*. _____

8. When salts are added to water, they *dissociate*. _____

9. The reaction between a salt and water to form an acid and a base is called a *neutralization* reaction. _____

10. A salt can be prepared by reacting a metal oxide with *an acid*. _____

TEST-TAKING TIP Look for clues in questions that tell you how to answer. For example, when you *compare and contrast* you must identify how two things are alike and how they are different. When you *explain,* you tell why something is true and provide evidence to support your answer.

Check Your Knowledge

Write the answer to each question in your notebook.

1. Compare each of the following sets of terms:
   a. acid and base
   b. hydrolysis and neutralization

2. a. Describe two methods of preparing an acid.
   b. Describe two methods of preparing a base.
   c. Describe three methods of preparing a salt.

3. Write an equation to show how each of the following ionizes in water:
   a. HNO_3 _____
   b. $Ca(OH)_2$ _____
   c. $MgCl_2$ _____
   d. H_3PO_4 _____
   e. KNO_3 _____

4. Complete and balance each of the following neutralization reactions:
   a. $KOH + H_2SO_4 \rightarrow$ _____
   b. $HCl + Ba(OH)_2 \rightarrow$ _____
   c. $NH_4OH + HCl \rightarrow$ _____

5. Complete and balance each of the following hydrolysis reactions:
   a. $Na_2SO_4 + HOH \rightarrow$ _____
   b. $NaHCO_3 + HOH \rightarrow$ _____
   c. $Zn(NO_3)_2 + HOH \rightarrow$ _____

Think Critically

Write the answer to each of the following questions in your notebook.

1. Complete the table.

Substance	Formula	Use
Sodium bicarbonate		
	H_2SO_4	
		Preparation of soap
Sodium nitrate		
		Manufacture of rocket fuel
Silver bromide		
	NH_4OH	
Calcium hydroxide		

2. Assume that you are given three solutions: an acid, a base, and distilled water. Explain what steps you would take to determine which is the acid, which is the base, and which is the distilled water.

Take It Further

1. Red cabbage is often used as an indicator of acidity. Find out how it can be used and then demonstrate an example for the class.

2. Understanding acids and bases can have an impact on your health. Research how acidity levels in the body affect processes for maintaining good health. Some treatments involve neutralizing the body or even making it acidic. Find out why. Choose an example to present to the class.

3. There are complex theories to differentiate between acids and bases. These include the Arrhenius theory, the Brönsted-Lowry theory, and the Lewis theory. Work with a group to research each theory. Have one student or a pair of students present each theory, and then compare them as a group.

CAREER

4. You may think that a chef does not need a knowledge of science, but that could not be further from the truth. For one thing, chefs need to know the properties of acids, bases, and salts to understand how they combine and how they affect the taste and texture of foods. Find out about careers as a chef along with the training required. Present your findings.

Acid Rain: Should People Be Paying More Attention?

In many parts of the world, acid rain is damaging buildings, statues, and even the glossy paint of cars. Those results are obvious. What may be more worrisome, however, is the damage you can't easily see. All rain contains some level of acidity. Normal rainwater, for example, has a pH of about 5.6. Any rain with a pH that is lower than 5.6 is considered acid rain.

Over time, acid rain can change the pH of surface water, such as lakes and ponds. If the pH drops too low, fish, plants, and other living things can die.

Pollutants released by factories can lead to acid rain affecting regions thousands of kilometers away.

Bacteria and other microorganisms that act as decomposers in ecosystems can also die. Entire forests can die as the acid rain destroys the waxy coating protecting their leaves. It's not just animals and plants that are in danger. Breathing problems have been linked to acid rain in the air. In addition, people may become sick as food crops are exposed to acid rain or they eat animals that have taken in acidic water.

Acid rain is a product of modern technology—the result of the desire for electricity, factory-made goods, and vehicles such as cars, buses, and trucks. To meet all of these desires, people use great amounts of energy. And most of this energy comes from the burning of fossil fuels, such as coal and oil products (mainly gasoline).

As you may know, coal and oil are not pure chemical compounds. Although they consist mostly of carbon and hydrogen, they do contain other elements such as sulfur and nitrogen. Since the process of burning involves oxidation, the burning of fossil fuels churns out oxides of sulfur and nitrogen. In fact, power plants that burn coal account for 70% of the sulfur oxides spewed into the air and 30% of the nitrogen oxides.

These oxides are gases, so, naturally enough, they float high up into the atmosphere. They get into clouds, fogs, snow, and any other kind of water in the air. Result? The water in the air becomes a dilute solution of sulfuric and nitric acids. So the next time raindrops start falling on your head, your family car, trees, buildings, statues, and lakes teeming with fish, so do these corrosive acids. Everything and everybody is the worse for the experience.

You might think that you don't need to worry about acid rain if you don't live near a factory. Think again. Emissions from smokestacks can be carried great distances by air currents. For example, pollutants released into the air in the Midwest are the main contributors to acid rain problems in the Adirondack Mountains of New York.

What's to be done?

First, not all forms of coal contain the same concentrations of sulfur. So people can use low-sulfur coal rather than high-sulfur coal. Unfortunately, low-sulfur coal is more expensive than high-sulfur coal. A switch to the low-sulfur variety, then, would mean higher prices of electricity and other products that use coal for energy. What's more, workers who mine high-sulfur coal might lose their jobs if the demand for this fossil fuel decreases.

There is another possible solution. The high-sulfur coal can be burned in much the same way, but the sulfur oxides can be removed from the smoke before they get loose in the atmosphere. This solution is known as *scrubbing* and employs combinations of chemical and physical techniques, all of which are expensive. So, once again, electricity rates would go up.

There is, of course, another partial solution, and it is one to which you can contribute—conserve electricity and fuels. You can help do this if you use more energy-efficient electrical appliances and avoid buying gas-guzzling cars no matter how attractive they appear. Are there other ways of reducing acid rain? Who should be concerned about acid rain? What do you think?

Organize It!

Use a method that your instructor describes to organize the information in this article.

Explain It!

1. The major source of acid rain is the burning of
   a. fossil fuels
   b. trees
   c. glossy paint
   d. air

2. The elements in coal and oil that produce acid rain are
   a. carbon and hydrogen
   b. carbon and sulfur
   c. sulfur and nitrogen
   d. carbon and nitrogen

3. An increase in the acidity of rain indicates
   a. a decrease in sulfur and nitrogen oxides in air
   b. an increase in sulfur and nitrogen oxides in air
   c. no change in sulfur and nitrogen oxides in air
   d. an increase of water vapor in air

Extend It!

4. Make a poster that identifies two problems associated with switching from high-sulfur coal to low-sulfur coal. Perform additional research to find details associated with the issue.

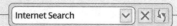

5. Propose and discuss other ways of reducing acid rain. Back up your proposals and discussion with data gathered from library or Internet research.

CAREER

6. To find out how plants in an ecosystem are being affected by acid rain, you would need to consult a botanist. Find out what a botanist does, what opportunities are open to botanists, and what kind of training might be required. Share your findings with the class.

CHAPTER

15

What Is Energy?

The passengers probably do not give it a thought as they speed through the loops of this thrilling ride, but their motion is all thanks to changes in energy. Designing a rollercoaster requires a thorough understanding of how an object's energy changes as it moves.

After reading this chapter, you should be able to answer the following questions:

What is the nature of energy?

How is energy related to work?

What are two general kinds of energy?

What are the different forms of energy?

Can energy be transformed?

What does the conservation of energy mean?

Sometimes you may feel that you can conquer the world, and at others you might just want to sit around and relax. No matter what you do, you have energy—even if you don't feel like it. In this inquiry investigation, you will explore the energy of matter at rest and in motion.

Materials:

✔ safety goggles
✔ string
✔ 2 steel spheres (equal mass)
✔ tape
✔ meterstick
✔ 100-cm dowel
✔ 2 ring stands and clamps
✔ crossbar

Part A Tape two strings 40 centimeters long to two steel spheres of the same size and suspend them as shown in Figure 15-1. Adjust the lengths and positions of the strings so that the spheres are at exactly the same height.

   Mount a meterstick about 10 centimeters above the spheres. Position the meterstick so that the 50-centimeter mark is centered between the two spheres.

Part B Raise the right sphere in an arc to the level of the meterstick, holding the string taut (See Figure 15-2). Release the sphere, allowing it to strike the left sphere.

1. **What happens to the left sphere?**

2. **At what point in the swing of the right sphere does it seem to be moving the fastest?**

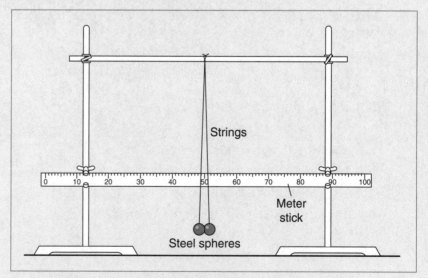

Figure 15-1.

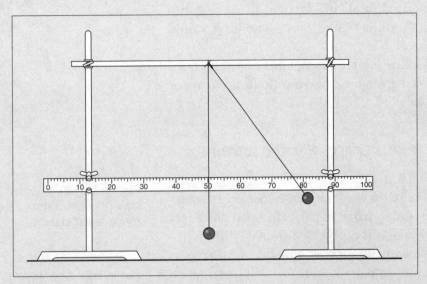

Figure 15-2.

3. *Upon being struck by the right sphere, what mark on the meterstick does the left sphere reach?*

Part C Raise the right sphere until the string is against the 60-centimeter mark on the meterstick. Make sure the string is taut. As in Part B, release the right sphere and allow it to strike the left sphere. Note the farthest mark reached by the string of the left sphere, measured against the meterstick.

In separate trials, repeat this procedure, raising the right sphere higher and higher so that the string is against the 70-centimeter mark, 80-centimeter mark, and so on. Measure the farthest mark reached by the string on the left sphere, measured against the meterstick. Record your results.

4. *How do the distances reached by the left sphere after being struck compare to the starting distances of the right sphere?*

What Is the Nature of Energy?

In the preceding chapters in this book, you learned about the properties of matter. Observations about matter are fairly easy to make because matter in any of its forms or states has substance. All liquids, solids, and gases occupy space and have mass. These substances are handled easily because you can see them, touch them, and, perhaps, taste and smell them.

In your study of chemical reactions, you learned that every chemical change is accompanied by a change in *energy*. In endothermic changes, energy is absorbed. In exothermic changes, energy is released.

Energy, like matter, is an important factor in the universe. Without energy, all matter—living and nonliving—would be at a standstill. Nothing would move—nothing would change.

Unlike matter, energy has no mass, does not occupy space, and has no form, taste, or odor.

How Is Energy Related to Work?

Scientists generally define **energy** as the ability to do work or cause change. In scientific terms, **work** is performed on an object only when the object is moved through a particular distance as a result of a **force**. A force is a push or pull. You will learn much more about work and forces in Part 5 of this book.

$$\text{Work} = \text{force} \times \text{distance}$$

$$W = Fd$$

When you lift books from your desk, you do work because you exert a force on the books that causes them to move some distance (see Figure 15-3). If, instead, you exert a force on a wall with all your might, you perform no work because the wall does not move (see Figure 15-4).

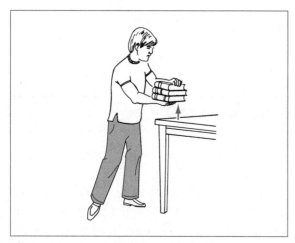

Figure 15-3. When you lift books some distance, you do work on them.

Figure 15-4. Although a force is exerted on the wall, no work is done because the wall does not move any distance.

What Are Two General Kinds of Energy?

Energy can be classified into two general kinds: *potential energy* and *kinetic energy*.

Potential energy. The energy stored in an object is called **potential energy**. In the inquiry investigation at the beginning of the chapter, you gave the steel sphere potential energy when you raised it to some height above the table. As you raised the sphere to higher positions, the amount of potential energy acquired by the sphere increased. You observed this increase when the left sphere moved as a result of collisions with the right sphere. The higher the right sphere was raised, the further the left sphere moved. Thus, the height to which an object is raised is one of the factors used in determining the amount of potential energy stored in the object.

A second factor used in determining potential energy is the weight of the object. When a heavier object is raised to the same height above the ground as a lighter object, the heavier object has more potential energy because the pull of gravity on the heavier object is greater. To determine the amount of potential energy in an object, you multiply the weight of the object by its height above the ground. The product of these factors is equal to the potential energy:

potential energy = weight of object × height

$$P.E. = wh$$

The equation reveals that either increasing the weight or increasing the height of an object increases the potential energy of the object.

Consider the situation shown in Figure 15-5. Fig. 15-5a shows two steel spheres of equal weight. Sphere A is raised to a height

of 5 meters, while sphere B is raised to a height of 10 meters. Sphere B is twice as high as A and therefore has twice the potential energy because the weight of the two spheres is the same. In the second case (Figure 15-5b), sphere A weighs 100 kilograms and sphere B weighs only 50 kilograms. The two spheres are raised to the same height, 10 meters from the ground. Since the height is the same, sphere A has twice as much potential energy as B because it is twice as heavy as sphere B.

It may help you to understand potential energy by recognizing that an object that has potential energy has the *potential* to do work. Consider a pile driver, in which a heavy weight is lifted high into the air and then dropped onto a pile or girder that is being sunk into the ground (see Figure 15-6). When the weight is dropped on the object, it exerts a force on the object that moves it some distance. In other words, the weight does work on an object. In order to do work, the weight must have energy. The higher the

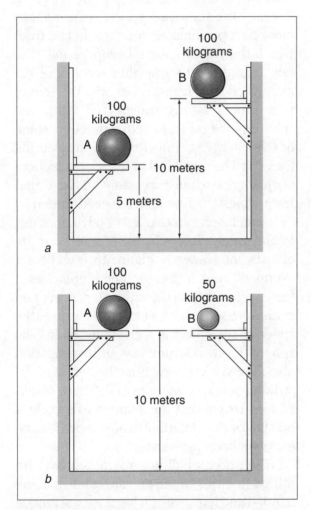

Figure 15-5. Potential energy is directly proportional to weight and height. In the top drawing, sphere B has twice the potential energy of sphere A because of B's greater height. In the bottom drawing, sphere A has twice the potential energy of sphere B because of A's greater weight.

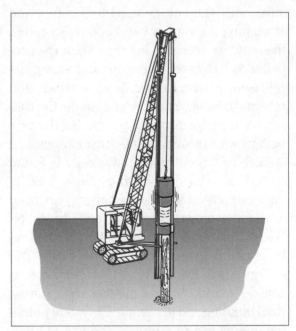

Figure 15-6. Various devices use the concept of potential energy to do work. For example, a pile driver raises a heavy weight to a height. When released, the weight falls and strikes a pile (log) that is driven into the ground.

weight is lifted and the heavier the weight is, the greater is the potential energy available for performing the work of sinking the pile.

In most roller coasters at amusement parks, a train of cars is pulled to the top of a tall hill by a machine-driven chain mechanism. At the top of the hill, the cars have potential energy. The cars are then released and "coast" down the track through a series of turns and dips. Whenever the cars reach the bottom of a dip, there is enough energy available to carry them up the next rise.

The type of potential energy that an object has as a result of its height is called *gravitational potential energy*. The object was given this energy because work was done on the object to lift it against the downward pull of gravity. Another type of potential energy results from stretching or squeezing an elastic object, such as a rubber band or a spring. This type of potential energy is called *elastic potential energy*. For example, a model airplane may be equipped with a rubber-band motor. When the rubber band is wound by turning the propeller, the rubber band is stretched. The energy used in twisting and stretching the rubber band is now stored in the band as potential energy. When the propeller is released, the potential energy is released. As the rubber band unwinds and returns to its original size and shape, the rubber band performs work by making the propeller move through a specific distance.

A third type of potential energy is found stored as *chemical potential energy*. Striking examples of such stored energy are seen in explosives, such as TNT and dynamite. When these explosives are set off, a rapid release of energy—an explosion—occurs. The energy made available by these explosions can do work, such as moving rock during road building and in mining. Chemical potential energy is also stored in foods and fuels, such as gasoline.

Kinetic Energy. You now know from the inquiry investigation that when a suspended sphere is raised, it acquires potential energy. When this sphere is released, its potential energy is changed into another kind of energy as the sphere is set into motion. The energy of an object in motion is called **kinetic energy**.

In the inquiry investigation, when the raised sphere was released, its potential energy decreased and its kinetic energy increased. When aimed properly, the raised sphere struck the sphere that was at rest, causing it to move. Thus, the kinetic energy of the moving sphere was transferred to the stationary sphere. When the sphere was raised to even greater heights and released, it struck the stationary sphere, causing it to move to approximately the same height from which the raised sphere began its fall. The fact that these two heights were approximately equal suggests that kinetic energy was almost totally transferred from one sphere to the other. In actual practice, some of this energy is converted into heat during transfer. The result is that the second sphere does not rise to quite the same height as that from which the first sphere was dropped.

It can be shown that as a body continues to fall freely, the velocity of the body increases. As shown in Figure 15-7, an object dropped from a greater height reaches a faster velocity than the same object dropped from a lesser height. Velocity describes the speed of the object in a given direction. The sphere that was struck in your investigation also moved more rapidly as the height of the striking sphere was increased. These observations reveal that the velocity of a body is one factor that determines how much kinetic energy a body possesses.

When a baseball is thrown gently (with little velocity), a player can catch it barehanded and hardly feel it because the kinetic energy of the ball is small. On the other hand, when a pitcher throws the same baseball with great velocity, the ball has much more kinetic energy and the catcher must wear a thick glove to protect his or her hand.

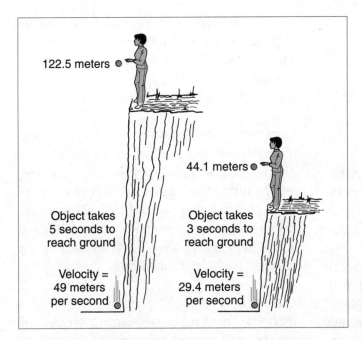

122.5 meters

44.1 meters

Object takes
5 seconds to
reach ground

Object takes
3 seconds to
reach ground

Velocity =
49 meters
per second

Velocity =
29.4 meters
per second

Figure 15-7. A number of factors, including velocity, determine the amount of kinetic energy generated by a moving object. Because it possesses greater velocity, the rock on the left has more kinetic energy than the rock on the right. Up to a point, the greater the distance an object falls, the greater its final velocity.

Suppose a baseball thrown with a velocity of 20 meters/second hits a wall. The ball will bounce away, doing little damage to the wall. However, should an automobile traveling at the same velocity strike the wall, the wall—and the car—probably will be destroyed (see Figure 15-8). In this case, the destruction is due to the large kinetic energy resulting from the greater mass of the car. Thus, the mass of an object is a second factor in determining how much kinetic energy a body possesses.

The kinetic energy possessed by an object in motion is determined by its mass and velocity. These two factors are related as follows:

$$\text{kinetic energy} = \frac{1}{2} \times \text{mass} \times \text{velocity} \times \text{velocity}$$

$$K.E. = \frac{1}{2}mv^2$$

Any moving object, regardless of size, possesses kinetic energy. This holds true for large objects, such as rockets propelled into space, as well as small objects, such as molecules in a sample of matter.

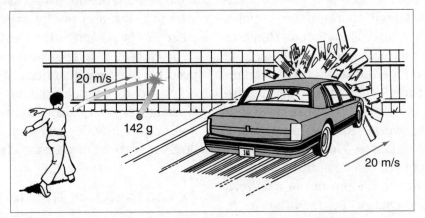

20 m/s

142 g

20 m/s

Figure 15-8. If two objects have the same velocity but different masses, the object with the greater mass has the greater kinetic energy.

What Are the Different Forms of Energy?

Energy may be further classified into six forms: chemical, mechanical, thermal, electromagnetic, electrical, and nuclear. See Table 15-1.

Chemical Energy. Potential energy stored in the bonds that hold matter together is **chemical energy**. Generally, chemical energy is the energy resulting from the attractive forces that bind atoms or molecules. When released, this type of energy can do work such as running a gasoline engine or propelling a rocket into space. When released suddenly (as in the explosion of dynamite), chemical energy can move a mountain. When released gradually, chemical energy is the energy that living things depend on for all of their life activities.

Mechanical Energy. The sum of an object's kinetic and potential energy is known as **mechanical energy**. It is the energy with which a hammer striking a nail does the work of driving the nail into a piece of wood. It is the energy that powers a baseball hit by a bat. It is the energy that moves a bicycle and powers a pile driver.

Thermal Energy. The particles that make up matter have both kinetic and potential energy. The total kinetic energy of the particles in a sample of matter is known as **thermal energy**. The thermal energy of a sample is related to its temperature, but the two quantities are not identical. Unlike thermal energy, which is a total, **temperature** is a measure of the average kinetic energy of the particles in the sample. Therefore, a cup of tea and a pot of tea can be at the same temperature. However, the pot of tea will have greater thermal energy because it has more particles of matter and therefore a greater total amount of energy.

Heat is another term related to thermal energy. Again, the two terms are not the same. The transfer of thermal energy from an object at a higher temperature to an object at a lower temperature is known as **heat energy**.

Electromagnetic Energy. Energy that is transferred by electromagnetic waves is known as **electromagnetic energy**. The light you see, x-rays, ultraviolet light, and microwaves are examples of this type of energy. Electromagnetic energy has an electrical component and a magnetic component, and is created by charged particles that vibrate.

Electrical Energy. The energy associated with the movement of electric charges is **electrical energy**. This type of energy can be carried through certain materials, such as wires, and used to do work. Electrical energy powers computers, televisions, and commuter trains. This form of energy will be studied in greater detail in Chapter 16.

Nuclear Energy. Energy is stored in the centers, or nuclei, of atoms. This energy, known as **nuclear energy**, can be released when atomic nuclei are broken apart through nuclear fission or joined together through nuclear fusion. During these processes, some of the mass of the nucleus is transformed into energy.

The discovery of this form of energy led to the invention of such weapons of war as the atomic bomb and the hydrogen bomb. Nuclear energy is used by the electrical industry to produce heat to spin large generators that produce the great quantities of electrical energy needed by people for modern daily living. Nuclear energy is also used to power submarines, to provide power for artificial satellites, and to treat diseases, such as cancer.

Can Energy Be Transformed?

Any form of energy can be changed, or transformed, into another form. Such changes in

Table 15-1.
What Are the Forms of Energy?

Energy	Where found	Examples
Chemical	Bonds between atoms	Energy to run a gasoline engine
Mechanical	Moving objects	Energy of a hammer driving a nail
Thermal	Motion of molecules	Energy in a hot liquid
Electromagnetic	Charged particles vibrating in a magnetic field	Energy carried by light or x-rays
Electrical	Movement of electric charges	Energy that powers computers
Nuclear	Atomic nuclei	Energy released through fusion and fission

the forms of energy are known as **energy transformations**. Consider these examples of energy transformations:

Mechanical Energy to Thermal Energy. Have you ever rubbed a block of wood with sandpaper? If so, you know that both the sandpaper and the wood gradually become warmer. The reason is that as the sandpaper rubs against the wood, it encounters friction. Friction is a force that opposes motion. It causes an increase in the motions of the particles of matter, which raises their thermal energy. Some of that thermal energy is released as heat energy you can feel. This same transformation can be observed when sawing wood, as shown in Figure 15-9.

Chemical Energy to Thermal Energy. When fuels such as coal or oil are burned, stored chemical energy is transformed into thermal energy that is released as heat. Similarly, when foods are digested in the body, some chemical energy is transformed into thermal energy that helps maintain proper body temperature.

Thermal Energy to Mechanical Energy. When water is heated, by burning a fuel for example, the water can turn to steam. That steam can be forced into a narrow tube and

Figure 15-9. The mechanical energy of the moving saw leads to the release of heat. Thus, mechanical energy has been transformed into thermal energy.

released onto the blade of turbine. The pressure exerted by the steam can spin the blades of a turbine. In this way, thermal energy is converted into mechanical energy.

Nuclear Energy to Thermal Energy. One way to heat water is to place it over burning coal or wood. Another way is through the release of nuclear energy from the fission or fusion of atoms. In some power plants, electric companies use nuclear reactions to release thermal energy that heats water until it becomes steam. Thus, they transform nuclear energy into thermal energy.

Mechanical Energy to Electrical Energy. Just as steam can be used to turn a turbine, so can the moving water in a stream or a waterfall. The spinning turbine can activate a device known as a generator, which produces electricity. In this way, mechanical energy is transformed into electrical energy.

Thermal Energy to Electromagnetic Energy. This energy transformation can be observed when a wire is placed in the flame of a Bunsen burner. As the wire becomes hot, it begins to glow, first with a dull red light and later with a white light. In this case, the thermal energy of the wire is transformed into electromagnetic energy that is visible as light.

Chemical Energy to Mechanical Energy. Not all of the chemical energy stored in the foods you eat is transformed into thermal energy. Some of that energy is transformed to the mechanical energy of moving muscles, which enable you to move.

Rarely will you encounter a single energy transformation in a natural process. Instead, energy is transformed into different forms through a series of changes. For example, consider the energy transformations that occur when turning a simple hand generator used to light a bulb (see Figure 15-10). The *chemical energy* released in your body is changed to *mechanical energy* as your mus-

cles move. This movement is used to turn the crank of the generator. The crank turns a coil of wire within the set of horseshoe magnets. This action produces *electrical energy*, which flows through other wires to the bulb. In the bulb, the electrical energy causes the filament wire to become hot, thus converting electrical energy to *thermal energy*, some of which is released as heat. When the generator is cranked fast enough, the heated wire begins to glow, giving off *electromagnetic energy* that you can see as light. Thus, even in this simple activity, you observe several transformations of one form of energy to another.

What Does the Conservation of Energy Mean?

In your earlier study of matter, you learned that matter can neither be created nor destroyed. This is the *law of conservation of mass.*

You have seen that energy transformations are common in daily life. There is neither a loss nor a gain of energy in these transformations. This is expressed in the **law of conservation of energy**, which states that energy can neither be created nor destroyed but can be changed from one form to another. Note the similarity between the laws concerning the conservation of matter and of energy. Add to this the knowledge that matter and energy are interchangeable and you can see why the two laws have been combined into one called the **law of conser-**

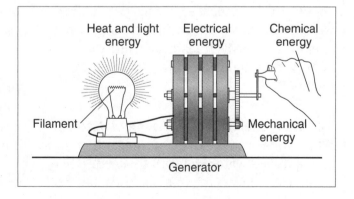

Figure 15-10. Often a number of energy transformations take place to produce a desired effect. Here, chemical energy in the body is used to contract muscles that produce mechanical energy by turning a wheel. The generator converts this energy to electrical energy, which passes through a filament producing thermal and electromagnetic energy.

vation of matter and energy. Accordingly, scientists now understand that the universe consists of matter and energy, which are both different forms of the same thing. Furthermore, since matter and energy may neither be created nor destroyed, the total amount of matter and energy in the universe is constant (remains the same).

Keep in mind that when measured carefully, there may appear to be a loss of energy during a transformation. However, in every transformation some energy is converted to thermal energy that is released into the environment as heat. Because the heat is not available to do useful work, it is sometimes called *waste heat* or said to be *lost as heat*. Despite the name, no energy is actually lost. It is simply converted to other forms.

Chapter Review

Science Terms

The following list contains all the boldfaced words found in this chapter and the page on which each appears.

chemical energy (p. 228)

electrical energy (p. 228)

electromagnetic energy (p. 228)

energy (p. 224)

energy transformation (p. 229)

force (p. 224)

heat energy (p. 228)

kinetic energy (p. 226)

law of conservation of energy (p. 230)

law of conservation of matter and energy (p. 230–231)

mechanical energy (p. 228)

nuclear energy (p. 228)

potential energy (p. 224)

temperature (p. 228)

thermal energy (p. 228)

work (p. 224)

Matching Questions

In your notebook, write the letter of the item in column B that is most closely related to the item in column A.

Column A

_____ 1. potential energy

_____ 2. nuclear energy

_____ 3. thermal energy

_____ 4. kinetic energy

_____ 5. electromagnetic energy

_____ 6. mechanical energy

_____ 7. electrical energy

_____ 8. chemical energy

_____ 9. work

_____ 10. change from one form of energy to another

Column B

a. movement of an object through a distance by a force

b. energy that is stored as a result of condition or position

c. energy of an object in motion

d. energy stored in the bonds that hold matter together

e. total kinetic and potential energy of an object

f. total kinetic energy of particles of matter

g. energy carried as waves, such as microwaves

h. energy associated with a flow of charge

i. transformation

j. produced by fission or fusion

Multiple-Choice Questions

In your notebook, write the letter preceding the word or expression
that best completes the statement or answers the question.

1. Energy is *best* defined as the ability to
   a. create matter
   b. fill some volume
   c. do work
   d. pull objects together

2. Which of these *best* constitutes a force?
   a. A student pulls open a door.
   b. A teacher reads a sentence.
   c. A child thinks about an idea.
   d. A dog sleeps in a bed.

3. Work is performed on an object when
   a. a force is exerted on the object
   b. energy is exerted on the object
   c. a force causes the object to move over a distance
   d. the object is at rest

4. Energy that is stored is called
   a. mechanical energy
   b. kinetic energy
   c. electromagnetic energy
   d. potential energy

5. The energy contained in a rock perched on a cliff is known as
   a. chemical energy
   b. potential energy
   c. kinetic energy
   d. electromagnetic energy

6. How can the gravitational potential energy of an object be increased?
   a. by lifting the object to a greater height
   b. by causing the object to move faster
   c. by squeezing the object into a smaller volume
   d. by transferring heat to the object

7. Two objects, A and B, are raised to the same height. A is twice as heavy as B. Therefore,
   a. A and B have the same potential energy
   b. B has more potential energy than A
   c. A has more potential energy than B
   d. A and B have no potential energy

8. In explosives, potential energy is generally stored in the form of
   a. thermal energy
   b. electromagnetic energy
   c. nuclear energy
   d. chemical energy

9. Which type of energy does a falling raindrop have because of its motion?
   a. potential energy
   b. kinetic energy
   c. chemical energy
   d. thermal energy

10. A moving object strikes an object at rest and causes it to move. This situation shows that
    a. potential energy is destroyed
    b. kinetic energy is destroyed
    c. kinetic energy can be transferred
    d. kinetic energy can be created

11. In general, the faster an object moves
    a. the more potential energy it has
    b. the less potential energy it has
    c. the more kinetic energy it has
    d. the less kinetic energy it has

12. A factor that determines the quantity of kinetic energy contained by a body is its
    a. mass
    b. volume
    c. direction of motion
    d. composition

13. As mechanical energy is transformed to thermal energy, the temperature of the object
    a. increases, then decreases
    b. decreases
    c. remains the same
    d. increases

14. The form of energy that is produced during every energy transformation is
    a. mechanical energy
    b. chemical energy
    c. heat energy
    d. electromagnetic energy

15. The form of energy produced by friction is
    a. chemical
    b. thermal
    c. electromagnetic
    d. mechanical

Modified True-False Questions

In some of the following statements, the italicized term makes the statement incorrect. For each incorrect statement, in your notebook, write the term that must be substituted for the italicized term to make the statement correct. For each correct statement, write the word "true."

1. The burning of fuels, such as wood, releases *electrical* energy. _____

2. *Nuclear* energy is stored in the centers of atoms. _____

3. The ability to do work is a description of *force*. _____

4. Living things obtain *electrical* energy that is stored in the foods they eat. _____

5. An x-ray that a doctor might use to see a broken bone is a form of *nuclear* energy. _____

6. *Work* is done when an object moves some distance as a result of a force. _____

7. The energy released by the fission of atoms is called *nuclear* energy. _____

8. A change from one form of energy to another is called an energy *formation*. _____

9. *Thermal* energy is transferred from warm objects to cooler objects as heat. _____

10. Your muscles do work by using *thermal* energy. _____

TEST-TAKING TIP As you study different kinds of energy, it may help to make a chart summarizing the different forms and giving examples of each. This will help you to avoid confusing them on a test.

Check Your Knowledge

Write the answer to each question in your notebook.

1. Define each of the following terms:
   a. energy
   b. work
   c. potential energy
   d. kinetic energy
   e. energy transformation

2. List and describe six forms of energy.

3. What is the law of conservation of energy? How is this law related to the law of conservation of matter?

Think Critically

Write the answer to each of the following questions in your notebook.

1. Complete the following table, indicating the energy transformation involved in each action described.

Action	Starting Form of Energy	Final Form of Energy
Sawing metal		
Heating a wire		
Walking		
Spinning of a wind turbine		
Movement of a car		

2. Describe the energy transformations that take place when coal burns to power a generator that produces electricity to light and heat homes.

3. Give a scientific explanation for each of the following:
    a. Object *A* is lifted to a height of 10 meters. Object *B*, which is the same weight as *A*, is lifted to a height of 20 meters. *B* has twice the potential energy of *A*.
    b. Two objects, *A* and *B*, are of equal mass and are in motion. *A* is moving twice as fast as *B*. *A* has four times the kinetic energy of *B*.

Take It Further

1. A pendulum continuously converts kinetic and potential energy into each other. Find out what a pendulum is, identify famous pendulums, and draw a diagram representing the energy changes.

2. A roller coaster involves many different kinds of energy changes and transformations. Create a model or diagram identifying some energy changes in the movement of a roller coaster. You can find a useful animation at ***http://www. physicsclassroom.com/mmedia/ energy/ce.cfm***.

3. Work with a partner to develop a booklet describing several examples of energy transformations from your everyday life. Show diagrams depicting each form of energy and the direction of transformation. Share your booklets with the class.

CAREER

4. Many varied careers depend on a thorough understanding of energy. For example, a radio frequency (RF) engineer uses the knowledge of electromagnetic energy to transfer information to and from cellular telephones. Find out what this type of engineer does, what training is required, and what job opportunities are available. Share your results with the class. You may find helpful information at the following sites: ***http://www. electromagneticcareers.com/*** and ***http://www.nspe.org/index.html***.

Fusion Energy: Future Fuel or Future Folly?

The population of Earth is soaring. Underdeveloped countries are becoming developed, and already developed countries are becoming even more developed. One obvious result of these changes is that the world's people continuously need more sources of energy. Where will all this energy come from?

Today, most of that energy comes from oil, natural gas, and coal. Some of that energy comes from nuclear-fission power plants. All of these energy resources are used to produce electricity. Unfortunately, each energy resource has drawbacks.

Figure 15-11. Current nuclear power plants rely on nuclear fission. A much greater amount of energy could be obtained by switching over to nuclear fusion, the process that occurs in the sun. The technology to make such a switch, however, is not yet possible.

Oil, natural gas, and coal, for example, are fossil fuels. When they are burned, they release harmful gases into the atmosphere. In addition, fossil fuels exist in limited amounts on Earth. At some point in the not-too-distance future, those resources will run out. Nuclear fission does not pollute the air. However, it results in hazardous wastes that remain dangerous for thousands of years and it creates the potential for deadly accidents.

Ideally, society needs a source of energy that is safe, nonpolluting, and unlimited in supply. As unbelievable as it may sound, there are such sources of energy. Nuclear fusion is one that has the potential to provide most of the world's energy needs for probably as long as people inhabit the planet. Nuclear fusion occurs when tremendous heat and pressure force the nuclei of hydrogen atoms to join together, or fuse. In the process, incredible amounts of energy are released in the form of light and heat. This is the same process that produces the heat and light of stars, like our sun.

In designs of nuclear fusion reactors, readily available forms of hydrogen called deuterium and

tritium are the fuel. Deuterium can be extracted from seawater, and tritium can be obtained from Earth's crust. Unlike other resources, it takes only a small amount of these materials to produce a tremendous amount of energy.

So why aren't we using this wonderful source of energy? This is a case in which the process is easier said than done. Getting nuclei to fuse requires raising the temperature of the fuel to at least 100 million degrees Celsius and/or causing the atoms to move at extremely high speeds! Technically, this was achieved years ago when the hydrogen bomb was developed. However, the energy release from that fusion reaction was violent and uncontrollable. Maintaining safe nuclear fusion reactions that can be controlled in nuclear power plants to produce electricity has not yet been achieved. Researchers have devised various methods for producing the temperatures and pressures required to make a controllable, ongoing fusion reaction. So far none has worked. Should the scientists keep trying at the expense of our tax dollars? Would our money be better spent on other types of energy research? What can society do to decrease the need for energy in the first place? What do you think?

Organize It!

Use a method that your instructor describes to organize the information in this article.

Explain It!

1. Which of the following is not considered a fossil fuel?
   a. oil
   b. natural gas
   c. coal
   d. deuterium

2. Which of the following is a drawback of nuclear fission?
   a. It produces hazardous waste.
   b. It occurs only in the sun.
   c. It releases pollutants into the air.
   d. It uses seawater as a fuel.

3. What drawback is preventing the use of nuclear fusion to produce electricity?
   a. Scientists cannot obtain fuel to run the reaction.
   b. Scientists do not understand the process occurring during fusion.
   c. Scientists cannot contain the reaction in a safe, controlled way.
   d. Scientists have not found a way to initiate the reaction.

Extend It!

4. There are two methods being explored to confine the materials involved in a fusion reaction. One method is known as magnetic and the other is inertial. Research these methods and summarize the main approach of each. Write a brief report of your findings.

5. Present your opinion as to whether the search for controlled fusion should continue. Back up your argument with research on the technical problems and costs involved.

CAREER

6. Perhaps you might be the one who makes nuclear fusion as an energy resource a reality. To accomplish this task, you may need to become a nuclear physicist or nuclear engineer. Find out what this type of career entails, what type of training is required, and where such a person might work. You may wish to begin your research at the following sites: *http://www.bls.gov/oco/ocos052.htm*, *http://www.calmis.ca.gov/file/occguide/engnuc.htm*, and *http://www.energy.gov/*. Share your findings with the class.

16 What Is the Nature of Electrical Energy?

The crackling of a bolt of lightning can be "shocking." Not only might it startle you, but the powerfully bright streak can cause great harm when it strikes the ground. As dramatic as it is, the cause of lightning can be traced to the movements of tiny, charged particles.

After reading this chapter, you should be able to answer the following questions:

What are electric charges and the law of electric charges?

How is static electricity detected?

How are conductors different from insulators?

How is an electric current produced?

What factors affect electric current?

What is Ohm's law, and how is it used?

What are the characteristics of series and parallel circuits?

Every time you plug in a video game, connect to your MP3 player, or turn on a light switch, you are using an electric circuit. In this inquiry investigation, you will explore some of the characteristics of electric circuits.

Materials:
✔ safety goggles
✔ 2 dry cells (1.5-V)
✔ 3 lamp sockets
✔ 3 lamps (1.5-V)
✔ knife switch
✔ 4 bell wires
✔ screwdriver

Part A Connect two dry cells, two lamp sockets, two lamps, and a knife switch as shown in Figure 16-1. Close the switch and observe how brightly the lamps light. Open the switch again.

Part B Disconnect the wire between the knife switch and the lamp socket. Add a third lamp in series to your circuit.

Close the switch again and observe how brightly the three lamps light. Open the switch again to conserve the dry cells.

1. *What effect does adding a third lamp have on the brightness of all three lamps?*

2. *How does the brightness of the lamps compare with each other?*

Part C Close the switch again. While the lamps are lit, unscrew one of the lamps from its socket. Then screw the lamp back into its socket. Open the switch.

3. *What effect does removing one lamp from the series circuit have on the brightness of the other lamps?*

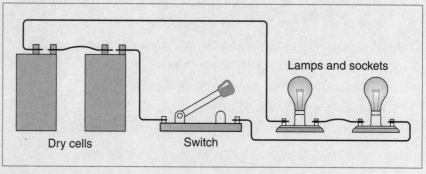

Figure 16-1.

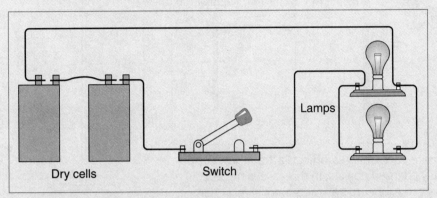

Figure 16-2.

Part D Disassemble the circuit. Reassemble the parts as shown in Figure 16-2. Close the switch and observe how brightly the lamps light. Open the switch again.

Part E Add a third lamp in parallel to the circuit. Close the switch again and observe how brightly the lamps light. Open the switch.

4. *What effect does adding a third lamp to the parallel circuit have on the brightness of the other lamps?*

Part F Close the switch again. While the lamps are lit, unscrew one of the lamps from its socket. Screw the lamp back into its socket. Open the switch again.

5. *What effect does removing one lamp from the parallel circuit have on the brightness of the other lamps?*

6. *Which of these two circuits do you think would be most useful in your home? Explain.*

What Are Electric Charges?

In Chapter 4, you learned that atoms are made up of smaller particles, including positively charged protons and negatively charged electrons. When the number of electrons and protons in a sample of matter are equal, the matter is **neutral**; that is, the matter has no net electric charge. Recall the inquiry investigation from Chapter 4 in which you were able to give an electric charge to certain materials by rubbing them. After rubbing, you found that these materials attracted other materials. Thus, when you rubbed a glass rod with silk and a hard rubber rod with fur, the glass rod and the rubber rod attracted each other. These rubbed objects would also attract small pieces of

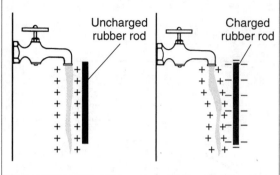

Figure 16-3. Charged objects attract other oppositely charged objects. In this case, a negatively charged rubber rod attracts a positively charged stream of water.

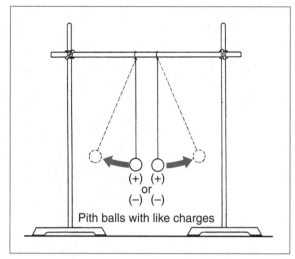

Figure 16-4. Pith balls with the same charge that are suspended freely repel each other.

paper or a fine stream of water (see Figure 16-3). No attraction was observed until the articles were rubbed.

What Is Static Electricity?

As you learned in Chapter 4, rubbing causes electrons to be transferred from one object to another, giving each of the objects a net electric charge. A neutral object that gains electrons acquires a negative charge because it has more electrons (negative electrical particles) than it had before. For example, rubbing a rubber rod with fur transfers electrons from the fur to the rod. A neutral object that loses electrons has fewer electrons than it had before. Consequently, it now has more protons (positive electrical particles) than electrons and, therefore, has a positive charge. For example, rubbing a glass rod with silk transfers electrons from the rod to the silk. Electric charges that accumulate on the surface of objects and remain there are referred to as static (nonmoving) electrical charges, or **static electricity**.

What Is the Law of Electric Charges?

Pith, which is a very light material, is ordinarily electrically neutral because it has equal numbers of electrons and protons. When a

small ball made of pith is touched with a positively charged glass rod, the pith ball also becomes positively charged. Suppose you suspend two pith balls by threads, as in Figure 16-4, and touch each with a charged glass rod. Each pith ball is thereby given a positive charge. If you try to bring two such positively charged balls together, you will find that they repel each other, or move apart.

Similarly, you can touch two suspended pith balls with a negatively charged rubber rod, thereby giving each a negative charge. If you try to bring two such balls together, they also repel each other. However, when a pith ball that has a positive charge is brought near another ball that has a negative charge, the two pith balls attract each other (see Figure 16-5). Such observations led to the **law of electrical attraction and repulsion**, which states that unlike electric charges attract one another, whereas like electric charges repel one another.

How Is Static Electricity Detected?

A device called an **electroscope** is used to detect the presence of a static electric charge. This instrument (see Figure 16-6a) usually consists of an insulated metal rod

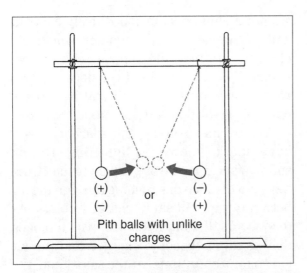

Figure 16-5. Pith balls with opposite charges that are suspended freely attract each other.

with a metal knob on one end. Attached to the other end of the rod are two thin pieces of metal foil, called leaves, which may be made of either aluminum foil or gold foil. The rod and leaves are enclosed in a container such as a flask. The container protects the delicate leaves. Only the knob projects from the flask.

When a charged object is brought close to the metal knob of an electroscope, both leaves become similarly charged. Since the same charges repel each other, the leaves move apart. If a more highly charged object is brought near the electroscope, the leaves move even farther apart. The leaves always draw apart regardless of whether the charged object brought near the electroscope is negative or positive because the two leaves always carry the same charge.

Thus, when a negatively charged rod (see Figure 16-6b) is brought near the knob of an electroscope, electrons from the rod repel the electrons in the knob. These electrons move down the rod to the leaves, causing both of the leaves to become negatively charged. Accordingly, the leaves repel each other. On the other hand, when a positively charged rod is near the knob, electrons from the leaves are attracted to the knob. Since the leaves have lost electrons, they become positively charged. Both leaves are now similarly charged, and again they repel each other (see Figure 16-6c).

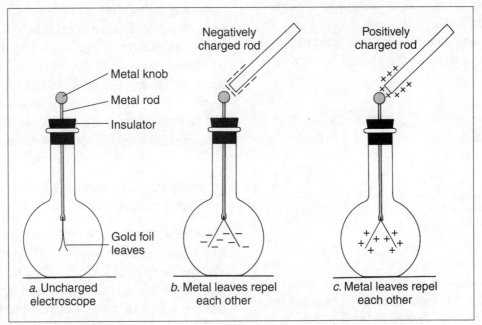

Figure 16-6. The leaves of an uncharged electroscope (a) remain together. However, when the electroscope becomes either negatively (b) or positively (c) charged, its leaves separate. This response indicates the presence of static electricity.

▶ What Is Electrical Discharge?

Have you ever walked across a carpet only to get a shock by touching a metal doorknob? The shock occurs because as you walk, you build up static electricity. When you touch the metal doorknob, the charges suddenly neutralize. In other words, the electric charges flow to your surroundings to even out the charge. The process through which excess charge is neutralized by flowing into the surroundings is known as **static discharge**.

You are familiar with a dramatic example of static discharge if you have ever watched a lightning storm. Lightning forms as a result of events that occur in clouds. Clouds are composed of water droplets so tiny that they are suspended in the air. Some of the droplets are larger than others and this tends to make them move downward. Smaller droplets tend to move upward with rising air currents. As they move up and down, the water droplets rub against one another and against gas molecules in the air. This rubbing, like that of glass against silk, causes static electricity to accumulate in clouds (see Figure 16-7).

Opposite electric charges accumulate in different regions of the cloud. The upper region of a cloud becomes positively charged and the lower region becomes negatively charged. At times, the opposite charges between regions of a cloud (or between two clouds or between a cloud and Earth) become so great that a tremendous static discharge occurs. You see this discharge as a large spark, known as **lightning**. During such a discharge, the bright light results from a stream of electrons rushing through the air between the oppositely charged points. As this occurs, the air is ionized, which means that its atoms become charged and the air glows for a short time. At the same time, the air is heated to such a degree that it expands suddenly. The rapid expansion of the heated air causes a shock wave that produces the loud noise known as **thunder**.

▶ What Happens When Electric Charges Flow?

Not all electric charges build up without flowing. Electrons, for example, can move steadily in a definite direction. This flow of electrons is called **current electricity** to distinguish it from static electricity. Such electrons flow from a point where there is an excess of electrons to a point where there is a deficiency of electrons. In static electricity, there is an excess or a deficiency of electrons on the *surface* of a particular material; in current electricity, however, electrons flow continuously *through* some material.

▶ How Are Conductors Different From Insulators?

Materials through which electrons flow freely are **conductors**. Recall that most metals are good conductors of electricity and that of all the metals, silver and copper are the best conductors. Copper is the more widely used conductor of electricity because it is cheaper than silver.

Materials that resist the flow of electrons through them are not good conductors of

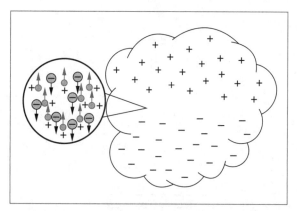

Figure 16-7. The top and bottom of a cloud may assume opposite charges as small, rising droplets and larger, falling droplets rub against each other. This process produces small droplets of positive charge and larger droplets of negative charge.

electricity. These materials are **insulators**. Examples of insulators are rubber, glass, air, wool, and silk. Although insulators do not conduct current electricity, they may store static electricity on their surfaces. Some insulators readily accept and hold electrons; other insulators readily give up electrons. As a result, some insulators can become negatively charged and some insulators can become positively charged. These properties of insulators help explain why rubbing a rubber rod with fur charges the rod negatively and the fur positively. Similarly, rubbing a glass rod with silk charges the rod positively and the silk negatively. Although insulators do not conduct electrons well, insulators generally hold a charge of static electricity that has accumulated on them.

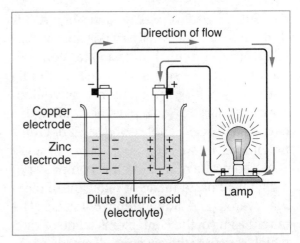

Figure 16-8. A wet cell consists of two electrodes made of different metals immersed in a liquid that conducts electricity. Electric current flows when the electrodes are connected by wires.

How Is an Electric Current Produced?

You may recall that some chemical reactions release chemical energy stored within the substances that react. You also know that all forms of energy can be transformed into other forms. Early in the nineteenth century, *Alessandro Volta*, an Italian physicist, produced the first steady flow of electric current by chemical means. He transformed chemical energy into electrical energy in a device called an **electrochemical cell**. One or more electrochemical cells make up a battery.

Today, Volta's experiments can be repeated by using a device known as a **voltaic cell**. One type of voltaic cell is the **wet cell**. Another type is the dry cell

Wet Cell. A wet voltaic cell is composed of strips of two different metals (electrodes) in an electrolyte, which is a liquid that conducts electricity. One such cell is shown in Figure 16-8. In this cell, a strip of zinc and a strip of copper are placed in dilute sulfuric acid. As a result of the chemical reaction of the zinc with the acid, an excess of electrons accumulates on the zinc. This causes the strip of zinc

to become negatively charged. The hydrogen ions of the acid are positively charged. (Recall from Chapter 14 that when sulfuric acid ionizes in water, positive hydrogen ions and negative sulfate ions are formed.) These charged atoms, or ions, accept electrons from the copper strip, become neutral, and form molecules of hydrogen gas. The hydrogen gas escapes from the solution in the form of bubbles. In giving away electrons to the hydrogen ions, the copper strip becomes positively charged.

The oppositely charged metals that are immersed in a conducting solution (such as zinc and copper in a voltaic cell) are called **electrodes**, or poles. The electrode that has an excess of electrons is the negative electrode, or anode. The other electrode, which has a deficiency of electrons, is the positive electrode, or cathode. When a conductor, such as copper wire, is connected to the electrodes of a voltaic cell, the excess electrons on the zinc electrode flow through the wire to the copper electrode, which has a deficiency of electrons. The flow of the electrons through the wire constitutes an electric current. In this type of cell, the accumulation of electrons usually continues until any one of the chemicals (acid, zinc, or copper) is used up.

Dry Cell. Since a wet cell contains liquid, it is difficult to use a wet cell as a portable source of electric current. For example, consider the problem of using such a cell in a radio you carry with you. A more convenient portable source of current is the familiar **dry cell**. The dry cell is not really dry; it operates much like the wet cell. As shown in Figure 16-9, the inside of a dry cell is composed of a chemical paste made of manganese dioxide, water, and ammonium chloride. The outer casing of the container is made of zinc, which serves as the negative electrode of the dry cell. The graphite (carbon) rod in the center of the dry cell serves as the positive electrode. The ammonium chloride paste serves as the electrolyte. The manganese dioxide aids in removing the hydrogen bubbles, which, if allowed to collect, would stop the chemical reactions generating the flow of electricity. When the electrodes are connected, an electric current flows between them. As in the case of the wet cell, the dry cell produces electric current until any one of the chemicals within the cell is used up.

How Are Electrical Circuits Related to Electric Current?

As you know, electrons flow from a point of excess electrons to a point of a deficiency of electrons. This condition, referred to as a **difference of potential**, produces an **electromotive force (emf)**, which can push electrons through a conductor. Such a complete path is known as an **electrical circuit**.

A complete electrical circuit, shown in Figure 16-10, consists of a source of electrons, a force that pushes the electrons through an appliance, such as an electric light bulb, a conducting path (such as a wire) through which the electrons can flow back to the source, and a switch for closing or opening the circuit.

Note that many books may show current as flowing from the positive terminal, through the circuit, and back into the negative terminal. In the 1700s when electricity was first explored, it was decided that current flowed from positive to negative. Although it was later learned that electrons are responsible for electric current, many sources continue to use this convention (appropriately named conventional current). The actual direction does not really matter as long as one or the other is used consistently.

Sources of Electrons. The most common sources of electrons are electrochemical cells and electric generators. Electrochemical cells, such as dry cells, are generally placed near the appliance or machine requiring electrical energy. Generators, on the other hand, are much larger than cells and are set

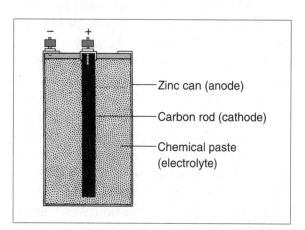

Figure 16-9. Like a wet cell, a dry cell consists of two electrodes, in this case carbon and zinc, and an electrolyte, which in a dry cell is a paste rather than a liquid.

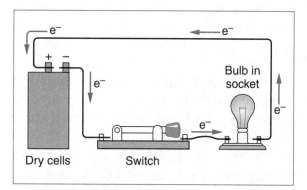

Figure 16-10. The diagram shows a complete electrical circuit in which electrons flow from and back to a source.

up in large buildings. Thus, they are usually set up some distance from homes, offices, or factories. Electric current supplied by generators reaches the appliance by means of connecting wires. Both electrochemical cells and generators require a conducting path to complete the electrical circuit.

The plug of any electrical appliance has two prongs. (See Figure 16-11.) This permits electrons to flow (1) through wires from the negative terminal of the source, (2) through a switch, (3) through one prong of a plug into an appliance, or **load**, (4) out of the load through the other prong, and (5) back to the positive terminal of the source.

Loads. A load is the electrical appliance that is powered by moving electrons (electrical energy). Since a load generally opposes the flow of electrons, a load is often referred to as a **resistance**. Examples of loads in a circuit include lamps, radios, buzzers, television sets, computers, and motors. Electrons from the source must move through the load before they can return to the source.

Switch. In a complete circuit, electrons flow continuously. A switch is a convenient way of operating the circuit, that is, a way of closing or opening the circuit. By *closing a switch,* you close, or complete, an electrical circuit,

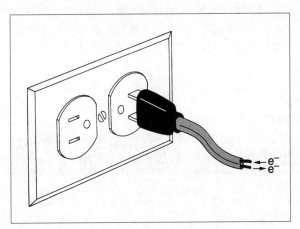

Figure 16-11. An electrical plug completes a circuit by allowing electrons to flow from and to a source.

and electrons flow. By *opening a switch*, you open, or break, the circuit and the flow of electrons stops. The control of circuits by this means is often provided by a knife switch, a push button, a snap switch, a fuse, or a circuit breaker. Fuses and circuit breakers are placed in the electrical circuits of homes and in other places as safety devices. When you use too many appliances at one time, you may overload a circuit, by producing a current that is too large. The fuse or circuit breaker is designed to break the circuit under these conditions and therefore stop the current. Since overloaded circuits usually overheat, they are fire hazards. The use of fuses and circuit breakers reduces the danger of fire.

▶ **What Factors Affect Electric Current?**

You can better understand the characteristics of a flow of electrons through a wire by using a model in which water flows through a hose. Like all models, the water model is limited in its application. However, the following major factors can be observed and measured in both the flow of water and the flow of electrons:

Rate of Flow. When a hose is attached to a faucet and the valve is opened, water flows from the faucet and through the hose. By using a stopwatch and a container marked to measure liters, you can study the rate of flow of the water. You can observe the number of liters per second that leave the hose and enter the measuring container. Thus, you can determine the rate of flow of the water, or the amount flowing into the container in some unit of time. You can express the rate of flow of water as the number of liters of water per second.

Similarly, you can determine the rate of flow of electrons, or current, by measuring the number of electrons flowing past a given point in a unit of time. The current is expressed as the number of electrons that pass a given point in a second. This number of electrons, called a **coulomb**, is very large: 6,300,000,000,000,000,000, or 6.3×10^{18}. The rate of flow of electrons is measured by a unit called an **ampere**, after the French scientist *André Ampère*. One ampere equals a flow of one coulomb of electrons per second. The rate of flow of electrons is known as **amperage**. The amperage of an electric current can be measured with an instrument called an **ammeter**, which must be properly connected to the circuit.

Driving Force. Water flows through a hose because there is a driving force behind the water. You can increase the rate of flow of the water by increasing the driving force. To do this, you might add one or more water pumps to the line. In an electrical circuit, the electromotive force (difference of potential) that causes electrons to move is produced in the current source. The electrochemical cell and the generator are common examples of a source of current. As the electromotive force is increased, the number of electrons flowing in the circuit increases. This electromotive force, abbreviated *emf*, is also known as **voltage**. It is measured in a unit called a **volt**, named after Volta, the Italian physicist. To measure voltage, an instrument known as a **voltmeter** is properly connected to the circuit.

Resistance to Flow. Water molecules, moving through a pipe, rub against the walls of the pipe and slow. The walls of the pipe oppose, or offer resistance to, the flow of water. Longer and narrower pipes offer more resistance to the flow of water than shorter and wider pipes. In a somewhat similar fashion, electrons flowing through a wire encounter resistance to flow. Longer and thinner wires offer more resistance to electron flow than shorter and thicker wires of the same material.

In addition, the nature of the conducting material influences the flow of electrons. For example, nichrome wire offers greater resistance than the same length and thickness of copper wire. When the resistance of a material to the flow of electrons is great enough, electrons do not flow. Such a material makes a good insulator. Electrical resistance is measured in a unit called the **ohm**, after *Georg Ohm*, a German physicist. An instrument called an **ohmmeter** is used to measure resistance. Table 16-1 summarizes the major factors that influence the flow of electrons in a circuit.

> ## What Electrical Phenomenon Does Ohm's Law Describe?

In 1827, Ohm studied the voltage, current, and resistance relationships in an electrical circuit. He summarized his findings in a statement, known as **Ohm's law**: In a complete, or closed, electrical circuit, current and voltage are directly proportional, whereas current and resistance are inversely

Table 16-1.
What Factors Affect Electric Current?

Name	Symbol	Meaning	Unit of Measurement	Measuring Instrument
Current	I	Rate of flow of electrons	Ampere (A)	Ammeter
Voltage	V	Driving or electromotive force behind electrons	Volt (V)	Voltmeter
Resistance	R	Opposition to the flow of electrons	Ohm (Ω)	Ohmmeter

proportional. This means that an increase in voltage causes an increase in current, and that a decrease in voltage causes a decrease in current. Also, an increase in resistance causes a decrease in current, and a decrease in resistance causes an increase in current. Mathematically, Ohm's law states:

$$\text{current} = \frac{\text{voltage}}{\text{resistance}} \qquad (1)$$

Since current is measured in amperes, voltage is measured in volts, and resistance is measured in ohms,

$$\text{amperes} = \frac{\text{volts}}{\text{ohms}} \qquad (2)$$

Using symbols (see Table 16-1), Ohm's law may be written as

$$I = \frac{V}{R} \qquad (3A)$$

The formula for Ohm's law can also be expressed in equivalent ways:

$$\text{volts} = \text{amperes} \times \text{ohms or } V = IR \quad (3B)$$

$$\text{ohms} = \frac{\text{volts}}{\text{amperes}} \quad \text{or} \quad R = \frac{V}{I} \qquad (3C)$$

▶ How Is Ohm's Law Used?

1. Find the amperage in a circuit that has a voltage of 120 volts and a resistance of 60 ohms.

   Write Ohm's law (equation 3A):

   $$I = \frac{V}{R}$$

   From the problem,

   $V = 120$ volts and $R = 60$ ohms.

   Substitute:

   $$I = \frac{120 \text{ volts}}{60 \text{ ohms}}$$

   Solve the equation:

   $$I = 2\,\frac{\text{volts}}{\text{ohms}} = 2 \text{ amperes}$$

   Notice that each factor affecting electric current has a numerical value as well as a unit. You must always divide (or multiply) the units as well as the numbers. Thus, 120 divided by 60 is 2; similarly, volts divided by ohms is amperes (equation 2). Be sure to always include units in the answer.

   The units you obtain as part of your answer act as a check on your work. In the preceding problem, suppose you accidentally wrote Ohm's law as $I = R/V$. You would get a numerical value of $\frac{1}{2}$ by dividing 120 into 60. But when you tried to divide volts into ohms, you would realize that something was wrong. None of your equations for Ohm's law gives ohms/volts; therefore, you would have to start over, and would realize that your equation $I = R/V$ was incorrect.

2. Determine the voltage in a circuit that has a current of 3 amperes and a resistance of 20 ohms.

   Write the formula for Ohm's law that has voltage (V) on the left (equation 3B):

   $$V = I \times R$$

   From the problem,

   $I = 3$ amperes and $R = 20$ ohms.

   Substitute:

   $$V = 3 \text{ amperes} \times 20 \text{ ohms}$$

   Solve the equation:

   $$V = 60 \text{ (amperes} \times \text{ohms)} = 60 \text{ volts}$$

3. Find the resistance of a circuit that has a voltage of 120 volts and a current of 4 amperes.

Write the formula for Ohm's law that has resistance (R) on the left (equation 3C):

$$R = \frac{V}{I}$$

From the problem,

$V = 120$ volts and $I = 4$ amperes.

Substitute:

$$R = \frac{120 \text{ volts}}{4 \text{ amperes}}$$

Solve the equation:

$$R = 30 \frac{\text{volts}}{\text{amperes}} = 30 \text{ ohms}$$

▶ What Are the Characteristics of Series Circuits?

Figure 16-1 (page 238) illustrates a circuit in which the electrons flow along a *single path* through two loads. This arrangement is an example of a **series circuit**. The distinguishing feature of such a circuit is that the electrons flow along a *single path* only, and pass through two or more loads before returning to the source. A series circuit has several important characteristics.

1. *Any break in a series circuit stops the entire electron flow.* In a series circuit, electrons must flow from the source through each load or section of the circuit and back to the source again. Any gap in this single pathway or line interrupts the flow of electrons. Thus, if one of the lamps shown in Figure 16-1 is removed from the circuit, as you did in your inquiry investigation, the circuit will be open and the other lamp will go out. Similarly, a break in a wire or a loose connection can prevent the electrons from flowing.

This situation can be compared to the model of water flowing through a small hose to a point 50 feet from the faucet. Any break in the hose prevents the water from reaching its destination, since the single path that the water follows has been broken. (The water model does not quite fit the electrical situation. A break in a wire permits *no* flow of electrons, whereas water still flows from a break in a hose, although not to its original destination.)

2. *When there are two or more loads in a series circuit, the voltage across each load is a part of the total voltage supplied by the source.* Every time an additional load is wired into a series circuit, the voltage across each load already in the circuit decreases. Figure 16-12 shows a lamp with a resistance of 1 ohm connected to a 3-volt source. Notice the readings on the voltmeter and ammeter.

　　Figure 16-13 shows the same series circuit, but with a second lamp of 1-ohm resistance added. When a voltmeter is connected across each of the lamps, the voltage reading is 1.5 volts. Since the voltage source is still 3 volts, the voltage across each lamp has decreased. An ammeter in the circuit reads 1.5 amperes.

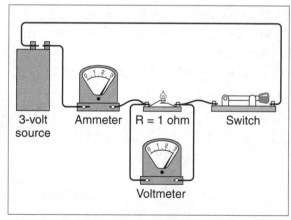

Figure 16-12. In a series circuit with a 1-ohm resistance and a 3-volt source, a voltmeter connected across the load registers 3 volts and an ammeter registers 3 amps.

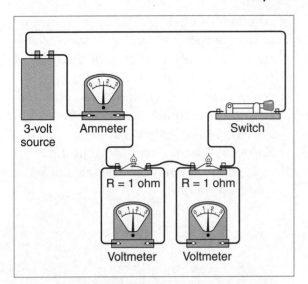

Figure 16-13. If two 1-ohm resistances are connected in series with a 3-volt source, voltmeters across each load will register 1.5 volts and the ammeter will register 1.5 amps.

Figure 16-14 shows the same series circuit, but with a third lamp of 1-ohm resistance added. The voltage reading across each of the lamps is now 1 volt, a further decrease in voltage. An ammeter in the circuit reads 1 amp.

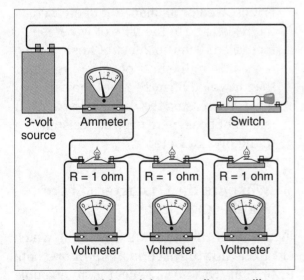

Figure 16-14. This and the preceding two illustrations reveal how Ohm's law applies to series circuits. In all cases, current is directly proportional to voltage and inversely proportional to resistance.

Notice that in each series circuit the *sum* of the voltages across each lamp is equal to the voltage source. In Figure 16-13, 1.5 volts + 1.5 volts = 3 volts; in Figure 16-14, 1 volt + 1 volt + 1 volt = 3 volts.

Ohm's law applies to all parts of an electrical circuit as well as to the entire circuit. According to Ohm's law, the current in the circuit in Figure 16-12 is 3 amperes:

$$I = \frac{V}{R}$$

$$I = \frac{3 \text{ volts}}{1 \text{ ohm}} = 3 \text{ amperes}$$

This agrees with the ammeter reading. In Figure 16-13, the current through either lamp is

$$I = \frac{V}{R}$$

$$I = \frac{1.5 \text{ volts}}{1 \text{ ohm}} = 1.5 \text{ amperes}$$

This also agrees with the ammeter reading. (Note that you use a voltage of 1.5 volts—the voltmeter reading—for this calculation since you are concerned with only *part* of the circuit.) In Figure 16-14, the current through any of the lamps is

$$I = \frac{V}{R}$$

$$I = \frac{1 \text{ volt}}{1 \text{ ohm}} = 1 \text{ ampere}$$

Once again, Ohm's law and the ammeter reading are in agreement.

The lamp in Figure 16-12 glows with characteristic brightness. When the second lamp is added to the circuit (Figure 16-13), both lamps glow—but with less brightness than before. This decrease in brightness occurs because each lamp now has a fraction of the total voltage. When a third lamp is added (Figure 16-14), the three lamps will glow with even less brightness. Again, each of the three bulbs now has an even smaller fraction of the total voltage, which causes a reduction in brightness.

To summarize: In a series circuit, (1) the voltage across each load decreases as additional loads are wired into the circuit, and (2) the sum of the voltages across each load in the circuit is equal to the voltage of the source.

In the model of water flowing through a hose, pressure or driving force is similar to voltage. Assume that water from some source at a given pressure passes through a series of pipes of different lengths and diameters and then returns to the source. If the driving force behind the water in each of the pipes is measured, you would find that the sum of the driving forces in each of the pipes equals the driving force of the water at the source.

3. *The current is the same in all parts of a series circuit.* In the circuit shown in Figure 16-12, for example, the ammeter will read 3 amperes when it is properly wired to *any point* in the series circuit. In any electrical circuit, all the electrons flowing from the source eventually return to the source. Since, in a series circuit, only one path is provided for the flow of electrons, all the electrons must pass through each of the loads in the circuit in order to reach the source again. This means that the current is the same in all parts of a series circuit.

4. *The resistance increases in a series circuit as the number of loads increases.* In a series circuit, where only one path is provided for the electrons, the wires and loads in the circuit offer resistance to the flow of electrons. Since the electrons travel along each

wire and through each load in returning to the source, the total resistance of the circuit is equal to the sum of the resistances of each wire and load. In the series circuit shown in Figure 16-13, for example, the total resistance offered by the two 1-ohm lamps is 2 ohms. Knowing the total resistance in the circuit, you may calculate the current by using Ohm's law:

$$I = \frac{V}{R}$$

$$I = \frac{3 \text{ volts}}{2 \text{ ohms}} = 1.5 \text{ amperes}$$

(Note that, since you use the total resistance, you must use the total voltage, that is, the voltage of the source.) With three 1-ohm lamps (Figure 16-14), the total resistance is 3 ohms and the current in this circuit is

$$I = \frac{V}{R} = \frac{3 \text{ volts}}{3 \text{ ohms}} = 1 \text{ ampere}$$

In the model of water passing through a hose, as the length of the hose is increased or its diameter decreased, the resistance to the flow of water is increased. Thus, in 2 feet of hose, the resistance to the flow of water is greater than it would be in 1 foot of the same hose. Decreasing the diameter of a given length of hose increases the resistance to the flow of water.

▶ **What Are the Characteristics of Parallel Circuits?**

Figure 16-15 illustrates a circuit in which electrons flow through *more than one* path or branch. This arrangement is an example of a **parallel circuit**, also called a **branching circuit**. The distinguishing feature of such a circuit is that the electrons can flow through *any one of the branches* of the circuit before returning to the source. Several important characteristics of parallel circuits follow:

1. *A break in one branch of a parallel circuit does not stop the flow of current in the other branches.* In Figure 16-15, each of the loads can be considered to be connected to the same source independently. Therefore, the removal of one of the lamps from the circuit, as you did in the inquiry investigation, eliminates only one branch of the circuit (see Figure 16-16). However, the electrons continue flowing in the other branch. This situation can be compared to the model of water flowing out of a can that has three spouts in its bottom, as shown in Figure 16-17. When all three spouts are open, water flows from all three. However, when a cork is placed in one of the spouts, the water stops flowing from this spout, but continues to flow from the other two.

2. *The total resistance in a parallel circuit decreases as the number of loads or individual resistances increases.* In a series circuit, all the electrons flow through each load by way of a single path and therefore meet more and more resistance along the way. On the other hand, in a parallel circuit, electrons flow into several branches containing loads or resistances. All the branches together act as one broad pathway that offers less resist-

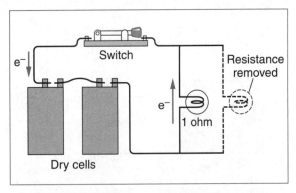

Figure 16-16. Note that, unlike in series circuits, the removal of a resistance in a parallel circuit does not interrupt the circuit existing with a remaining resistance.

ance to the flow of electrons than does a narrow pathway. In fact, the total resistance in a parallel circuit is *less* than the smallest single resistance. If, for example, each lamp in Figure 16-15 has a resistance of 1 ohm, the total resistance of the circuit is $\frac{1}{2}$ ohm. (In a *series* circuit, such as that shown in Figure 16-13, two 1-ohm lamps would have a total resistance of 2 ohms.) When a third 1-ohm lamp is wired into a parallel circuit (Figure 16-18 on page 252), the total resistance of the three 1-ohm lamps is $\frac{1}{3}$ ohm. (In a *series* circuit, such as that shown in Figure 16-14, three 1-ohm lamps would have a total resistance of 3 ohms.)

This situation can be compared to a pipe of given diameter that branches into three smaller pipes. The three pipes

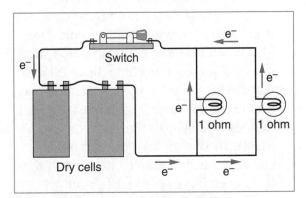

Figure 16-15. This illustration shows a parallel circuit, that is, a circuit in which electrons can follow more than one path.

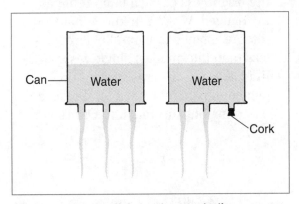

Figure 16-17. Parallel circuits are similar to water flowing from three spouts in a can. If one spout is blocked off, water continues to flow from the other two spouts.

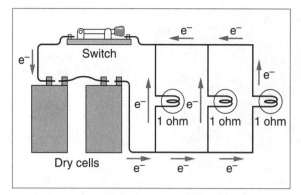

Figure 16-18. In a parallel circuit, voltage remains constant across each resistance regardless of the number of resistances in the circuit. Thus, the lamps depicted glow with equal brightness.

offer less resistance to the flow of water than does the single pipe.

3. *The voltage is the same in all branches of a parallel circuit.* Recall that Ohm's law applies to *portions* of an electrical circuit. Given a 3-volt source and a lamp with a resistance of 1 ohm, the current is 3 amperes:

$$I = \frac{V}{R}$$

$$I = \frac{3 \text{ volts}}{1 \text{ ohm}} = 3 \text{ amperes}$$

The lamp glows with a characteristic brightness. When two such lamps are connected in parallel to the same source, as in Figure 16-15 on page 251, the brightness of each lamp remains unchanged. Why? You know that the total resistance of a parallel circuit is less than the smallest single resistance. In fact, two 1-ohm resistances connected in parallel have a total resistance of $\frac{1}{2}$ ohm. Substituting into Ohm's law:

$$I = \frac{V}{R}$$

$$I = \frac{3 \text{ volts}}{\frac{1}{2} \text{ ohm}} \left[3 \div \frac{1}{2} = 3 \times 2 = 6 \right]$$
$$= 6 \text{ amperes}$$

Thus, 6 amperes flow through the entire circuit. However, the circuit has *two* branches of equal resistance and each branch must carry half the current, or 3 amperes. This was the current in the 1-lamp circuit previously used. The voltage across each lamp equals $I \times R$ $= 6 \times \frac{1}{2}$ ohm $= 3$ volts, which is the same as the voltage of the source.

You can use the same reasoning to show that the addition of another lamp (or any number of lamps) does not diminish the brightness of each lamp in the parallel circuit. The current flowing through each lamp must remain 3 amperes. The total resistance using three lamps in parallel is $\frac{1}{3}$ ohm (Figure 16-18). The total current $I = V/R = 3$ volts/$\frac{1}{3}$ ohm $= 9$ amperes. The current divides into three branches, each carrying $\frac{1}{3}$ of the total, or 3 amperes. The voltage is still $I \times R = 9$ amperes $\times \frac{1}{3}$ ohm $= 3$ volts. Thus, the brightness remains the same.

4. *The amperage (current) is not necessarily the same in all branches of a parallel circuit.* In a parallel circuit, as in a series circuit, all the electrons flowing from the source eventually return to the same source. In a parallel circuit, however, electrons enter each branch of the circuit before reaching the source again. Since each branch may offer different resistance, the flow of current in one branch may differ from the flow in another. The sum of all the currents in the branches of the circuit must equal the total current flowing in the circuit. This idea was illustrated in the previous paragraph. The total current in the two-lamp parallel circuit is 6 amperes, and the current in each lamp is 3 amperes.

This is similar to the situation in Figure 16-19, where, if the can holds 3 gallons of water, about 1 gallon will flow from each large spout and about $\frac{1}{2}$ gallon will flow from each half-size spout. The two half-gallons equal one single gallon.

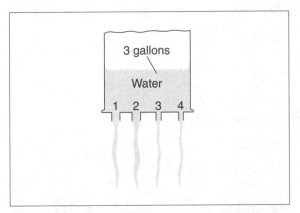

Figure 16-19. This drawing illustrates that in a parallel circuit, although the current flowing through various resistances (spouts 1–4) may differ, the total current ("3 gallons") will remain unchanged.

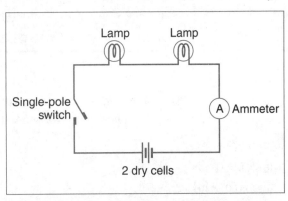

Figure 16-20. Electrical symbols are used to represent various circuits. Many manuals for audio, video and other electronic equipment use symbols to show circuits and components.

What Electrical Symbols Are Used to Describe Electric Circuits?

Representing electric circuits through actual drawings is time-consuming and difficult. Figure 16-20 uses common electrical symbols to illustrate a series circuit containing two dry cells, two lamps, an ammeter, and a single-pole switch. Figure 16-21 shows the same items connected in a parallel circuit. See Figure 16-22 for other common electrical symbols that are used to represent electric circuits. Note that ammeters are always attached to a circuit in series and voltmeters are always attached to a circuit in parallel.

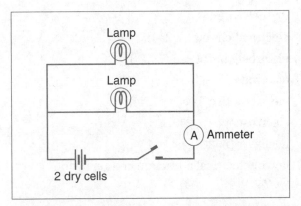

Figure 16-21. This diagram shows a parallel circuit in which two lamps are connected to a source and an ammeter.

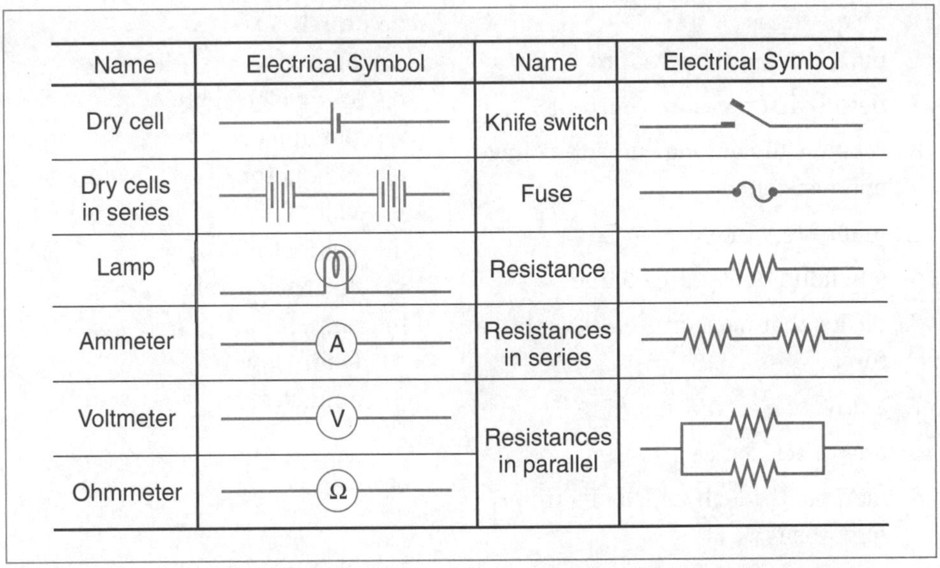

Name	Electrical Symbol	Name	Electrical Symbol
Dry cell	—⊣⊢—	Knife switch	— ▪ —
Dry cells in series	—⊣⊢⊣⊢—	Fuse	—∿—
Lamp	(lamp symbol)	Resistance	—WWW—
Ammeter	—(A)—	Resistances in series	—WW—WW—
Voltmeter	—(V)—	Resistances in parallel	(two resistors in parallel)
Ohmmeter	—(Ω)—		

Figure 16-22. The diagram shows electrical symbols and what they represent.

Chapter Review

Science Terms

The following list contains all the boldfaced words found in this chapter and the page on which each appears.

ammeter (p. 246)

amperage (p. 246)

ampere (p. 246)

branching circuit (p. 250)

conductor (p. 242)

coulomb (p. 246)

current electricity (p. 242)

difference of potential (p. 244)

dry cell (p. 244)

electrical circuit (p. 244)

electrochemical cell (p. 243)

electrode (p. 243)

electromotive force (p. 244)

electroscope (p. 240)

insulator (p. 243)

law of electrical attraction and repulsion (p. 240)

lightning (p. 242)

load (p. 245)

neutral (p. 239)

ohm (p. 246)

ohmmeter (p. 246)

Ohm's law (p. 246)

parallel circuit (p. 250)

resistance (p. 245)

series circuit (p. 248)

static electricity (p. 240)

static discharge (p. 242)

thunder (p. 242)

volt (p. 246)

voltage (p. 246)

voltaic cell (p. 243)

voltmeter (p. 246)

wet cell (p. 243)

Matching Questions

In your notebook, write the letter of the item in column B that is most closely related to the item in column A.

Column A

_____ 1. unit of electromotive force

_____ 2. device that measures current

_____ 3. relationship among current, voltage, and resistance

_____ 4. unit of rate of electron flow

_____ 5. a buildup of electric charge

_____ 6. device that measures electromotive force

_____ 7. a flow of electric charge

_____ 8. unit of resistance

_____ 9. material through which electrons flow easily

_____ 10. device that measures resistance

Column B

a. ohm

b. static electricity

c. ohmmeter

d. conductor

e. volt

f. voltmeter

g. electric current

h. ampere

i. Ohm's law

j. ammeter

Multiple-Choice Questions

*In your notebook, write the letter preceding the word or expression
that best completes the statement or answers the question.*

1. A material that loses electrons becomes
   a. electrically neutral
   b. positively charged
   c. negatively charged
   d. insulated from charge

2. Static electricity is produced when
   there is
   a. the flow of electric charges
   b. the discharge of electric charges
   c. the accumulation of electric charges
   d. the destruction of electric charges

3. Which pair of objects will experience a
   force of attraction between them?
   a. two positively charged pith balls
   b. two negatively charged pith balls
   c. two pith balls that are each electrically
      neutral
   d. a negatively charged pith ball and a
      positively charged pith ball

4. An object brought near the knob of an
   electroscope causes the leaves to spread
   apart. What can you conclude about the
   object?
   a. It is electrically neutral.
   b. It is positively charged.
   c. It is negatively charged.
   d. It is electrically charged.

5. In a cloud, the rubbing of water droplets
   against air molecules produces
   a. current electricity
   b. magnetism
   c. static electricity
   d. thunder

6. What causes a bolt of lightning to occur?
   a. Static electricity in clouds is dis-
      charged.
   b. Heated air expands rapidly.
   c. Electric current flows through water
      droplets in a series of storm clouds.

   d. Electric charges are converted into
      electromagnetic waves.

7. Which of the following is an example of
   an insulator?
   a. copper   c. silver
   b. iron   d. rubber

8. Which scientist is credited with producing
   the first steady flow of electric current by
   chemical means?
   a. Volta   c. Ampère
   b. Ohm   d. Galvani

9. Two strips of different metals placed in a
   liquid electrolyte constitute
   a. a dry cell   c. a battery
   b. a voltaic cell   d. none of these

10. In a voltaic cell, an electrode that has a
    deficiency of electrons is called the
    a. cathode   c. conductor
    b. electrolyte   d. anode

11. Which energy transformation takes place
    in a battery?
    a. chemical to electrical
    b. static to current
    c. electrical to electromagnetic
    d. nuclear to electrical

12. Which of these devices produces an elec-
    tric current?
    a. lamp   c. transformer
    b. motor   d. generator

13. What is the role of a fuse in an electric
    circuit?
    a. to prevent the circuit from becoming
       overloaded
    b. to turn the flow of electrons on and off
    c. to push electrons around the circuit
    d. to slow the flow of electrons in a con-
       ductor

14. In general, the greatest resistance is offered by
    a. short, thick wires
    b. long, thick wires
    c. long, thin wires
    d. short, thin wires

15. How is current related to voltage in a closed circuit?
    a. They are always equal.
    b. They are opposite values.
    c. They are directly proportional.
    d. They are inversely proportional.

16. In a series circuit containing four bulbs, when one bulb burns out,
    a. all four bulbs go out
    b. the remaining three bulbs remain lit
    c. one other bulb goes out
    d. the brightness of the bulbs increases

17. In a series circuit, the sum of the voltages in each load
    a. is less than the voltage at the source
    b. is greater than the voltage at the source
    c. is equal to the voltage at the source
    d. equals the voltage across the smallest resistance

18. In a series circuit, as the number of loads increases,
    a. the total amperage increases
    b. the total resistance increases
    c. the total voltage increases
    d. the total amperage decreases

19. In a parallel circuit, a break in one branch of the circuit
    a. stops the flow of electrons in all branches
    b. decreases the flow of electrons in other branches
    c. does not stop the flow of electrons in other branches
    d. produces a short circuit

20. In all branches of a parallel circuit,
    a. the voltage across each load is the same as the voltage of the source
    b. the voltage across each load varies
    c. the amperage is the same
    d. the resistance is the same

Modified True-False Questions

In some of the following statements, the italicized term makes the statement incorrect. For each incorrect statement, in your notebook, write the term that must be substituted for the italicized term to make the statement correct. For each correct statement, write the word "true."

1. An object acquires a *negative* charge when it gains electrons. _____

2. Electric charges that accumulate on the surface of objects and remain there are called *current* electricity. _____

3. A device used to detect the presence of a static electric charge is *a dry cell*. _____

4. A large discharge of static electricity in the atmosphere is called *lightning*. _____

5. A flow of electrons in a definite direction is called an electric *charge*. _____

6. Materials with the same electric charge *repel* one another. _____

7. Rubbing two materials together causes electrons to be *destroyed*. _____

8. Materials that resist the passage of electrons are called *insulators*. _____

9. An electrochemical cell converts *nuclear* energy stored in chemicals into electricity. _____

10. Strips of metal placed into a wet cell are called *anodes*. _____

11. The outer casing of a dry cell is made of *ammonium chloride*, which serves as the negative electrode. _____

12. A complete path for electrons through a conductor is called an *electric circuit*. _____

13. A computer in an electric circuit is considered a *load*. _____

14. The rate of flow of electrons is known as *voltage*. _____

15. As the electromotive force in a circuit increases, the number of electrons flowing in the circuit *decreases*. _____

16. An engineer using an ohmmeter is measuring *resistance*. _____

17. Any break in a *parallel* circuit stops the flow of current through the entire circuit. _____

18. The total resistance in a series circuit is found by *multiplying* the individual resistances. _____

19. The voltage is the same in all branches of a *parallel* circuit. _____

20. A symbol in a circuit diagram consisting of the letter A inside a circle represents a device used to measure *current*. _____

TEST-TAKING TIP Symbols will appear in many types of electrical diagrams. Make sure you are familiar with them so you understand what is being presented in the diagram.

Check Your Knowledge
Write the answer to each question in your notebook.

1. Explain the differences between the terms in each of the following pairs:
   a. static and current electricity
   b. anode and cathode
   c. conductor and insulator
   d. series and parallel circuits
   e. amperage and voltage

2. Why is an electroscope not useful for differentiating between positively charged and negatively charged objects?

3. Complete the table.

Name	Meaning	Unit of Measurement	Measuring Device
Current			
Voltage			
Resistance			

4. Explain how lightning is formed in the atmosphere.

Think Critically
Write the answer to each of the following questions in your notebook. Include the correct equation and show your work along with your answers.

1. Solve each of the following problems using Ohm's law.
   a. Find the amperage in an electric circuit when the voltage is 120 volts and the resistance is 40 ohms.
   b. Find the voltage in an electric circuit when the amperage is 5 amperes and the resistance of the current is 25 ohms.

c. Find the resistance of an electric circuit when the voltage is 220 volts and the amperage is 5 amperes.

2. Draw each of the following using electrical symbols.
   a. A series circuit that contains 2 dry cells, an ammeter, 2 lamps, and a single-pole switch.
   b. A parallel circuit that contains 2 dry cells, an ammeter, 2 lamps, and a single-pole switch.

3. Using some or all of the following materials, draw a design for a burglar alarm. The drawing should include your front door or a window to your home.

   Materials: dry cell, wire, buzzer, push-button switch, lamp and lamp holder, any other materials you wish to use.

Take It Further

1. Many of the plugs attached to the devices you use have a third prong on them. Research the reason for the third prong and why it is used. Draw a diagram or poster to present your findings.

2. Select a scientist named in the chapter or otherwise related to the discovery of the nature of electricity. Write a brief report describing the contributions of the scientist and the circumstances under which that scientist worked.

CAREER

3. You would not have lights to help you read these words right now without the help of an electrician. Conduct research to investigate the role of electricians, the environments in which they might work, and the training they need to do their job. Share a specific example with the class. You may wish to visit the following site as you begin your research: *http://www.bls.gov/k12/build06.htm*.

17

What Is the Nature of Magnetism?

These antique compasses may once have been used to navigate treacherous seas or majestic mountain ranges. A compass is useful for finding direction thanks to the fact that Earth behaves as if it has a giant magnet running through it!

After reading this chapter, you should be able to answer the following questions:

What are the characteristics of magnetic materials?

What makes materials magnetic?

How can you make a magnet?

How can a magnet be demagnetized?

What law describes magnetic poles?

What is a magnetic field?

Perhaps you played with magnets when you were younger. Maybe you have a magnet on your locker or refrigerator. What makes magnets different from other materials? In this inquiry investigation, you will explore how magnets affect the regions around them.

Materials:

- ✔ safety goggles
- ✔ 2 bar magnets
- ✔ sheet of clear, stiff plastic
- ✔ iron filings
- ✔ horseshoe magnet
- ✔ dish for filings

Part A Lay a bar magnet on your desk. Cover the bar magnet with a sheet of clear, stiff plastic. Sprinkle iron filings onto the plastic. Gently tap the edge of the plastic with your finger. Note what happens to the positions of the iron filings.

1. Draw the pattern formed by the iron filings in your notebook.

Remove the plastic from the magnet and shake the iron filings into the dish intended for this purpose.

Part B Lay two bar magnets on your desk. The magnets should be placed end to end, about 2.5 centimeters (1 inch) apart, and with the same poles facing each other.

Cover the magnets with the sheet of plastic. Gently sprinkle iron filings onto the plastic, especially over the space between the two magnets. Tap the edge of the plastic with your finger. Note what happens to the positions of the iron filings.

2. Draw the pattern formed by the iron filings in your notebook.

Remove the plastic from the magnets and return the iron filings to the dish.

Part C Position the two bar magnets on your desk so that they are end to end, about 2.5 centimeters (1 inch) apart, and with the north pole of one magnet facing the south pole of the other magnet.

Cover the magnets with the sheet of plastic. Gently sprinkle iron filings onto the plastic, especially over the space between the two magnets. Tap the edge of the plastic with your finger.

Note what happens to the positions of the iron filings.

3. Draw the pattern formed by the iron filings in your notebook.

Remove the plastic from the magnets and return the iron filings to the dish.

Part D Lay a horseshoe magnet on your desk. Cover the magnet with the sheet of plastic. Gently sprinkle iron filings between the poles of the magnet. Tap the edge of the plastic with your finger. Note what happens to the positions of the iron filings.

4. *Draw the pattern formed by the iron filings in your notebook.*

Remove the plastic from the magnet and return the iron filings to the dish.

5. *Based on your findings in Parts B and C, how would you describe the force that exists between the poles of the horseshoe magnet? Propose an explanation for your observations.*

6. *Based on your findings in Parts B and C, draw a figure showing the positions of iron filings when two horseshoe magnets are positioned with opposite poles facing each other about 2.5 centimeters (1 inch) apart.*

What Are the Characteristics of Magnetic Materials?

Stories about the discovery of magnets can be found in writings dating back thousands of years. People noticed that a type of rock known as a **lodestone** (roughly, a stone that "leads") could attract certain metals. They quickly discovered that if an elongated piece of this rock were suspended from a cord, one end of the rock always pointed toward the north. Using this crude device, the captain of an ancient sailing ship could keep his vessel on course, even when the sky was overcast and the stars were hidden.

Today, scientists know that the lodestone points toward the north because of the property called **magnetism**. This property is the ability of a substance to attract certain materials such as iron. An understanding of magnetism explains the behavior of the lodestone as well as the operation of many modern devices such as telephones, electric generators, and various kinds of electric motors.

All substances can be classified as either magnetic or nonmagnetic. A **magnetic** substance is one that is attracted to a magnet. Examples include iron, cobalt, nickel, and lodestone. These are also called **ferromagnetic** substances. A **nonmagnetic** substance is not attracted to a magnet; however, magnetism passes through such a substance. For example, if you were to place an iron nail on a sheet of thin cardboard and hold a magnet under the cardboard, the nail would be attracted to the magnet. As you moved the magnet about, the nail would "follow" it. It is apparent that the magnetism passes through the nonmagnetic cardboard. Other examples of nonmagnetic substances are plastic, wood, and nonferrous metals such as copper.

▶ What Makes Materials Magnetic?

You know that matter consists of atoms. Each atom contains a positively charged nucleus and negatively charged electrons moving around the nucleus. Not only do electrons revolve around the nucleus, but each electron spins around on its own axis, just as Earth does. The spinning motions of the electrons produce oppositely charged magnetic poles. In most elements, however, the spins of electrons oppose one another; that is, the motions are in opposite directions and thus the magnetic forces cancel each other. Most substances, therefore, do not display any magnetic properties.

In ferromagnetic elements, spinning motions of the electrons do not oppose each other. Instead, they reinforce each other. The atoms in a piece of iron can be thought of as groups of tiny magnets called **domains**. Ordinarily, these domains are arranged in a random fashion, as shown in Figure 17-1a. Note that the poles of these tiny magnets are arranged in every possible direction, which tends to weaken or cancel any net magnetic effect. However, when the majority of domains are lined up as shown in Figure 17-1b, there is a net magnetic effect and the object has magnetic properties. Breaking or cutting a large magnet does not disturb the regular arrangement of magnetic domains and hence the remaining smaller pieces retain their magnetism.

Lodestone is classed as a **natural magnet** because it is a naturally occurring iron ore called **magnetite**, Fe_3O_4. Except for such iron ores, most magnets in use today are artificial and, therefore, are called **artificial magnets**. Artificial magnets are usually made of alloys (combinations of iron and other metals). For example, a very powerful artificial magnet, called an **alnico magnet**, consists of aluminum, nickel, cobalt, and iron.

▶ **How Can You Make a Magnet?**

Magnets are made by several methods:

1. *By Contact.* When a bar of magnetic material is stroked in *one direction* with a magnet, the bar becomes magnetized. For example, when a bar of steel is stroked in one direction with a magnet, the steel itself becomes a magnet (see Figure 17-2). After stroking the steel with a magnet, the steel can attract several paper clips. This method is known as magnetizing by contact. According to the theory of magnetism, stroking a magnetic substance properly realigns

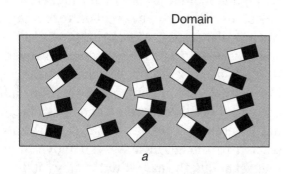

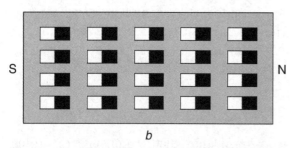

Figure 17-1. In an unmagnetized substance (a), the domains are arranged in random fashion. In a magnetized substance (b), the domains line up with north poles facing one end and south poles facing the other end.

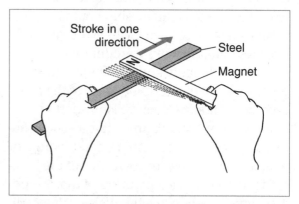

Figure 17-2. To make a magnet by contact, a magnet should be rubbed along an unmagnetized steel bar in one direction only. The steel bar then becomes magnetized.

the domains into a regular north-south arrangement.

It is interesting to note that when a bar of soft iron is magnetized, it does not remain a magnet for very long. It slowly loses its magnetism and is therefore called a **temporary magnet**. On the other hand, when steel is magnetized, it remains a magnet for a long period of time and is called a **permanent magnet**.

2. *By Induction.* When a magnetic substance, such as a bar of soft iron, is brought close to a magnet—but does not touch the magnet—the soft iron itself becomes a magnet. As shown in Figure 17-3, when an iron bar is held near (not touching) a magnet, the bar attracts the paper clips. When the magnet is moved away, the paper clips fall from the iron bar. This method of making a magnet is known as **induction**. According to the theory of magnetism, the presence of a magnet near a magnetic object rearranges the domains in the magnetic object. Most of the north poles point in one direction and most of the south poles point in the opposite direction. Apparently, the magnetic force extends outward to some distance. Beyond this region, the magnet loses its power.

3. *By Electricity.* In 1819, the Danish scientist *Hans Christian Oersted* discovered that a wire carrying an electric current possesses magnetic properties (see Figure 17-4). In 1820, André Ampère wound a long piece of copper wire, a nonmagnetic substance, into a spring-like coil. He then attached the ends of the coil to a source of electric current. He found that the coil attracted iron and acted like a bar magnet as long as the circuit was closed. When the circuit was broken, the coil lost its magnetism. Thus, the flow of electricity produced a magnetic field.

When a magnetic substance is inserted into a coil of wire and the wire is connected to the poles of a dry cell,

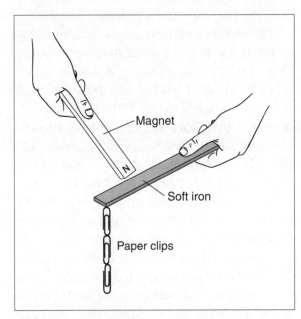

Figure 17-3. To make a magnet by induction, a magnet should be brought near an unmagnetized soft iron bar. The iron bar then becomes magnetized.

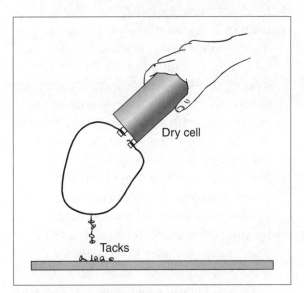

Figure 17-4. To make a magnet by using electricity, allow an electric current to flow through a wire, causing the wire to become magnetic.

the magnetic substance becomes a magnet. If this substance is soft iron, it becomes an **electromagnet** (a temporary magnet). If the substance is steel or some other hard iron alloy, it becomes a permanent magnet. Since electromagnets can be turned on and off, they can be used to lift, carry, and deposit large magnetic objects such as scrap steel.

How Can a Magnet Be Demagnetized?

Just as a magnet can be made, a magnetic material can lose its magnetism. Magnets can be demagnetized in several ways:

1. *By Heat.* When a magnet is placed in a flame and heated until it is red hot, it becomes demagnetized.
2. *By Contact.* When one magnet is stroked by another magnet alternately in one direction and then the other, the stroked magnet becomes demagnetized. Note that this procedure is the opposite of the procedure used in making a magnet by contact.
3. *By Hammering or Jarring.* When a magnet is repeatedly struck with a hammer or when it is struck against a tabletop or some other hard object, the magnet loses its magnetism. This can be shown as follows: First, pick up some paper clips with a magnet. Then remove the paper clips and strike the magnet solidly against a hard object four or five times. Now try to pick up the paper clips again. The clips are no longer attracted—the magnet has become demagnetized. The theory of magnetism explains what happens during demagnetization. Heating, rubbing, and hammering a magnet disturb the regular arrangement of magnetic domains—a necessary requirement for magnetism.

What Law Describes Magnetic Poles?

As you noticed in the inquiry investigation, iron filings tend to concentrate at the ends of a magnet. It is at these ends, called **magnetic poles**, that the power of a magnet is the strongest. When a bar magnet is suspended horizontally by a string from a ring stand, the magnet usually swings and then comes to rest in an approximate north-south position. The pole pointing toward the north is called the **north pole** of the magnet, while the pole pointing southward is called the **south pole** of the magnet.

When the north pole of a second magnet is brought close to the north pole of the suspended magnet, the two north poles repel each other. If the south pole of a magnet is brought close to the south pole of a suspended magnet, the two south poles also repel each other. On the other hand, when the south pole of a magnet is brought close to the north pole of the suspended magnet, the two poles attract each other (Figure 17-5). The attraction or repulsion between magnetic poles is the **magnetic force**.

These observations about magnets are summarized in the **law of magnetic poles**. This law states that like poles of magnets repel each other and unlike poles of magnets attract each other. Note the similarity between this law and the law of electric charges studied earlier. (See Chapter 16.) In both cases, opposites attract and similar charges or similar poles repel each other.

The force of attraction between two unlike poles or the force of repulsion between two like poles depends on the strength of the magnets and the distance between the poles. At a fixed distance, stronger magnets produce stronger attractions or stronger repulsions. With magnets of the same strength, the magnetic force increases as the distance between the poles decreases. The magnetic force decreases as the distance between the poles increases.

ing the bar magnet brings the poles closer together.

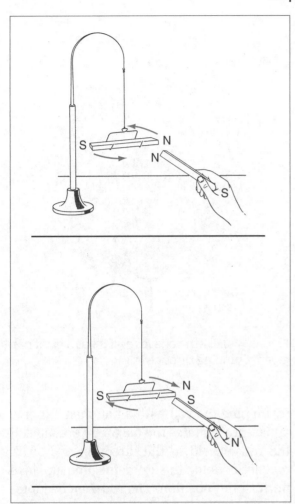

Figure 17-5. According to the law of magnetic poles, like poles repel one another whereas opposite poles attract one another.

In calculating the attractive or repulsive forces between two magnets, the distance between poles has a more pronounced effect than does the strength of the magnets. For example, if you double the strength of a magnet, you double the attractive or repulsive forces. But, if you double the distance between two unlike poles, the attractive force is decreased to one-fourth of its original strength. If you halve the distance between two unlike poles, the attractive force becomes four times greater than the original strength. This relationship is an inverse square law. This law helps explain why a bar magnet becomes stronger when bent in the form of a horseshoe. Bend-

What Is a Magnetic Field?

You have already seen in your inquiry investigation that iron filings tend to cluster near the poles of a magnet. Magnetic effects can be observed not only at the poles of a magnet but also, as you learned earlier, for some distance away from the poles. The magnetic force in the region around a magnet constitutes a **magnetic field**. This magnetic field is invisible, but its effect can be observed with the aid of iron filings. The field around a magnet can be described by a pattern of lines extending from the north pole of the magnet to its south pole (see Figure 17-6). These lines, known as **lines of force**, form closed arcs around the magnet and never cross each other. The lines of force are most concentrated at the poles, indicating that the magnetic field is strongest at these regions.

You also observed the patterns showing the magnetic field between the poles of two magnets. Between two similar poles, the lines of force appear to repel each other (Figure 17-7). When the north pole of one bar magnet is placed near the south pole of another

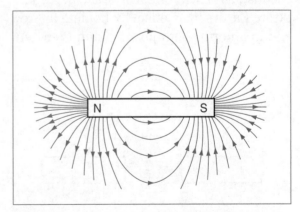

Figure 17-6. The magnetic field around a bar magnet can be represented by a series of lines that extend from the north pole to the south pole of the magnet.

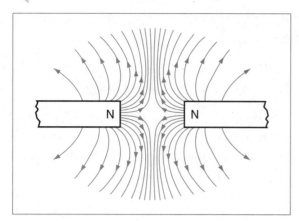

Figure 17-7. The pattern of iron filings shows the lines of force between two like poles.

magnet, the lines of force indicate the attraction between these poles (Figure 17-8).

In 1600, *William Gilbert*, an English scientist, published an essay in which he claimed that Earth behaved like a giant bar magnet. To support his view, he shaped a piece of lodestone into a sphere resembling Earth. He then demonstrated that a compass needle, placed anywhere on the sphere, took a north-south position. Recall that the same observation can be made when a bar magnet is suspended from a string. The freely suspended magnet also takes a north-south position.

If you represent Earth with a cardboard sphere and place a bar magnet inside the sphere as in Figure 17-9, the lines of force around the bar magnet will correspond to the magnetic field of Earth. You can demonstrate Earth's magnetism by holding an iron rod in a north-south position and then gen-

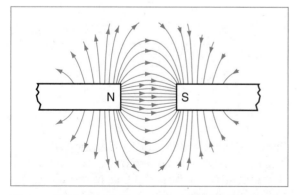

Figure 17-8. The pattern of iron filings shows the lines of force between two unlike poles.

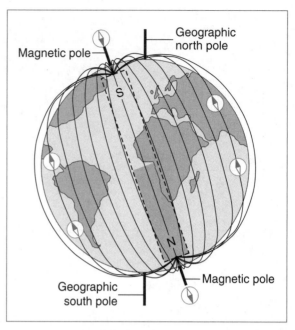

Figure 17-9. Earth behaves as if it has a giant bar magnet running through it.

tly tapping the rod with a hammer. Tapping apparently agitates the magnetic domains. If the rod is held in the direction of Earth's magnetic field, the domains line up in a north-south position. The rod then becomes magnetized by induction.

The response of the compass to Earth's magnetism makes the compass useful as a navigational instrument. However, in most places on Earth, the compass needle does not point to true north, which is the geographic North Pole. Instead, the compass needle points to the north magnetic pole, as shown in Figure 17-9, which is located in northern Canada, about 2000 km (1200 mi) south of the geographic North Pole. The angle made by lines from the observer to the magnetic and geographic north poles is called the **magnetic declination** of the particular location of the observer. In certain places on Earth, the declination is 0°. In these places only, the compass needle assumes a true north-south position. This means that when the declination is 0°, the geographic North Pole, the magnetic north pole, and the observer are all aligned in a straight line. Navigators use special maps that show the declination in dif-

ferent locations. By knowing the proper declination, and by using a compass, one can
then determine the direction of true north,
that is, the geographic North Pole.

The north and south magnetic poles of
Earth can be located by using a **dipping needle** (Figure 17-10). This device is a compass
needle suspended so that it rotates in a vertical plane; a protractor that is part of the instrument permits a person to measure the
angle through which the needle moves. This
angle, called the **angle of dip**, is the angle
that Earth's magnetic field makes with the
horizontal at any specific location on Earth.
At the equator, the angle of dip is 0°. As you
move from the equator closer to Earth's north
magnetic pole, the angle of dip increases until
it reaches 90°—a vertical position—at the
magnetic north pole. At the magnetic south
pole, the dipping needle also indicates a 90°
angle of dip.

Measurements of magnetic declination
and dip show that the Earth's magnetic field
is continually changing. Although these
changes are slight, they make it necessary
for mapmakers to undertake regular mag-

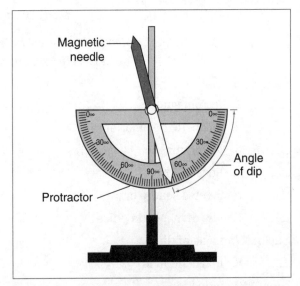

Figure 17-10. A dipping needle indicates the difference between the geographic pole and the
magnetic pole.

netic surveys of Earth to keep their maps up
to date. In addition, evidence indicates that
Earth's magnetic poles have completely reversed several times in history and will most
likely do so again in the future. Much still remains to be learned about Earth's behavior
as a magnet.

Chapter Review

Science Terms

*The following list contains all the boldfaced words found in this
chapter and the page on which each appears.*

alnico magnet (p. 262)

angle of dip (p. 267)

artificial magnet (p. 262)

dipping needle (p. 267)

domain (p. 262)

electromagnet (p. 264)

ferromagnetic (p. 261)

induction (p. 263)

law of magnetic poles (p. 264)

lines of force (p. 265)

lodestone (p. 261)

magnetic (p. 261)

magnetic declination (p. 266)

magnetic field (p. 265)

magnetic force (p. 264)

magnetic pole (p. 264)

magnetism (p. 261)

magnetite (p. 262)

natural magnet (p. 262)

nonmagnetic (p. 261)

north pole (p. 264)

permanent magnet (p. 263)

south pole (p. 264)

temporary magnet (p. 263)

Matching Questions

In your notebook, write the letter of the item in column B that is
most closely related to the item in column A.

Column A

_____ 1. ferromagnetic

_____ 2. magnetic declination

_____ 3. electromagnet

_____ 4. lines of force

_____ 5. inverse square law

_____ 6. law of magnetic poles

_____ 7. angle of dip

_____ 8. magnetic field

_____ 9. induction

_____ 10. domain

Column B

a. pattern used to represent the direction of the magnetic field around a magnet

b. opposite poles attract whereas like poles repel

c. difference between magnetic and geographic poles

d. a measure used to differentiate between Earth's magnetic and geographic poles

e. magnetic effect some distance from magnet

f. a region in which the magnetic fields of atoms are grouped together

g. a way of magnetizing a magnetic substance

h. description of a material that is attracted to a magnet

i. a magnet that can be turned on and off

j. relationship that describes how the strength of a magnet varies with distance

Multiple-Choice Questions

In your notebook, write the letter preceding the word or expression
that best completes the statement or answers the question.

1. Which rock has been used for navigational purposes?
   a. hematite   c. bauxite
   b. lodestone   d. calcite

2. Which of the following is a nonmagnetic substance?
   a. cobalt   c. iron
   b. nickel   d. zinc

3. Which of the following substances can be used to test for a magnetic substance?
   a. iron filings   c. zinc
   b. copper   d. sand

4. Magnetic effects are produced by
   a. stationary electrons
   b. protons locked into place
   c. electrons spinning around their own axis
   d. an irregular arrangement of atoms

5. What must happen to the domains of a material in order for it to be magnetic?
   a. The majority of domains must be aligned in the same direction.
   b. The domains must disappear so the fields of the atoms do not conflict.
   c. No two domains can point in the same direction.
   d. The material must have a single, large domain.

6. Breaking a magnet in half results in
   a. the destruction of the magnet
   b. the formation of two half magnets
   c. the formation of two complete magnets
   d. disruption of the magnetic domains

7. Which elements make up the ore known as magnetite?
   a. iron and oxygen
   b. nickel and copper

c. cobalt and aluminum
d. silver and zinc

8. A magnet can be made by
a. stroking a magnetic material in one direction with a magnet
b. striking a magnetic material with a hammer
c. heating a magnetic material
d. stroking a magnetic material in both directions with a magnet

9. Placing a magnetic material near (but not touching) a magnet produces a magnet by
a. contact   c. conduction
b. induction   d. reaction

10. Which scientist discovered that a wire carrying an electric current has magnetic properties?
a. Volta   c. Oersted
b. Ampère   d. Maxwell

11. Why can hammering a magnet cause it to become demagnetized?
a. It forces electrons in the material to start flowing.
b. It stops the regular spinning of electrons in the atoms of the material.
c. It causes the domains in the material to become aligned.
d. It disturbs the regular pattern of domains.

12. The force of attraction between the poles of two magnets is most greatly affected by
a. the distance between the poles
b. the size of the magnets
c. the strength of the magnets
d. the composition of the magnets

13. When the south poles of two magnets are brought close together,
a. they attract each other
b. they have no effect on each other
c. they repel each other
d. they first repel and then attract each other

14. The ends of a magnet are known as
a. electrodes   c. the field
b. poles   d. domains

15. When the distance between unlike poles of two magnets is tripled, the force of attraction between these poles is decreased
a. 4 times   c. 3 times
b. 6 times   d. 9 times

16. The magnetic effects in the region around a magnet form the
a. magnetic domain
b. magnetic field
c. magnetic pole
d. magnetic induction

17. A magnetic field is represented by
a. domains   c. charged atoms
b. iron filings d. lines of force

18. Which instrument that operates on the principle of magnetism is used currently for navigation?
a. map   c. compass
b. lodestone   d. circuit

19. Which scientist proposed the theory that Earth is a giant magnet?
a. Gilbert   c. Ampère
b. Maxwell   d. Oersted

20. To find the relationship between the magnetic north pole of Earth and the geographic north pole, scientists use an instrument known as a
a. compass   c. lodestone
b. dipping needle d. sextant

TEST-TAKING TIP As you prepare for a test, it may help to make an outline using the headings from each chapter. Write the headings as questions and then make sure you can answer each question.

Modified True-False Questions

In some of the following statements, the italicized term makes the statement incorrect. For each incorrect statement, in your notebook, write the term that must be substituted for the italicized term to make the statement correct. For each correct statement, write the word "true."

1. *Magnetism* is the ability to attract certain materials, such as iron._____

2. A substance that is not attracted to a magnet but allows magnetism to pass through it is said to be *artificial*.

   _____

3. The magnetism of nickel is called *ferro-magnetism*. _____

4. Lodestone is an example of a *natural magnet*. _____

5. When steel is magnetized, it becomes a *temporary magnet*. _____

6. The observation that opposite magnetic poles attract each other is stated in the *law of domains*. _____

7. An invisible magnetic field can be detected by using *wood shavings*.

   _____

8. The angle that the magnetic field of the Earth makes with the horizontal as measured by a dipping needle is called the *angle of declination*. _____

9. At the equator, the angle of dip is *90°*.

   _____

10. The magnetic north pole is located in *northern Canada*. _____

Check Your Knowledge

Write the answer to each question in your notebook

1. Define each of the following terms:
   a. magnetic substance
   b. natural magnet
   c. temporary magnet
   d. magnetic poles
   e. magnetic field

2. Explain the theory of magnetism. What evidence supports this theory?

3. Describe three methods for making a magnet.

4. Describe three methods of destroying a magnet.

5. Explain why a suspended magnet will line up in a north-south position when it comes to rest.

Think Critically

Write the answer to each of the following questions in your notebook.

1. Suppose you were to place several compasses around a bar magnet. Draw a diagram showing how the position of the compass needle would change with location.

2. The N on a compass points toward Earth's magnetic north pole. What does this indicate about the end of the compass needle relative to Earth's magnetic pole?

3. At your position, the angle of dip on a dipping needle measures 45°. Approximate your position with respect to the magnetic pole and the magnetic equator.

Take It Further

1. Unlike electric charges, magnetic poles are never found alone. In other words, no

magnet has only a north pole or a south pole. Research this phenomenon and present an explanation for it. Include evidence and perhaps diagrams in your presentation.

2. Investigate the movement of Earth's magnetic pole over time. Make a map showing its movement and predict its future movement. Explain how this has affected explorers and hikers. Include specific examples of maps that have changed over time. For example, signs on runways at Tampa International Airport were changed to reflect the new position of Earth's magnetic poles. You may wish to read the articles at *http://www.dailymail.co.uk/sciencetech/article-1344899/Shift-magnetic-north-pole-affects--Tampa-airport.html*.

3. Some animals are believed to be able to use Earth's magnetic field for migratory movements. Investigate this possibility and present an example to the class.

CAREER

4. Navigators are people who use compasses, radar, GPS, and other equipment. Find out what a navigator can do, where a navigator might work, and what training is required. You may wish to use the following sites as you begin your research: *http://www.career-descriptions.co.uk/navigator-career-description.htm* and *http://www.careersinthemilitary.com/index.cfm?fuseaction=main.career detail&mc_id=134*.

18 How Are Electricity and Magnetism Related?

Would you be surprised to learn that this crane can lift heavy objects using magnetism? It is quite different from the magnets you might have on your refrigerator or locker. The crane has a very strong magnet that can be turned on and off.

After reading this chapter, you should be able to answer the following questions:

What is an electromagnet?

What factors affect the strength of electromagnets?

What are some of the uses of electromagnets?

How is electricity produced from magnetism?

How is an alternating current different from a direct current?

What are some applications of electromagnetic induction?

You have studied electricity and you have studied magnetism. In this inquiry investigation, you will have an opportunity to explore the relationship between electricity and magnetism.

Materials:
- ✔ safety goggles
- ✔ 2 iron nails
- ✔ 30-cm length of bell wire
- ✔ 2 dry cell (1.5 V)
- ✔ knife switch
- ✔ paper clips
- ✔ magnetic compass

NOTE: Be sure to use the same length of bell wire for all the experiments in this inquiry investigation.

Part A Using a 30-cm length of insulated bell wire, wind 10 turns around an iron nail. Connect the bell wire, the dry cell, and the knife switch in a series circuit, as shown in Figure 18-1. Leave the switch open.

Place a few paper clips on your desk and touch one end of the nail to them.

1. Describe what happens.

Part B Close the switch in the circuit and again touch the end of the nail to the paper clips. You have made an electromagnet. Open the switch again.

2. Describe what happens when the switch is closed.

Part C Repeat Part B. This time, however, wind 20 turns of bell wire around the nail before closing the switch. Open the switch when you are finished.

3. What happens to an electromagnet when you increase the number of turns around the nail?

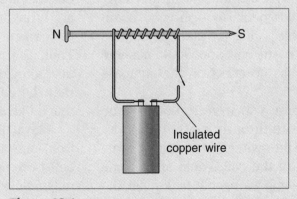

Figure 18-1.

Part D Wind 20 turns of bell wire around *two* iron nails. Close the switch on the electromagnet and touch the ends of the nails to the paper clips. Open the switch again when you are done.

4. *What happens to an electromagnet when you increase the thickness of the core, that is, increase the number of nails?*

Part E Connect a second dry cell into the circuit in series. There are still 20 turns of bell wire wrapped around two iron nails. Close the switch on the electromagnet.

5. *What happens to an electromagnet when you increase the current through the circuit?*

Part F Remove the second dry cell from the circuit. Place a magnetic compass near the nails and close the switch on the electromagnet. Open the switch when you are finished.

6. *What effect does the electromagnet have on the compass needle?*

Part G Reverse the wires connected to the dry cell and close the switch again. Observe the compass needle. Open the switch when you are done.

7. *What effect does reversing the wires have on the compass needle?*

What Is an Electromagnet?

You learned in the previous chapter that when an electric current passes through a straight wire, a magnetic field is produced in the space surrounding the wire. Suppose, for example, you were to wind an insulated copper wire around a pencil to form a coil. If you then remove the pencil and place a compass near one end of the coil, you would observe that the coil has no effect on the compass needle.

Then suppose you were to connect the ends of the wire through a switch to a dry cell and close the switch, you would observe that one end of the coil would attract one pole of the compass needle and repel the other. If the compass were placed near the other end of the coil, the reverse would happen (Ampère's experiment, Figure 18-2).

The behavior of the compass needle resembles its behavior near a bar magnet. Recall that attraction occurs when unlike poles are brought together and that repulsion occurs when like poles are brought together. Thus, the behavior of the compass needle near a coil carrying an electric current shows that the coil has magnetic properties very much like a bar magnet.

As you observed in your inquiry investigation, an iron nail in a coil connected to a dry cell becomes a magnet and attracts ferromagnetic substances such as paper clips. Such a magnet, produced by electrons flow-

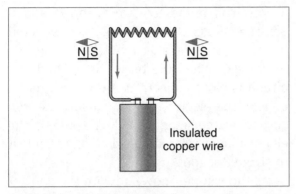

Figure 18-2. The diagram represents a modern version of Ampère's experiment.

ing through a coil of wire, is an *electromagnet*. The nail is called the **core** of the electromagnet.

To determine which end of the core is the north pole, you use a procedure known as the **left-hand rule** (Figure 18-3). Wrap the four fingers of your left hand around the coil so that the fingers point in the direction in which the electrons are flowing, that is, from the negative terminal of the dry cell to the positive terminal. When you extend your left thumb along the core, your thumb points to the north pole of the electromagnet. Thus the left-hand rule explains why the polarity

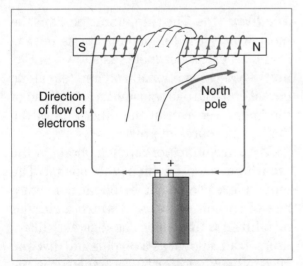

Figure 18-3. The illustration demonstrates the left-hand rule. When the curved fingers of your left hand are pointing in the direction of electron flow in the coiled wire, your thumb points toward the north pole of the magnet created.

of the electromagnet was reversed when you reversed the wires connected to the dry cell in the inquiry investigation.

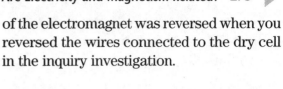

What Factors Affect the Strength of Electromagnets?

The strength of an electromagnet can be changed in several ways, some of which you discovered in your inquiry investigation.

1. *Varying the number of turns of wire around the core.* When you increased the windings of the coil from 10 turns to 20, the core picked up more paper clips than before. Therefore, when you increase the number of turns or loops of insulated wire, the strength of the electromagnet increases.
2. *Varying the thickness of the core.* When you wound a coil of wire around two nails instead of only one, the electromagnet became stronger. Thus, when the thickness of the core of an electromagnet is increased, the strength of the electromagnet is increased.
3. *Varying the current.* When you added a second dry cell in series to the circuit containing a coil of 20 turns of wire, the electromagnet picked up still more paper clips. Therefore, when you increase the amount of the current through the coil of wire by increasing the voltage, the strength of the electromagnet increases.
4. *Changing the core.* As you learned earlier, when an empty coil of wire is connected to a source of voltage, a compass needle indicates the presence of a magnetic field at the ends of the coil. If a wooden core is inserted in the coil, the strength of the electromagnet does not change. When a magnetic substance such as iron is used as a core, the strength of the electromagnet may be increased as much as 1000 times. If a weaker magnetic substance, such as

cobalt, is used as a core, the strength of the electromagnet is increased about 170 times.

To summarize:

- There is a magnetic field around a straight wire that carries current. If you bend the wire in the form of a number of loops, each loop behaves as a separate magnet. Adding more coils adds more magnets, which increases the strength of the electromagnet.
- Recall Oersted's discovery that a movement of electrons in a wire produces a magnetic field around the wire. Increasing the number of electrons (current) through an electromagnet thus increases its strength.
- Some objects become magnetized by induction when magnetic lines of force pass through them. As a result, the magnetic field near these objects becomes stronger. This effect on the lines of force is called **magnetic permeability**. Soft iron possesses greater magnetic permeability than cobalt. Both metals possess greater magnetic permeability than either air or wood. Therefore, iron and cobalt are used in cores to strengthen electromagnets.
- Using a larger or thicker core in an electromagnet provides more magnetic domains and thus increases the strength of an electromagnet.

What Are Some Uses of Electromagnets?

Electromagnets of varying strengths are used in many of the household and industrial devices people use all the time. Some of these devices include the electric bell, the telephone, and the electric motor.

The Electric Bell. A common type of electric bell consists of a horseshoe electromagnet,

a soft iron **armature**, or clapper, and a gong (see Figure 18-4). The bell is connected through a switch or push button to a source of voltage. When the button is pushed, the circuit is closed; electrons flow through the coils of the electromagnet, causing the iron core to become magnetized. The poles of the electromagnet attract the clapper, causing it to strike the gong.

As the clapper moves toward the gong, it also moves away from a contact screw. Thus the circuit is broken at the contact point and the flow of electrons stops. The iron core of the electromagnet loses its magnetism and the clapper is pulled back to its original position by a spring. In this position, the clapper makes contact with the contact screw, thereby completing the circuit. The electromagnet again attracts the armature and the cycle repeats itself over and over, as long as the circuit is closed (the button is pushed). When the button is released, the circuit is opened, the flow of electrons stops, and the bell stops ringing.

Buzzers operate like bells. However, since a buzzer lacks a hammer on the clapper and a gong, the sound is the buzz of the vibrating armature.

The Telephone. The **telephone**, perhaps the most widely used communications device, also uses electromagnets. As shown in Figure 18-5, a conventional land-line telephone circuit consists of a transmitter at one end of the line, a receiver at the other end of the line, and a source of power.

The transmitter of any telephone is the mouthpiece into which you speak. The mouthpiece of an older telephone contains a box of carbon granules to which a circular metal disk is attached. The disk acts like a drum head, known as a diaphragm, that can vibrate back and forth. The receiver is the earphone of the telephone and reproduces the sounds entering the transmitter. The receiver is a horseshoe electromagnet in which

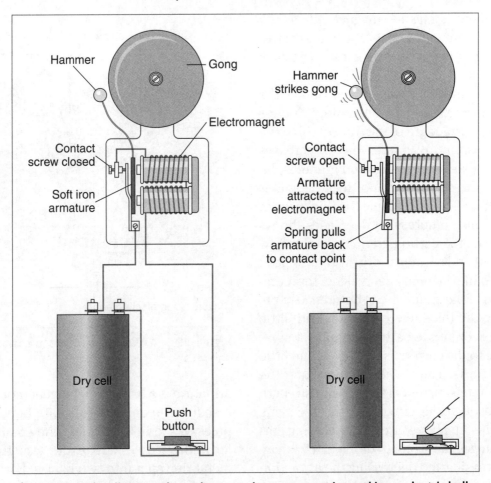

Figure 18-4. The diagram shows how an electromagnet is used in an electric bell.

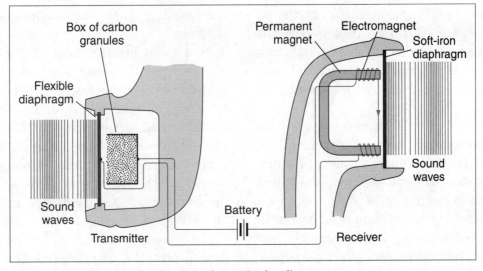

Figure 18-5. A telephone circuit is shown in the diagram.

a permanent horseshoe magnet acts as the core. A diaphragm made of a thin sheet of soft iron is attached to the poles of the electromagnet.

How does the receiver reproduce the sounds that enter the transmitter? Sounds cause the diaphragm of the transmitter to vibrate. This, in turn, increases or decreases the compression of the carbon granules. Increasing the compression of these granules can be likened to increasing the thickness of a wire. This compression decreases the resistance of the carbon granules to the flow of current and permits more current to flow. In the same manner, decreasing the compression of the granules can be likened to decreasing the thickness of a wire. With little compression of the carbon granules, the resistance to the current is strongest, and little current flows. Thus, when sounds enter the transmitter, a current that varies in strength flows through the circuit. At the receiving end of the telephone circuit this varying current changes the strength of the electromagnet, increasing and decreasing the attraction of the electromagnet for the diaphragm. This produces vibrations of the diaphragm, corresponding to the vibrations of the diaphragm of the transmitter. In this manner, the sounds that enter the transmitter are reproduced in the receiver.

Modern telephones and cell phones no longer use carbon granules. Nonetheless, the same basic principles of older telephones still apply and electromagnets are still used to change electrical signals into sounds.

The Electric Motor. Electromagnets are important to **electric motors**, which in turn are used to power trains, elevators, and many household devices such as vacuum cleaners and electric drills.

An electric motor is composed of a **field magnet**, an armature, a **commutator**, and **brushes**. The field magnet may be a permanent horseshoe magnet or a horseshoe electromagnet, as shown in Figure 18-6. The

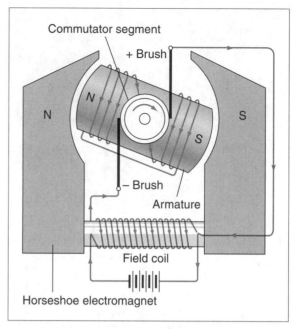

Figure 18-6. A direct-current electric motor is shown above.

armature is a bar electromagnet mounted on a shaft, or axle, free to rotate between the poles of the field magnet. The commutator, located on the shaft of the armature, is a metal ring split into two halves. Each half is insulated from the other. The same current that enters the horseshoe electromagnet is brought to the commutator by brushes. The brushes are metallic strips mounted so that each brush is always in contact with one of the commutator segments. From the commutator, wires lead to the coil of the armature.

In a complete circuit containing a motor, the electrons flow from the field magnet to the brushes, into one segment of the commutator, and into the armature. As a result, the armature coil is magnetized. When one pole of the armature becomes a north pole, the north pole of the field magnet repels it, and the armature rotates, making a half-turn. As the armature rotates, each brush makes contact with a different commutator segment. This changes the direction of the electron flow through the armature coil. According to the left-hand rule, the poles of the electromagnet of the armature are reversed. Like poles again face each other, and the armature makes another half-turn. As the commutator continues to reverse the direction of the flow of electrons, the armature continues to rotate. When a mechanical device is connected to the shaft of the armature, the device operates. Thus, electrical energy is transformed to mechanical energy.

Electric Meters. Recall (Chapter 16) that Ohm's law describes the relationship of amperage, voltage, and resistance. You will now see how each of these characteristics can be measured using electric meters.

In its simplest form, an electric meter resembles an electric motor. Both devices contain an armature (moving coil), free to rotate on its axle between the poles of a magnet. (In the electric meter, this is usually a permanent horseshoe magnet.) The armature in an electric motor, owing to the action of the commutator, makes complete rotations; the armature of an electric meter, however,

makes only a partial turn. When current enters the coil of a meter, the coil becomes magnetized. Since no commutator is present, the attraction and repulsion between the poles of the coil and the poles of the horseshoe magnet cause the coil to make a partial turn. The greater the current, the greater is the turn. A needle attached to the coil points to a scale designed to give the proper reading. When the circuit is broken, a spring pulls the needle back to its original position.

Tiny electric currents are measured by a **galvanometer** (Figure 18-7). Note that the zero (0) position on this meter is in the center of the scale. This permits a galvanometer to detect the direction of the current (polarity). Larger electric currents are measured with an *ammeter* (see Figure 18-8). To protect the windings of the coil in the ammeter from burning out, a bar of metal called a **shunt** is connected in parallel with the coil.

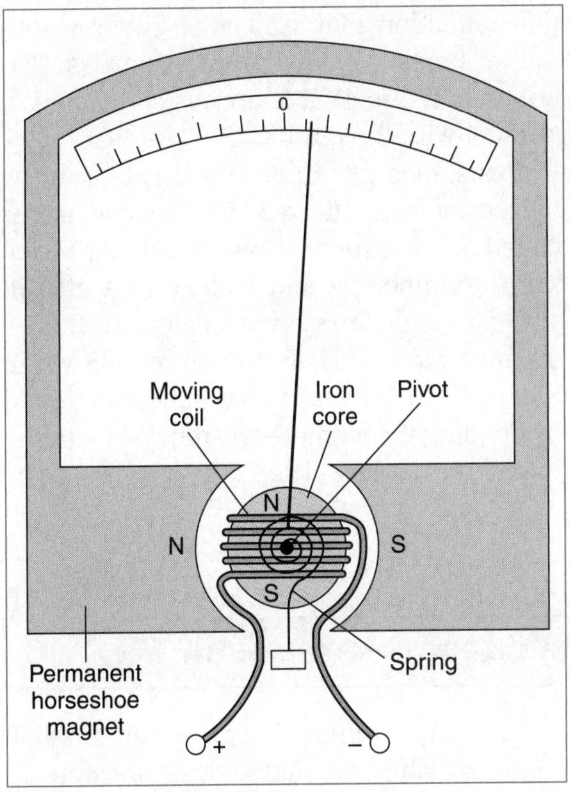

Figure 18-7. The diagram shows a simple galvanometer.

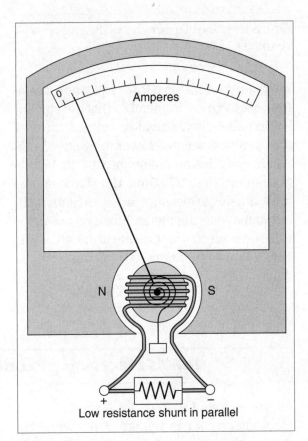
Figure 18-8. The diagram shows a simple ammeter.

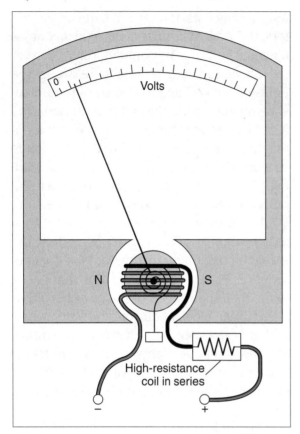

Figure 18-9. The diagram shows the parts of a voltmeter.

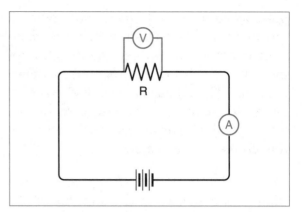

Figure 18-10. The diagram illustrates how resistance is measured

The shunt offers very low resistance to the flow of electrons. Remember that the current in a parallel circuit divides and that most of the current enters the lower resistance. This means that, in the ammeter, very little current enters the coil. Thus, the shunt allows the ammeter to measure large currents without damage to the meter. Since an ammeter measures electrons flowing through a circuit, it is always connected in series with the circuit.

Voltage is measured by a *voltmeter*, which is a high-resistance galvanometer (see Figure 18-9). Hence, only a very small amount of current enters the voltmeter itself, thus protecting the delicate coil in the voltmeter. It is the flow of electrons, or current, that magnetizes the coil of the meter and turns the needle. Recall from Ohm's law that current *(I)* depends on the voltage *(V)*: $I = V/R$. Thus, changes in the voltage will determine the deflection of the needle. Since a voltmeter measures the voltage across two points in a circuit, it is always connected in parallel with the circuit.

Resistance *(R)* in an electrical circuit is measured with the aid of a special meter called an *ohmmeter*. However, if you measure the amperage and voltage in a circuit, you can use Ohm's law to calculate the resistance *(R = V/I)*. In the circuit shown in Figure 18-10, the resistance *(R)* can be found by dividing the ammeter reading *(A)* into the voltmeter reading *(V)*.

How Is Electricity Produced from Magnetism?

As you know, Oersted discovered that an electric current passing through a wire produces a magnetic field around the wire. This discovery is the basis of all modern inventions containing electromagnets.

In 1831, *Michael Faraday*, an English scientist, showed that it was possible to produce the reverse effect—that is, he discovered how to obtain electricity from magnetism. Faraday placed a permanent magnet

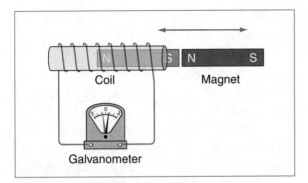

Figure 18-11. An electric current can be generated by moving a magnet back and forth through a coil.

in a coil. A galvanometer connected to the ends of the coil indicated that no current was flowing. Upon moving the magnet out of the coil, Faraday noted that the galvanometer needle moved, indicating the presence of current (see Figure 18-11). When he placed the magnet back into the coil, the needle of the meter moved—but in the opposite direction.

Note that Faraday succeeded in producing an electric current only when he *moved* the magnet into or out of the coil of wire. He also found that he could produce a current in a coil by holding the magnet still and moving the coil back and forth. In this case, the direction in which the needle of the meter moves depends on the direction in which the coil is moved. Producing an electric current by moving a magnet through a coil of wire (or by moving the coil of wire back and forth) is called **electromagnetic induction**. It does not matter whether the coil moves or the magnet moves. Electromagnetic induction takes place whenever a coil of wire cuts the lines of force of a magnet.

If the ends of the coil are not connected to a complete circuit, electrons will not flow; instead, an induced electromotive force, or voltage, is produced between the ends of the wire in the coil. When the circuit is complete, however, the induced voltage will produce an induced current. Thus, electrons will flow through the circuit as long as the coil cuts the lines of force of the magnet. (Recall from Ohm's law that current depends on voltage: $I = V/R$.)

How Do Scientists Explain Electromagnetic Induction?

Recall that a magnet is surrounded by a field composed of lines of force that spread out from the magnet. Recall also that a conducting wire is metallic and is composed of atoms that contain electrons. When a magnet is moved in and out of a coil of wire, the lines of force of the magnet are cut by the wire. When a conductor cuts the lines of force of a magnet, electrons are forced to one end of the conductor. As this occurs, the other end of the wire becomes deficient in electrons. Accordingly, when the two ends of the wire are connected to a galvanometer, electrons flow from the end of the wire where they are in excess through the galvanometer to the end of the wire where they are deficient. The electrons continue to flow as long as the magnetic lines of force are cut by the wire, that is, as long as either the magnet or the coil is in motion.

How Can the Strength of an Induced Current Be Varied?

Remember that the strength of an electromagnet can be varied in many ways. Somewhat similar methods are used to vary the strength of an induced current.

1. *Varying the speed of motion.* When the speed of motion of either the coil or the magnet is increased, the strength of the induced current increases. Suppose you slowly push a magnet into a coil connected to a galvanometer and note how far the needle moves. Then remove the magnet and push it rapidly into the coil. You would note that the galvanometer needle deflects to a much greater extent. This indicates that the amount of current induced in the coil has increased. The same results are obtained regardless of whether the magnet or the coil is moving. Thus, it appears that the strength of an induced current is related

to the speed with which the coil of wire cuts the lines of force of the magnet.

2. *Varying the strength of the magnet.* Now suppose you push a bar magnet into a coil connected to a galvanometer. Again, you note how far the needle moves. Then you place two magnets side by side, with similar poles together, and push them into the coil, moving at the same speed as before. The galvanometer connected to the coil registers a larger movement of the needle than when the single magnet was pushed into the same coil. A stronger single magnet produces the same effect as the two individual magnets. Since stronger magnets have stronger magnetic fields, the coil cuts more lines of force and thus the strength of the induced current increases.

3. *Varying the number of turns.* When the speed of motion and the strength of the magnet remain the same, the amount of current induced in a coil is increased by increasing the number of loops in the coil. Thus, it appears that when more turns of wire cut the magnetic lines of force, more electrons in the coil are disturbed. As a result, the amount of induced current is increased.

▶ **How Is an Alternating Current Different from a Direct Current?**

Two types of current can be produced depending on how the current flows. They are known as alternating current and direct current.

Alternating Current. When a current is induced by plunging a magnet into a coil of wire connected to a galvanometer, the needle of the galvanometer deflects in a particular direction. As you learned, when the magnet is withdrawn from the coil, the galvanometer needle deflects in the opposite direction. This shows that the direction of current depends on the direction in which the magnet is moved. An electric current that reverses its direction at regular intervals is known as an **alternating current**. When the electrons make one complete trip back and forth in the circuit, two alternations have occurred and the electrons are said to have completed one **cycle**. Most homes in this country are supplied with 60-cycle alternating current, that is, current that changes its direction approximately 120 times every second.

Direct Current. A flow of electrons traveling in one direction in a circuit is known as a **direct current**. Batteries are common sources of direct current.

Both alternating-current and direct-current circuits are useful in the home and for commercial and industrial needs. However, most power companies supply only alternating current for these purposes because alternating current, as you will learn later, is transmitted from generating stations to the user more economically than direct current.

What Are Some Applications of Electromagnetic Induction?

Being able to induce an electric current makes many important devices possible.

Electric Generators

An electric **generator** is a device that produces electric current by means of electromagnetic induction. Generators resemble electric motors. In a motor, a flow of electrons through the windings causes a continuous rotation of the armature. In a generator, on the other hand, the rotation of the armature between the poles of a magnet induces voltage in the armature. The voltage, in turn, induces current.

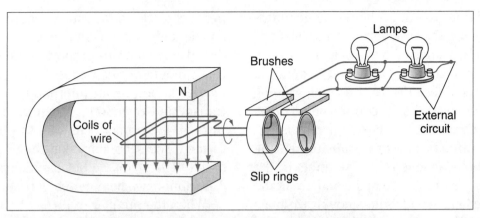

Figure 18-12. The diagram shows an alternating-current generator.

The mechanical energy required to drive the armature of a generator may be derived directly or indirectly from falling water, from burning coal, or from nuclear energy. An alternating current generator consists of an armature coil mounted on a shaft between the poles of either a permanent magnet, shown in Figure 18-12, or an electromagnet. A half-turn of the armature causes a flow of electrons in the coil in one direction. Completing the rotation of the armature with another half-turn means motion through the magnetic field in the opposite direction. This causes a flow of electrons in the coil in the opposite direction. To complete the circuit, the alternating current passes through two metal rings, called **slip rings**, which are mounted on the same shaft as the armature. From the slip rings, brushes lead the alternating current to the load (lamps) or to the user.

In some generators, a commutator, such as the one used in the electric motor, is mounted on the shaft in place of the slip rings. Recall that the commutator reverses the direction of electron flow in the motor. In the same way, each half of the commutator in this type of generator changes from one brush to another at the exact instant that the direction of electron flow in each half of the commutator is reversed. This produces a flow of electrons in one direction only, and such a generator is called a **direct-current generator** (see Figure 18-13).

Transformers

It is impossible to transmit electricity over long distances without some loss of power. These losses generally occur as heat. Wires carrying electric current generate heat, and the quantity of heat is roughly dependent on the amperage. It is therefore more economical to transmit low-amperage electricity.

The **transformer** is a device designed to change the voltage produced by power

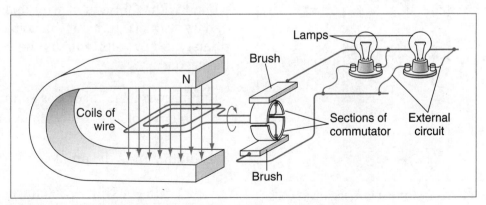

Figure 18-13. The diagram shows a direct-current generator.

companies for use in the home and in industry. Basically, the transformer is an electromagnet consisting of two coils, a **primary coil** and a **secondary coil**, both wound on the same core (see Figure 18-14). Alternating current changes its direction many times every second. If alternating current is fed into the primary coil of a transformer, the coil becomes magnetized. The effect of the alternating current is to make and break the magnetic field, which is like moving the magnet into and out of a coil. Magnetic lines of force are cut in the same manner as moving a magnet in and out of a coil at the same rate. When the current in the primary coil magnetizes the coil, lines of force move first in one direction and then the other.

The transformer's primary and secondary coils are on the same core. Therefore, when the primary becomes an alternating electromagnet, the lines of force of the primary induce a corresponding alternating voltage in the secondary coil. When the number of turns in the secondary coil is greater than that of the primary coil, the voltage induced in the secondary is greater than that in the primary. Such a device is called a **step-up transformer**.

It would appear that, in the transformer, something is being gotten for nothing, which violates the conservation laws. However, the total electrical energy is roughly equal to the product of the voltage and the current. Thus, as the induced voltage increases, the induced current drops proportionately and the total amount of electrical energy remains unchanged. Before an alternating voltage is transmitted over long distances, it is sent through the primary coil of a step-up transformer. The secondary coil then supplies a much higher voltage but a smaller current. This minimizes heat losses in transmission.

When the number of turns of wire in the secondary coil is less than the number of turns in the primary coil, the voltage in the secondary is less than the voltage in the primary. The current in the secondary is proportionately higher, which keeps the total amount of electrical energy unchanged. This type of transformer is called a **step-down transformer**.

When the secondary coil has twice as many turns of wire as the primary coil, the voltage induced in the secondary is twice that of the primary. Accordingly, the ratio of the number of turns in the primary to the number of turns in the secondary determines the ratio of the voltages between the primary and the secondary coils. Thus, when you know the number of turns of wire in the primary and secondary coils, as well as the voltage in *one* of the coils, you can find the voltage in the other by using the formula

$$\frac{\text{primary voltage}}{\text{secondary voltage}} = \frac{\text{turns in primary}}{\text{turns in secondary}}$$

For example, suppose the primary is wound with 300 turns of wire and the secondary with 600 turns. If the voltage of the primary is 115 volts, what is the voltage of the secondary?

$$\frac{\text{primary voltage}}{\text{secondary voltage}} = \frac{\text{turns in primary}}{\text{turns in secondary}}$$

Substituting from the problem,

$$\frac{115 \text{ volts}}{\text{secondary voltage}} = \frac{300 \text{ turns}}{600 \text{ turns}} = \frac{1}{2}$$

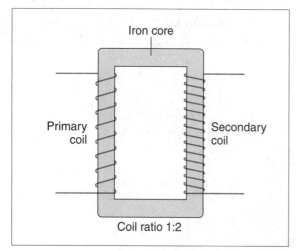

Figure 18-14. A transformer is made up of coils of wire as shown in the diagram.

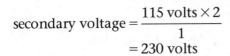

$$\text{secondary voltage} = \frac{115 \text{ volts} \times 2}{1}$$
$$= 230 \text{ volts}$$

The use of step-up transformers in generating stations permits power companies to use thin wires to carry high-voltage–low-current electricity to transformer stations near the user's home. By using step-down transformers installed near the users, the high voltages can be reduced to 220 or 110 volts, which are the voltages usually required by electrical devices in homes.

Chapter Review

Science Terms

The following list contains all the boldfaced words found in this chapter and the page on which each appears.

alternating current (p. 282)

armature (p. 276)

brushes (p. 278)

commutator (p. 278)

core (p. 275)

cycle (p. 282)

direct current (p. 282)

direct-current generator (p. 283)

electric motors (p. 278)

electromagnetic induction (p. 281)

field magnet (p. 278)

galvanometer (p. 279)

generator (p. 282)

left-hand rule (p. 275)

magnetic permeability (p. 276)

primary coil (p. 284)

secondary coil (p. 284)

shunt (p. 279)

slip rings (p. 283)

step-down transformer (p. 284)

step-up transformer (p. 284)

telephone (p. 276)

transformer (p. 283)

Matching Questions

In your notebook, write the letter of the item in column B that is most closely related to the item in column A.

Column A

_____ 1. magnetic permeability

_____ 2. electromagnetic induction

_____ 3. commutator

_____ 4. ammeter

_____ 5. left-hand rule

_____ 6. direct current

_____ 7. galvanometer

_____ 8. step-up transformer

_____ 9. alternating current

_____ 10. generator

Column B

a. a method for finding the north pole of an electromagnet

b. the production of current by the movement of a magnet relative to a coil of wire

c. a device that measures larger electric currents

d. the effect a magnetic core has on the lines of force

e. an electric current that reverses direction

f. a metal ring split in two halves

g. a device that increases voltage

h. a device that produces current by electromagnetic induction

i. a flow of electrons in one direction

j. a device that measures tiny electric currents

Multiple-Choice Questions

In your notebook, write the letter preceding the word or expression
that best completes the statement or answers the question.

1. When you use the left-hand rule, you extend your thumb in the direction
   a. in which electrons are flowing
   b. opposite to the direction of electric current
   c. of the north pole of the magnet
   d. of the south pole of the magnet

2. When the number of turns of wire around the core of an electromagnet is increased, the strength of the electromagnet
   a. increases
   b. decreases
   c. remains the same
   d. increases, then decreases

3. A decrease in the amount of current supplied to an electromagnet causes the strength of the electromagnet to
   a. increase
   b. decrease
   c. remain the same
   d. first decrease, then increase

4. Which of the following substances, used as the core of an electromagnet, produces the strongest magnet?
   a. copper   c. wood
   b. cobalt   d. soft iron

5. In general, when the thickness of the core of an electromagnet is increased, the strength of the electromagnet
   a. increases
   b. decreases
   c. remains the same
   d. first increases, then decreases

6. What causes an electric bell to stop ringing once the button is no longer being pushed?
   a. The iron core of the electromagnet becomes magnetized.
   b. Electrons flow through the coils of the electromagnet.
   c. The clapper moves away from the contact screw.
   d. The electromagnet attracts the armature.

7. Part of a telephone transmitter is a box containing granules of
   a. carbon   c. cobalt
   b. sulfur   d. silicon

8. What must the diaphragm in a telephone receiver do in order for sound to be produced?
   a. It must become magnetic.
   b. It must vibrate back and forth.
   c. It must transmit an electric current.
   d. It must become compressed like a spring.

9. A tiny electric current can be measured with
   a. a voltmeter
   b. an ohmmeter
   c. a galvanometer
   d. a shunt

10. What is the role of a shunt in an ammeter?
    a. to protect the ammeter from burning out
    b. to provide large currents to the ammeter
    c. to point to the measure of current on a scale
    d. to continuously reverse the direction of current

11. Large electric currents are best measured with
    a. an ammeter
    b. a galvanometer
    c. a voltmeter
    d. an ohmmeter

12. That electricity can be produced from magnetism was first proposed by
    a. Oersted
    b. Ampère
    c. Volta
    d. Faraday

13. As the motion of a magnet in a coil of wire increases, the current induced in the coil
    a. increases
    b. remains the same
    c. decreases
    d. decreases, then increases

14. When a strong magnet moving in a coil is replaced by a weaker magnet, the current induced in the coil
    a. decreases
    b. increases
    c. remains the same
    d. decreases, then increases

15. An electric current that reverses its direction frequently is known as
    a. a direct current
    b. a reversing current
    c. an alternating current
    d. a steady current

16. A device that produces an electric current by means of electromagnetic induction is called
    a. a meter
    b. a generator
    c. a galvanometer
    d. an amplifier

17. Which type of energy is used to drive a generator?
    a. electrical
    b. mechanical
    c. chemical
    d. solar

18. In an alternating-current generator, the current produced is carried to the load by the
    a. magnet
    b. transformer
    c. commutator
    d. brushes

19. In a step-up transformer, as the induced voltage increases, the induced current
    a. increases
    b. decreases
    c. remains the same
    d. increases, then decreases

20. When the secondary coil of a transformer has twice as many turns of wire as the primary coil, the induced voltage in the secondary coil is
    a. half as great as in the primary
    b. the same as in the primary
    c. twice that in the primary
    d. four times that in the primary

TEST-TAKING TIP It can be helpful to use flashcards or diagrams to study direct and inverse relationships. This will help you to avoid confusion when faced with questions providing options for increase, decrease, or remains the same.

Modified True-False Questions

In some of the following statements, the italicized term makes the statement incorrect. For each incorrect statement, in your notebook, write the term that must be substituted for the italicized term to make the statement correct. For each correct statement, write the word "true."

1. *Decreasing* the number of turns of wire in an electromagnet increases its strength. _____

2. The iron around which the wires of an electromagnet are wrapped is known as the *core*. _____

3. In an electric bell, the electromagnet attracts the *clapper*. _____

4. A transmitter and receiver are parts of a *generator*. _____

5. In an electric motor, current is brought to the commutator by a *slip ring*. _____

6. In a circuit, a voltmeter is always connected in *series*. _____

7. A magnet moving in a coil produces a current by *electromagnetic induction*.

8. In a motor, the direction of current flow is reversed by the *armature*. _____

9. A device used to change the voltage entering it is called a *generator.* _____

10. The input voltage of a *step-down transformer* is less than the output voltage. _____

Check Your Knowledge

Write the answer to each question in your notebook.

1. Describe four methods that you can use to increase the strength of an electromagnet.

2. Describe how an electric bell works.

3. Describe how electricity is produced from magnetism.

4. Discuss three methods by which the strength of an induced current can be increased.

5. What is the difference between alternating and direct current?

Think Critically

Write the answer to each of the following questions in your notebook.

1. The number of turns of wire in the primary of a step-up transformer is 200. The secondary contains 800 turns of wire.

What is the voltage produced by the secondary coil if 120 volts enter the primary coil?

2. In a step-down transformer, the primary has 1000 turns of wire whereas the secondary has 500 turns of wire. What voltage is produced by the secondary if the primary is supplied with 120 volts?

Take It Further

1. The Danish physicist Hans Christian Oersted made his discovery while giving a lecture. Research the details of that lecture, such as where and when it occurred. Find out why he was surprised, what he concluded, and what developments came from his discovery. Share your findings with the class.

2. The left-hand rule is not the only rule in physics. Find out what the right-hand rule is and when it is used. Provide a comparison of the rules to the class.

3. Electromagnets were once used in a device known as a telegraph. Research the history of the telegraph and how it led to the development of telephones. Present your findings to the class. Include such information as how telegraphs were built, how they relied on electromagnets, how they were used, and how Morse code made them useful.

4. Electric generators require a mechanical force to move them. Identify several sources of that force. For example, moving water from a dam or steam from heated water can provide the force. Choose one example and create a diagram showing how electricity is generated.

CAREER

5. So many modern devices use electric motors that it is essential to have people who know how to build and repair them. Find out what an electric motor professional does, what training might be required, and what job opportunities exist. Share your findings with the class. You may wish to begin your research at *http://www.bls.gov/oco/ocos184.htm* or *http://www.campusexplorer.com/ careers/AEB86032/electric-motor-power-tool-and-related-repairers/*.

19

What Is the Nature of Heat Energy?

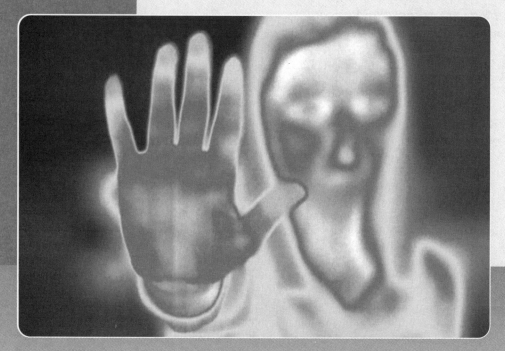

This photo did not record visible light as conventional photos do. Instead, it recorded the heat given off by the woman's body. The colors indicate the amount of heat, with white areas being the warmest and black areas being the coolest.

After reading this chapter, you should be able to answer the following questions:

What is heat?

How is heat related to the expansion of solids, liquids, and gases?

How is heat related to temperature?

What instruments and scales are used to measure temperature?

How is heat transferred?

How is heat measured?

How is heat related to changes in state?

How are heat calories related to food?

Objects change in some way when they are heated or cooled. You probably know this from experience. In this inquiry investigation, you will have an opportunity to explore some specific examples of these types of changes.

Materials:
- ✔ safety goggles
- ✔ ball and ring apparatus
- ✔ Bunsen burner or hot plate
- ✔ container of cold water
- ✔ Erlenmeyer flask (250-mL) with one-hole stopper fitted with a piece of glass tubing
- ✔ food coloring
- ✔ tripod
- ✔ wire gauze
- ✔ rubber balloon
- ✔ rubber band
- ✔ water

NOTE: Wear safety goggles during this activity.

Part A Using the ball-and-ring apparatus provided by your teacher, push the ball in and out of the ring several times.

Holding the ball by its insulated handle, heat the ball in a flame. Now try to push the ball through the ring again.

1. *Describe what happens.*
   Cool the ball by plunging it into a container of cold water. Try to push the ball through the ring again.

2. *Describe what happens.*

3. *What effect does heating have on the ball?*

Part B Push the ball through the ring and keep it there. Heat the ball in a flame. Try to pull the ball through the ring.

4. *Describe what happens.*

5. *How can you remove the ball without first cooling it?*

6. *Try your procedure as described in 5 above. What is the result?*

Part C Fill an Erlenmeyer flask with colored water. Insert a one-hole stopper into the neck of the flask. Your teacher will fit the stopper with a length of

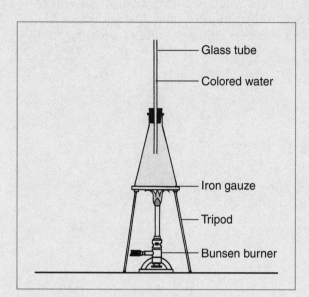

Figure 19-1.

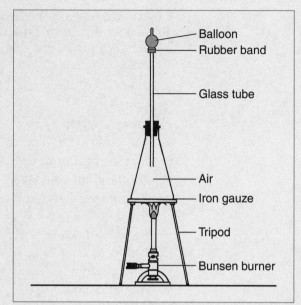

Figure 19-2.

glass tubing, as shown in Figure 19-1. Set the flask on a circle of iron gauze mounted on a tripod. Gently heat the flask. Observe the glass tube.

7. *What happens to the water in the glass tubing as the water in the flask is heated?*

Allow the Erlenmeyer flask to cool.

8. *What happens to the water in the glass tubing as the water in the flask cools?*

Part D Obtain a dry Erlenmeyer flask from your teacher. Stretch a wide-mouth balloon directly over the mouth of the flask, or secure the balloon to a glass tube with a rubber band. See Figure 19-2. Gently heat the flask over a flame.

9. *What happens to the balloon as the flask heats up? Why?*

10. *What common effect does heat have on the substances you experimented with in this inquiry investigation?*

11. *Would you expect that heat would have the same effect on other substances? Explain.*

What Is Heat?

You probably use the word *heat* all the time. You might say that you can't take the heat or you're going to heat up a snack. What exactly is heat and what does it do? In Chapter 15, you learned that heat is the transfer of thermal energy. In this chapter, you will study the effects of heat on matter.

Have you ever rubbed sandpaper across a wooden surface to make it smooth? If so, you know that both the sandpaper and the wood become warm. Around 1800, an American-British scientist named *Count Rumford* made a similar observation. He noted that when a drill was used to bore a cannon, the end of the drill, the drill bit, and the cannon both became very hot. To keep the metals cool, he placed a cylinder of water around the end of the cannon. As the boring continued, the water became warmer and eventually boiled. Because the drill bit and the cannon were cold at the start, Rumford concluded that friction created by the particles of the metal bit rubbing against the particles of the metal cannon produced heat. Further, he theorized that the motions of the particles in the metals themselves (atoms or molecules) generated the heat.

Recall (Chapter 15) that various forms of energy can be converted into other forms. In each conversion, some amount of heat is produced. For example, when electrical energy passes through a thin wire, as in a toaster, the wire becomes hot (electrical energy to heat energy). When you rub your hands together, heat is produced from the friction between the rubbed surfaces (mechanical energy to heat energy). This may be explained by the kinetic-molecular theory: The energy excites particles in matter, causing them to move faster and to collide more frequently. Thus the thermal energy of the matter increases, and some of that energy es-

capes as heat. As more collisions take place, more heat is produced.

The effect of heat energy on the motion of molecules can be demonstrated by using a sealed tube containing a little mercury with some glass beads floating on the surface of the mercury (see Figure 19-3). At ordinary temperatures, the glass beads merely float on the surface of the mercury. However, when the tube of mercury is heated, the glass beads bounce up and down in a violent but random fashion. As still more heat is supplied to the sealed tube, particles of mercury begin to move more swiftly. The glass beads are repeatedly struck by many mercury particles at the same time. As a result, the glass beads begin to move randomly themselves. Thus, Rumford's theory that heat is related to the motions of molecules appears to be correct.

According to the kinetic-molecular theory, heat energy acquired by an object is transformed into increased kinetic energy of the molecules of the object, and therefore increased thermal energy. You observe this increased kinetic energy whenever a solid, a liquid, or a gas expands on heating. A further

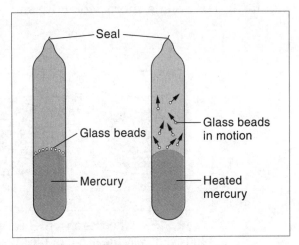

Figure 19-3. Heat causes molecules to move faster.

increase in kinetic energy will eventually cause the particles of a solid to separate as the solid melts. In the same manner, an increase in kinetic energy causes the particles of a liquid to separate as the liquid vaporizes.

Recall that when an ice cube (a solid) is heated, it melts and becomes liquid water. When the water is heated, it vaporizes and becomes water vapor. According to the kinetic-molecular theory, as increasing amounts of heat are supplied to a piece of ice, the water molecules move more rapidly until they gain enough energy to overcome the attractive forces holding them together. This permits the ice to liquefy and become water. Similarly, as still more energy is received, the water molecules move at even greater speeds. The attractive forces in the liquid are weakened and the water is converted into water vapor. (See Figure 19-4.)

How Is Heat Related to the Expansion of Solids?

Your inquiry investigation with the ball-and-ring apparatus showed the effect of heat on volume. The increase in size is *not* due to an increase in the size of the particles that make up the solid ball, but instead to an increase in the average distance between the particles. When an object is heated, its particles vibrate faster, collide more violently, and consequently move farther apart. The result is that the volume of the object increases. This increase is called *expansion.*

When the object is cooled, the opposite change occurs. The particles vibrate slower, collide gently, and the volume of the object decreases. This decrease in volume is called *contraction.*

The expansion of solids by heating may cause serious practical problems. For example, the expansion of railroad tracks, bridges, or the concrete in a roadbed can create dangerous situations. Thus, engineers must account for the expansion of solids during hot weather when they design rails, bridges, and roads. For example, when rails are laid, gaps between the ends of the rails provide for expansion. If this were not done, consider what would happen to the railroad tracks on a very hot day. The metal would expand, making the tracks bend and buckle, which might cause an oncoming train to be derailed. In bridge construction, expansion joints allow for changes in the length of the bridge. Concrete roadbeds and sidewalks are built with spaces between the sections of concrete to allow for expansion.

The contraction of solids by cooling may also present problems. Telephone and electrical wires are purposely strung loosely to prevent their snapping as contraction takes place during the colder times of the year.

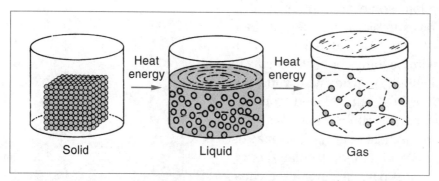

Figure 19-4. When ice absorbs heat energy, the molecules move faster and eventually break out of their positions. The ice melts into a liquid. If the liquid water absorbs heat energy, the particles move faster and farther apart. Eventually, they move fast enough to escape the liquid and enter the gas state.

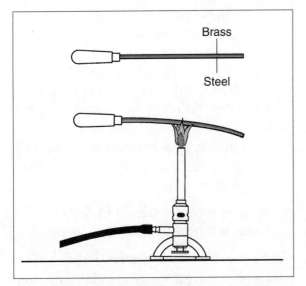

Figure 19-5. The two metals in a compound bar expand at different rates when heated. This causes the bar to bend in one direction.

Different metals expand at different rates when they are heated. For example, when a piece of iron and a piece of aluminum of equal size are heated together, the aluminum expands more than twice as much as the iron. When two strips of different metals are fastened together, they form a **compound bar**, or **bimetallic strip**, which is used in devices such as thermostats and bimetallic thermometers. In these devices, the two dif-

ferent metals, usually brass and steel, are welded together. When the bar is heated (see Figure 19-5), the brass expands more than the steel and therefore becomes longer than the steel. This causes the strip to bend. The brass strip will be on the outside of the bend. As it cools, the bar returns to its original shape.

A **thermostat** is a device that uses a compound bar to regulate a heating system. You probably have one on the wall of your home. When the temperature in your home falls below the setting on the thermostat, the compound bar cools and contracts. This causes it to close a circuit and turn on the heating system. As the room is warmed, the compound bar in the thermostat expands, bends, and thereby breaks the circuit, turning off the heating system (see Figure 19-6).

A bimetallic thermometer is often used as an oven thermometer to indicate the temperature within an oven, or within a piece of meat that is cooking.

▶ **How Is Heat Involved in the Expansion of Liquids?**

Liquids, like solids, expand when heated. In the inquiry investigation, you saw that water

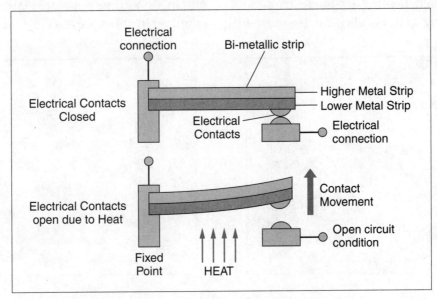

Figure 19-6. A thermostat uses the fact that different metals expand and contract at different rates to control a heating system.

expands as it is heated. When the same water is cooled to its original temperature, the water contracts to its original volume. Many other liquids, such as alcohol and mercury, behave in the same way.

At lower temperatures, however, the behavior of water is an exception to this rule. As water is cooled from 100°C to 4°C, it contracts—like other liquids do. However, when water is cooled below 4°C, the water *expands*—unlike other liquids. Water continues to expand until it reaches 0°C, its freezing point. As shown in Figure 19-7, the spaces between the water molecules in ice are larger than the spaces between the water molecules in liquid water. Ice is therefore said to have an *open structure*. Thus, as ice is formed, the need for increased space between the molecules causes the volume of the ice to be greater than that of the water from which it was formed. (This expansion in volume begins as liquid water is cooled below 4°C.) Since the volume of ice is greater than the volume of water from which the ice is formed, the density of ice is less than the density of water. (Recall that density equals mass divided by volume.) This is why ice floats on water.

The expansion of liquids must be considered in certain heating systems. In a hot-water heating system, allowances must be made for the expansion of heated water. As the furnace heats the water in the heating system, the water expands. If the expansion continued, pressure would build up in the pipes and could damage the entire system. To avoid this difficulty, an expansion tank is provided. Excess heated water enters the expansion tank and thereby reduces the pressure in the system.

How Is Heat Involved in the Expansion of Gases?

Gases, like solids and liquids, expand when heated. Your inquiry investigation indicated that air expands as it is warmed. Scientists have made similar observations with other gases: gases confined in an elastic container expand when they are heated and contract when they are cooled.

The expansion of gases by heat must be considered by automobile tire manufacturers, because tires may burst if allowed to remain in the sun indefinitely. A less serious hazard caused by expanding gases is that bottles of carbonated drinks may crack or even explode if they are exposed to heat for a considerable length of time.

Products such as whipped cream, shaving cream, deodorants, and insect repellents are supplied in aerosol cans. These cans contain

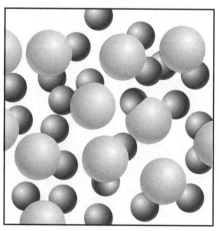

Ice   Water

Figure 19-7. Water molecules in ice are farther apart than in liquid water. It is the structure of the molecules that gives ice different properties from liquid water.

the product itself and a gas that forces the product out of the can when the valve is open. When the product is used up, the can still contains unused gas. If this can is thrown into an incinerator, the gas becomes heated, expands, and may cause the can to explode. Such aerosol cans should be discarded in a manner that does not involve heating.

Different solids and liquids expand at different rates when heated. Gases, however, generally expand at the same rate when heated to the same temperature at a given pressure.

How Is Heat Related to Temperature?

As you learned in Chapter 15, thermal energy, heat, and *temperature* are terms that are often confused. A sample of matter has *thermal energy* because of the total energy of the particles of which it is composed. The average kinetic energy of those particles is the *temperature* of the sample. Any thermal energy that is transferred from the sample is *heat*. Consider an example in which the temperature of a small sample of molten iron is considerably higher than the temperature of the water in the ocean. However, the total thermal energy in a sample of molten iron is much less than the total thermal energy of the water in the ocean. Therefore, heat will be transferred from the molten iron to the ocean.

Scientists now accept Rumford's theory that thermal energy, and in turn heat, is related to the motions of particles in matter. Thus, thermal energy depends on the total kinetic energy of the particles in a body. Recall (Chapter 15) the equation relating kinetic energy to mass (m) and velocity (v):

$$K.E. = \frac{1}{2}mv^2$$

Thus, the total kinetic energy of the particles in a body depends on the number of particles (mass) and the velocity of these particles.

Because the water in the ocean is colder than the sample of molten iron, the velocity of the particles in the water is slower than the velocity of the particles in the molten iron. However, the much larger quantity (mass) of water compensates for the smaller velocity of the particles and thus the particles of water in the ocean possess greater kinetic energy. This means that there is more thermal energy in the water in the ocean than in a small sample of molten iron.

Why then is the temperature of molten iron higher than that of ocean water? Temperature, unlike thermal energy, depends on the *average* kinetic energy of the particles, that is, the kinetic energy per particle. To find this average, divide the total kinetic energy by the number of particles. In any fraction, the larger the denominator, the smaller will be the quotient. For example, $\frac{16}{2} = 8$; $\frac{16}{4} = 4$; $\frac{16}{8} = 2$. Thus, the large mass of ocean water has a smaller average kinetic energy per particle and consequently has a lower temperature than a small sample of molten iron.

What Instruments Are Used to Measure Temperature?

Instruments designed to measure temperature are called **thermometers**. Most thermometers are based on the principle that matter expands when heated and contracts when cooled. In general, matter expands and contracts regularly. This means that the amounts of expansion or contraction in length are generally equal for the same increase or decrease in temperature. This regular expansion and contraction of certain materials has made it possible to construct three different types of thermometers: gas (air) thermometers, liquid (mercury and alcohol) thermometers, and solid (bimetallic) thermometers.

The Gas (Air) Thermometer. An air thermometer can be constructed as shown in Figure 19-8. In this thermometer, the glass

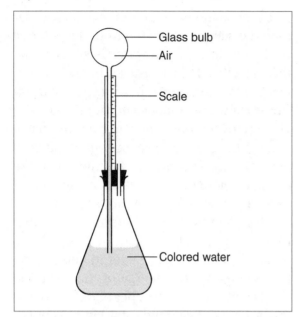

Figure 19-8. In an air thermometer, air in the glass bulb expands as it is warmed and pushes the colored water farther down in the tube.

bulb contains air. When the bulb is warmed, the air in the bulb expands and forces some of the colored water out of the tube. This changes the level of the liquid in the tube. By placing a suitable scale alongside the tube, temperature changes can be measured. Air thermometers, while interesting, are not very accurate because the volume of a gas is also influenced by the air pressure around it. (Note that the flask contains a tube open at both ends. Why?)

Liquid Thermometers. Thermometers containing liquids such as alcohol and mercury are useful and accurate because these liquids usually expand and contract uniformly (regularly). Alcohol thermometers are produced by filling a thin glass tube with colored alcohol at a temperature greater than the maximum to be measured. The tube is then cut and sealed at the top. When the alcohol cools, it contracts, leaving a partial vacuum above the alcohol. (Liquids expand and contract to a much greater extent than do solids. Thus, in the given temperature range, the glass tube is scarcely affected by

the temperature change.) The partial vacuum eliminates the effect of air resistance on the expansion of the alcohol. The same procedure is used to make thermometers that contain mercury. However, mercury is toxic, which means it can harm the human body. In particular, mercury can interfere with the normal processes of the nervous system. Mercury thermometers therefore pose a risk if they break. For that reason, most modern thermometers no longer use mercury.

The scale of the thermometer is generally fixed by locating the boiling and freezing points of water on the scale. The distance between the boiling and freezing points is then divided into units depending on the temperature scale used. Modern battery-powered digital display thermometers are replacing liquid thermometers.

Because mercury freezes at $-39°C$, it cannot be used to measure very low temperatures. However, mercury boils at $357°C$, which means that a mercury thermometer can be used to measure temperatures above the boiling point of water. On the other hand, alcohol freezes at $-114°C$. Accordingly, alcohol thermometers are used to measure low temperatures. However, because alcohol boils at $78°C$, alcohol thermometers cannot be used to measure high temperatures.

Solid (Bimetallic) Thermometers. Recall that a bimetallic strip (see Figure 19-5 on page 295) behaves as it does because different metals expand at different rates. Because most metals melt only at very high temperatures, a thermometer that uses a bimetallic strip can measure temperatures as high as 1000°C. The *dial thermometer*, often used as an oven thermometer, is an example of a bimetallic thermometer (see Figure 19-9). A curved bimetallic strip, with the faster-expanding metal on the outside of the bend, is attached to a pointer. Upon heating, the bimetallic strip moves, causing the pointer to indicate the temperature on a circular scale.

Figure 19-9. An oven thermometer contains a curved bimetallic strip attached to the pointer.

Other metallic thermometers, called *resistance thermometers*, use the principle that the resistance of a wire changes with temperature. Such thermometers also measure high temperatures. In industrial applications they are used to measure temperatures between −200 and 500 °C (−328 and 932 °F).

▶ **What Scales Are Used to Measure Temperature?**

Temperature markings on thermometers are indicated in Fahrenheit degrees or Celsius degrees. The **Fahrenheit** and **Celsius** scales are named after their originators, *Gabriel Fahrenheit* and *Anders Celsius*. Both Fahrenheit and Celsius scales are calibrated by using the boiling and freezing points of water. The Fahrenheit scale is used in the English system of measurement and the Celsius scale in the SI system. In the Fahrenheit scale (see Figure 19-10), the freezing point of water is 32°F, and the boiling point of water is 212°F. The remainder of the scale between these two points is marked off into 180 equal divisions (212 − 32 = 180). In the Celsius scale (see Figure 19-10), the freezing point of water is 0°C, and the boiling point of water is 100°C. The remainder of the scale between these points is divided into 100 equal divisions (100 − 0 = 100).

Note that there are 180 divisions between the freezing and boiling points of water in the Fahrenheit scale and 100 divisions between these points in the Celsius scale. Thus,

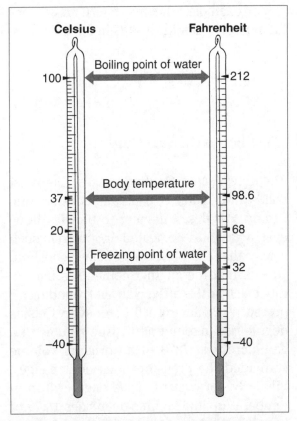

Figure 19-10. The diagram compares the Celsius and Fahrenheit temperature scales.

each Celsius division (degree) is 180/100, or 9/5, as large as a Fahrenheit division (degree). This relationship, together with the fact that there are 32 Fahrenheit divisions (degrees) between 0°F and 32°F, makes it possible to convert one scale into the other by using the following formulas:

$$\text{degrees C} = \frac{5}{9} \times (\text{degrees F} - 32 \text{ degrees})$$

$$\text{degrees F} = \left(\frac{9}{5} \times \text{degrees C}\right) + 32 \text{ degrees}$$

These formulas may be written as

$$°C = \frac{5}{9}(°F - 32°) \text{ (formula 1)}$$

$$°F = \frac{5}{9}°C + 32° \text{ (formula 2)}$$

For example, to convert 40°C to degrees Fahrenheit, substitute 40°C in formula 2:

$$°F = \frac{9}{\cancel{5}} \times \cancel{40}^{8} + 32$$

$$°F = 72 + 32 = 104$$

Thus, 40°C is equivalent to 104°F.

The Kelvin Scale. Confined gases, like most solids and liquids, expand and contract uniformly. For this statement to be true, however, a gas must be heated or cooled in such a way that the pressure remains constant. (Recall that the air thermometer is inaccurate because it is affected by surrounding air pressure.) Beginning at 0°C, for every Celsius degree rise in temperature, the volume of a gas increases 1/273 of its original volume (provided the pressure does not change). Similarly, for every Celsius degree drop in temperature, the volume decreases 1/273 of its original volume. At −273°C, the volume of a gas would shrink to zero and all molecular motion would cease. This, in turn, means that the gas would contain no heat. (Actually, gases generally liquefy before this temperature is reached.) Scientists refer to −273°C as **absolute zero**, a temperature that has been approached, but never reached.

Absolute zero, −273°C, is also called 0 Kelvin (0 K). Note that Kelvin temperatures do not include the degree symbol. The **Kelvin scale**, named after its originator, *Sir William Thomson, Lord Kelvin,* is based on absolute temperatures. Thus, it is often called the absolute scale. Because the Kelvin scale begins with absolute zero (–273°C), the following formula can be used to convert the Celsius scale to the Kelvin scale:

Kelvin temperature = Celsius temperature + 273

This formula may be written as

$$K = °C + 273$$

Let us find the freezing point of water (0°C) in the Kelvin scale:

$$K = 0 + 273 = 273$$

Thus, 0°C is equivalent to 273 K.

Now, let us find the boiling point of water:

$$K = 100 + 273 = 373$$

Thus, 100°C is equivalent to 373 K.

▶ How Is Heat Transferred?

You may know from experience that if you place a metal spoon in a bowl of hot soup, the entire spoon soon becomes hot. Heat travels from the soup to the bowl-shaped part of the spoon and then to the handle. In another example, ice soon melts when placed in warm water. Both these examples show that heat travels from one body to another.

Generally, when objects are at different temperatures, heat is transferred from the warmer object to the cooler object until both objects are at the same temperature. Heat transfer can occur through one of three methods: conduction, convection, or radiation.

Conduction. When one end of a metal rod is held in a flame, the entire rod will become hot enough to burn a hand that might be holding it. The heat from the flame reaches the hand by **conduction**, that is, by traveling through the rod. Substances that allow heat to travel through them are called **conductors**. In general, as you learned before, metals are good conductors. However, some metals conduct heat more readily than others. This can be demonstrated by inserting rods of aluminum, copper, iron, nickel, and brass into a brass sphere or disk such as that shown in Figure 19-11 and then attaching a small ball of wax to the end of each rod. When the center of the brass disk is heated,

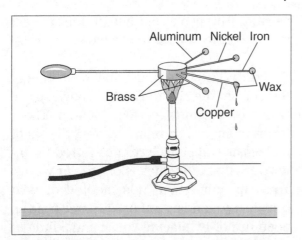

Figure 19-11. Metals conduct heat at different rates.

the wax at the tip of each metal melts in the order in which the different metals conduct heat. The wax at the tip of the copper melts first and the wax at the tip of the iron melts last.

Conduction in most materials can be explained by the kinetic-molecular theory. When one end of a rod is heated, the molecules in that end of the rod vibrate faster and strike other nearby molecules, causing them to vibrate faster. In this manner, the increased molecular motion is transferred from one end of the rod to the other, permitting the heat to travel through the rod.

Substances that do not readily allow heat to pass through them are called **insulators**. Gases and liquids are generally poor conductors of heat because their molecules are farther apart than are the molecules in solids. Therefore, neighboring molecules in a gas or in a liquid are less affected by the increased motions of heated molecules, and consequently heat is not conducted rapidly.

Substances such as wood or plastic are poor conductors of heat, so they are used to make handles for metallic objects that are to be heated. Porous material is generally nonconducting because it contains layers of trapped air, which do not permit heat transfer.

Convection. Although gases and liquids are poor conductors of heat, heat is transferred through them by the process of **convection**. Convection is the transfer of heat due to the motion of the liquid or gas itself. For example, when a beaker of water is heated, as shown in Figure 19-12, the water layer closest to the heat source is warmed slowly by conduction. As the water becomes warmer, it expands, becomes less dense, and rises. This brings heat to the upper layer. At the same time, cooler water from the upper portion of the beaker sinks, takes the place of the rising water, and becomes heated itself. When warm enough, this water rises and carries heat upward. As these processes continue, heat that enters the bottom of the beaker is distributed throughout the beaker until all the water is at the same temperature. The moving water in such a case is said to have set up a **convection current**.

Heat is also transferred through gases by convection. It is by this means, in part, that a stove or a radiator heats a room. Heat from the radiator warms the air above it, causing the air to expand, become less dense, and rise. The cooler air that sinks in to take the place of the warmed air is also soon warmed. As this air rises, a convection current is

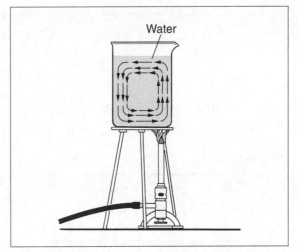

Figure 19-12. Convection currents can form in fluids, such as water.

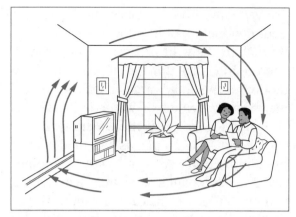

Figure 19-13. Convection currents can transfer heat in air.

established (see Figure 19-13). The convection current continues to distribute heat throughout the room until the entire room is warmed.

The formation of a convection current in air is demonstrated with a convection box apparatus (see Figure 19-14). First the candle is lighted; then a smoking wad of paper is placed over the chimney opposite the candle. The smoke, coloring the air, can be seen to move down this chimney, across the box, and out through the other chimney. This occurs because the air over the candle is heated, becomes less dense, and rises, leaving a partial vacuum. Cooler, denser air from the first chimney moves in to fill the partial

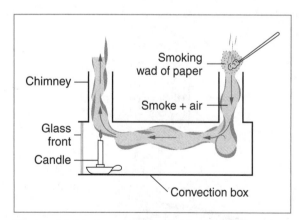

Figure 19-14. A convection box apparatus demonstrates the formation of a convection current.

vacuum. This cycle continues as long as heat is given off by the burning candle.

Radiation. Light energy and heat energy travel from the sun to Earth through space, which is an almost perfect vacuum. These forms of energy, traveling without the aid of molecular collisions, are transferred by **radiation**, that is, by means of rays, or waves. You can understand this method of heat transfer by standing a short distance from an open fire or by placing your hand a little to one side of, but not touching, a hot radiator. Since neither source of heat is being touched, you cannot receive heat by conduction. Since warm air rises vertically from the heat source, the heat cannot reach you by convection. The heat that is transferred to you from the fire or radiator reaches you by radiation.

The heat radiated by one object (the sun, for example) is most rapidly absorbed by other objects that are black in color and rough in texture. In warm climates, white clothing—which reflects the radiant heat of the sun—stays cooler than dark clothing—which quickly absorbs the radiant heat. Similarly, objects that are rough and dark tend to radiate heat better than shiny smooth objects. This is why steam radiators are often dark and have a roughened surface. It is for the same reason that coal-burning stoves are black.

Objects that are shiny and smooth do not absorb heat readily. Instead, these objects reflect heat. Thus, aluminum used for roofing keeps homes cool in the summer and warm in the winter. This principle is used in the thermos (vacuum) bottle, which is constructed to permit liquids to retain their temperatures for a long time. A thermos bottle is double-walled, with a partial vacuum between the walls to prevent heat transfer by conduction or convection. A cork stopper also prevents heat transfer by conduction. The inner glass walls are silvered to reflect

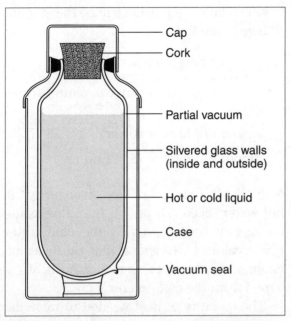

Figure 19-15. A thermos bottle is designed to prevent the flow of heat into or out of a liquid.

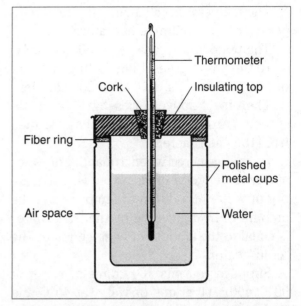

Figure 19-16. A calorimeter is used to measure amounts of heat energy.

radiant heat back into the liquid, thereby minimizing heat loss by radiation (see Figure 19-15). Thus, a hot liquid remains hot because heat is lost very slowly. A cold liquid remains cold in thermos bottles because outside heat enters very slowly by conduction, convection, or radiation.

▶ **How Is Heat Measured?**

You learned (page 228) that temperature is a measure of the *average* kinetic energy of the molecules of a substance. This is the same as saying that temperature represents the average intensity of the motion of the molecules, or the degree of hotness of a substance.

The temperature of matter can increase or decrease when heat is added to or removed from matter. The amount of heat needed to raise the temperature of 1 gram of water 1 Celsius degree is called the **calorie**. The calorie is a SI unit whereas heat is measured by a unit called the **British Thermal Unit** (BTU) in the English system. A BTU is the amount of heat needed to raise the temperature of 1 pound of water 1 Fahrenheit degree.

An amount of heat energy is measured by observing its effect on a given quantity of water in a device called a **calorimeter**. One type of calorimeter, shown in Figure 19-16, consists of two polished metal cups surrounded by air, a poor conductor of heat. An insulating cover, holding a thermometer, makes up the top of the calorimeter. The polished cups reflect heat, thus maintaining the temperature of the liquid in the container.

To determine the amount of heat energy absorbed (or lost) by a given quantity of water, multiply the mass of the water in grams by the change in temperature of the water in Celsius degrees. Thus:

amount of heat = mass of water
(calories) (grams)
× change in temperature
(Celsius degrees)

In a calorimeter, when 20 grams of water at 20°C are heated to a temperature of 30°C, how much heat is absorbed?

amount of heat = mass of water
(calories) (grams)
× change in temperature
(Celsius degrees)

The temperature change = the final temperature − the initial temperature.

The temperature change = 30°C − 20°C = 10 Celsius degrees. Substituting, amount of heat = 20 grams × 10 C° = 200 calories.

Therefore, 200 calories have been absorbed. (Assume that no heat has escaped from the calorimeter.)

In a calorimeter, when a quantity of water at a given temperature is mixed with a quantity of water at a different temperature, the amount of heat given up by the "hot" water is equal to the amount of heat gained by the "cold" water.

Suppose you mix 100 grams of water at 90°C with 100 grams of water at 40°C and find that the final temperature of the mixture is 65°C. The temperature of the hot water dropped from 90°C to 65°C, which is a decrease of 25 Celsius degrees. Use the following relationship to determine the amount of heat lost:

amount of heat = mass of water
(calories)   (grams)
× change in temperature
(Celsius degrees)

amount of heat = 100 grams × 25 C°

amount of heat = 2500 calories

[Note: To avoid possible confusion, scientists often indicate heat given up with a minus sign. Using this method, the above equation would be solved as follows:

amount of heat = mass of water
× change in temperature

amount of heat = 100 grams × (−25 C°)

amount of heat = −2500 calories

The minus sign in the answer indicates that 2500 calories of heat have been *given up*.]

The temperature of the cold water increased from 40°C to 65°C, an increase of 25 Celsius degrees. Again, you can use the following relationship to determine the amount of heat gained:

amount of heat = mass of water
(calories)   (grams)
× change in temperature
(Celsius degrees)

amount of heat = 100 grams × 25 C°

amount of heat = 2500 calories

Note that the amount of heat given up by the hot water (2500 calories) is the same as the amount of heat gained by the cold water (2500 calories). (Assume that the heat exchange was "perfect" and that no heat escaped from the calorimeter.)

The quantity of heat needed to raise the temperature of 1 gram of a substance 1 Celsius degree is called the **specific heat** of the substance. For water, the specific heat is 1. This means that 1 calorie of heat will raise the temperature of 1 gram of water 1 C°. Water is the only substance for which this is true. Other substances vary in the quantity of heat needed to raise the temperature of 1 gram of the substance 1 Celsius degree. Consequently, the formula you have been using applies only to water.

▶ How Is Heat Related to Changes in State?

Remember that heat is required to change a solid to its liquid form (page 190) and that the amount of heat needed to change 1 gram of a solid to a liquid at its melting point is the heat of fusion. As an example, in order to melt 1 gram of ice at 0°C to liquid water at 0°C, 80 calories of heat are necessary. How many calories of heat are necessary to change 10 grams of ice at 0°C to water at 0°C? To find the answer, simply multiply the mass of the solid by its heat of fusion.

total heat = mass × heat of fusion

total heat = 10 grams × 80 calories/gram

total heat = 800 calories

Similarly, heat is required to change a liquid to its gaseous form. Recall that the amount of heat needed to change 1 gram of liquid to its gaseous form at its boiling point is called the heat of vaporization (page 188). For example, the heat of vaporization of water is 540 calories/gram. This means that 540 calories of heat are necessary to change 1 gram of water at 100°C to water vapor at 100°C. How many calories of heat are needed to change 10 grams of water to water vapor? To find the answer, simply multiply the mass of the substance by the heat of vaporization.

total heat = mass × heat of vaporization

total heat = 10 grams × 540 calories/gram

total heat = 5400 calories

During the time that a change in state is occurring, that is, that a solid is becoming a liquid or a liquid is becoming a gas, all the heat supplied to the substance is used for this change. No temperature increase occurs until all the substance has changed state. At that time, the heat supplied increases the temperature of the substance.

How Are Heat Calories Related to Food?

Your body requires energy to perform its daily tasks. Most of this energy comes from energy-rich foods such as carbohydrates and fats. This energy is released when the body uses these foods. Using special calorimeters, scientists have measured the energy content, or the number of calories present, in fixed quantities of certain foods. For example, a slice of white bread contains about 60,000 calories; a typical chocolate bar may contain about 300,000 calories.

Nutritionists use a special kind of notation when discussing the caloric content of foods. They define a food **Calorie** (written with a capital letter) as 1000 calories. On a calorie table, therefore, you would read that a slice of white bread contains about 60 Calories and that a chocolate bar contains about 300 Calories.

Chapter Review

Science Terms

The following list contains all the boldfaced words found in this chapter and the page on which each appears.

absolute zero (p. 300)
bimetallic strip (p. 295)
British Thermal Unit (p. 303)
calorie (p. 303)
Calorie (p. 305)
calorimeter (p. 303)
Celsius (p. 299)
compound bar (p. 295)
conduction (p. 300)
conductors (p. 300)

convection (p. 301)
convection current (p. 301)
Fahrenheit (p. 299)
insulators (p. 301)
Kelvin scale (p. 300)
radiation (p. 302)
specific heat (p. 304)
thermometer (p. 297)
thermostat (p. 295)

Matching Questions

In your notebook, write the letter of the item in column B that is most closely related to the item in column A.

Column A

_____ 1. specific heat

_____ 2. absolute zero

_____ 3. Calorie

_____ 4. Kelvin scale

_____ 5. Celsius scale

_____ 6. convection

_____ 7. insulator

_____ 8. calorie

_____ 9. radiation

_____ 10. conductor

Column B

a. quantity of heat needed to raise the temperature of 1 gram of a substance 1°C

b. system in which the water freezes at 0 degrees

c. a material that allows heat to pass through easily

d. transfer of heat by waves

e. amount of heat needed to raise the temperature of 1 gram of water 1 Celsius degree

f. transfer of heat by currents in a fluid

g. amount of heat needed to raise the temperature of 1000 grams of water one Celsius degree

h. lowest possible temperature

i. a material that does not conduct heat well

j. system in which the freezing point of water is 273

Multiple-Choice Questions

In your notebook, write the letter preceding the word or expression that best completes the statement or answers the question.

1. The scientist who proposed that heat results from the motion of molecules was
   a. Celsius
   b. Fahrenheit
   c. Rumford
   d. Newton

2. How does the absorption of heat affect the molecules in a sample of matter?
   a. It causes them to slow.
   b. It causes them to move more rapidly.
   c. It causes them to increase in size.
   d. It causes them to stick together.

3. As heat energy is absorbed by a liquid, the attractive forces holding the molecules together are
   a. not affected
   b. weakened
   c. strengthened
   d. eliminated

4. Which of the following will cause a brass ball to contract?
   a. Rubbing it with sandpaper.
   b. Cooling it in a freezer.
   c. Heating it in a flame.
   d. Painting it a darker color.

5. A metal railroad track expands on a hot summer day due to
   a. an increase in the size of its molecules
   b. a decrease in the size of its molecules
   c. a decrease in the distance between its molecules
   d. an increase in the distance between its molecules

6. How is a bimetallic strip useful in a thermostat?
   a. It bends because the two metals expand and contract at different rates.

b. It acts as a conductor when it expands and an insulator when it contracts.

c. It removes heat with one side and produces heat with the other side.

d. It transfers heat by radiation on one side and by convection on the other side.

7. What happens to water as it is cooled from 40°C to a temperature below 4°C?
   a. It expands, then contracts.
   b. It contracts.
   c. It expands.
   d. It contracts, then expands.

8. Which statement is true about what happens to liquids when they are heated?
   a. Liquid molecules shrink when heated.
   b. Liquids contract when heated.
   c. Different liquids expand at different rates.
   d. All liquids expand at the same rate.

9. To avoid excess pressure in a hot-water heating system, engineers make use of
   a. an expansion tank
   b. a boiler
   c. a circulator
   d. an oil tank

10. What most likely will happen if an aerosol can is placed in an incinerator?
    a. It will contract.
    b. It will melt.
    c. It will not be affected.
    d. It will explode.

11. In an alcohol thermometer, the amount of expansion of the alcohol for each degree increase in temperature
    a. increases
    b. decreases
    c. is the same
    d. increases, then decreases

12. Which of the following thermometers is the one best suited to measure temperatures below the freezing point of water?
    a. dry ice   c. mercury
    b. alcohol   d. water

13. In the Fahrenheit scale, the number of equal divisions between the freezing and boiling points of water is
    a. 100   c. 180
    b. 160   d. 212

14. Each Celsius degree is
    a. $\frac{5}{9}$ of a Fahrenheit degree
    b. $\frac{9}{5}$ of a Fahrenheit degree
    c. twice as large as a Fahrenheit degree
    d. half as large as a Fahrenheit degree

15. For each one-degree rise in Celsius temperature, the volume of a gas increases its original volume by
    a. $\frac{1}{273}$ c. $\frac{1}{3}$
    b. $\frac{1}{200}$ d. $\frac{1}{2}$

16. The Celsius equivalent for absolute zero is
    a. 0°C   c. −459.7°C
    b. −273°F   d. −273°C

17. The temperature scale that is based on absolute temperatures was proposed by
    a. Celsius
    b. Fahrenheit
    c. Kelvin
    d. Maxwell

18. What is the freezing point of water in the absolute temperature scale?
    a. 273 K   c. 273°F
    b. 273°C   d. 0°C

19. When objects are at different temperatures,
    a. heat is not transferred
    b. heat is transferred from the cooler object to the warmer object
    c. heat is transferred from the warmer object to the cooler object
    d. heat in the warmer object is destroyed

20. Which heat transfer can occur through the vacuum of space?
    a. conduction   c. convection
    b. radiation   d. insulation

Modified True-False Questions

In some of the following statements, the italicized term makes the statement incorrect. For each incorrect statement, in your notebook, write the term that must be substituted for the italicized term to make the statement correct. For each correct statement, write the word "true."

1. Heat is *chemical* energy transferred from one object to another._____

2. When two strips of different metals are fastened together, they form a *bimetallic strip.* _____

3. The air inside a balloon *contracts* as it is heated. _____

4. The average kinetic energy of the particles of matter is known as *heat.* _____

5. An instrument used to measure temperature is known as a *radiometer.* _____

6. Alcohol boils at a temperature of *78°C.* _____

7. Resistance thermometers are used to measure *high* temperatures. _____

8. A temperature of −273°C is known as *the freezing point.* _____

9. Heat travels through a metallic rod by a process called *convection.* _____

10. A substance that does not readily allow heat to pass through it is called an *insulator.* _____

11. The transfer of heat by the motion of a liquid or gas is called *radiation.* _____

12. As the air in a room is warmed, it rises. Cool air moves down to take its place and a *convection current* is formed. _____

13. The transfer of heat without the aid of molecular collisions is called *radiation.* _____

14. In the SI system, the amount of heat needed to raise the temperature of 1 gram of water 1 C° is called a *degree.* _____

15. The amount of heat in an object can be measured with a/an *anemometer.* _____

TEST-TAKING TIP Check any mathematical calculations by performing them twice or using the reverse operation.

Check Your Knowledge

Write the answer to each question in your notebook.

1. Contrast each of the following sets of terms:
   a. expansion and contraction
   b. thermal energy and temperature
   c. one Celsius degree and one degree Celsius
   d. conduction and convection
   e. conductor and insulator

2. a. Change 77°F to the comparable Celsius temperature.
   b. Change 212°F to the comparable Celsius temperature.
   c. Change 20°C to the comparable Fahrenheit temperature.
   d. Change 5°C to the comparable Fahrenheit temperature.

3. Convert the following Celsius temperatures to the Kelvin scale:
   a. 16°C   d. 70°C
   b. 30°C   e. 44°C
   c. 100°C

4. Explain how a thermos bottle relies on the principles of conduction, convection, and radiation to do its job.

Think Critically

Write the answer to each of the following questions in your notebook.

1. Find the quantity of heat (in calories) needed to raise the temperature of 100 grams of water at 20°C to a temperature of 70°C.

2. Find the quantity of heat (in calories) added when 60 grams of water are heated until the temperature changes by 10°C.

Take It Further

1. Conditions that make it suitable for life on Earth depend on heat transfer by conduction, convection, and radiation. Find out how Earth is heated, how Earth gives off heat, and how heat is trapped near Earth's surface. Present your findings in a poster or diagram.

Internet Search

2. Scientists continue to work to reach absolute zero. Conduct research to learn about some of their attempts, how close they have come, and why many scientists consider this an important goal. You may wish to begin your research by reading the following article: *http://www.time. com/time/magazine/article/ 0,9171,996621,00.html.*

CAREER

3. Nutritionists need a thorough understanding of heat energy and how to measure it. Conduct research to find out what a nutritionist does, what education is required, and what opportunities are available. You may wish to begin your search at *http://www.bls.gov/oco/ ocos077.htm.*

20

What Is the Nature of Sound Energy?

The beautiful sounds of this orchestra are very different from the unpleasant sounds of traffic noise. The way that sounds are produced and interact determines how they can be enjoyed and used.

After reading this chapter, you should be able to answer the following questions:

How is sound produced and transmitted?

What are the characteristics of sound waves and how are they related?

How is the speed of sound determined?

What happens when sound is reflected or absorbed?

What are pitch and amplitude?

What is interference?

You hear different sounds around you all the time. They vary in their characteristics according to how they were made. In this inquiry investigation, you will make different sounds and describe their characteristics.

Materials:
✔ safety goggles
✔ clamp
✔ metal ruler
✔ meterstick
✔ 5 test tubes (150-mm)
✔ test-tube rack
✔ water

NOTE: Wear safety goggles during this activity.

Part A Clamp a metal ruler to the edge of your desk so that the ruler extends about 20 cm beyond the desk (see Figure 20-1). Force the overhanging end of the ruler down about 15 cm and then release the ruler suddenly.

Observe the rate at which the ruler vibrates and listen to the sound produced by the vibrating ruler. The rate at which the ruler vibrates is its *frequency*. The sound produced by the vibration is called its *pitch*.

Part B Shorten the amount that the ruler extends from the desk to 15 cm. Again, force the overhanging end of the ruler down and then release the ruler suddenly.

1. *How does the rate of vibration compare with the rate of vibration in Part A?*

2. *How does the pitch of the vibrating ruler compare with the pitch produced in Part A?*

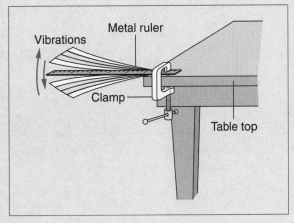

Figure 20-1.

Part C Shorten the amount that the ruler extends from the desk to 10 cm. Again, force the overhanging end of the ruler down and then release the ruler suddenly.

3. *How does the rate of vibration compare with the rates of vibration in Parts A and B?*

4. *How does the pitch of the vibrating ruler compare with the pitch produced in Parts A and B?*

5. *What is the relation between the frequency at which the ruler vibrates and the pitch produced by the ruler?*

Part D Pour water into the five 150-mm test tubes as shown in Figure 20-2. Place them in a rack.

Part E Pick up the first test tube and blow gently across the opening. Do the same with the other test tubes in turn.

6. *What is the relation between the amount of water in each test tube and the pitch of the sound produced?*

7. *What similarity exists between the sounds produced by a vibrating ruler as you change its length and the sounds produced by the vibrating air in a test tube as the height of the water in the tube changes?*

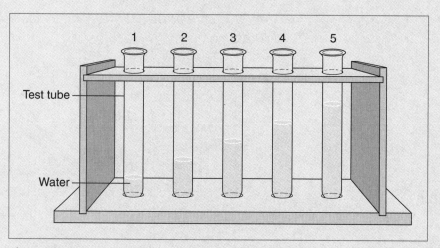

Figure 20-2.

How Is Sound Produced?

Sound plays an important role in modern life. You communicate with others by making sounds with your mouth. In other words, you talk. You might make sounds by playing a musical instrument, kicking a ball, or tapping your fingers. Some sounds warn you of dangers, such as police, fire, or ambulance sirens and smoke alarms. Some sounds let you know that a certain amount of time has passed, such as an alarm clock. Other sounds are just noise.

No matter what type of sound you hear, all sounds are produced by vibrations. A **vibration** is a back-and-forth movement. In the inquiry investigation at the beginning of the chapter, you caused the ruler to vibrate. Once it began vibrating, the ruler made a sound.

If you were to pluck a string of a guitar or a banjo, you would produce a sound by causing the string to vibrate. Similarly, a tuning fork produces a sound when it is struck, because it vibrates. Sometimes the vibrations are so rapid that you cannot see them. You can show evidence for such vibrations by striking the fork and quickly placing the tips of its prongs just at the surface of a dish of water. The water splashes out of the container, and small waves can be seen on the surface of the water coming from the prongs of the tuning fork (see Figure 20-3). Because sound is produced when matter moves (vibrates), sound is really a form of mechanical energy.

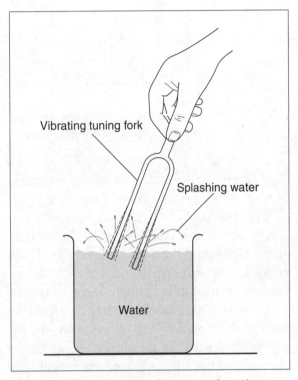

Vibrating tuning fork

Splashing water

Water

Figure 20-3. You can see that a struck tuning fork vibrates by dipping it in water.

How Is Sound Transmitted?

Suppose a bell rings down the hall to tell you that class is over. How did the sound get to your ear? For you to hear a sound, the sound must be transmitted from its source to your ear. Sound travels by disturbing a **carrying medium**, which is the matter through which it travels.

That some form of matter, or a medium, is needed for the transmission of sound can be demonstrated with the apparatus shown in Figure 20-4 on page 314. When the switch is closed, the electric bell in the bell jar begins to ring and can be heard in all parts of the room. As the vacuum pump takes air from the inside of the bell jar, the sound of the bell becomes fainter and fainter until it almost disappears. When the pump is stopped and air is let back into the bell jar, the sound of the bell is again heard normally. This shows that a **vacuum**, which is

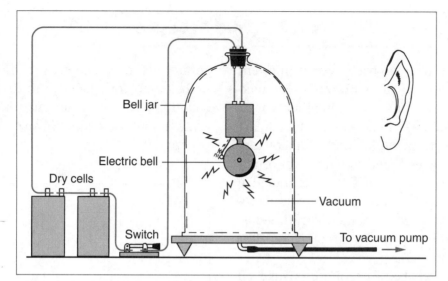

Figure 20-4. Sound is not transmitted through a vacuum. It can travel only through a carrying medium.

the absence of matter, cannot transmit sound. A carrying medium is necessary.

The carrying medium may be matter in any state—solid, liquid, or gas. Matter that transmits sound possesses **elasticity**. Elasticity is the property of matter that allows molecules moved apart by a force to return to their original positions after the force is removed. A coiled spring is a common example of a solid that possesses elasticity. A force stretches the spring; when the force is removed, the spring returns to its original shape.

In general, solids transmit sound faster than either liquids or gases because solids are more elastic. Similarly, liquids are more elastic than gases so they transmit sounds more rapidly than gases.

Density also affects the transmission of sound. For example, sound is transmitted more rapidly through a less dense gas such as hydrogen than through the denser carbon dioxide (both gases being at the same pressure). The very small mass of the hydrogen molecules permits these molecules to vibrate more readily than the more massive carbon dioxide molecules.

Sound-resistant materials such as cork or fiberboard are used to deaden sound or to insulate against sound. These materials are generally porous and inelastic. Thus, they absorb sounds, but cannot transmit them effectively.

You constantly hear sounds traveling through the air, which is a gas, so you know that gases transmit sound. You can easily demonstrate that sound travels through a solid, as shown in Figure 20-5. A student taps one end of a metal pole while another student has his ear near the other end of the pole. The sound is clearly heard at the other end of the pole.

You may have had the opportunity to hear sounds while swimming underwater. You can

Figure 20-5. Solids transmit sound from one end to the other.

verify that liquids transmit sound by placing your ear in the water of your bathtub as you gently scratch the side of the tub with your fingernail. The sounds you hear are the vibrations of the tub transmitted to your ear by the water.

What Are the Characteristics of Sound Waves?

You know that a sound is produced when matter vibrates and that the vibration is transmitted through a medium. Now you will consider the way in which the vibration is transmitted. Look at the motion of a tuning fork when struck as shown in Figure 20-6. As each prong moves outward, the surrounding air molecules are crowded together. As the prongs move back, the crowded air molecules are allowed to move apart. The region where the molecules of the elastic medium are crowded together is called a **compression**, and the region where the air molecules are farther apart is called a **rarefaction**. The compressions and rarefactions make up a sound wave, which travels outward in all directions. Thus, sound energy results from the motions of molecules. Recall that heat

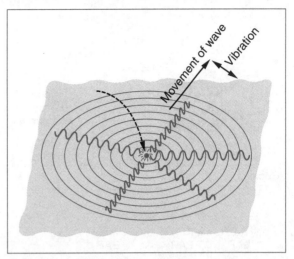

Figure 20-7. Unlike sound waves, water waves are transverse waves.

energy also results from the motions of molecules.

A sound wave is a wave in which the vibrating molecules move parallel to the path of the wave. This type of wave is called a **longitudinal wave**. Water waves are **transverse waves** in which the vibrating water molecules move at right angles to the path of the wave. Note what happens when a pebble is dropped into water (see Figure 20-7). You will learn more about transverse waves in Chapter 21.

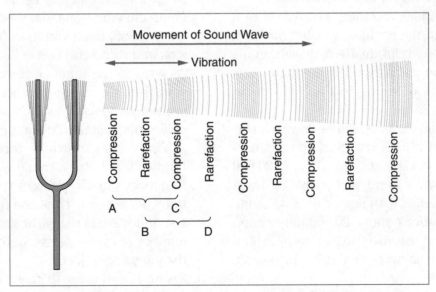

Figure 20-6. The motion of the prongs of a struck tuning fork affects the surrounding air molecules.

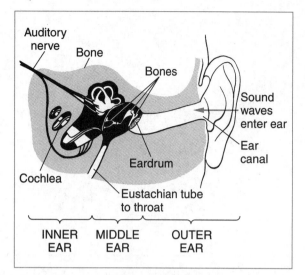

Figure 20-8. The human ear collects sound waves and converts them into messages sent to the brain.

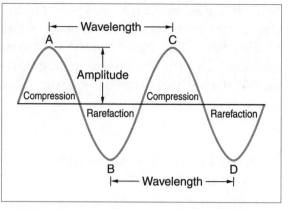

Figure 20-9. A sound wave can be described by its characteristics, such as wavelength and amplitude.

How does the human ear hear sounds? The human ear (Figure 20-8) consists of three parts: the outer ear, the middle ear, and the inner ear. The outer ear is shaped so as to collect sound waves. The sound waves travel through the ear canal to the eardrum. The eardrum is a membrane that separates the outer ear from the middle ear. The sound waves cause the eardrum to vibrate. The sound vibrations are reinforced (amplified) by three small bones in the middle ear and are then transmitted to the inner ear.

The vibrations are then transferred to a membrane in the cochlea, causing the fluid in the cochlea to vibrate. Here, the vibrations stimulate the auditory nerves, which carry the sensation of sound to the brain as an electrical message.

The human ear is sensitive only to a certain range of vibrations. Thus, you can usually hear sounds between 20 and 20,000 vibrations per second. The range of hearing can decrease with age or illness. Longitudinal vibrations above 20,000 per second are called **ultrasonic**. Dogs, dolphins, and many other animals can hear ultrasonic sounds.

Sound waves may be described in terms of certain characteristics: **wavelength, frequency, speed, and amplitude**. Figure 20-9 shows a convenient way of representing these characteristics.

1. *Wavelength.* Wavelength is the distance between two successive compressions; this is the same as the distance between two successive rarefactions. For example, the wavelength of the wave shown in Figure 20-6 on page 315 is either the distance between points A and C (compressions) or between points B and D (rarefactions). These distances are equal. Figure 20-9 shows the same relationships.
2. *Frequency.* Frequency is the number of complete vibrations that pass a point in one second. Each vibration (compression and rarefaction) is called a **cycle**. As a result, the number of waves that start from the vibrating object every second is the same as the number of cycles per second. The unit cycles per second is also known as **hertz** (Hz). Figure 20-9 shows a sound wave with a frequency of two cycles or two vibrations per second. Thus, the frequency of a sound wave is really the same as the number of cycles per second made by the vibrating object.
3. *Speed.* Speed is the distance that the wave travels in a unit of time, usually the distance per second.

4. *Amplitude.* Amplitude is the amount of vibration, that is, the loudness of a sound. In the figure used to represent sound waves (see Figure 20-9), the amplitude is represented by the height of the curve. The amplitude of the wave formed by a vibrating tuning fork, for example, depends on how much energy was used to strike the prongs of the fork. The greater the amount of energy with which the fork is struck, the more air is set in vibration, and the greater is the amplitude of the sound (Figure 20-10).

▶ How Is the Speed of Sound Determined?

During a thunderstorm, you have probably noticed that you see a flash of lightning before you hear the sound of thunder. The lightning and the thunder occur simultaneously, but light, which travels at a speed of 300,000 kilometers per second (186,000 miles per second), reaches you almost instantaneously. Sound, on the other hand, travels at a much slower rate. Depending on how far away the thunder occurred, the sound may take several seconds to reach you.

The speed of sound was first determined by firing a cannon on one hill while a person on another hill measured the interval of time between seeing the flash of the cannon and hearing the sound. By dividing the difference in time into the distance between the two hills, the speed of sound in air was determined.

You learned earlier that the state of matter and its density affect the speed of sound. Temperature also affects the speed of sound. This is because temperature changes the density of the air without necessarily changing its pressure. Recall that gases with lower densities (hydrogen) transmit sound more rapidly than gases with higher densities (carbon dioxide). The speed of sound at 0°C is 332 meters per second (m/s). For every Celsius degree increase in air temperature, the speed of sound increases by approximately 0.6 meters per second. Thus, when the temperature is 5°C, the increase in the speed of sound is 5°C × 0.6 meters per second, or 3 meters per second. Adding 3 meters per second to the speed of sound at 0°C (332 meters per second), the speed of sound in air at 5°C is 335 meters per second. See Table 20-1.

At a temperature of 20°C, the increase in the speed of sound is 20°C × 0.6 meters per second, or 12 meters per second. Adding 12 meters per second to the speed of sound in air at 0°C, the speed of sound in air at 20°C is found to be 344 meters per second.

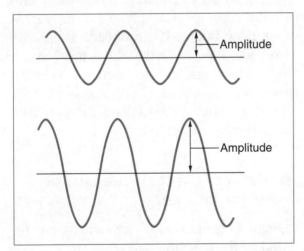

Figure 20-10. The amplitude of a wave is the distance from rest to the point of greatest vibration. The harder a tuning fork is struck, the greater is the amplitude of its sound.

Table 20-1.
How Does the Speed of Sound Change with Temperature?

Temperature (°C)	Speed of Sound (m/s)
0	332
5	335
10	338
15	341
20	344

The relationship of temperature to the speed of sound and your knowledge of the speed of light can help you determine how far away a bolt of lightning is. Suppose that the temperature of the air is 25°C and that the thunder is heard 3 seconds after the lightning is seen. Because light travels at 300,000 kilometers per second, assume that light rays reach you instantaneously. To find out how far away the lightning is, you must first determine the speed of sound at 25°C. At 0°C, the speed of sound is 332 meters per second. Since the speed increases by 0.6 meters per second for each Celsius degree increase in temperature, the speed of sound at 25°C is 15 meters per second faster than at 0°C. Thus, the speed of sound is 15 meters per second + 332 meters per second, or 347 meters per second at 25°C. Since it takes the sound of thunder 3 seconds to reach you, the distance traveled by the sound is 347 meters per second multiplied by 3 seconds:

$$347 \frac{\text{meters}}{\text{second}} \times 3 \text{ seconds} = 1041 \text{ meters}$$

The speed of sound in solids and liquids, unlike the speed of sound in gases, varies only slightly with changes in temperature. This is probably because the densities of solids and liquids are less affected by temperature changes than are the densities of gases.

What Does It Mean to Break the Sound Barrier? A speed of 335 meters per second is 1200 kilometers per hour (750 miles per hour) and is referred to as a speed of Mach 1. The Mach number (named for the German physicist *Ernst Mach*) describes how fast a body is moving compared to the speed of sound. An airplane moving at slower speeds sets up sound waves, which move in front of it at the speed of sound. These sound waves continue to pile up and reinforce one an-

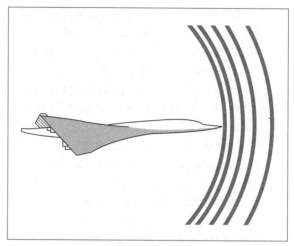

Figure 20-11. An aircraft breaks the sound barrier when it penetrates the buildup of sound waves in front of it.

other. When the airplane reaches a speed of Mach 1, it has caught up with its own sounds which, by this time, have taken the form of a giant compression (longitudinal) wave. This wave, called the **sound barrier**, subjects the plane to tremendous stress. To continue in motion, the airplane must penetrate the compression wave in front of it; it must break the sound barrier (see Figure 20-11). Planes are designed with sharpened noses and swept-back wings so as to reduce air friction which, in turn, permits them to break the sound barrier safely. When the plane breaks through the barrier, an explosive sound, or boom, is produced. The same problems face rockets, which must attain tremendous speeds to reach the velocity necessary to escape Earth's gravity. This speed is about 40,000 kilometers per hour (25,000 miles per hour).

How Are the Characteristics of Waves Related?

Speed, frequency, and wavelength are related by the equation

$$\text{speed} = \text{frequency} \times \text{wavelength}$$

Substituting the letters v for speed, f for frequency, and λ for wavelength, the equation may be written as

$$v = f \times \lambda \qquad \text{(equation 1)}$$

This formula can be transformed into

$$f = \frac{v}{\lambda} \qquad \text{(equation 2)}$$

or

$$\lambda = \frac{v}{f} \qquad \text{(equation 3)}$$

To find the speed of a wave when the frequency and the wavelength are given, use equation 1. For example, find the speed of a wave with a frequency of 500 hertz and a wavelength of 2 meters. Remember, 1 hertz is the same as 1 cycle per second.

$$v = f \times \lambda = 500 \text{ hertz} \times 2 \text{ meters}$$

$$v = 1000 \text{ meters per second}$$

Therefore, the speed of a wave with a frequency of 500 hertz and a wavelength of 2 meters is 1000 meters per second.

To find the frequency of a wave with a speed of 1100 meters per second and a wavelength of 2 meters, use equation 2.

$$f = \frac{v}{\lambda}$$

$$v = 1100 \text{ meters per second or } 1100 \, \frac{\text{meters}}{\text{second}}$$

$$\lambda = 2 \text{ meters}$$

$$f = \frac{1100 \, \dfrac{\text{meters}}{\text{second}}}{2 \text{ meters}}$$

As usual, you must compute both the number and the unit of the answer. To compute the unit, recall how to divide fractions:

$$\frac{\dfrac{\text{meters}}{\text{second}}}{\text{meters}} = \frac{\text{meters}}{\text{second}} \div \text{meters}$$

$$= \frac{\text{meters}}{\text{second}} \times \frac{1}{\text{meter}}$$

$$= \frac{1}{\text{second}}$$

Thus,

$$f = \frac{1100}{2} \times \frac{1}{\text{second}}$$

$$= 550 \text{ cycles per second or } 550 \text{ hertz}$$

To find the wavelength of a wave with a speed of 2000 meters per second and a frequency of 500 hertz, use equation 3.

$$v = 2000 \text{ meters per second or } 2000 \, \frac{\text{meters}}{\text{second}}$$

$$f = 500 \text{ hertz or } 500 \, \frac{1}{\text{second}}$$

$$\lambda = \frac{2000 \, \dfrac{\text{meters}}{\text{second}}}{500 \, \dfrac{1}{\text{second}}}$$

To compute the unit, recall how to divide fractions:

$$\frac{\dfrac{\text{meters}}{\text{second}}}{\dfrac{1}{\text{second}}} = \frac{\text{meters}}{\text{second}} \div \frac{1}{\text{second}}$$

$$= \frac{\text{meters}}{\text{second}} \times \frac{\text{second}}{1}$$

$$= \text{meters}$$

Thus,

$$\lambda = \frac{2000}{500} \text{ meters} = 4 \text{ meters}$$

What Happens When Sound Is Reflected or Absorbed?

When a sound wave strikes a smooth, hard surface such as a wall, floor, or mountain wall, it may be reflected back toward the source, much like a handball bouncing back from a wall. When such a sound reflection is heard, it is called an **echo**. Echoes can be heard only when the reflecting surface is more than 17 meters away because the ear cannot detect different sounds that are less than $\frac{1}{10}$ second apart. This means that the sound must travel 17 meters to the reflecting surface and 17 meters back to the source, a total of 34 meters. Because sound travels about 34 meters in $\frac{1}{10}$ second, the reflecting surface must be farther away than 17 meters so that the return of the sound occurs after $\frac{1}{10}$ second. If the distance were less than 17 meters, the total distance traveled by the sound would be less than 34 meters. Sound can travel this distance in less than $\frac{1}{10}$ second.

To avoid echoes in large rooms or auditoriums, soft materials such as drapes, rugs, and special ceiling materials are used to absorb the sound waves. This prevents the sounds from being reflected. Recall that sounds are absorbed by porous, inelastic materials.

Ships use a device called **sonar** to detect underwater objects. The word *sonar* is derived from *so*und *na*vigation *r*anging. In using sonar, a sound signal of ultrasonic frequency is sent out. When the sound wave strikes an object, the sound bounces back and is picked up by a receiver. If you know the speed of sound in the medium through which it is traveling and the time it takes for the sound to return, the distance of the reflecting object can be determined. For example, if a sound is sent out from a submarine and the echo is received 10 seconds later, you can determine the distance of the submarine from the object as follows:

1. Divide the time in half, since it will take half the time to reach the object and the other half to return to the sonar device. Thus, the time it will take for the sound to reach the object is 5 seconds.
2. In seawater, sound travels at a speed of about 1490 meters per second.
3. Multiply the speed of sound (1490 meters per second) by the time (5 seconds), or 1490 meters per second × 5 seconds = 7450 meters. The distance from the submarine to the object is 7450 meters.

How Are Sounds Described?

In your daily life, you are constantly exposed to many sounds—automobile horns, cell phones, airplane engines, speech, music, singing, explosions, hammering, and many others. In general, sounds can be classified as either *noises* or *musical tones* (or combinations of both). Musical tones are produced by the *regular* vibrations of an object, that is, vibrations that have uniform compressions and rarefactions. Noises are produced by *irregular* vibrations. Such sounds as the roar of a train, an explosion, or the striking of a hammer are noises because the vibrations of the objects producing them are irregular.

The difference between regular and irregular vibrations can be demonstrated in the following manner: Figure 20-12a shows a disk that has a series of evenly or regularly spaced holes and Figure 20-12b shows another disk with a series of irregularly spaced holes. When we rotate the disks, air blown through the evenly spaced holes produces regular vibrations. The sound we hear is a musical note, that is, a sound of fixed frequency. Air blown through the irregularly spaced holes, however, produces an unpleasant noise. Patterns of these sounds are shown in Figure 20-13. The smooth curve (regular vibrations) represents a pleasant sound such as a musical

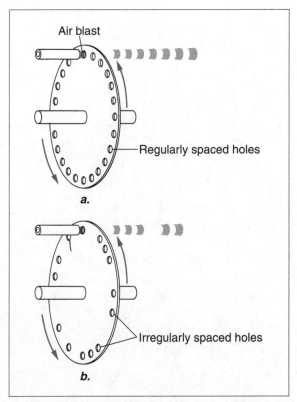

Figure 20-12. Air blown through rotating disks is affected by the spacing of the holes to form either a regular or an irregular pattern.

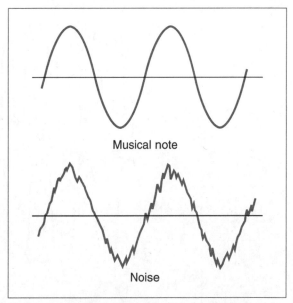

Figure 20-13. Regular and irregular vibrations produce music or noise, respectively.

note. The jagged curve (irregular vibrations) represents an unpleasant sound such as noise.

Figure 20-14 shows a disk with several series of evenly spaced holes, each series a different distance from the center of the disk. When this disk is rotated, a blast of air directed through the holes produces notes of different frequency. Why? This device can be used as a siren.

What Is Pitch? When a musical note is played, **pitch** refers to how high or how low the sound is. In the inquiry investigation you observed how pitch is related to vibrations by clamping the ruler at varying points from its end. As you shortened the vibrating part of the ruler, the pitch of the sound produced became higher as the frequency of vibration increased. The greater the number of vibra-

tions per second (frequency), the higher the pitch becomes. Figure 20-15 on page 322 shows three sound waves with different frequencies. The wave with the lowest frequency has the lowest pitch. The wave with the greatest frequency has the highest pitch.

Changing the Pitch of a Vibrating String. Stringed instruments such as the violin, banjo, and guitar produce a range of sounds

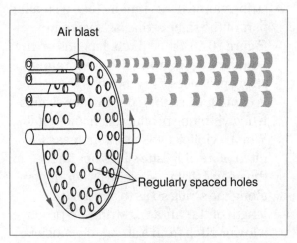

Figure 20-14. The diagram shows one way that a siren's sound is generated.

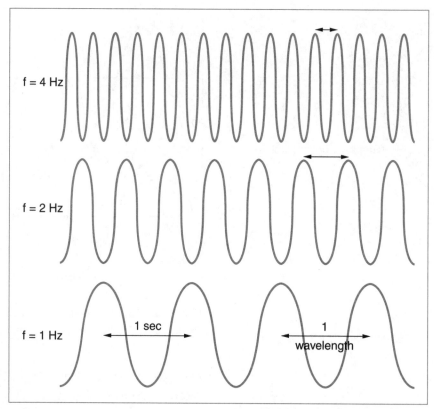

Figure 20-15. Pitch increases when frequency increases.

that result from varying the frequency of the vibrating strings. The frequency of a vibrating string can be varied in several ways:

1. *Varying the length of the string.* As a string is lengthened, its vibration frequency decreases. This means that a long string vibrates less rapidly than a smaller part of the same string, as shown in Figure 20-16. Since pitch depends on the number of vibrations, a long vibrating string produces a low pitch. If the string is cut in half, each of the smaller strings when vibrating produces a higher pitch. When a violinist wishes to increase the pitch of a string, she slides her finger "up the neck," that is, she moves her finger along the string so as to shorten the length of the vibrating string. To produce a lower pitch from a string, the musician moves her finger the other way, thereby allowing more of the string to vibrate (see Figure 20-17).

2. *Varying the thickness of the string.* In general, thick or heavy strings vibrate more slowly than do thin strings, and therefore thick strings produce musical notes of lower pitch. The strings of a violin vary in thickness. The thinnest of the four strings, the E string, produces a higher pitch than the thickest, the G string.

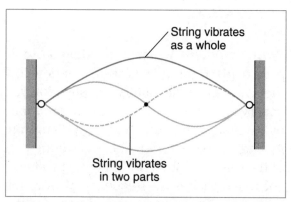

Figure 20-16. Smaller parts of a vibrating string vibrate faster than the entire string.

Figure 20-17. The pitch of a vibrating string depends on the string's length, thickness, and tightness.

3. *Varying the tension or tightness of the string.* In the case of two strings of equal length and equal thickness, the tighter string produces a note of higher pitch than the looser string. You can hear the change of pitch with tension when a guitar or violin is tuned. As the tuning key is turned to loosen or tighten the vibrating string, you hear the changes in pitch until the desired tension and pitch are reached.

Changing the Pitch of Pipes. A cylinder open at both ends is called an **open pipe**. A cylinder open at only one end is called a **closed pipe**. As with a vibrating string, the length of a pipe determines its pitch. In your inquiry investigation, you filled test tubes to various heights with water and demonstrated that

the shorter the pipe (that is, the more water there is in the test tube), the higher the pitch.

The relation of pipe length to pitch can also be shown by trimming and tapering one end of a drinking straw. Place the tapered end of the straw into the mouth and blow through it to produce a sound. (You have made a crude oboe.) Cut off a piece of the straw and blow through it again. You will note that as the straw (pipe) becomes smaller, the pitch of the note produced becomes higher.

Musical instruments such as the flute, clarinet, and oboe are based on the principle that the pitch of a pipe can be increased by shortening the length of the pipe, and can be decreased by lengthening the pipe. By opening and closing the keys of the instrument, a musician in effect lengthens or shortens it, varying the pitch.

Experiments have shown that the wavelength of the sound produced by an open pipe is approximately equal to twice the length of the vibrating air column. Thus, in an open pipe 1 meter in length, the wavelength of the sound produced is about 2 meters (Figure 20-18 *left*).

In a closed pipe, the wavelength of the sound produced is found to be four times the length of the pipe. Thus, the wavelength of a sound produced by a 1-meter closed pipe is about 4 meters (Figure 20-18 *right*).

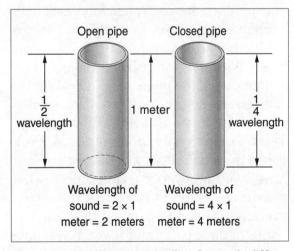

Figure 20-18. The wavelengths of sounds differ between open and closed pipes.

What Is Amplitude? You saw that amplitude corresponds to the loudness of the sound and depends on the force used in producing the sound. When a string is plucked gently, a quiet note is produced. However, when the string is plucked violently, a much louder note is produced. Although the pitch of the two notes is the same, their loudness, or intensity, is different. The louder sound is produced because greater energy was applied to the string. This increase in energy causes the string to vibrate through a larger distance, or range, than before. An increase in amplitude affects the compressions and rarefactions of the sound wave in opposite ways. During compression, the air molecules are crowded together even closer. During rarefaction, the air molecules are spread apart even farther. Thus, the loudness of a note depends on the amount of energy given to a vibrating body—that is, the greater the energy given, the louder the sound that is produced.

What is Sound Quality? When a trumpet and a violin sound the same note, you can easily distinguish between the two sounds. The difference in the sounds is called **quality**. The difference in quality among musical instruments is based on differences in the complexity of the vibrations of the instruments. All the instruments playing the same musical note produce the same main tone, called the **fundamental tone**. In a stringed instrument, the fundamental tone is produced when the string vibrates as a whole.

Because of the materials of which different instruments are constructed, musical instruments vibrate in many complex ways. These complex vibrations produce **overtones** (see Figure 20-19). In a stringed instrument, the first overtone is produced when the string vibrates in two parts; the second overtone is produced when the string vibrates in three parts; and so on. The sounds of the overtones differ in frequency as shown in Figure 20-19.

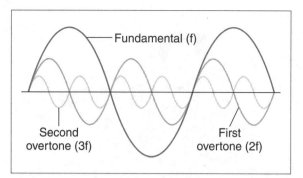

Figure 20-19. The diagram compares fundamentals and overtones.

When listening to a musical instrument, you actually hear a combination of the fundamental tone plus the overtones. Because the fundamental tones of all instruments producing the same note are the same, the differences in the quality of the sounds they produce are caused by the differences in their overtones.

The human voice is produced by vibrating membranes, which are stretched across the *larynx*, or Adam's apple. These membranes are called the *vocal cords*. Muscles can change the tension on these cords, thus changing the pitch of the sounds. Correct usage of the palate, tongue, lips, and teeth provides for modulation, or regulation, of the voice. As with musical instruments, voice quality depends on the proper blending of the overtones.

▶ What Is Resonance?

Have you ever watched an acrobat jumping on a trampoline (a stretched, flexible piece of canvas securely mounted on vertical supports)? To get the maximum bounce from each vibration of the canvas, the acrobat must time his jumps properly. As shown in Figure 20-20, he comes down when the canvas drops and he bounces up when the canvas comes up. In this manner, he can increase the height of his bounce greatly.

A sounding object—a vibrating body—is very much like the vibrating canvas of a trampoline. An elastic body in contact with

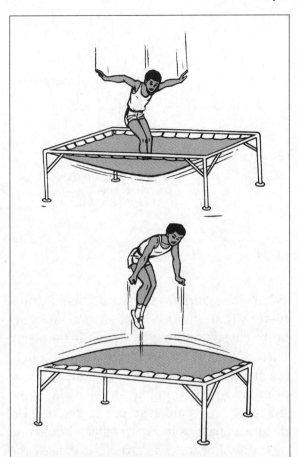

Figure 20-20. An acrobat times his jumps to increase the height of his jumps.

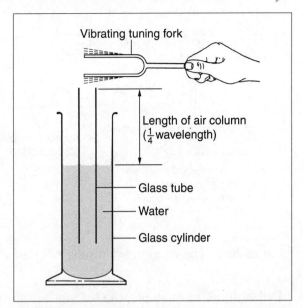

Figure 20-21. The diagram shows an example of resonance.

or near the sounding body can be made to vibrate. If the frequencies of the two bodies match properly, the intensity of the sound that is produced increases. This phenomenon is called **resonance**.

You have already learned that an *open* tube, or pipe, is a tube that is open at both ends. Observe the open tube in a cylinder of water shown in Figure 20-21. One end of the tube is closed by the water, and the tube is now a *closed* tube. Raising the tube in the water, without removing it completely, provides an air column of variable length. Now place a vibrating tuning fork over the open end of the tube and slowly raise the tube. At some height of the air column, the intensity of the sound reaches a maximum. The air column is said to be resonating. At this point, the compressions and rarefactions of the vibrating tuning fork match the compressions and rarefactions of the sound wave that is reflected from the surface of the water in the tube. This increases the amplitude of the wave, and the intensity of the sound increases. Experiments show that a closed tube resonates best when the height of the air column is one quarter of the wavelength of the sound wave that it reinforces.

The reinforcement of sound by resonance is used in wind instruments such as a saxophone or harmonica. In these instruments, a vibrating air column resonates and reinforces the air jet produced by a vibrating reed.

Voice resonance is produced by the vibrations of the vocal cords reinforced by air in the *resonant cavities* formed by the base and roof of the mouth, or by the larynx, or by the nose. This is why a cold or a stuffed nose affects the resonance of the voice.

Forced Vibrations. An elastic body has its own natural frequency of vibration. However, it may be forced to vibrate at another frequency by touching it with a vibrating body that has a different natural frequency

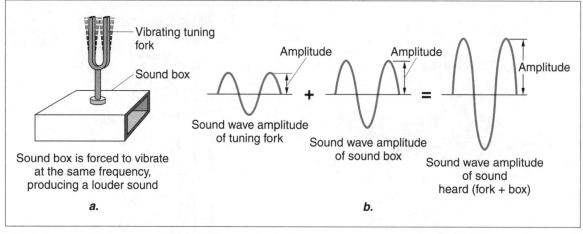

Figure 20-22. The setup shown results in forced vibrations.

of vibration. For example, the tuning fork in Figure 20-22a is struck and its stem is placed on a sound box. The sound box is forced to vibrate at the same frequency as the tuning fork, a phenomenon called **forced vibration**. The sound coming from the box has greater intensity because the larger amount of air around the box has been made to vibrate. This is the same as saying that the amplitude of the sound wave has been increased, as shown in Figure 20-22b. Forced vibrations are used to reinforce the sounds produced in a violin. The wood of the violin acts like the sound box previously described and the forced vibrations increase the intensity of the sound.

What Are Sympathetic Vibrations? Sympathetic vibrations occur when one vibrating body causes another body, with the same *natural* frequency, to vibrate without touching it. To demonstrate sympathetic vibration, set up two tuning forks of the same frequency on similar sound boxes a short distance apart as in Figure 20-23. When one of the tuning forks is struck, it causes the second tuning fork to vibrate at the same frequency. When the vibration of the first tuning fork is stopped, the second tuning fork continues to vibrate. Some opera singers can cause a thin glass to shatter as they stand away from the glass and sing a certain note. This occurs when the singer reaches a note

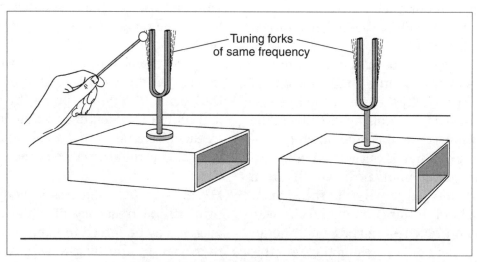

Figure 20-23. Sympathetic vibrations can be produced by using the setup shown.

that causes the glass to vibrate sympathetically at the same frequency as the note. Since glass is not sufficiently elastic to bend rapidly as it vibrates, it shatters.

What Is Interference?

You learned that when the frequencies of two vibrating bodies match—that is, when the compressions and rarefactions occur at the same time—reinforcement of the sound occurs. When sound waves from two tuning forks reinforce one another, they are said to be in phase, or in step. When the waves are out of phase, that is, when one vibrating tuning fork produces a compression while the other vibrating tuning fork produces a rarefaction, the intensity of the sound can lessen to the point approaching complete silence. This phenomenon is called **interference**.

Beats. Sound waves of slightly differing frequencies may alternately interfere and reinforce one another. When this happens, a throbbing effect called **beats** is produced.

Figure 20-24 shows how beats may be formed when two notes of slightly different

frequencies are struck at the same time. *A* and *B* represent the wave forms of the two notes. At point *x*, both waves are out of step. The total amplitude, shown in wave *C*, is the difference between the two amplitudes. The sound decreases in intensity (is softest) because interference between both waves occurs. At point *y*, both waves are in step. The total amplitude, shown on wave *C*, is the sum of the two amplitudes. The sound increases in intensity (is loudest) because reinforcement of both waves occurs at this point. The same situation can be described as you move farther along waves *A* and *B*. Beats are formed from the variations in sound produced by alternate interference and reinforcement.

The number of beats per second equals the difference between the frequencies of the sounds. When the difference between the frequencies of two tuning forks (30 hertz and 27 hertz) is 3 hertz, three beats can be heard when both forks are struck. The ear can distinguish only a limited range of beats. If the notes C (256 hertz) and G (384 hertz) are struck at the same time, 128 beats per second are produced. Since the ear cannot detect beats that are so close to one another,

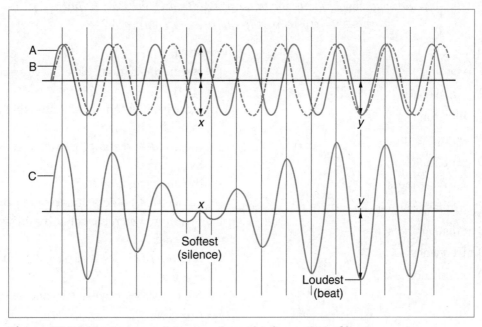

Figure 20-24. These wave diagrams show the formation of beats.

a pleasing sound is heard. However, if C (256 hertz) and D (288 hertz) are struck at the same time, the sound is unpleasant because the ear hears 32 beats per second.

When you hear music, you constantly hear beats. The sounds, however, are pleasant because the beats are properly blended with other notes.

Chapter Review

Science Terms

The following list contains all the boldfaced words found in this chapter and the page on which each appears.

amplitude (p. 316)
beats (p. 327)
carrying medium (p. 313)
closed pipe (p. 323)
compression (p. 315)
cycle (p. 316)
echo (p. 320)
elasticity (p. 314)
forced vibration (p. 326)
frequency (p. 316)

fundamental tone (p. 324)
hertz (p. 316)
interference (p. 327)
longitudinal wave (p. 315)
open pipe (p. 323)
overtones (p. 324)
pitch (p. 321)
quality (p. 324)
rarefaction (p. 315)
resonance (p. 325)

sonar (p. 320)
sound barrier (p. 318)
speed (p. 316)
transverse wave (p. 315)
ultrasonic (p. 316)
vacuum (p. 313)
vibration (p. 313)
wavelength (p. 316)

Matching Questions

In your notebook, write the letter of the item in column B that is most closely related to the item in column A.

Column A

_____ 1. vacuum
_____ 2. wavelength
_____ 3. ultrasonic
_____ 4. compression
_____ 5. amplitude
_____ 6. carrying medium
_____ 7. rarefaction
_____ 8. sonar
_____ 9. frequency
_____ 10. resonance

Column B

a. region of air molecules that are spread apart
b. increase in intensity of sound due to matching frequencies
c. the greatest distance particles are disturbed by a wave
d. the absence of matter
e. device that detects underwater objects
f. region in which particles are crowded together
g. number of cycles that pass a point in one second
h. the distance between two successive compressions
i. more than 20,000 vibrations per second
j. matter that transmits vibrations

Multiple-Choice Questions

*In your notebook, write the letter preceding the word or expression
that best completes the statement or answers the question.*

1. Which of the following devices is used to
   detect underwater objects?
   a. laser   c. maser
   b. radar   d. sonar

2. Of the following, sound is most closely
   associated with
   a. mechanical energy
   b. chemical energy
   c. heat energy
   d. potential energy

3. A tuning fork making a sound is inserted
   into a beaker of water. What property of
   sound will be demonstrated by this act?
   a. Sounds cannot travel through liquids.
   b. Sounds are created by vibrations.
   c. Sounds transfer chemical energy.
   d. Sounds cannot travel from one medium
      to another.

4. Sound is transmitted best through
   a. liquids   c. a vacuum
   b. gases   d. solids

5. Which property makes for the best insulator of sound?
   a. being of low density
   b. being elastic
   c. being porous
   d. being solid

6. Why does the sound decrease when the
   air in a bell jar containing a ringing bell is
   removed?
   a. The removal of the air prevents an elec-
      tric current from flowing.
   b. Sound cannot travel in a vacuum.
   c. Sound cannot travel through the glass.
   d. Sound cannot travel through air.

7. What characteristic of a sound wave is
   described as a rarefaction?
   a. a region where the molecules of the
      medium are spread apart

   b. a region where the molecules of the
      medium are crowded together
   c. the distance from the beginning of one
      wave to the end
   d. the greatest distance molecules of the
      medium move

8. In a sound wave, the molecules
   a. vibrate perpendicular to the movement
      of the wave
   b. do not move
   c. vibrate in all directions
   d. vibrate parallel to the movement of the
      wave

9. The range of human hearing is between 20
   hertz and
   a. 200 hertz   c. 2000 hertz
   b. 1,000 hertz   d. 20,000 hertz

10. In a sound wave, the distance between
    two successive compressions is called the
    a. wavelength   c. wave height
    b. frequency   d. amplitude

11. The height of a wave when drawn as a
    graph is known as the
    a. wavelength   c. wave distance
    b. amplitude   d. frequency

12. How is the speed of sound related to tem-
    perature at a given pressure?
    a. The speed is equal to the temperature.
    b. The speed increases with temperature.
    c. The speed decreases with
       temperature.
    d. The speed is independent of
       temperature.

13. The sound barrier is
    a. the tone produced when an object
       vibrates as a whole
    b. a device that transmits a sound and
       receives its echo

c. a material through which sound cannot pass

d. a giant compression formed by an object traveling at Mach 1

14. When a sound wave strikes a smooth hard surface, it is
a. reflected   c. transmitted
b. absorbed   d. refracted

15. How is noise different from other kinds of sounds?
a. Noise is produced by irregular vibrations.
b. Noise is produced by regular vibrations.
c. Noise is produced when matter is not vibrating.
d. Noise is produced when there is more than one sound wave.

16. The pitch of a sound depends on the
a. frequency   c. temperature
b. wavelength   d. amplitude

17. How does the pitch of a sound change as the length of a vibrating string is increased?
a. increases, then decreases
b. increases
c. decreases
d. remains the same

18. As the tension on a vibrating string is increased, the pitch of the sound produced by the string
a. is increased
b. is decreased
c. remains the same
d. increases, then decreases

19. The amplitude of a sound is determined by the
a. frequency
b. amount of energy used
c. wavelength
d. pitch

20. When the compressions and rarefactions of an air column match those of a vibrating tuning fork, the sounds produced
a. are different in pitch
b. have different wavelengths
c. have different frequencies
d. are resonating

Modified True-False Questions

In some of the following statements, the italicized term makes the statement incorrect. For each incorrect statement, in your notebook, write the term that must be substituted for the italicized term to make the statement correct. For each correct statement, write the word "true."

1. The rapid back-and-forth movement of matter that produces sound is known as *vibration.* _____

2. Sound-resistant materials are generally porous and *elastic.* _____

3. In a sound wave, the area of separation of molecules is called *compression.*

4. A sound wave is a *transverse* wave. _____

5. Sounds with frequencies above 20,000 hertz are called *ultrasonic.* _____

6. One compression and rarefaction in a sound wave is called a *cycle.* _____

7. The speed of sound increases as the temperature of the air *decreases.* _____

8. The speed of a sound wave is *inversely* proportional to its frequency. _____

9. Planes are designed with sharp noses and swept-back wings to reduce friction when they break the *sound barrier.* _____

10. A sound reflection is known as *a noise*.
   _____

11. Musical tones are produced by *regular* vibrations of matter. _____

12. The wavelength of a sound produced by an open pipe is approximately equal to *twice* the length of the pipe. _____

13. The main tone produced by a musical instrument is called *an overtone*.
   _____

14. Fluids in the *eardrum* of the human ear vibrate to stimulate auditory nerves.
   _____

15. A *forced vibration* occurs when a vibrating object causes another object to vibrate without touching it. _____

TEST-TAKING TIP You may find it helpful to draw and label a simple diagram as you answer questions. This may help you avoid confusion between related topics. For example, make sure you can draw and label a sound wave diagram.

Check Your Knowledge
Write the answer to each question in your notebook.

1. List and discuss three characteristics of sounds.

2. Describe three ways by which the pitch of a vibrating string may be increased.

3. Explain how the sound barrier is formed.

4. Give a scientific reason for each of the following:
   a. A vibrating object at one end of a room causes a glass to shatter at the other end of the room.
   b. When a vibrating tuning fork is touched to a sound box, the sound becomes louder.
   c. The sound of a vibrating tuning fork lessens when the tuning fork is placed over a column of air.

Think Critically
Write the answer to each of the following questions in your notebook.

1. a. A thunderclap is heard 5 seconds after a bolt of lightning is seen. Find how far away the lightning bolt struck if the air temperature is 10°C.
   b. A thunderclap is heard 10 seconds after a bolt of lightning is seen. The lightning bolt strikes a tree at a distance of 3470 meters from you. (1) Find the velocity of sound in this situation. (2) Find the air temperature.

2. a. Find the velocity of a sound wave whose frequency is 480 hertz and whose wavelength is 2 meters.
   b. Find the wavelength of a sound wave traveling at a velocity of 1200 meters per second at a frequency of 400 hertz.

3. a. A research ship discovers a whale by receiving a transmitted sonar signal 10 seconds after it was sent. How far away is the whale?
   b. How deep is the ocean bottom if the echo of a transmitted sonar signal is received 20 seconds after it was sent?

Take It Further
1. In old western movies, cowboys were often shown putting their ear to railroad tracks to determine if a train was coming. Investigate this phenomenon and explain why it would be more useful to listen through the tracks than through air.

Internet Search ⌄ ✕ ↺

2. Chuck Yeager is credited as the first person to break the sound barrier. Research his historic flight and find out why it was easier for him to accomplish this feat at a higher altitude than on the ground. Expand your research to find the conditions under which the sound barrier was broken on land. Consult sources such as the following to begin your research: *http://www.centennialofflight.gov/ essay/Explorers_Record_Setters_and _Daredevils/yeager/EX30.htm* and *http://www.achievement.org/autodoc/ page/yea0bio-1*.

CAREER

3. Acoustical engineers deal with limiting unwanted sounds and maximizing desired sounds. Research careers in acoustical engineering to find out what training is required and what job opportunities exist. You may wish to begin your search at a site such as the following: *http:// education-portal.com/articles/ Acoustic_Engineer_Job_Description_ and_Requirements_for_a_Career_in_ Acoustic_Engineering.html*. Share your findings with the class.

21

What is the Nature of Electromagnetic Energy?

Light of the sun signals the start of a new day. It lets people see the world around them and it enables plants to make food. The properties of light make it possible for it to travel millions of kilometers to Earth in just 8 minutes.

After reading this chapter, you should be able to answer the following questions:

What is the origin of light?

What theories explain the nature of light?

How fast does light travel?

How does matter affect the transmission of light?

How is light reflected from surfaces?

How can wave motion be described?

What is polarized light?

You may look in a mirror all the time, but do you know what makes it possible for you to see yourself in a mirror? It has to do with the nature of light. In this inquiry investigation, you will explore how light is reflected from a mirror.

Materials:

✔ safety goggles
✔ plane mirror
✔ block of wood
✔ rubber band
✔ piece of white paper or cardboard
✔ long dissecting pin
✔ meterstick
✔ drawing board
✔ tacks or tape
✔ pencil

Part A Secure a sheet of white paper or cardboard to a drawing board with either tape or tacks. Use a ruler to draw line *EF*. Draw and label points *A*, *B*, *C*, and *D* in the approximate locations shown in Figure 21-1.

Part B Using a rubber band, attach a plane mirror to a block of wood and stand the mirror upright on line *EF*. Stick a pin in the paper at point *A*.

Part C Move a little to the right of the pin to point *C*. Sight the image of the pin in the mirror by placing a ruler at point *C*, looking along the edge of the ruler to the image of the pin in the mirror. Draw a line from point *C* to line *EF* to indicate this sighting. Mark point *N* where the line touches the mirror.

1. ***With respect to the mirror, where does the image of the pin appear to be?***

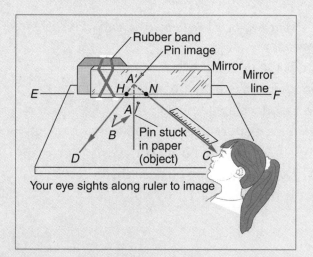

Figure 21-1.

Part D Move to the left of the pin to point *D* and again sight the image of the pin along a ruler between point *D* and the mirror. Draw a line to indicate this sighting by connecting point *D* with line *EF*. Mark point *H* where the line touches the mirror.

Part E Remove the mirror and extend line *CN* behind the mirror using a dotted line. Extend line *DH* behind the mirror by a dotted line also. Mark point *A'* where line *CN* crosses line *DH*. This is the apparent position of the image.

Part F Move the pin from point *A* to point *B*. Repeat procedures *C*, *D*, and *E* for the image of the pin at point *B*. Mark point *B'* behind the mirror where the dotted lines meet. Connect points *A'* and *B'* with a dotted line. This represents the image of an object, line *AB*.

Part G Make the following measurements and record them in a table:

    a. Length of *object AB* =
    b. Length of *image A'B'* =
    c. Distance from point *A* to mirror line =
    d. Distance from point *A'* to mirror line =
    e. Distance from point *B* to mirror line =
    f. Distance from point *B'* to mirror line =

    2. *How does the size of the object AB compare to the size of the image A'B'?*

    3. *What conclusion can you draw concerning the distance of the object to the mirror and the distance of the image to the mirror?*

    4. *What does the mirror appear to do to the position of the image A'B' as compared to the position of the object AB?*

What Is the Origin of Light?

Light, like heat and sound, is a form of energy. It may be described as either natural or artificial. **Natural light** is light that comes from objects in the environment. Most natural light that you use comes from the sun. Other stars also produce natural light. **Artificial light** is manufactured and is usually associated with burning fuels or devices powered by electricity.

Some objects appear to produce light when, in fact, they do not. For this reason, it is necessary to distinguish between **luminous** or **illuminated** objects. A luminous body, such as the sun or a shining lightbulb, manufactures its own light. An illuminated body, such as the moon or a mirror or a person, is visible because it reflects light.

Heat energy is often a vital factor in producing light energy. If a piece of iron, such as a horseshoe or a large nail, were clamped to a ring stand and then heated with a Bunsen burner, the iron would glow as it becomes heated. It would glow red at first, then white, and finally—if the source of heat is great enough—blue. When the burner is removed, the iron will continue to glow until it cools. This example shows that a heated body can produce light as well as heat.

The introduction of energy (such as heat) into a body can cause the emission, or release, of light energy. The emitted energy results from movements of electrons in the atoms of the body. When electrons return to their normal positions, energy is emitted. The emitted energy sometimes takes the form of visible light. At other times, the energy given off may be in the form of ultraviolet light or x-rays, which are invisible to the human eye. Interactions in the atoms of elements present in the sun are responsible for the sun's heat and light.

Unlike luminous bodies, which give off their own light, illuminated bodies give off light that reaches them from other sources, that is, by reflection. Examples of illuminated bodies, in addition to the moon and the planets, include clouds, the pages of this book, and all other objects that you see that do not emit their own light.

What Theories Are Used to Explain the Nature of Light?

Although everyone is familiar with light energy, scientists still puzzle over just what it is. Investigations to determine the nature of light began in the seventeenth century and continue today. The major theories that have been proposed to explain the nature of light are the corpuscular theory, the wave theory, the electromagnetic theory, and the quantum theory.

The Corpuscular Theory. The corpuscular theory of light was first proposed in the seventeenth century by the English scientist *Sir Isaac Newton.* According to this theory, the light emitted by luminous bodies consists of tiny particles of matter, or *corpuscles.* These emitted corpuscles are propelled outward in all directions, and travel in straight lines much like bullets from a gun. Newton thought that when corpuscles strike a surface, each particle is reflected in much the same way that a handball bounces off a wall. From his studies of gravitation, Newton predicted that light traveling from air into water would *increase* its speed. Because water is denser than air, he reasoned, the corpuscles of light on entering water would be attracted more to the water and hence the speed of the corpuscles would increase.

The Wave Theory. Christian Huygens, a Dutch scientist, proposed his wave theory of light at about the same time that Newton proposed his corpuscular theory. Huygens proposed that light is emitted as a series of waves that spread out from the light source in all directions, much like the ripples formed when a pebble is dropped into water. These waves, unlike corpuscles, are not affected by gravity. Disagreeing with Newton, Huygens predicted that light on entering water from air would *decrease* in speed. When the speed of light through different media (air, glass, water) was determined two centuries later, Huygens' prediction was found to be correct.

About 100 years later, the English scientist *Thomas Young* showed that under certain conditions, light waves could interfere with each other in a way similar to that of sound waves. Remember that interference between sound waves results in beats (intervals of loud sound followed by intervals of comparative quiet). Similarly, interference between light waves results in bright bands of light and bands of darkness. Young's discovery gave great support to the wave theory and almost destroyed the corpuscular theory. The fact that light can be polarized (see page 344) also goes against the corpuscular theory.

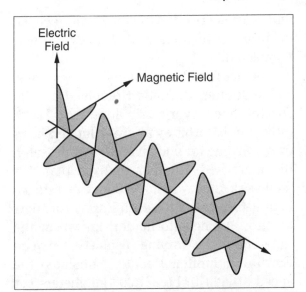

Figure 21-2. An electromagnetic field is composed of vibrating electric and magnetic fields.

The Electromagnetic Theory. The wave theory of light, as developed by Huygens, assumes that light waves, like sound waves, require a medium for transmission. Toward the end of the nineteenth century, *James Clerk Maxwell,* a Scottish physicist, proposed that light waves do not require a medium for transmission. According to Maxwell, light waves possess electrical and magnetic properties and can travel through a vacuum. An electromagnetic wave consists of electric and magnetic fields that vibrate perpendicular to one another and to the direction of the wave. (See Figure 21-2.)

Later experiments by Maxwell and other scientists showed that light waves are only a small part of a larger family of electromagnetic waves and make up what is called the **electromagnetic spectrum**. Light, therefore, is just one form of energy that can be described as **electromagnetic energy**. The energy is carried by a disturbance that does not require matter through which to travel.

According to the electromagnetic theory of light, different electromagnetic waves are produced by the interactions of various forms of energy and atomic particles. Only a small portion of these waves (or *rays*, as they are sometimes called) can be seen by the human eye. Most of the waves are invisible and can be detected only with specific instruments. Each type of wave in the electromagnetic spectrum possesses a particular wavelength and a particular frequency (hertz). Thus, a radio wave that is 1000 meters long has a frequency of 300,000 hertz (3.0×10^5 Hz). A visible light ray that is five ten-millionths of a meter long has a frequency of 600,000,000,000,000 hertz (6.0×10^{14} Hz). An x-ray that is one ten-billionth of a meter long has a frequency of about 3,000,000,000,000,000,000 hertz (3.0×10^{18} Hz). The shorter the wavelength is, the greater the frequency is, as shown in Figure 21-3.

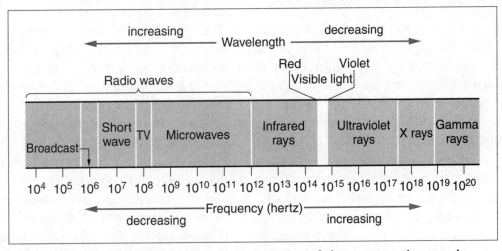

Figure 21-3. The electromagnetic spectrum consists of electromagnetic waves in order of frequency and wavelength.

Radio waves with frequencies between 10^9 and 10^{12} hertz are called microwaves. These **microwaves** are used for communication as well as for cooking. Microwaves are particularly useful in cooking because foods absorb the microwaves and cook from within. As a result, the cooking is rapid and uniform.

The Quantum Theory. By the end of the nineteenth century, experiments had shown that electromagnetic waves possess energy and that each wave possesses a different amount of energy from the others. In 1900, the German scientist *Max Planck* proposed the theory that light waves travel as separate packets of energy called **quanta** or **photons**. In some respects, Planck's photons resemble the corpuscles of Newton's theory. However, instead of considering the photons to be particles of matter, Planck considered them to be bundles of energy.

In recent years, it has become evident that, in some respects, light seems to behave as corpuscles; in others, light behaves as visible and invisible waves; and in still others, light behaves as bundles of energy. Because the **quantum theory** merges the ideas of the three theories that preceded it, this theory explains the nature and behavior of light better than does any other theory.

▶ How Fast Does Light Travel?

You see a flash of lightning from a distant storm long before you hear the sound of the thunder generated by the lightning. It is therefore apparent that the speed of light is much greater than the speed of sound.

As long ago as 1676, *Olaus Roemer*, a Danish scientist, devised a method to accomplish the difficult task of finding the speed of light. Through a telescope, he observed the motions of the planet Jupiter and one of its moons. This moon's revolution could be accurately timed because, at some point in its orbit, the satellite passed behind Jupiter and was eclipsed. Whenever this eclipse occurred, a revolution of the satellite was completed.

Roemer found that when Earth was closest to Jupiter, the moon revolved around Jupiter once every $42\frac{1}{2}$ hours. As Earth moved in its orbit away from Jupiter, however, the time for one revolution of the satellite increased. Roemer realized that this increase in time was due to the extra distance light had to travel to reach Earth at its new position. Using information known at the time about the varying distances between Earth and Jupiter, Roemer calculated the speed of light to be 227,000 kilometers per second, which is close to the actual value.

Modern experimenters have improved on Roemer's determination of the speed of light. Among these was *Albert A. Michelson*, who in 1926 used rotating mirrors to measure the time required for light to make one round trip from Mt. Wilson to Mt. San Antonio in California, a distance of about 44 miles. He checked his results by measuring the time it took light to travel through a specially constructed tunnel that was one mile long. From his precise experiments, Michelson calculated the speed of light to be 186,285 miles per second, or 299,796 kilometers per second. For most purposes, however, the approximate figures of 186,000 miles per second, or 300,000 kilometers per second are acceptable. This value is most often written as 3.00×10^8 meters per second.

Recall that the wavelength of any sound wave multiplied by its frequency equals the speed of sound; $v = f \times \lambda$. In the same manner, the wavelength of any electromagnetic wave multiplied by its frequency equals the speed of the electromagnetic wave. Scientists have determined that the speed of *any* electromagnetic wave equals the speed of light—300,000 kilometers per second.

Even though an electromagnetic wave does not require a medium, it can travel through matter. The type of medium can affect the speed of an electromagnetic wave.

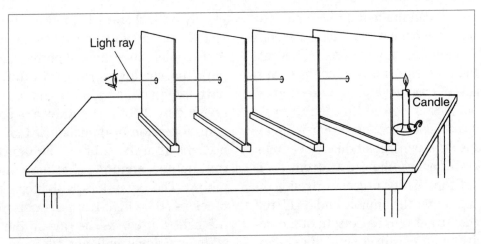

Figure 21-4. Light travels in a straight line.

The value for the speed of light is about the same in air as it is in a vacuum. However, the speed of light does decrease as light passes through liquids and solids. You will deal with some of these effects in the next chapter.

How Does Matter Affect the Transmission of Light?

Recall the example of the electric bell that rang in a vacuum (Figure 20-4 on page 314). As the vacuum was produced in the bell jar, the sound of the ringing bell diminished even though the bell could be seen ringing. This experiment shows that light continued to be transmitted from the bell even in the absence of a material medium.

Light waves easily pass through a vacuum, undergoing little change. When light waves come in contact with matter, however, they slow and may otherwise change. In traveling through matter, light may be blocked (or absorbed), either partially or completely; it may be distorted; or it may pass through the medium with little change. Objects that completely block light and through which you cannot see are described as being **opaque**. Examples include wood, stone, and steel. Objects that readily transmit light and through which you can see clearly are described as **transparent**. Plate glass, air, and clear plastics are examples of transparent objects. Objects that allow light to pass through partially or that distort the light so that you cannot see through them are called **translucent** objects. Frosted glass, cloth window shades, and oiled paper are examples of translucent objects.

How Does Light Interact with Matter?

What do you think would happen if you set up the demonstration shown in Figure 21-4? Because light rays from the candle can reach your eye only by traveling along the path through the holes, it is reasonable to conclude that light travels in straight lines.

Pinhole Camera. This fact helps in understanding how a pinhole camera (see Figure 21-5) forms an image of an object viewed

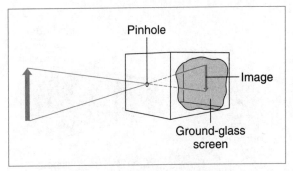

Figure 21-5. A pinhole camera takes advantage of the fact that light travels in straight lines.

through it. You can make a pinhole camera by using a pin to make a small hole the center of one side of an opaque box. After cutting out the opposite side, replace it with a screen made of ground glass or waxed paper. When an object is viewed through the pinhole, its image is seen on the screen in an inverted (upside down) position. It becomes upside down because light rays from each part of the top of the object, traveling in straight lines, enter the pinhole and reach the screen. Light rays from the bottom of the object reach the screen in a similar manner. Light rays from all parts of the object passing through the pinhole cross each other's path. After crossing, the lower rays reach the upper part of the screen and the upper rays reach the lower part of the screen, thereby producing the inverted image.

Shadows. The fact that light travels in straight lines helps explain the formation of shadows. When light from a luminous body strikes an opaque object, the light is blocked and a dark space called a **shadow** is formed behind the object. As shown in Figure 21-6*a*, a point source of light, such as a laser or a tiny high-intensity bulb, produces a com-

pletely dark shadow behind the opaque object. However, when the light source is larger than a point (an ordinary lightbulb, for example), the shadow formed is often seen to have two parts: an *umbra* and a *penumbra* (see Figure 21-6*b*). The **umbra** is the darker central portion of the shadow that receives no light from the source. The **penumbra** is the lighter shadow that surrounds the umbra. The penumbra is lighter because it receives some light from the outer edges of the light source. As the rays in the diagram show, shadows will not form unless light travels in straight lines.

How Is Light Reflected from Surfaces?

In general, when light strikes opaque objects, it is absorbed. If the object is dark in color, the light energy is transformed into thermal energy. You already know that when light strikes transparent or translucent objects, it passes through them and continues on its path. However, when light strikes certain surfaces, it is reflected, which means that the light bounces off the surface in much the same manner as a handball bounces off a wall. It is the reflection of light from objects to your eyes that enables you to see the objects around you.

Law of Reflection. When you play handball, you return a ball best when you place yourself near where you expect the ball to be after it rebounds from the wall. Light rebounds from an object in much the same way as a ball rebounds from a wall. As shown in Figure 21-7, when a ray of light strikes a smooth shiny surface, the ray is reflected. The light ray that strikes the surface is called the **incident ray**; the light ray that bounces off the surface is called the **reflected ray**. The line drawn at right angles to the surface is called the **normal**. When a light ray strikes a surface such as a flat mirror (plane mirror) along the normal, the light ray rebounds from the mirror along the same

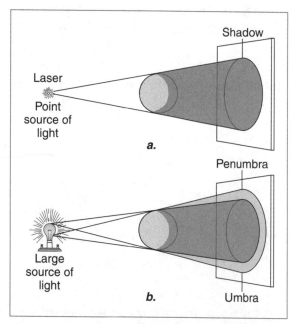

Figure 21-6. The formation of shadows results from the straight-line paths of light rays.

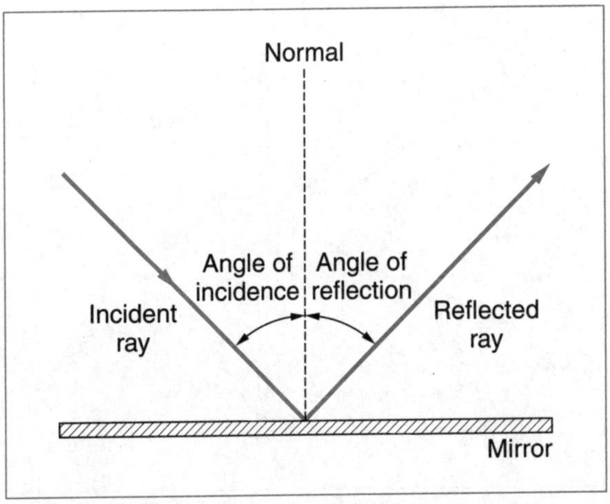

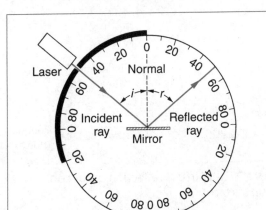

Figure 21-7. According to the law of reflection, the angle of incidence is always equal to the angle of reflection.

Figure 21-8. An optical disk is used to measure angles of incidence and reflection.

line. When a light ray strikes the mirror at an angle to the normal, it is reflected from the mirror at an angle equal to the original angle. The angle between the incident ray and the normal is called the **angle of incidence**; the angle between the reflected ray and the normal is called the **angle of reflection**. Thus, when light strikes a mirror at an angle, the angle of incidence is equal to the angle of reflection. This relationship is called the **law of reflection**.

The law of reflection is readily demonstrated by a device called an *optical disk* (see Figure 21-8). The mirror of this device is lined up so that the normal to the mirror crosses the zero point of the scale. When an incident ray strikes the mirror at an angle of 50° from the normal, the beam of light is reflected and crosses the scale at the 50° mark on the other side of the normal. You can test the law of reflection by using different angles for the incident ray.

Regular and Diffuse Reflection. You have just seen that a single ray of light behaves according to the law of reflection when the ray is reflected from a smooth shiny surface. However, when a beam of light, which is composed of many parallel light rays, strikes a given surface, the manner in which the beam is reflected depends on the nature of the sur-

face. The surface determines whether the reflection will be *regular* or *diffuse*.

Reflection that occurs from a smooth flat surface, such as a mirror or a quiet pool of water, is called **regular reflection**. In this type of reflection, when many parallel rays of light strike the surface at some angle from the normal, all of the rays remain parallel and are reflected from the surface in the same direction and at the same angle of reflection (see Figure 21-9).

Reflection from a rough surface is called **diffuse reflection**. When a beam of light composed of many parallel light rays strikes a rough surface, each individual light ray

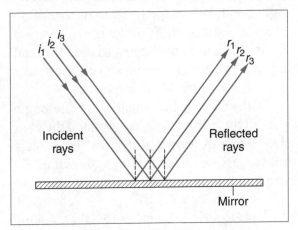

Figure 21-9. Regular reflection occurs on a smooth surface.

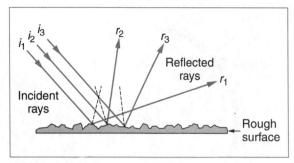

Figure 21-10. Diffuse reflection occurs on a rough surface.

obeys the law of reflection according to the position of each portion, or facet, of the surface. Because the surface is not smooth, the reflected rays that leave it are no longer parallel. As shown in Figure 21-10, the reflected rays bounce off the surface in all directions. Diffuse reflection is the type of reflection by which you see many illuminated objects. For example, you see the paper of this page because of the diffuse reflection of light from the individual fibers of which the paper is made.

Reflection From a Plane Mirror. You observe a familiar example of regular reflection every time you look into an ordinary mirror. If you stand 5 feet from a full-length mirror and examine your image, it will appear to be 5 feet behind the mirror. Your image will also appear to be as tall as you are. Furthermore, you will find your position and that of your image to be reversed laterally, from left to right. That is, your left hand is your image's right hand, and so forth. The reversal of position is best seen by holding this page in front of a mirror and trying to read it. Reading will be difficult because you must read backwards or upside down!

In the inquiry investigation at the beginning of the chapter you, determined the characteristics of an image formed by a plane mirror. These characteristics, shown in Figure 21-11, may be summarized as follows:

1. The size of the image (I) seen in a plane mirror is the same as the size of the object (O).

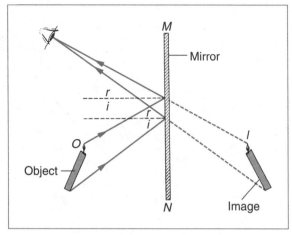

Figure 21-11. The diagram shows how an image is formed by a plane mirror.

2. The actual distance of the object from a plane mirror is the same as the distance the image appears to be behind the mirror.
3. The image seen in a plane mirror is reversed laterally when compared to the object.

How Can Wave Motion Be Described?

Have you ever fastened one end of a rope to a fixed support and shook the free end of the rope as in Figure 21-12? If so, you know that a wave travels along the rope. Shaking disturbs the rope and the disturbances travel along the length of the rope. The rope is said to be vibrating. Similarly, a pebble or stone dropped into a body of quiet water acts as a center of disturbance. The particles in the water vibrate as the disturbances move as waves. In each of these cases, the disturbances—not the particles of the medium—travel outward. For example, when a specific spot on the rope is marked and the rope is shaken, the spot moves up and down in the same position whereas the disturbances travel along the rope. Similarly, a piece of wood floating on the surface of a quiet, windless pond remains bobbing in the same position as waves pass by it.

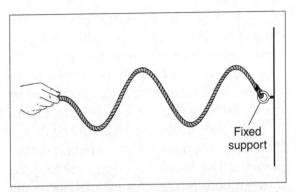

Figure 21-12. The rope vibrates as a wave travels along it. The disturbance, or wave, moves, but the rope itself stays in the same place.

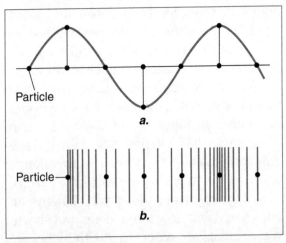

Figure 21-13. (a) Transverse waves result from a disturbance perpendicular to the direction of the wave. (b) Longitudinal waves result from a disturbance parallel to the direction of the wave.

The direction of the disturbances (waves) compared with the direction of motion of the vibrating particles determines the type of wave. Scientists recognize two common wave types:

1. *Transverse waves* vibrate at right angles to the direction of the wave (see Figure 21-13a). The vibrating rope and water waves are examples of transverse waves.
2. *Longitudinal waves* vibrate back and forth, parallel to the direction the wave travels (see Figure 21-13b). Recall that sound waves consist of series of compressions (condensations) and rarefactions in which air molecules move back and forth while the wave travels through them. Sound waves are examples of longitudinal waves.

Both types of waves can be described in terms of the same characteristics: wavelength, frequency, and amplitude. Because both types of waves represent vibrations, or disturbance displacements, they can be pictured graphically in the same manner.

▶ What Are the Properties of Light Waves?

If you have been in a small boat, you may have experienced the up-and-down bobbing of the boat as a series of waves passes you. The waves travel horizontally while the boat

moves up and down. Light waves behave in a manner similar to these transverse waves.

The quantum theory (see page 338) proposes that light waves travel as bundles of energy resembling somewhat the corpuscles in Newton's theory of light. The quantum theory, combining the corpuscular theory and the wave theory, states that corpuscles vibrate *at right angles* to the direction in which the wave travels. Thus, in a transverse light wave, the corpuscles move in an up-and-down direction similar to that of a water wave.

As shown in Figure 21-14 a transverse wave has high points, or **crests**, and low

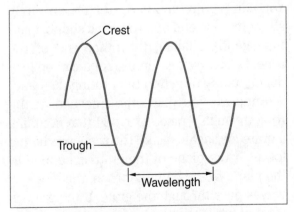

Figure 21-14. Like other waves, transverse waves can be described by properties that include wavelength and frequency.

points, or **troughs**. The wavelength of such waves is the distance between two successive crests or troughs. The frequency of a transverse wave is the number of vibrations (crests or troughs) per second the wave makes. Two complete vibrations, or cycles, are shown in Figure 21-14. Refer to Figure 21-3 on page 337 and note that there is a specific relationship between the wavelength and frequency of the waves of the electromagnetic spectrum—long wavelengths are associated with low frequencies and shorter wavelengths are associated with higher frequencies. As with any electromagnetic wave, the wavelength of light multiplied by its frequency gives its velocity.

Visible light, which consists of six basic colors, appears white when all of the colors are seen together. The basic colors are red, orange, yellow, green, blue, and violet. Each color has a characteristic wavelength and frequency. Of the visible light rays, red rays have the longest wavelength and the lowest frequency; violet rays have the shortest wavelength and the highest frequency.

What Is Polarized Light?

A light source, such as the sun or a lamp, emits waves that vibrate vertically, horizontally, and in all directions. Because the wave is transverse, the vibrations are at right angles to the plane in which the waves travel. Such light waves are said to be **unpolarized**. You can picture unpolarized light waves by attaching one end of a rope to a support and then gently shaking the other end of the rope. Loops (waves) in the rope can be produced in any direction by rotating the hand.

Suppose you place the free end of the rope through a piece of wood that contains a grate and again shake the rope, producing loops. If the plane of the grate is parallel to the plane of the vibrating rope, the loops or waves pass through the grate. If the grate is rotated while the plane of the vibrating rope remains unchanged, fewer and fewer waves

can pass through. When the plane of the grate is at right angles to the plane of the vibrating rope, no waves pass through.

You can get the same effect by passing the free end of the rope through two pieces of wood, each containing a grate (see Figure 21-15). Gently shake the rope up and down. If the planes of both grates are parallel to the plane of the vibrating rope, waves pass through both grates. However, suppose the grate nearer the rope support is rotated, as the rope is shaken vertically. When the two grates are at right angles to one another (crossed), no waves pass through to the support.

In certain naturally occurring crystals, the atoms in the crystals are arranged in rows. The space between any two rows of atoms resembles the grate discussed previously. All the vibrations associated with a light wave cannot pass through these crystals. Only those vibrations that are parallel to the rows of atoms will pass through. The light that emerges consists of waves that vibrate in a single plane and is called **polarized light**. Note that the polarization of light has been explained by assuming that light is a trans-

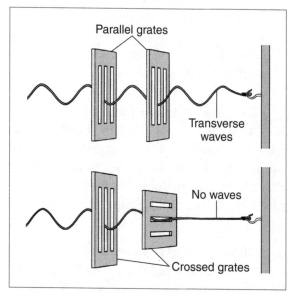

Figure 21-15. Transverse waves can pass through gratings only if the vibration is in the same direction as the grating.

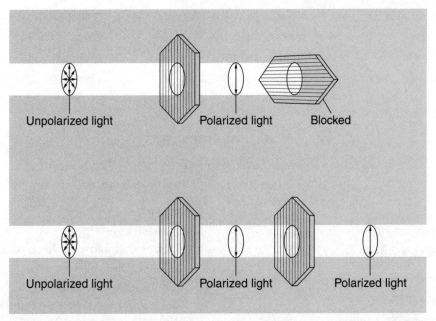

Figure 21-16. Light can be polarized by materials that resemble gratings.

verse wave. The corpuscular theory cannot account for this behavior.

The crystal that produces polarized light is called a **polarizer**. An artificial material, called Polaroid™, acts as a polarizer. Two sheets of Polaroid™, placed on one another so that their axes are at right angles, will not permit any light to pass through them (see Figure 21-16). When both sheets of Polaroid™ are arranged so that their axes are parallel, polarized light passes through each sheet.

Polarized light has many applications. Polarizing lenses in eyeglasses or cameras help to reduce glare. Glare is produced when light reflects off a surface, causing it to shine brightly into a person's eyes. Polarized light is used by engineers to locate points of stress in automobiles and machinery. As a research tool, polarized light is extremely useful. Since different crystals polarize light differently, the identities of these crystals can be determined.

Chapter Review

Science Terms

The following list contains all the boldfaced words found in this chapter and the page on which each appears.

angle of incidence (p. 341)

angle of reflection (p. 341)

artificial light (p. 335)

crests (p. 343)

diffuse reflection (p. 341)

electromagnetic energy (p. 337)

electromagnetic spectrum (p. 337)

illuminated (p. 335)

incident ray (p. 340)

law of reflection (p. 341)

luminous (p. 335)

microwaves (p. 338)

natural light (p. 335)

normal (p. 340)

opaque (p. 339)

penumbra (p. 340)

photons (p. 338)

polarized light (p. 344)   reflected ray (p. 340)   transparent (p. 339)
polarizer (p. 345)   regular reflection (p. 341) troughs (p. 344)
quanta (p. 338)   shadow (p. 340)   umbra (p. 340)
quantum theory (p. 338)   translucent (p. 339)   unpolarized (p. 344)

Matching Questions

*In your notebook, write the letter of the item in column B that is
most closely related to the item in column A.*

Column A

_____ 1. transparent
_____ 2. microwaves
_____ 3. quanta
_____ 4. opaque
_____ 5. transverse wave
_____ 6. regular reflection
_____ 7. luminous
_____ 8. penumbra
_____ 9. polarized light
_____ 10. translucent

Column B

a. packets of energy
b. matter that allows light to pass through as frosted glass does
c. lighter part of a shadow
d. description of object that produces light energy
e. light waves that vibrate in a single plane
f. matter that readily transmits light
g. light bouncing off a mirror as parallel rays
h. vibrations perpendicular to wave direction
i. electromagnetic waves used for cooking and communication
j. matter through which light cannot pass
k. darker part of a shadow

Multiple-Choice Questions

*In your notebook, write the letter preceding the word or expression
that best completes the statement or answers the question.*

1. Which of the following is an illuminated object?
a. the moon   c. light bulb
b. the sun   d. a star

2. The corpuscular theory of light was proposed by
a. Maxwell   c. Planck
b. Huygens   d. Newton

3. Which theory of light was proposed by Christian Huygens?
a. corpuscular theory
b. wave theory
c. quantum theory
d. electromagnetic theory

4. Which discovery showed that the corpuscular theory is not true?
a. Light requires a medium through which to travel.
b. Light travels in straight lines.
c. Light can be polarized.
d. Light changes speed as it travels from one medium to another.

5. James Maxwell proposed the idea that light
a. has electrical and magnetic properties
b. travels as particles
c. is composed of quanta
d. travels in waves

6. Objects that block all light are said to be
   a. transparent   c. opaque
   b. luminous   d. translucent

7. An example of a translucent substance is a
   a. windowpane   c. book
   b. frosted glass   d. movie screen

8. In a pinhole camera, the image formed on the film is
   a. right side up   c. inverted
   b. reversed   d. enlarged

9. The blocking of light produces
   a. shadows
   b. streaks of light
   c. interference
   d. dark and light lines

10. The lighter fringe of a shadow is called the
    a. filter
    b. penumbra
    c. polarized light
    d. umbra

11. What does it mean to say that light is absorbed?
    a. It is taken in and not released.
    b. It becomes brighter.
    c. It changes color.
    d. It bounces off in the same direction it came from.

12. When light energy is absorbed by a dark object, it is generally changed to
    a. mechanical energy
    b. potential energy
    c. thermal energy
    d. chemical energy

13. Reflection from a rough surface is said to be
    a. diffuse   c. regular
    b. irregular   d. translucent

14. Compared to the object, the image produced by the object in a plane mirror is
    a. larger   c. the same size
    b. smaller   d. distorted

15. If you stand at a distance of 1 meter from a full-length mirror, your image in the mirror appears to be
    a. 1 meter behind the mirror
    b. 1.5 meters behind the mirror
    c. 2 meters behind the mirror
    d. 1 meter in front of the mirror

16. Light travels as a
    a. longitudinal wave
    b. transverse wave
    c. polarized wave
    d. compressional wave

17. What happens to light when it is polarized?
    a. It is canceled out by a wave traveling in the opposite direction.
    b. The speed is slowed down by the medium.
    c. Only vibrations in a single plane are allowed to advance.
    d. It is reflected from an irregular surface.

18. The scientist who first measured the speed of light was
    a. Huygens   c. Maxwell
    b. Planck   d. Roemer

19. An incident ray strikes a mirror at an angle of 36°. What must be true about the angle of reflection?
    a. It is along the normal.
    b. It is equal to 18°.
    c. It is equal to 36°.
    d. It is greater than 36°.

20. What must be true for a shadow to form?
    a. An opaque object must block light rays.
    b. Light rays must be reflected from a surface.
    c. Light must travel as longitudinal waves.
    d. The wavelength of light must be decreased.

Modified True-False Questions

In some of the following statements, the italicized term makes the statement incorrect. For each incorrect statement, in your notebook, write the term that must be substituted for the italicized term to make the statement correct. For each correct statement, write the word "true."

1. *Natural* light is manufactured. _____

2. According to the corpuscular theory of light, the corpuscles are tiny particles of *energy.* _____

3. Visible light makes up a *small* part of the electromagnetic spectrum. _____

4. The quantum theory of light was proposed by *Max Planck.* _____

5. Objects that allow light to pass through them without distortion are said to be *opaque.* _____

6. Michelson used rotating mirrors to measure the *wavelength* of light._____

7. That the angle of incidence is equal to the angle of reflection is stated in the *law of angles.* _____

8. A device used to demonstrate that the angles of incidence and reflection are equal is the *optical disk.* _____

9. Reflection from a smooth flat surface is called *diffuse reflection.* _____

10. The high point of a transverse wave is called the *trough.* _____

TEST-TAKING TIP Make sure you are familiar with direct and inverse relationships. For example, know that as wavelength increases, frequency decreases, which is an inverse relationship. This will help you relate quantities in test questions.

Check Your Knowledge

Write the answer to each question in your notebook.

1. Define each of the following terms and give an example of each:
    a. luminous   d. translucent
    b. illuminated   e. opaque
    c. transparent

2. How is regular reflection different from diffuse reflection?

3. Compare the image of an object in a plane mirror with the object itself with respect to each of the following:
    a. size
    b. distance from the mirror
    c. position

4. Explain the properties of a light wave.

5. Describe how Roemer determined the speed at which light travels. Would you expect his method to provide an exact value or an approximate value? Explain.

Think Critically

Write the answer to each of the following questions in your notebook.

1. The human eye detects light with a wavelength of about 560 nm (5.60×10^{-7} m) to be brightest. This corresponds to yellow-green light. What is the frequency of this light?

2. When you shine a flashlight in a room, you see the beam of light on the wall. Why don't you see the light in the air?

3. As you move toward a plane mirror on a wall, do you see more of yourself, less of yourself, or the same image?

Take It Further

1. The brightness of light decreases with the square of the distance from the source. Research this relationship. Work with a partner to create a poster representing the phenomenon.

2. Astronomers studying distant galaxies talk about looking backward in time. Explain, in terms of light energy, why this is true. Conduct additional research to develop your answer.

3. Eclipses are described in terms of umbra and penumbra. Research the different types of eclipses and what causes them to occur. Draw and label a diagram describing an eclipse in terms of light.

4. The discovery of the photoelectric effect added to the current understanding of the nature of light. Investigate this discovery and write a paragraph describing the photoelectric effect.

CAREER

5. Some careers combine science with art. Lighting is one such career. Investigate careers in this field by learning what training is required, what certifications can be achieved, and what opportunities exist. You may wish to begin your search at the following site: *http://www.ncqlp.org/careers/index.html*.

Investigating Issues in Science, Engineering, Technology, and Society

Talk Now, Pay Later?

Where would you be without a cell phone? Society has become dependent on instant communication with friends and business associates, not to mention having the ability to make reservations, conduct banking, and even do research all at the push of a button. Cell phones and related hands-free devices are a benefit of modern technology. Therefore, people should forge ahead without ever looking back ... or should they?

The collection of electromagnetic waves is known as electromagnetic radiation (EMR). Each day, you are bombarded with EMR from many technologies that are part of modern life—from the alarm clock near your bed to the power lines above your home. Unlike some of the other technologies, however, cell phones and related hands-free devices are often used right next to your brain. This makes them deserve additional study.

The form of electromagnetic energy specifically emitted by cell phones is called radio frequency (RF) energy. Living organisms also produce electromagnetic energy at the cell, tissue, and organ levels. Often called the biofield, this energy is involved in maintaining the proper function of the body. Any interference with the biofield by RF energy may cause damage to cells, disrupt communication between cells, interfere with DNA replication, and harden cell membranes.

Numerous studies have been completed to determine if there is a link between this radiation and

People rely on cell phones to stay in contact with friends and coworkers no matter where they go. Are there risks associated with that convenience?

an increased risk of brain cell damage. Results have shown such radiation produces brain tumors in mice, but results in humans have been contradictory. In 2007, for example, the researchers who conducted a huge Danish study concluded that cell phones do not pose any health risk. However, in 2009, the World Health Organization stated, following a decade-long study, that excessive use of cell phones increases the risk of tumors later in life. Many additional studies have reached similar contradictory conclusions. A study reported in 2011 that when using a cell phone, brain activity increased on the side of the head closest to the phone's antenna. However, researchers say that they do not know if there are long-lasting effects from this exposure to the weak electromagnetic radiation produced by cell phones.

While the research continues and until completely safe technologies are developed, you can reduce your radiation exposure in several ways. Corded headsets, for example, emit much less RF energy and allow you to move the phone away from your body tissues. Keep in mind that an earpiece is not a piece of jewelry. Even though they reduce the radiation, they still emit some even after you hang up from a call. Be sure to take out an earpiece between calls.

Another way to reduce health risks is to think about where you place your phone. A study published in the *Journal of Craniofacial Surgery* showed a link between cell phone radiation and decreased bone density in the pelvis. Another study, conducted by the Cleveland Clinic, related cell phone radiation to decreased fertility in men. Keeping your phone in a separate bag or backpack, therefore, is safer than keeping it in your pocket.

The risks to children are greater than those for adults because the younger skull is thinner and the brain is still forming. Children should limit their use of cell phones to decrease their exposure to RF radiation.

No one knows for sure what the long-term effects of cell phone use will be. Should you ignore the concerns? Should you worry about it later? Or should you do what you can now because years from now, it may just be too late? Because there is no definitive answer for now, the decision lies in your hands.

Organize It!

Use a method that your instructor describes to organize the information in this article.

Explain It!

1. The type of energy emitted by cell phones is
   a. chemical energy
   b. nuclear energy
   c. RF energy
   d. electrical energy

2. What is a biofield?
   a. the damage to cells caused by cell phones
   b. the space through which a call from a cell phone travels
   c. an area over which a cell phone emits radiation
   d. electromagnetic energy produced by living things

3. Children are at greater risk from cell phone use than adults because
   a. they do not get as much sleep
   b. their skulls are thinner
   c. they talk longer
   d. they have poorer diets

4. Why might keeping a cell phone in a pants pocket increase the health risks of RF radiation?

5. Why has general exposure to electromagnetic radiation increased greatly in the past several decades?

Extend It!

6. Dr. George Carlo, a leading epidemiologist, was hired by the Cellular Telephone Industry Association in 1993 to prove that cell phones were safe. Investigate his work and findings.

7. Dr. Salford is an outspoken opponent of cell phone use. He has referred to them as a human biological experiment and suggests that today's teenagers will suffer the effects, including Alzheimer's, by the time they reach middle age. Research Dr. Salford's credentials and research.

CAREER

8. Some of the people working to make cell phones safer are radiofrequency engineers (RF). Find out what an RF engineer does, what training is required, and what opportunities exist. Share your findings with the class.

22
How Is Light Refracted and How Does It Produce Color?

The bright points at the end of the thin optical fibers are formed by light. The nature of the fibers makes it possible for light to bounce through them without escaping.

After reading this chapter, you should be able to answer the following questions:

What is refraction?

What is total internal reflection?

How do lenses refract light?

How do curved mirrors affect light?

How does white light separate into colors?

How is color related to wavelength?

How do transparent and opaque objects get their colors?

Have you ever noticed that a straw in a glass of water can look bent or broken? Or perhaps you have reached for an object under water only to discover that it was deeper than it looked. These and other phenomena can be explained by the bending of light. In this inquiry investigation, you will observe the bending of light.

Materials:
- ✔ safety goggles
- ✔ coin
- ✔ shallow metal tray
- ✔ water
- ✔ jar
- ✔ ruler
- ✔ spectroscope
- ✔ projected light of different colors
- ✔ screen

Part A Place a coin in the center of a shallow metal tray. While lowering your head, look at the coin until the coin just disappears behind the rim of the tray, as shown in Figure 22-1. Remain in this position while someone else slowly fills the tray with water, being careful not to move the coin.

1. Describe what you observe as the water fills the tray.

Part B Fill a large jar about three-quarters full of water. Place a ruler in the water so that it stands up straight. Lower your head so that your eye is at the level of the water and observe the appearance of the ruler.

Part C Tip the ruler so that it is resting at an angle in the jar. Again lower your head so that your eye is at the level of the water and observe the appearance of the side of the ruler.

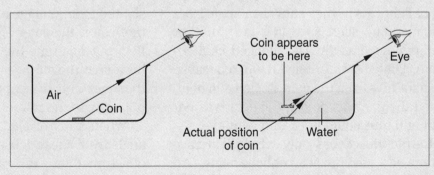

Figure 22-1.

2. *Describe any differences in the appearance of the ruler as you moved it in the jar from an upright to a tilted position.*

3. *How do you account for the changes in the positions of the ruler?*

Part D Observe the light that illuminates your room.

4. *Describe the color of light.*

   Observe the light through a spectroscope.

5. *Describe what you see.*

6. *Suggest an explanation for your observation.*

Part E Your teacher will project light of different colors on a screen. The colors will first be projected separately, then together.

7. *List the colors that are projected separately.*

8. *What happens when these colors are projected together on the same spot?*

9. *From the results of Parts D and E, what can you conclude about the nature of white light?*

What Is Refraction?

In your inquiry investigation, you observed what happens to light as it passes through different media. You observed that a coin in water appears to be higher than it really is. This type of optical illusion is caused by the *refraction* of light. **Refraction** is the bending of light rays as they pass at an angle from one medium, such as water, into another medium, such as air. The blocked coin became visible as water filled the pan because the light rays from the coin slowed and bent. When the pan was empty, the light was not bent and thus could not reach your eye.

Refraction occurs only when light rays enter a new medium at an oblique angle. (An oblique angle is any angle that is neither a right angle nor a straight line.) As you observed in your inquiry investigation, the portion of the ruler below the surface seemed to be magnified and appeared to be a straight-line extension of the portion of the ruler above the surface. When the ruler was slanted at an oblique angle to the surface of the water, the ruler again appeared magnified, but this time the ruler appeared to be broken at the surface. The magnification of the ruler and the apparent break in it are both due to the refraction of the light rays.

When a ray of light passes at an oblique angle from a less dense medium into a more dense medium, the ray bends *toward the normal*. The normal, you will recall, is the line drawn at right angles to the surface of the medium. However, when a ray passes at an oblique angle from a more dense medium into one that is less dense, the ray bends *away from the normal.* This behavior of light rays is described as the **law of refraction**. Reviewing the coin and ruler experiments will show you that the light rays in both cases behave according to this law.

Another example of the law of refraction is shown in Figure 22-2. When a ray of light passes from air into a triangular piece of glass (a medium of greater density than air) at point *A*, the ray bends toward the normal. When the light ray reaches the end of the glass at point *B* and re-enters the air (a medium of lesser density than glass), it bends away from the normal. As a result of the two refractions, the horizontal light ray entering at point *A* is bent downward as it emerges from point *B*. In order to see the light entering at the left side, the observer's eye would have to be in line with the light ray emerging from point *B*.

▶ What Causes Refraction?

When light travels through media such as water or glass, its speed is less than 300,000 kilometers per second (3.0×10^5 km/s). In water, the speed of light is roughly three-quarters of its speed in air. In glass, the speed

of light slows to about two-thirds of its speed in air. This decrease in the speed of light occurs because the molecules in water and glass are packed more tightly than the molecules in air. The closeness of the molecules, called **optical density**, acts as a barrier to the passage of light.

When parallel rays *A*, *B*, *C*, and *D* in a beam of light pass from air into water along the normal (at right angles to the surface), all the rays are slowed at the same time. Because all the rays remain in step (are parallel), the beam does not bend. Therefore, the beam continues in the same direction (see Figure 22-3*a*). When light rays pass from air into water at an angle (see Figure 22-3*b*), they do not remain parallel. Because the ray labeled *A* enters the water first, it slows sooner than the ray labeled *B*. Accordingly, the rays pivot around *A* as all the rays continue to move. This

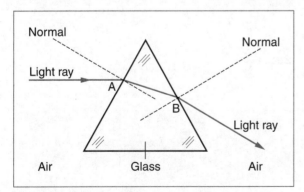

Figure 22-2. According to the law of refraction, light bends toward or away from the normal depending on the difference between the density of the medium it enters and leaves.

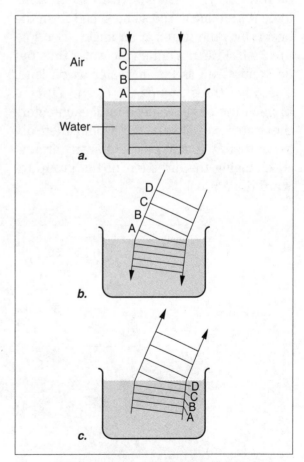

Figure 22-3. A beam of light bends as it moves from one medium to another at an oblique angle.

difference in the speed of the rays causes the beam to bend toward the normal. After all parts of the light beam are in the water, the rays continue in a straight line in a new direction because all the rays now travel at the same speed. When passing from water to air, as shown in Figure 22-3c, the opposite effect occurs—the light rays bend away from the normal. The ray labeled D enters the air first and increases in speed. The succeeding rays pivot around D. Thus, the direction of the beam is changed. When all parts of the beam re-enter the air, the rays continue in a straight line in a new direction because all the rays again travel at the same speed.

You may better understand this bending of a light beam by considering what happens to a group of people running at an angle from one type of ground surface onto another. Assume that you are watching a group of four of your friends, with their arms locked, running at the same speed from the beach into the water at an angle. (See Figure 22-4.) Friend A enters the water first, but he cannot run as fast in water as on land. The other three friends (B, C, and D) continue at the original speed until each enters the water and slows. You would then observe that B, C, and D would swing around A, changing the direction of the group toward the normal.

What Is Total Internal Reflection?

When the angle of incidence is small, the angle of the refracted ray is also small (position A). As the angle of incidence increases, the angle of refraction increases. As the angle of incidence increases still more, a point is reached where the refracted ray does not enter the air, but instead travels along the surface of the water. The angle of incidence at which this occurs is called the **critical angle**. In Figure 22-5, line AB represents an incident ray that is at the critical angle. Note that an observer at position B cannot see the light source. Line BC represents the corresponding refracted ray. When the angle of incidence of a ray of light exceeds the critical angle, the ray does not leave the denser medium, but is reflected by the surface of the medium. This ray undergoes total reflection. In Figure 22-5, line DE represents a ray that is totally reflected. In other words, the incident ray is not refracted, but is reflected as if the surface of the water were a mirror. If you wanted to see an underwater object under these conditions, it would be necessary to look upward to the surface of the water (position C). Because the bending of incident light rays in this type of situation occurs within one medium without any refraction, it is called **total internal reflection**.

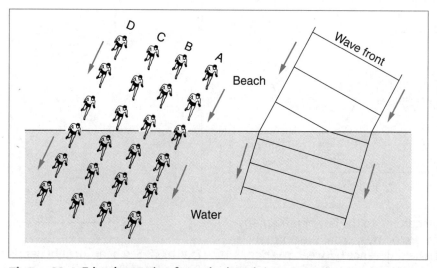

Figure 22-4. Friends running from the beach into water behave in much the same way as light rays do when they enter a new medium at an angle.

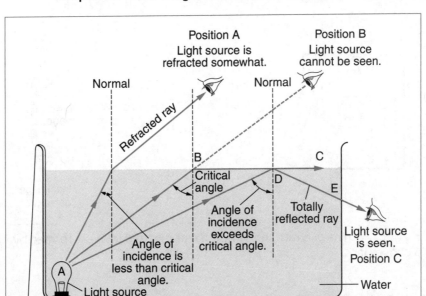

Figure 22-5. Total internal reflection occurs when the angle of incidence exceeds the critical angle.

Total internal reflection commonly occurs in a home aquarium. By looking upward at the surface of the water, you can see fish at the opposite end of the aquarium. Another example is observed in the transmission of light through a curved Lucite™ rod. Regardless of how the rod is curved, when light enters the rod at one end, it is totally reflected within the rod from each curved section. As a result, the light leaves the rod at the other end. In this manner, a ray of light can be made to go around corners.

> ## How Do Lenses Refract Light?

If you wear eyeglasses, you are using lenses. A **lens** is a thin disk of transparent material, such as glass, whose opposite sides are smooth, curved surfaces. Lenses are found in devices such as contact lenses, telescopes, microscopes, cameras, and binoculars. There are two general types of lenses: convex and concave.

Convex Lenses. A **convex lens** is a lens that is thicker in the middle than at the edges. As shown in Figure 22-6, when parallel rays of light pass through a convex lens, they are re-

fracted and are brought together, or converged, at a point called the **principal focus**, or *F*. Note that a ray of light passing through the center of the lens is not refracted. The distance measured from the center of the lens to the principal focus is called the **focal length**. The **principal axis** is a line normal to the curved surface that passes through the center of the lens. Because a convex lens can converge parallel rays of light, it is often called a **converging lens**. In general, the greater the curvature of a convex lens, the shorter the focal length. Thus, a completely spherical convex lens has the shortest focal length possible for a convex lens.

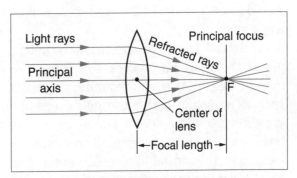

Figure 22-6. A convex lens is thicker in the middle than at the edges. This type of lens brings parallel rays of light together.

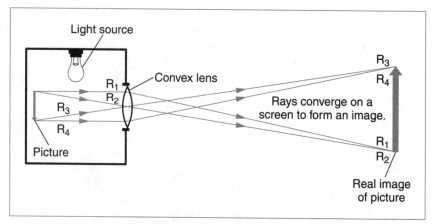

Figure 22-7. The diagram shows how a real, inverted image is formed by a convex lens.

Images Formed by Convex Lenses. In general, the images formed by convex lenses are of two types, real and virtual. A **real image** is an image formed by actual rays of light. The image produced by a "magic lantern," a device for projecting pictures onto a screen, is an example of a real image. Figure 22-7 is the ray diagram of a magic lantern. Notice that the rays of light converge to form the image (R_1 and R_2 meet; R_3 and R_4 meet; these two points fall on the same plane). Also, by following the rays in the diagram, you will discover that the image is upside-down (inverted). R_1 and R_2 come from the top of the picture, but these rays form the bottom of the image; R_3 and R_4 come from the bottom of the picture, but these rays form the top of the image.

All real images have the following characteristics: (1) A real image is formed by actual rays of light. (2) A real image can be projected onto a screen. (3) A real image is always inverted.

A **virtual image** is an imaginary image; that is, the image only *seems* to be formed by rays of light. When you examine an object such as a postage stamp through a magnifying glass, for example, the stamp appears to be larger. While the stamp really remains the same size, the virtual image seen in the lens creates the illusion called magnification. Figure 22-8 shows the ray diagram of a magnifying glass being used to examine a stamp.

Notice that the actual rays of light (indicated by solid lines) do not converge to form an image. Because you see an image in the lens, however, you know that an image is formed. To explain this, study the ray diagram. Note that by extending the rays downward (as indicated by the dashed lines), an image is formed. By following the rays in the diagram, you will discover that R_1 and R_2 come from the left side of the stamp and R_3 and R_4 come from the right side. The image, therefore, has not been reversed. The image of the stamp is

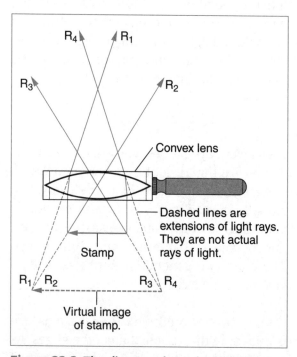

Figure 22-8. The diagram shows how a virtual, erect image is formed by a convex lens.

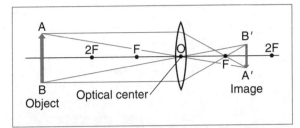

Figure 22-9. An image formed when an object is beyond 2F is reduced, inverted, and real.

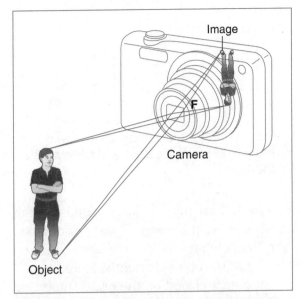

Figure 22-10. A camera forms an image that is smaller than the actual object and inverted.

also larger than the stamp itself. Note that the image is not formed by actual rays of light—it is imaginary. However, because the word "imaginary" suggests something that cannot be seen, scientists use the word "virtual" to describe such an image.

All virtual images have the following characteristics: (1) A virtual image is formed by *extensions* of light rays (that is, the image is not formed by actual rays of light). (2) A virtual image cannot be projected onto a screen. (3) A virtual image is always erect, that is, right side up.

The type of image produced by a convex lens depends on the distance of the object from the lens. The object may be anywhere, from a point an infinite distance from the lens to a point inside the principal focus. In each case, the image formed will be different from the others.

An object at an infinite distance from the lens is very far away. Light rays reaching the lens from this distance are parallel to each other. When such parallel light rays pass through a convex lens, an image the size of a dot can be formed on a screen placed at the principal focus of the lens. When the image

of the sun is thus brought into focus by a convex lens, the lens is often called a "burning glass" because the focused light can cause paper or other materials to catch fire.

When an object is at a distance that is greater than twice the focal length, an image is formed on a screen on the opposite side of the lens. The image formed is smaller than the object, inverted and real (see Figure 22-9). This is the type of image produced when you take a picture with a camera. The object photographed is large, but the image formed on the film or digital sensor is small and inverted (see Figure 22-10).

An image in the eye is formed in the same way. Light from an object is converged by the convex lens (see Figure 22-11). The image formed on the retina in the eye is small and

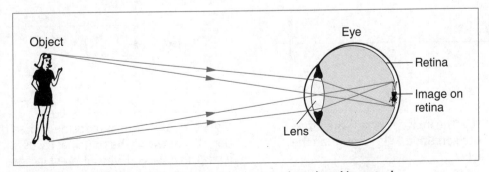

Figure 22-11. The image formed in the eye is reduced and inverted.

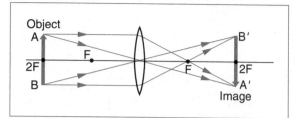

Figure 22-12. The image formed when the object is at 2F is real, inverted, and the same size as the object.

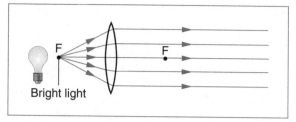

Figure 22-14. A spotlight uses the fact that an object placed at the principal focus of a lens produces a bright disc of light.

inverted. This image starts impulses that reach the brain by way of the optic nerve. The brain interprets the impulses and you "see" that the object is right side up.

An object placed on the principal axis at a point that is exactly twice the focal length (2F) forms an image at the same distance on the other side of the lens. This image is real, inverted and the same size as the object (see Figure 22-12).

When an object lies between F (the principal focus) and a point twice that distance (2F), an image is formed on the other side of the lens at a distance of more than 2F. The image formed is real, inverted, and larger than the object. Convex lenses are used in this manner in motion-picture projectors. In these, the object is a small film placed in an inverted position close to the principal focus. The image formed on the screen is far from the lens and upright (Figure 22-13).

If the object is placed exactly at the principal focus of the lens, the light rays emerging from the opposite side are parallel to each other. When projected on a screen, no image

is formed—only a bright disc of light is visible (see Figure 22-14). This arrangement is used for a spotlight or headlight of a car.

When an object is placed at a point that is between the principal focus and the lens, an image cannot be formed on a screen. As shown in Figure 22-15, the actual rays from the object do not form an image. However, by extending the diverging rays backward through the lens until their extensions meet at a point, a virtual image is formed. Thus, if you look through the lens at the object, you see a larger, erect, virtual image. A convex lens used in this way becomes a magnifying glass.

Convex lenses are used in eyeglasses to correct the near vision of farsighted people. (See Figure 22-16.) In farsightedness, an image of a nearby object falls behind the retina because the lens of the eye is not convex enough. Thus, the image appears blurred. A stronger convex lens brings the image forward enough to fall on the retina.

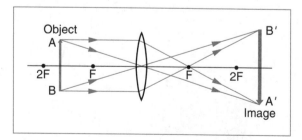

Figure 22-13. The image formed when the object is between F and 2F is larger than the object.

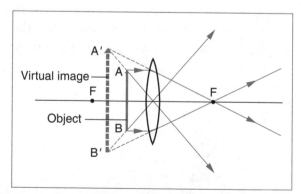

Figure 22-15. The image formed when the object is between the principal focus and the lens is an enlarged, virtual, erect image.

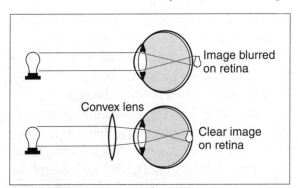

Figure 22-16. A convex lens corrects farsightedness.

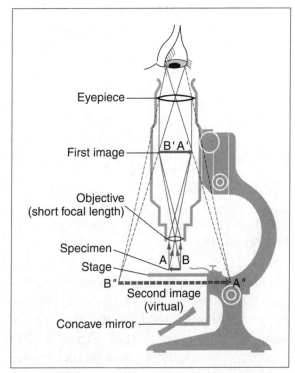

Figure 22-18. A microscope uses a convex objective lens and eyepiece to magnify small objects.

Combinations of convex lenses are used in refracting telescopes and in microscopes. In a refracting telescope (see Figure 22-17), the convex objective lens has a long focal length. This produces a real, smaller, and inverted image of a distant object that is viewed through a convex eyepiece lens. This image appears at less than a focal length of the eyepiece and produces a virtual, larger, and erect second image. However, as shown in Figure 22-17, this virtual image is inverted with respect to the distant object. As the objective lens of a refracting telescope is made larger, its ability to gather light increases.

In a microscope (see Figure 22-18), the specimen is examined through a convex *objective* lens of short focal length. Because the specimen is beyond one focal length of the lens, the first image is real, larger, and inverted. This image falls within one focal length of a convex eyepiece of long focal length. This second image that the eye observes is virtual, larger, and erect, thus producing magnification. As in the telescope, the virtual image is inverted with respect to the object being examined. (See Figure 22-18.)

Concave Lenses. A **concave lens** is a lens that is thicker at the edges than in the middle. When parallel rays of light pass through a concave lens, they are refracted and separated, or *diverged.* For this reason, concave lenses are also called **diverging lenses**. The refracted light rays from a concave lens

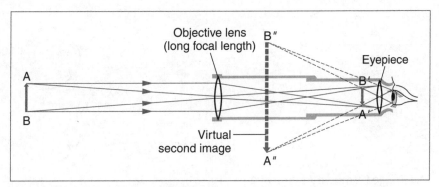

Figure 22-17. A refracting telescope uses a combination of convex lenses to produce an image of a distance object.

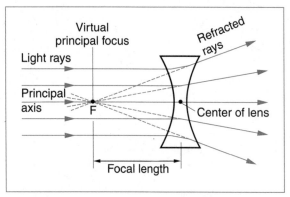

Figure 22-19. A concave lens is thinner in the middle than at the edges. This type of lens spreads rays of light.

never meet. The principal focus of such a lens is found by extending the diverging rays backward through the lens until their extensions meet at a point. (See Figure 22-19.) This point is called a **virtual focus** because the light rays do not actually meet there. The focal length of this lens is found by measuring the distance from the center of the lens to the point where the extensions of the diverging rays meet.

Unlike the images formed by convex lenses, the images produced by concave lenses are always virtual, erect, and smaller than the object. The properties of these images are the same no matter where the object is placed with regard to the principal focus of a concave lens. Study Figure 22-20 and note that, except for the light ray that travels along the principal axis, all other rays are refracted away from the center of the lens. As a result

of the diverging rays, no image can form on a screen on the side of the lens opposite that of the object. However, a virtual image can be seen (but cannot be formed on a screen) on the same side of the lens as the object.

Concave lenses are used in eyeglasses to correct the vision of nearsighted people. (See Figure 22-21.) In nearsightedness, an image of a distant object falls in front of the retina. The light rays that reach the retina are not in focus. When a concave lens is placed in front of such an eye, this lens diverges the rays and allows a clear image to fall on the retina.

Concave lenses in combination with convex lenses are used in such devices as opera glasses. The opera glass is a kind of telescope containing an eyepiece that is a concave lens. The focal length of this lens matches the focal length of the convex lens of the eye. Because a concave lens diverges light while a convex lens converges light, the net effect of a concave eyepiece is to neutralize the convex lens of the eye. This means that the convex *objective* lens of the opera glass forms the image on the retina. This image is real and between three and six times larger than the object viewed.

▶ **How Do Curved Mirrors Affect Light?**

Curved mirrors have properties similar to those of convex and concave lenses. A mirror that curves inward, as shown in Fig-

Figure 22-20. The image formed by a concave lens is always virtual, erect, and smaller than the object.

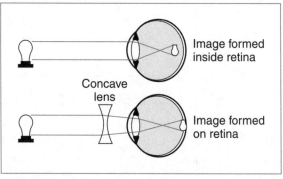

Figure 22-21. A concave lens corrects nearsightedness.

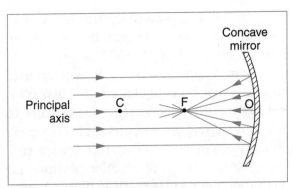

Figure 22-22. A concave mirror converges light rays.

ure 22-22, is called a **concave mirror**. The silvered surface converges light rays by *reflection*, and can be used in much the same way as a convex lens. Used in combination with a convex lens and a plane mirror, a concave mirror is part of a reflecting telescope. The function of the concave mirror in the reflecting telescope is to gather light. The larger the mirror, the greater is the light-gathering power. As the objective lens in the refracting telescope is made larger, the lens also gathers more light. However, it is easier to make a large mirror than a large lens. Thus, reflecting telescopes, some with mirrors over 500 cm in diameter, are more widely used than refracting telescopes.

A mirror that curves outward, as shown in Figure 22-23, is called a **convex mirror**. This type of mirror diverges light rays by reflection. Like a concave lens, a convex mirror forms only small virtual images. Such mirrors are used as rearview mirrors, in

which a large area can be viewed in a small space.

How Does White Light Separate Into Colors?

A beam of light entering a prism (a triangular piece of glass) is refracted in the prism and again refracted when it emerges from the prism. Observation reveals that the emerging light splits into a series of colors very much like a natural rainbow. This phenomenon, called **dispersion**, is shown in Figure 22-24.

An artificial rainbow and a natural rainbow are formed in the same manner. Both the prism and water droplets in the air separate white light into the colored rays of which it is composed. Sir Isaac Newton first demonstrated that white light is composed of a mixture of colors. He found that when a beam of white light passes through a prism, the light is separated into six colors arranged in the following order: red, orange, yellow, green, blue, and violet.

To prove that white light is composed of separate colors, Newton allowed these six colored rays of light to pass through a second inverted prism. He showed that the colors recombined and produced a beam of white light.

To understand why dispersion occurs, recall than when a light beam enters a more dense medium (such as the glass of the prism) at an oblique angle, the speed of the light is decreased and the beam is refracted. However, the red rays of the white light are

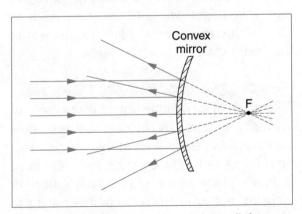

Figure 22-23. A convex mirror diverges light rays.

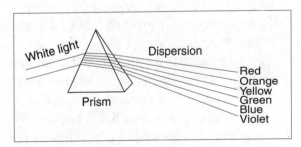

Figure 22-24. Dispersion of light.

slowed the least, whereas the violet rays of the white light are slowed the most. As a result of these differences in speed, the rays are refracted to different degrees. Red light, which has the longest wavelength, is refracted least; violet light, which has the shortest wave length, is refracted the most. When the rays of colored light re-enter the air from the prism, they are refracted again. Thus, these rays cannot rejoin to form white light and are seen as separate colors spread in a rainbow-like band called a **spectrum**.

As mentioned previously, the dispersion of white light to form a natural rainbow takes place in a similar manner. After a rain, tiny water droplets present in the air act in much the same manner as does the prism. The water droplets cause the white light passing through them to undergo dispersion, producing a spectrum.

Another optical device that affects a beam of light in the same manner as a prism is the **diffraction grating**. This is usually a flat piece of transparent material on which thousands of parallel lines have been ruled on every square inch of surface. The space between any two lines is less than one wavelength of light. When a beam of light enters such a grating, it is spread out, or **diffracted**, and a typical spectrum is formed. It is significant to note that light could not behave in this fashion unless it consisted of waves. Thus, the phenomenon of diffraction supports the wave theory of light.

How Is Color Related to Wavelength?
Wavelengths of visible light range from approximately 400 to 700 nanometers. The wavelengths of the six colors of white light fall into this range, with each color having a different wavelength.

Electromagnetic waves somewhat longer than those of red light are called **infrared rays**. This band of waves contains the radiant heat rays discussed earlier (Chapter 19). Infrared rays are invisible to the human eye, but can affect a special type of photographic film. Microwaves and radio waves are electromagnetic waves longer than infrared. (See Figure 21-3 on page 337.)

Electromagnetic waves somewhat shorter than those of violet light are called **ultraviolet rays**. Ultraviolet rays are also invisible to the human eye, but can affect photographic film. These rays tan the skin (or cause sunburn), stimulate the production of vitamin D in the body, and kill bacteria in the air. X-rays, gamma rays, and cosmic rays are electromagnetic waves shorter than ultraviolet. The shorter the wavelength, the more penetrating is the ray. Thus, great caution must be exercised in using rays of short wavelength.

How Do Transparent Objects Get Their Colors? The color of a transparent object is the color of the light that the object transmits. Ordinary window glass transmits *all* colors equally well and, therefore, appears to be colorless in white light. However, when white light strikes a piece of red glass, the glass absorbs orange, yellow, green, blue, and violet light. Because this glass transmits only red light, the glass appears red. Similarly, blue glass transmits only blue light and absorbs the remaining colors; green glass transmits green light and absorbs the remaining colors. When a beam of red light shines on a piece of blue glass, no light is transmitted because the blue glass absorbs all the red light. In such a case, the blue glass may appear black, which is the absence of color. Thus, light is transmitted by a transparent object only when light waves of the same color as that of the transparent object are present in the beam that reaches the object.

How Do Opaque Objects Get Their Colors?
The color of an opaque object is the color of the light reflected by the object. A red apple absorbs all of the colors of light except red. It reflects red light to your eye. Similarly, a green grape absorbs all of the colors of light except green. It reflects green light to your eye.

What, then, makes a sheet of paper appear white? The paper reflects all the colors in a beam of white light. If the same white paper were viewed through a red filter that lets only red light through it, the paper would appear red because that is the only color of light allowed to reach the eye. Whereas white objects reflect all the light that reaches them, black objects absorb all the light that reaches them. When white light strikes a black shoe, the shoe appears black because the coloring matter of the shoe absorbs all the colored rays that strike it. As a result, no colors of light are reflected to the eye. Colored objects can be made to look black by shining light on them that is not reflected. A blue cloth, for example, reflects blue light. If the cloth is viewed in red light, there is no blue light to reflect. The cloth appears black because the blue dye in it absorbs the red rays and reflects no light at all.

In general, an object appears white (or colorless) when it either reflects or transmits all colors of light at the same time. On the other hand, an object appears black when it absorbs the light reaching it and neither reflects nor transmits any light.

How Do Light Spectra Form?

Whenever an object is heated sufficiently, it glows and emits heat. As you learned earlier, a prism or a diffraction grating can disperse light into the band of colors. This band of colors is called a *spectrum*. The spectra (plural of spectrum) from various glowing objects differ from one another. With the aid of a device called a **spectroscope**, which contains either a prism or a diffraction grating, it is possible to study the spectra of various substances and to identify them. (See Figure 22-25.) By comparing the spectrum of the light coming from the sun with the spectra of the elements present on Earth, scientists have learned which elements are present in the sun. The same technique is used to determine the contents of other distant stars.

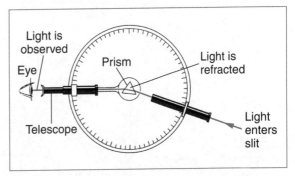

Figure 22-25. A spectroscope is used to study the spectra produced by luminous objects.

There are three important types of spectra: the continuous spectrum, the bright-line spectrum, and the absorption spectrum.

A **continuous spectrum** is the type of spectrum you observe when you view white light through either a diffraction grating or a glass prism. In this spectrum, the colors blend into each other without separations. Gases under high pressure that are made to glow and glowing solids produce continuous spectra.

A **bright-line spectrum** is composed of several brightly colored narrow lines separated by large dark spaces. This type of spectrum is formed when a gas under low pressure is subjected to heat or electrical energy, a phenomenon called *excitation*. The gas begins to glow and is then observed through the spectroscope. Each element, when converted to a gas and made to glow, produces its own characteristic bright-line spectrum. This type of spectrum originates from the motions of electrons in the atoms of elements. Heat excites these electrons, causing them to move to higher (unstable) energy levels. When the electrons return to their stable energy levels, they emit energy of a definite wavelength and color. It is possible to identify an unknown element by matching its spectral lines with the spectral lines of known elements.

You know that an element, when excited, emits specific wavelengths (colors). It has been found that such an element can absorb these wavelengths *and no other.* Thus, the

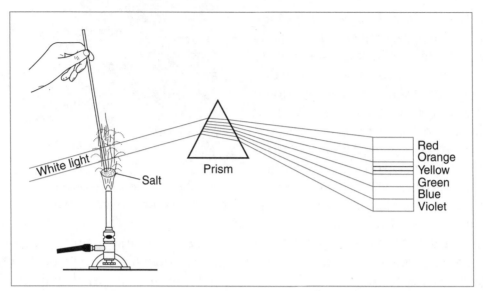

Figure 22-26. An absorption spectrum has dark areas where light has been absorbed.

spectrum of sodium vapor shows two bright yellow lines. Suppose a beam of white light that contains all the colors of the spectrum is passed through sodium vapor. When the resulting light is observed in a spectroscope, you see a continuous spectrum with dark areas in the exact position where the yellow sodium lines would normally appear. (See Figure 22-26.) The sodium atoms have apparently absorbed the yellow wavelengths from the continuous spectrum. The dark areas form an **absorption spectrum**.

Because the dark lines (absorbed wavelengths) are characteristic for each element, they can also be used to identify unknown elements. The dark lines observed in the absorption spectrum of the sun were first noted by the German physicist *Joseph von Fraunhofer*, in 1817. These lines are called *Fraunhofer lines*.

Chapter Review

Science Terms

The following list contains all the boldfaced words found in this chapter and the page on which each appears.

absorption spectrum (p. 366)

bright-line spectrum (p. 365)

concave lens (p. 361)

concave mirror (p. 363)

continuous spectrum (p. 365)

converging lens (p. 357)

convex lens (p. 357)

convex mirror (p. 363)

critical angle (p. 356)

diffracted (p. 364)

diffraction grating (p. 364)

dispersion (p. 363)

diverging lenses (p. 361)

focal length (p. 357)

infrared rays (p. 364)

law of refraction (p. 355)

lens (p. 357)

optical density (p. 355)

principal axis (p. 357)

principal focus (p. 357)

real image (p. 358)

refraction (p. 354)

spectroscope (p. 365)

spectrum (p. 364)

total internal reflection (p. 356)

ultraviolet rays (p. 364)

virtual focus (p. 362)

virtual image (p. 358)

Matching Questions

In your notebook, write the letter of the item in column B that is most closely related to the item in column A.

Column A

_____ 1. principal focus

_____ 2. refraction

_____ 3. retina

_____ 4. convex mirror

_____ 5. concave lens

_____ 6. real image

_____ 7. convex lens

_____ 8. concave mirror

_____ 9. virtual image

_____ 10. dispersion

Column B

a. image formed by actual light rays

b. clear glass or plastic that is thicker in the middle than at the edges

c. device that is part of a reflecting telescope, along with a convex lens

d. phenomenon that forms a rainbow

e. the bending of light rays

f. part of the eye on which images are formed

g. type of image formed through a magnifying glass

h. point at which parallel rays refracted by a convex lens converge

i. device used as a rear-view mirror

j. clear glass or plastic that is thicker at the edges than in the middle

Multiple-Choice Questions

In your notebook, write the letter preceding the word or expression that best completes the statement or answers the question.

1. How is refraction different from reflection?
a. Refraction occurs when light bounces off a flat surface.
b. Refraction occurs when light passes from one medium to another.
c. Refraction occurs when light is absorbed by matter.
d. Refraction occurs when light is made to vibrate in only one plane.

2. The closeness of the particles of matter in a sample determine its
a. focal length
b. color
c. optical density
d. dispersion

3. When light enters a medium such as water or glass from the air, its speed
a. decreases
b. increases
c. remains the same
d. increases, then decreases

4. When light passes at an oblique angle from a medium that is less dense to a medium that is more dense, it
a. continues in a straight line
b. is reflected
c. bends away from the normal
d. bends toward the normal

5. A ray of light passes from air into glass. After the entire ray enters the glass, the light
    a. continues to bend
    b. travels in a straight line
    c. is reflected
    d. bends toward the normal

6. As the angle of incidence of a light ray increases, the angle of refraction
    a. increases
    b. decreases
    c. remains the same
    d. increases, then decreases

7. When the angle of incidence of a light ray is greater than the critical angle, the ray
    a. bends toward the normal as it is refracted
    b. bends away from the normal as it is refracted
    c. is reflected by the surface of the medium
    d. travels in a straight line out of the medium

8. By looking upward at the surface of water in an aquarium, you can see the other end due to
    a. polarization
    b. refraction
    c. dispersion
    d. total internal reflection

9. A lens that is thicker in the middle than at the ends is called
    a. concave   c. diverging
    b. convex   d. chromatic

10. What happens to parallel rays of light that pass through a convex lens?
    a. They are dispersed.
    b. They are diverged.
    c. They are converged.
    d. They are diffracted.

11. Lenses that separate parallel light rays are called
    a. convex   c. prismatic
    b. converging   d. concave

12. How is a real image different from a virtual image?
    a. A real image can be projected on a screen.
    b. A real image is right side up.
    c. A real image is formed by extensions of light rays.
    d. A real image has different colors than the object.

13. A virtual image is seen when using a
    a. magic lantern
    b. movie projector
    c. magnifying glass
    d. camera

14. Where, in relation to a lens, should the object be placed to produce an image that is real, inverted, and smaller than the object?
    a. at F
    b. beyond $2F$
    c. between F and the lens
    d. between F and $2F$

15. When the object on the principal axis is exactly on $2F$, the image is formed on a screen at a point that is
    a. at $2F$
    b. at F
    c. between F and $2F$
    d. between the lens and F

16. When an object is placed at the principal focus of a convex lens, what happens to the rays emerging from the opposite side of the lens?
    a. They converge.
    b. They diverge.
    c. They are reflected.
    d. They are parallel.

17. Compared to the object, images produced by concave lenses are
   a. virtual, upright, and smaller
   b. real, upright, and larger
   c. real, inverted, and smaller
   d. virtual, inverted, and larger

18. A reflecting telescope consists of a convex lens, a plane mirror, and a
   a. convex mirror
   b. concave lens
   c. magnifying glass
   d. concave mirror

19. Eyeglasses used by nearsighted people consist of lenses that are
   a. convex   c. concave
   b. converging   d. chromatic

20. Why is violet light refracted more than red light in a prism?
   a. Brighter colors are refracted more than duller colors.
   b. Shorter wavelengths are refracted more than longer wavelengths.
   c. Light that travels faster is refracted more than light that travels slower.
   d. Higher frequencies are absorbed more than lower frequencies.

21. The band of colors of light, ranging from red to violet that is produced by a prism, is called a
   a. rainbow
   b. spectrum
   c. diffraction grating
   d. prism display

22. Which of the following electromagnetic waves have shorter wavelengths than ultraviolet light?
   a. infrared rays
   b. microwaves
   c. radio waves
   d. gamma rays

23. A transparent object is the color of the light that the object
   a. transmits   c. absorbs
   b. reflects   d. refracts

24. When a beam of red light shines on a piece of green glass, what color does the glass appear to be?
   a. red   c. black
   b. green   d. white

25. When an object reflects all light, it appears to be
   a. black   c. green
   b. red   d. white

Modified True-False Questions

In some of the following statements, the italicized term makes the statement incorrect. For each incorrect statement, in your notebook, write the term that must be substituted for the italicized term to make the statement correct. For each correct statement, write the word "true."

1. A *pinhole camera* is used to identify the spectra of various substances._____

2. A series of narrow dark lines that separate parts of a continuous spectrum is an *absorption spectrum.* _____

3. Because of *dispersion*, a refracting ray does not leave the medium, but instead travels along the surface. _____

4. A convex lens converges light rays at a point called the *principal axis.* _____

5. The distance from the center of the lens to the principal focus is calledthe *focal length.* _____

6. An image that seems to be formed but cannot be projected is a *real image.* _____

7. A magnifying glass consists of a *concave lens.* _____

8. The scientist who determined that white light is composed of colored rays was *Isaac Newton.* _____

9. The separation of white light into its component colors is called *refraction.* _____

10. A device that separates white light into its colors is a *diffraction grating.* _____

11. Radiant heat rays are also called *ultraviolet rays.* _____

12. Invisible rays that affect photographic film are called *ultraviolet rays.* _____

13. A red glass transmits *white light.* _____

14. When blue cloth is viewed in red light, the cloth appears *black.* _____

15. The color of an opaque object is the color that it *transmits.* _____

Think Critically
Write the answer to each of the following questions in your notebook.

1. Complete the following table for convex lenses:

Object Distance	Image Distance	Image Size	Type of Image	Erect or Inverted
At infinity				
Greater than 2F				
At 2F				
Between F and 2F				
At F				
Between lens and F				

Check Your Knowledge
Write the answer to each question in your notebook.

1. Explain what happens to the path and speed of a ray of light in each of the following situations:
   a. Light passes from air to glass at an oblique angle.
   b. Light passes from water to air at an oblique angle.
   c. Light passes through a convex lens at the normal.
   d. Light, traveling in water, strikes the surface of the water at an angle greater than the critical angle.

2. Describe how concave lenses can be used to help nearsighted people see better.

3. Explain the dispersion of light as it passes through a prism.

TEST-TAKING TIP As you study, construct a chart that describes the properties of images formed by each type of lens and in each location. This will help you describe the images on an exam.

2. Explain the color observed for each of the following when struck with white light:
   a. a red transparent object
   b. a blue opaque object

Take It Further

1. Fiber-optic cables take advantage of total internal reflection. Research fiber-optic cables as used in communication. Find out how they work and why they are useful. Present your findings to the class. Include a diagram if possible.

2. The mnemonic ROY G BV is often used to help people remember the order of the colors of visible light. Create a poster showing how the colors are organized according to wavelength, and how this mnemonic is useful.

CAREER

3. Ophthalmologists and optometrists use the refraction of light to interpret and correct vision problems. Find out the difference between these two professions and the training required for each. You may wish to consult the following sites as you begin your research: *http://www.eyecareprofessions.com/ophthalmologist-vs-optometrist.html*, *http://www.aoa.org*, or *http://www.aao.org/*

Investigating Issues in Science, Engineering, Technology, and Society

Sunscreens: Do They Make It Perfectly Safe to Stay Out in the Sun?

Every second of your life, an uncountable variety of chemical reactions takes place within each cell of your body. These tiny chemical factories churn out all sorts of products vital to your health. What's more, these factories have the capability of reproducing themselves, so you are never at a loss for the products they manufacture.

Sunlight can cause serious damage to skin over time. Sunscreens can prevent some of that damage, but not all of it.

Both processes—production of vital chemicals and cellular reproduction—are made possible by "blueprints" in cells called genes. Normally, these genes remain relatively unchanged, so cell functions tend to remain stable.

Unfortunately, the structure of genes can be changed by factors outside the cell. One of these factors is a form of high-energy radiation. One source of this radiation is sunlight, or, more precisely, certain parts of sunlight.

As you may know, sunlight consists of three major parts. The part you see is called visible light. The part you feel is called infrared radiation, or heat. But the high-energy, potentially dangerous part, which you cannot see or feel, is called *ultraviolet radiation,* or UV for short.

Ultraviolet radiation comes in two varieties, UVA and UVB. The effects of UVB are obvious. Sunburn! Pain! Sleepless nights! Ruined vacations! Those of UVA are less obvious but much more damaging. UVA penetrates more deeply into the skin. Over time, UVA can cause skin to age, that is, become leathery and wrinkled. It can weaken your immune system, making you more susceptible to infections. What's worse, UVA and UVB working together can damage the genes in cells and cause skin cancer. One kind of skin cancer, called melanoma, can be deadly if not treated early. That's why it is important to reduce the amount of UVA and UVB that strikes your skin. Since you can't stay indoors forever and you can't cover every square millimeter of your skin with clothing when outdoors, what can you do? Here's where sunscreens can play a role.

Sunscreens are products that contain chemicals that absorb ultraviolet radiation. Which sunscreen agents are appropriate for an individual? The answer depends on a number of factors. These include (1) the color of a person's skin: People with fair or light-colored skin are more sensitive to sunlight than are people with darker skin; (2) the latitude where a person lives: The lower the latitude (the closer to the equator), the greater the danger of damage from sunlight; (3) the duration of exposure to the sun and the time of day of exposure. Obviously, the longer a person is exposed to sunlight, the greater are the chances for injury. Moreover, exposure between 10:00 A.M. and 3:00 P.M., when the sun's rays hit Earth's surface more directly, is riskier than exposure at other times.

A person's sensitivity to sunlight is measured using a unit called the minimum erythema dose, or MED. The MED is "the smallest amount of sunlight exposure necessary to induce a barely perceptible redness of the skin within 24 hours after exposure." Sunscreens allow people to increase their MED, that is, to increase the amount of time they can stay in the sun without becoming burned. How much does each sunscreen product increase the MED?

Today, every sunscreen has what is known as a sun protection factor, or SPF number, written on its bottle, package, or tube. SPF is an acronym for *sun protection factor*. The number is determined indoors, experimentally by mimicking noontime sun and comparing the skin redness of test subjects.

If the sunscreen has an SPF of 15, it will increase your MED 15 times. For example, if your MED is 20 minutes and you use a sunscreen with an SPF of 15, your MED will jump to 20 minutes times 15, or 300 minutes (5 hours). But since MED is a unit of skin redness, which is caused by UVB, how do you know whether you are being protected from UVA, too? .

Many products claim to be "broad spectrum," protecting against UVA and UVB. Under Food and Drug Administration rules, effective in 2012, products labeled "broad spectrum" must provide equal protection against UVA and UVB rays, and only SPF 15 and higher products can claim to protect against skin cancer and premature aging.

In addition, don't be fooled by SPF ratings. You might be tempted to conclude that a sunscreen with an SPF of 30 is twice as effective as one with an SPF of 15. This is not the case. Generally, an SPF of 15 blocks about 94% of UVB rays, an SPF of 30 blocks about 97% of UVB rays, and an SPF of 45 blocks about 98% of UVB rays.

Based on what you have read above, can the sun's rays be made harmless by using a sunscreen? What do you think?

Organize It!

Use a method that your instructor describes to organize the information in this article.

Explain It!

1. The part of sunlight that is most dangerous to people is
   a. visible light
   b. infrared radiation
   c. ultraviolet radiation
   d. avobenzone

2. Which of the following factors BOTH increase the risk of skin damage from sunlight?
   a. light-colored skin and high latitude
   b. light-colored skin and low latitude
   c. dark-colored skin and high latitude
   d. dark-colored skin and low latitude

3. If your normal MED was 40 minutes and you applied a sunscreen with an SPF of 20, what would your MED become under these new conditions?
   a. 20 minutes
   b. 40 minutes
   c. 60 minutes
   d. 800 minutes

4. Using your own words, define MED.

5. What can you learn by checking the SPF of a sunscreen?

Extend It!

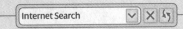

6. Investigate the procedures for determining the SPF of sunscreens and rules controlling the labeling on sunscreen packaging. Present your findings to the class.

CAREER

7. Dermatologists are some of the most outspoken proponents of sunscreen use. Find out what a dermatologist does, what education is required, and what opportunities they have. You may wish to begin your search at the following site: *http://www. aad.org/*.

23 What Is the Nature of Nuclear Energy?

These rods provide the fuel for nuclear reactions to occur in a reactor. The material in them, often uranium-235, can be made to undergo a reaction in which particles and energy are released. The energy can be used to produce electricity and the particles go on to cause more reactions.

After reading this chapter, you should be able to answer the following questions:

What is radioactivity?

What are the characteristics of elements and their isotopes?

What happens during radioactive decay?

How is radiation detected?

What is transmutation?

What is the half-life of a radioisotope?

How can nuclear energy and radioactive isotopes be used?

What are the dangers of radioactivity?

You might be exposed to radiation, but how would you know? In this inquiry investigation, you will have an opportunity to detect radiation.

Materials:
- ✔ safety goggles
- ✔ glass jar with clear bottom
- ✔ alcohol
- ✔ dry ice (solid carbon dioxide)
- ✔ metal tray
- ✔ flashlight
- ✔ source of radioactivity
- ✔ Geiger-Müller counter
- ✔ sheet of cardboard
- ✔ sheet of lead
- ✔ pair of tongs or cloth towel

CAUTION: While these sources are weak emitters and present no health risk, handle them with care as you would any other possibly dangerous material.

Part A Set up the materials as shown in Figure 23-1. Your teacher will provide the alcohol and a source of radioactivity. Lay the lid of the jar upside down on the table. Place the radioactive source inside the lid. Soak the black lining in the jar with the alcohol and screw the jar into the lid, which should remain upside down on the table.

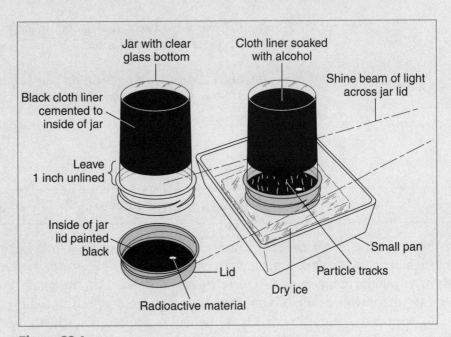

Figure 23-1.

CAUTION: Dry ice can cause serious burns. Do not handle the dry ice with your bare hands.

Part B Using a pair of tongs or a cloth towel, place a flat piece of dry ice in the metal tray. Place the jar, which should still be upside down, on the piece of dry ice.

    1. Describe what you see inside the jar.

Part C Allow the jar to cool for 15 minutes. Turn out the lights in the room. Shine a flashlight into the jar, just above the lid, so that the beam of light passes completely through the jar as shown in Figure 23-1.

    2. Describe the appearance of any particles or tracks that you may see inside the jar.

    3. How do you account for the presence of these particles or tracks?

Part D Remove the jar from the dry ice, unscrew the lid (making sure the jar is still upside down), and place the lid on the table. Hold a Geiger-counter probe 6 inches from the radioactive source. Note how rapidly the clicks occur.

    4. Cover the lid with a sheet of cardboard. Is there any change in how rapidly the clicks occur? Explain.

    5. Cover the lid with a sheet of lead. Is there any change in how rapidly the clicks occur? Explain.

    6. If the rate of clicking between the cardboard and the lead is different, how do you account for the difference?

    7. Which substance, cardboard or lead, do you believe offers greater protection against harmful radiation? Explain.

What Is Radioactivity?

In 1896, *Antoine Henri Becquerel*, a French physicist, conducted experiments with crystals of a uranium compound. He stored these crystals in a drawer on top of a photographic plate, wrapped securely with black, light-proof paper. When Becquerel developed this plate, he noticed that there were black streaks on the plate. Puzzled as to how the streaks got there, he placed a fresh photographic plate in the same drawer, but this time he removed the uranium crystals. Later, when he developed this plate, he found that there were no black streaks. He reasoned that the uranium compound was emitting invisible rays that had enough energy to affect the chemicals in a covered photographic plate.

At the request of Becquerel, *Marie* and *Pierre Curie* investigated the mysterious rays coming from the uranium compound. As a source of the uranium compound, they used an ore of uranium called *pitchblende*. In 1898, they succeeded in isolating radium and polonium, two elements that release even more energy than uranium. Such **atomic energy**, or **nuclear energy**, comes from the nucleus of atoms. Elements that spontaneously release nuclear energy are said to be **radioactive**, or to have the property of radioactivity. To understand radioactivity and its relation to energy, you must first recall some basic ideas about atoms that you learned in earlier chapters.

What Are the Characteristics of Elements and Their Isotopes?

An atom of any element consists of a central nucleus around which electrons move. The nucleus is composed of protons, which are positively charged, and neutrons, which have no charge. The orbital electrons have a negative charge equal to that of the protons in the nucleus.

Recall that the orbital electrons account for the chemical properties of an element. These electrons take part in chemical changes when atoms bond. The bond is usually accomplished by the sharing or the transfer of orbital electrons. The mass of an electron is tiny when compared with the mass of either a proton or a neutron. Thus, the mass of an atom is the combined mass of its protons and neutrons and is concentrated in the nucleus.

It is possible for the same element to exist in different forms. Each form has the same chemical properties, but each form has a slightly different atomic mass due to a difference in the number of neutrons in the nucleus. Recall that these varieties of the same element are called *isotopes*. For example, the element carbon (atomic number 6) has several isotopes. Among these is the isotope with an atomic mass of 12 and another with an atomic mass 14. Common carbon (coal, diamond, black deposits on spark plugs) is composed largely of atoms of atomic mass 12. Any other isotopes in such examples of carbon are present in extremely small quantities. Carbon of atomic mass 12 (carbon-12) is not radioactive. Therefore, it is a stable isotope of carbon. On the other hand, carbon of atomic mass 14 (carbon-14) is radioactive and is unstable.

All the elements from atomic number 1 through 83 exist as both stable (nonradioactive) and unstable (radioactive) isotopes. Unstable isotopes are called **radioisotopes**. All the elements above atomic number 83, whether natural or artificial, are radioactive.

An example of an element that has stable and unstable isotopes is hydrogen (atomic number 1). This element has three isotopes, all of which have one proton in the nucleus and 1 electron in the first energy level. When representing the isotopes of elements, the atomic number is written as a subscript to the left of the symbol; the atomic mass (number of protons and neutrons) is written as a superscript to the left of the symbol. Common hydrogen, also called **protium**, which has 1 proton in its nucleus but has no neutrons, is written $_1^1H$. **Deuterium**, another isotope of hydrogen, has 1 proton and 1 neutron in its nucleus. Because the atomic mass is 2, deuterium is written $_1^2H$. Deuterium, often called heavy hydrogen, is not radioactive. The third isotope of hydrogen, **tritium**, has 1 proton and 2 neutrons in its nucleus.

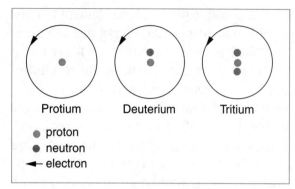

Figure 23-2. Hydrogen has three isotopes.

Tritium, written ^3_1H, is heavier than deuterium and is radioactive. Deuterium and tritium are relatively rare. (See Figure 23-2.)

Uranium is an example of an element that has only unstable isotopes. This element, and others like it, will be discussed later in this chapter.

What Happens During Radioactive Decay?

When an unstable isotope emits radiation, the isotope may change to another element that is lighter in atomic mass or different in atomic number or both. Such a change in an unstable element is called **radioactive decay**. For example, when atoms of carbon-14 decay, a neutron in the nucleus changes into a proton, an electron, and an antineutrino. The electron and the antineutrino, fly out of the nucleus. The proton remains in the nucleus. Because an element is defined by the number of protons it has, the original element has changed into a different element. In this example, carbon with an atomic number of 6 changes into nitrogen with an atomic number of 7.

This change can be shown in a type of equation called a **nuclear equation**:

$$\text{carbon} \rightarrow \text{nitrogen} + \text{electron}$$

$$^{14}_{6}C \rightarrow ^{14}_{7}N + ^{0}_{-1}e$$

Each superscript represents the number of protons and neutrons in the particle (atomic mass) and each subscript represents the number of protons or electrons (atomic number). Note that the superscripts on both sides of the nuclear equation are balanced: $14 = 14 + 0$. Similarly, the subscripts are also balanced: $6 = 7 + (-1)$.

All radioactive elements undergo radioactive decay and, in so doing, change to other elements. In this process, energy is released. When the element that is formed is a stable one, the decay process stops and no more energy is released.

Types of Radiation

In 1903, *Ernest Rutherford* investigated the nature of the radiations emitted from pitchblende. He placed a sample of the ore in a lead box open on one side. By allowing the radiation to pass through the opening and then between a positively charged plate and a negatively charged plate, he identified three types of radiation (see Figure 23-3).

Alpha Rays. As the figure shows, one component of the beam of radiation turns toward the negatively charged plate. According to the law of electric charges, opposite charges attract each other. Therefore, the particles that are attracted to the negative plate must be positively charged. These

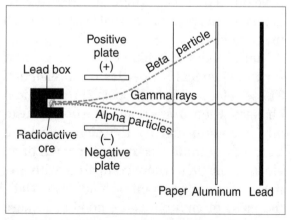

Figure 23-3. Rutherford's experiment enabled him to identify three types of radiation.

particles are called **alpha particles**. Many experiments have shown that alpha particles are actually the nuclei of helium atoms; that is, they are composed of 2 protons and 2 neutrons. Therefore, an alpha particle has an atomic mass of 4 and a charge of +2. The abbreviation for an alpha particle is $^4_2$He. The speed at which alpha particles travel is approximately one-tenth the speed of light. Traveling at this relatively slow speed, these relatively heavy particles can pass through a thin sheet of paper. However, they can be stopped by a barrier of greater thickness.

Beta Particles. Figure 23-3 also shows that one component of the beam turns sharply toward the positive plate and, therefore, must be negatively charged. This component of the beam consists of electrons that, in this case, are called **beta particles**. These particles turn toward the positive plate to a far greater degree than the alpha particles turn toward the negative plate. The degree of deflection shows that alpha particles are more massive than beta particles. These observations, and other experiments, indicate that beta particles are high-speed electrons emitted from the nuclei of atoms. The abbreviation for the beta particle is the same as the symbol for an electron, $^0_{-1}e$. These electrons travel at a speed close to that of light. Beta particles can pass through paper because of their great speed. However, because they are so light, they cannot pass through a sheet of aluminum.

Gamma Rays. The third component of the beam of radiation shown in Figure 23-3 is not deflected from the path between the oppositely charged plates. Therefore, this component must be electrically neutral. This type of radiation is called **gamma radiation**, or **gamma rays**. These rays are high-frequency electromagnetic waves similar to x-rays. Gamma rays have no mass but possess high

energy. They are the most penetrating of the rays emitted from radioactive elements and are, accordingly, the most dangerous. Gamma rays can pass through paper, aluminum, and living tissue. They can be stopped only by thick sheets of lead or concrete.

When any one of the three types of radiation collides with an atom, electrons are stripped from the atom, forming a charged particle. The atom is said to be ionized. Consequently, alpha, beta, and gamma rays are described as **ionizing rays**.

How Is Radiation Detected?

The ionizing ability of alpha, beta, and gamma rays makes it possible to detect their presence. Detection is accomplished by devices that indicate when ionization takes place. Some of these are described briefly below.

Film Badges. Remember that radiation from radioactive substances was first discovered by its effect on a photographic plate. Although invisible, the radiation ionizes the photographic chemicals in film and changes them. People working near radioactive materials, including some scientists, doctors, and nurses, wear buttons containing film, called film badges. At the end of each workday, the film is developed to determine their exposure to radiation.

The Electroscope. In Chapter 16, you learned that the electroscope is used to detect a static electric charge. This device can also be used to detect radioactivity. When a charged electroscope, which has its leaves separated, is placed near a radioactive source, the radiations ionize the air molecules near the electroscope. The ionized air molecules neutralize the charge of the electroscope and cause its leaves to collapse. The rate at which the electroscope discharges is a measure of the amount of radioactivity present; that is, the faster the rate of discharge, the greater is the amount of radiation present.

The Geiger-Müller Counter. This device is composed of a gas-filled tube (Geiger-Müller tube), shown in Figure 23-4, and a signaling device such as a lamp or a sounder. The tube contains argon gas under low pressure and two electrodes that are separated by the gas. The electrodes are part of an electric circuit that connects them to the signaling device. When charged particles or gamma rays pass into the tube, the gas inside becomes ionized for a split second. The gas conducts an electric current to the signaling device, which then produces a flash of light or a clicking sound. The greater the number of signals per second, the greater is the degree of radioactivity of the substance being studied.

The Cloud Chamber. In 1911, *C. T. R. Wilson* designed an apparatus in which radioactive particles could be tracked and studied. This device, the **cloud chamber** (see Figure 23-5), consists of a reservoir and a rubber bulb. Water containing a black dye is placed in the reservoir and the material to be studied is placed on a little shelf above the water. The black dye makes it easier to observe tracks made by particles. In a short time, the air above the water becomes saturated

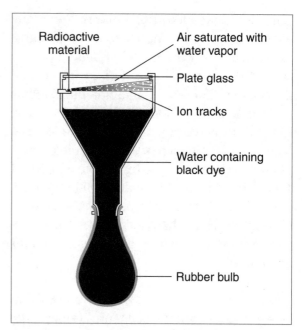

Figure 23-5. The Wilson cloud chamber made it possible to track and study radioactive particles.

with water vapor. Then the rubber bulb is squeezed, thereby compressing the saturated air. As the bulb is released, the air expands and cools and becomes supersaturated with water vapor. Alpha particles (or any other ionizing material) striking the molecules in the air cause these molecules to become ionized. The ions act as centers around which the water vapor can condense. As water vapor condenses on the ions, the path of the ions becomes visible.

Your inquiry investigation used a variation of Wilson's cloud chamber. The bright streaks coming from the radioactive source can be accounted for as follows: The alcohol evaporates into the air of the jar, which is cooled by the dry ice. When an ionizing particle passes through the cold vapor, condensation takes place along the path of the particle, making the track visible. Using a Geiger-Müller counter probe, you also observed how certain solids stop radioactive particles, such as alpha particles.

The Bubble Chamber. This is a highly specialized piece of equipment used to observe the tracks of particles that move too rapidly for

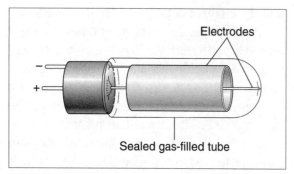

Figure 23-4. A Geiger-Müller tube can be used to detect nuclear radiation.

observation in a cloud chamber. In one type of bubble chamber, liquid hydrogen is heated under pressure to a temperature slightly above its normal boiling point. The liquid becomes superheated but does not boil. When high-energy particles enter the chamber, they create a trail of ions. These ions, in turn, pass through the liquid and cause the liquid to boil, producing a track of small bubbles. The properties of the track of bubbles make it possible to identify the type of particle producing the track.

What Is Transmutation?

All radioactive elements undergo radioactive decay. For example, when carbon-14 decays and emits radiation, the carbon is transformed into another element—nitrogen. Such a transformation of one element into another is called **transmutation**.

The natural decay of uranium to a stable element involves several transmutations. Each transmutation is accompanied by the release of energy. When an atom of uranium-238 ($^{238}_{92}U$) decays, it emits an alpha particle (helium nucleus, ^4_2He). Accordingly, the atomic mass of the atom decreases by 4 mass units (2 protons + 2 neutrons) and its atomic number decreases by 2. These changes result in an atomic nucleus of 234 mass units and an atomic number of 90, the element thorium. These changes can be summarized as follows:

$$\text{uranium} \rightarrow \text{thorium} + \overset{\text{alpha}}{\text{particle}} + \text{energy}$$
$$^{238}_{92}U \rightarrow ^{234}_{90}Th + ^4_2He + \text{energy}$$

Note that the atomic masses (superscripts) balance: $238 = 234 + 4$. The atomic numbers (subscripts) also balance: $92 = 90 + 2$.

Like uranium, thorium is radioactive and decays as follows:

$$\text{thorium} \rightarrow \text{protactinium} + \overset{\text{beta}}{\text{particle}} + \text{energy}$$
$$^{234}_{90}Th \rightarrow ^{234}_{91}Pa + ^{0}_{-1}e + \text{energy}$$

The atomic masses balance: $234 = 234 + 0$; the atomic numbers balance: $90 = 91 + (-1)$.

Protactinium is also radioactive and decays. This decay results in another element which, in turn, also decays. The process continues for several more such radioactive transmutations, each of which is accompanied by the release of energy. The final stable element that results after 14 transmutations is an isotope of lead, $^{206}_{82}Pb$.

The transmutation of uranium and other radioactive isotopes to lead is a natural process that has been going on since Earth formed. Artificial transmutation began in 1919. At that time, Ernest Rutherford bombarded the nuclei of nitrogen atoms with alpha particles and produced an isotope of oxygen and common hydrogen as shown in the following equation:

$$\text{nitrogen} + \overset{\text{alpha}}{\text{particle}} \rightarrow \text{oxygen} + \text{hydrogen}$$
$$^{14}_{7}N + ^4_2He \rightarrow ^{17}_{8}O + ^1_1H$$

What Is the Half-Life of a Radioisotope?

The rate at which a radioactive element decays is expressed as the **half-life** of the element. The half-life of a radioactive element is the time it takes for one-half of a given amount of the element to undergo change into another element. For example, the half-life of radium is 1620 years. Thus, if a sample of 10 grams of radium existed 1620 years ago, only 5 grams of the radium would exist today. This sample would decrease to 2.5 grams of radium 1620 years from now. The sample would continue to decay at the same rate. As you will learn later in this chapter, the knowledge of the half-lives of some elements is useful in determining the age of materials containing radioactive elements. Table 23-1 on page 382 shows the half-life of some radioactive elements.

Table 23-1.
What Are the Half-Lives of Some Elements?

Isotope	Symbol	Half-Life
Carbon-14	$^{14}_{6}C$	5700 years
Cobalt-60	$^{60}_{27}Co$	5.25 years
Iodine-131	$^{131}_{53}I$	8.04 days
Iron-53	$^{53}_{26}Fe$	8.9 minutes
Phosphorus-32	$^{32}_{15}P$	14.3 days
Polonium-210	$^{210}_{84}Po$	138 days
Radium-226	$^{226}_{88}Ra$	1620 years
Sodium-24	$^{24}_{11}Na$	14.9 hours
Uranium-238	$^{238}_{92}U$	4.5 billion years

▶ What Is the Purpose of Smashing Atoms?

Since Rutherford carried out the first artificial transmutation, many other experimenters used radiation from certain elements to bombard samples of nonradioactive elements. Among these experimenters were *Irène* and *Frédéric Joliot-Curie*. In 1934, they fired alpha particles onto aluminum, which then became unstable. The aluminum underwent transmutation, becoming the radioactive isotope phosphorus-30, which does not occur naturally. Thus, by using "atomic bullets," a radioisotope of phosphorus was artificially created. Radioactive phosphorus, half-life 2.5 minutes, decays rapidly to form silicon.

In recent years, several devices have been invented that shoot out nuclear particles with great energy. When such particles reach certain atoms, the atomic nuclei often break up into fragments as transmutations occur. Research concerning these fragments has led to the discovery of particles other than electrons, protons, and neutrons. The devices used in this type of research are called **particle accelerators**. Among the more com-

monly known particle accelerators are the cyclotron, the synchrotron, and the betatron.

The *cyclotron* (see Figure 23-6), designed by *Ernest O. Lawrence* in 1931, is a large, circular, flat box, divided into two halves called *dees*. The box is placed between the poles of a powerful electromagnet and the air is removed from the box. (The presence of air molecules might interfere with the movement of charged particles in the box.) Usually, positively charged particles are introduced into the center of the chamber. Alternating current entering the dees, together with the action of the magnetic field, increases the speed of the particles and makes them follow a circular path. When the particles have been sufficiently accelerated, they are fired through a window into a target element. The particles released from the target are then studied with one of the radiation detectors described earlier in this chapter.

The *synchrotron* operates on a principle similar to that of the cyclotron. The synchrotron controls the path of accelerated particles better than the cyclotron and imparts even greater energy to them.

The *betatron* accelerates electrons in much the same manner as a synchrotron accelerates positively charged particles. The high-speed electrons produced may be used

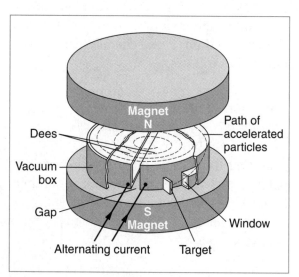

Figure 23-6. A cyclotron is one type of particle accelerator.

either to bombard the nuclei of radioactive substances or to produce very high-energy x-rays.

More recently, another tool for investigating particle interactions has been developed. The Large Hadron Collider (LHC) is a huge instrument built 100 meters underground along the border of France and Switzerland at Geneva. The circular track of the LHC is about 27 kilometers (about 16 miles) long, and there are four detection chambers along the track with a network of computers to process information. The LHC collides particles much like other accelerators. However, it gives them up to seven times as much energy. This may make it possible to recreate energies and conditions that existed when the universe first formed.

▶ How Can Nuclear Energy Be Used?

In 1905, *Albert Einstein* proposed his famous equation $E = mc^2$, which indicates the amount of energy released when matter becomes energy. In the Einstein equation, E represents energy, m represents mass, and c^2 represents the square of the speed of light. According to this equation, 1 gram of matter can produce 25 million kilowatt-hours of energy—the amount of energy that can be released by burning almost 4500 tons of coal. The energy released by the decay of the naturally radioactive elements is seldom useful because these elements are relatively scarce. Yet, since the discovery of how to convert matter to energy by means of nuclear fission and nuclear fusion, certain atoms have become an important source of power for everyday needs.

▶ Nuclear Fission

In 1939, *Otto Hahn, Fritz Strassman,* and *Lise Meitner* confirmed the idea that a uranium nucleus can be split by a neutron. When the isotope uranium-235 ($^{235}_{92}U$) is bombarded with neutrons, its nucleus suddenly splits into two fragments as a burst of energy is released. As shown in the following equation, the uranium nucleus accepts a neutron, becomes unstable, and then splits, forming an atom of barium and an atom of krypton. As this occurs, both nuclear energy and three neutrons are released.

$$\text{Uranium} + \text{neutron} \rightarrow$$
$$^{235}_{92}U + ^{1}_{0}n \rightarrow$$

$$\text{barium} + \text{krypton} + 3 \text{ neutrons} + \text{energy}$$
$$^{138}_{56}Ba + ^{95}_{36}Kr + 3^{1}_{0}n + \text{energy}$$

The splitting of a nucleus into two fragments of approximately equal size with the release of nuclear energy is called **nuclear fission**. As shown in Figure 23-7, the three neutrons released during the fission of the first uranium atom can cause the fission of three other uranium atoms, thereby releasing nine

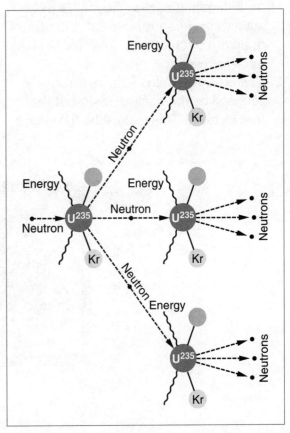

Figure 23-7. A chain reaction is a self-continuing fission reaction.

additional neutrons. These neutrons, in turn, can cause the fission of nine other uranium atoms, and so on. Such a self-continuing fission reaction is called a **chain reaction**. If the chain reaction is allowed to continue, more uranium fissions and increasing amounts of nuclear energy become available.

When a chain reaction is uncontrolled, vast quantities of nuclear energy are released instantaneously. It is this type of chain reaction that is responsible for the destructiveness of an atomic bomb. When a chain reaction is controlled, the energy released can be regulated and used for many peaceful purposes.

Nuclear Reactor. Nuclear chain reactions can be controlled in a device called a **nuclear reactor**. As shown in Figure 23-8, there are five main parts of a nuclear reactor:

1. The *fuel element* is a substance capable of undergoing nuclear fission. Substances such as uranium-235 and plutonium are often used as fuels for the nuclear reactor.
2. The *moderator* slows the neutrons released by the nuclear fission of the fuel element. This makes the fissioning

process more efficient. Pure graphite (carbon) is generally used as the moderator in a nuclear reactor.

3. The *control rods* absorb neutrons readily. Such rods are composed of cadmium steel or boron. When the control rods are withdrawn from the reactor, the chain reaction begins as neutrons are permitted to bombard the fuel element. To stop the chain reaction, the control rods are pushed back into the reactor. Since they absorb neutrons, they stop the chain reaction.
4. A *pump* circulates a fluid, called a *coolant*, inside the shielded chamber in which fission is occurring. The coolant conducts away the heat released by fission to a heat exchanger. In the heat exchanger, water in the coil is converted to steam, which is drawn off and used to run electrical generators. Some common coolants used in reactors are heavy water or liquid sodium.
5. The *shielding* prevents the leakage of radiation. The danger of radiation produced by a nuclear reactor is decreased by proper shielding. The shielding material usually consists of concrete and thick blocks of lead.

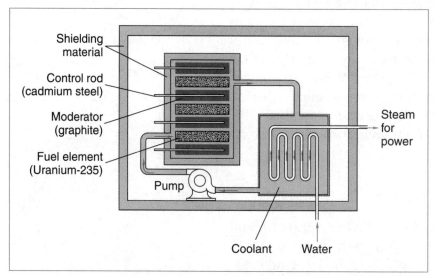

Figure 23-8. A nuclear reactor uses controlled chain reactions to harness large amounts of energy.

The energy provided by nuclear reactors has been put to use in powering submarines, aircraft carriers, and other seagoing vessels. Nuclear reactors are used increasingly by large utility companies to produce electricity. Two such reactors are located at Entergy Nuclear Northeast's Indian Point Energy Center in Buchanan, New York. It produces a large portion of the electric power consumed by New York City.

In addition to providing power, nuclear reactors are used to prepare some artificial radioactive isotopes. For this purpose, an element is placed in the reactor and exposed to neutrons. The absorption of neutrons by the nuclei of atoms results in the production of radioactive elements. Examples of such elements include cobalt-60, which is used in treating some forms of cancer, and plutonium (an artificial element), which is used as a fuel element in some reactors and in nuclear bombs.

Nuclear Fusion

In contrast to nuclear fission, **nuclear fusion** is the process in which the nuclei of two light atoms combine to produce a nucleus of a heavier atom. For example, when 4 hydrogen atoms fuse, 1 helium atom is formed and 2 positrons (electrons with a positive charge) and nuclear energy are released:

$$\text{4 hydrogen atoms} \xrightarrow{\text{fusion}}$$
$$\text{helium atom} + \text{2 positrons} + \text{energy}$$

$$4{}_1^1\text{H} \xrightarrow{\text{fusion}} {}_2^4\text{H} + 2{}_{+1}^{0}e + \text{energy}$$

This type of reaction is capable of releasing even larger amounts of energy than does nuclear fission. Fusion reactions, also called *thermonuclear reactions*, appear to be the source of the energy released by the sun. The enormous destructiveness of the hydrogen bomb is the result of an uncontrolled fusion reaction.

How Can Radioactive Isotopes Be Used?

Small quantities of radioisotopes are not useful sources of energy. However, when these isotopes are properly used, they are valuable in medical diagnosis and treatment, industry, and research.

The radioactive and nonradioactive isotopes of any element have the same chemical properties. Consequently, either type of isotope may be used in a specific chemical reaction. When a radioisotope is used, its chemical pathway can be followed with one of the types of radioactivity detectors. A radioisotope used in this way is called a *tracer*. Many of the valuable applications of radioactivity depend upon such tracers.

Medical Uses. Phosphorus-32, one of the radioisotopes of phosphorus, is sometimes used to find certain types of cancer deep inside the body. If the cancerous tissue is a kind that ordinarily absorbs phosphorus, the absorption of phosphorus-32 by the tissue makes it possible to locate the cancer by means of one of the detectors. Since the half-life of P-32 is about 14 days, it does not accumulate in the body.

Iodine-131, one of the radioisotopes of iodine, is used to treat an overactive thyroid gland. This gland normally absorbs iodine. When iodine-131 is given to a patient in an "atomic cocktail," the iodine-131 is absorbed by the gland. There, the radiation from the iodine-131 destroys the excess thyroid tissue. Since the half-life of iodine-131 is about 8 days, the dose can be adjusted in order to prevent damage to other tissues of the body.

Cobalt-60, a radioactive isotope that has become widely available as a result of its manufacture in nuclear reactors, is a strong emitter of gamma rays. Gamma rays have properties similar to those of x-rays. Accordingly, cobalt-60 is used in x-ray photography and in treating cancers.

Radioactive salts of iron or sodium are used to trace the circulation of blood in various parts of the body. After injecting the isotope, a doctor can follow its course in the body by means of a Geiger-Müller counter.

Industrial Uses. Radioisotopes are used as tracers to follow the flow of oil through pipelines. Since these pipes transport samples of different kinds of oil one after the other, it is important to know where one kind of oil begins and another ends. By placing a small quantity of a radioisotope into the pipeline at the point of entry of a batch of oil, workers at the receiving end of the pipeline can use a Geiger-Müller counter to identify the point of separation between two types of oil.

Radioisotopes are also used to measure the uniformity of thickness of sheets of paper, plastic, glass, or metal as they are being manufactured. The radiation from cobalt-60 is allowed to penetrate the sheet and is then detected by a Geiger-Müller counter. When differences in thickness cause the Geiger-Müller counter reading to change, it is a signal to a worker to adjust the manufacturing process.

Research Uses. Carbon-14 has been used as a tracer in the study of photosynthesis, the process by which green plants make food. As a result, the chemistry of this process is better understood.

Radioisotopes that have long half-lives may be used to determine the age of an ancient object, which usually contains radioactive material. In this process, called **radioactive dating**, the proportion of a radioactive element remaining in the object to that of the element into which it has changed is first determined. Then, the knowledge of the half-life of the radioactive element enables scientists to calculate how long it took for the transmutation of the radioactive element to a stable one. For example, the half-life of uranium-238 is approximately 4.5 billion years. Thus, by comparing the propor-

tion of uranium-238 to lead-206 (the last stable element formed in the decay of uranium-238) in rocks, the age of the rocks can be determined. Using such methods, scientists believe the age of the oldest rocks on Earth to be close to 4.5 billion years.

Carbon-14 has a half-life of about 5700 years, eventually decaying into stable nitrogen-14. Living things contain mostly carbon-12, but take in carbon-14 as long as they are alive. By calculations similar to those used for uranium and lead, the age of the remains of some living things can be found. In this type of research, the proportion studied is that of carbon-14 to carbon-12.

▶ What Are the Dangers of Radioactivity?

You are exposed to low levels of radioactivity every day. Radioactive elements are found naturally in rock, soil, water, and air. Cosmic rays from space interact with Earth's upper atmosphere and create another source of natural radiation. Fortunately, the levels of radiation from these sources are relatively low. Some people, such as workers in nuclear power plants, find themselves exposed to high levels of radioactivity on a regular basis. These people need to protect themselves carefully because the rays emitted by radioactive substances and other sources can penetrate the body without being felt. Prolonged exposure to penetrating radiation can injure the body enough to cause death. Radiation can damage or destroy both surface and internal tissues. Not only can radiation cause burns, but radiation can also damage the genes within cells and thereby cause **mutations**. Mutations are changes in genetic information and are generally harmful. As you learned earlier in this chapter, proper shielding can prevent excessive exposure to radiation.

When a nuclear device is exploded in the atmosphere, radioactive materials are released. These fall to the ground and continue to emit radiation. Materials that fall to the ground any time after a nuclear explosion are called *fallout*. Frequently, fallout contains radioisotopes that have long half-lives. When these isotopes are inhaled or when they land on food materials and are eaten, they can inflict radiation damage for a long time afterward. It is for these reasons that every nation should be interested in taking steps to limit future tests of nuclear explosions to underground regions or to abolish all nuclear tests.

Nuclear power plants produce radioactive waste as well as electricity. How to dispose of this waste remains a difficult problem. No method devised so far can be guaranteed to keep the waste products isolated from the environment forever. Leakage from storage containers can release long-lived radioactive particles that have effects similar to fallout. It is in every nation's interest to take steps to limit future nuclear tests and to work together to find a way to dispose of nuclear wastes safely.

▶ What Are the Dangers of Nuclear Accidents?

In addition to radioactive wastes normally produced by nuclear power plants, radiation can also be leaked during accidents that might occur at facilities in which nuclear fuels are used. For example, in 1986, a series of explosions occurred at the Chernobyl Nuclear Power plant in Ukraine. The fire that resulted sent radioactive smoke fallout into the atmosphere over a large area of land. Many people were harmed or even killed as a result, and hundreds of thousands of people had to leave their homes forever because the land was no longer safe to inhabit. Up to three million acres of farmland were contaminated with radiation that entered the food chain.

In 2011, an earthquake knocked out electricity at Japan's Fukushima Daiichi nuclear plant. Although generators were available to make sure coolant continued to be pumped to the fuel rods, a tsunami then struck, damaging the generators. Without coolant, heat from the fuel rods led to the buildup of superheated water. The superheated water split into oxygen and hydrogen, and some of the escaping hydrogen exploded. Throughout the disaster, radioactive elements were released into the air and later found to be in the water supply and food chain.

Some of the radioactive materials that enter the soil, water, or food chain decay quickly but others remain for thousands of years. People who consume foods laced with radioactive materials are likely to suffer serious and often fatal health problems, including cancers and genetic disorders.

Chapter Review

Science Terms

The following list contains all the boldfaced words in this chapter and the page on which each appears.

alpha particle (p. 379)

atomic energy (p. 377)

beta particle (p. 379)

chain reaction (p. 384)

cloud chamber (p. 380)

deuterium (p. 377)

gamma radiation (p. 379)

gamma rays (p. 379)

half-life (p. 381)

ionizing rays (p. 379)

mutations (p. 386)

nuclear energy (p. 377)

nuclear equation (p. 378)

nuclear fission (p. 383)

nuclear fusion (p. 385)

nuclear reactor (p. 384)

particle accelerator (p. 382)

protium (p. 377)

radioactive (p. 377)

radioactive dating (p. 386)

radioactive decay (p. 378)

radioisotopes (p. 377)

transmutation (p. 381)

tritium (p. 377)

Matching Questions

In your notebook, write the letter of the item in column B that is most closely related to the item in column A.

Column A

_____ 1. cloud chamber

_____ 2. radioisotope

_____ 3. transmutation

_____ 4. LHC

_____ 5. beta particle

_____ 6. nuclear fusion

_____ 7. pitchblende

_____ 8. chain reaction

_____ 9. nuclear fission

_____ 10. alpha particle

Column B

a. uranium ore

b. helium nucleus

c. unstable form of an element

d. process in which neutrons released during fission initiate other reactions

e. the splitting of a nucleus

f. process through which one element changes into another

g. process through which smaller nuclei join together

h. a high-speed electron

i. particle accelerator that creates high-energy collisions

j. apparatus in which radioactive particles can be tracked

Multiple-Choice Questions

In your notebook, write the letter preceding the word or expression that best completes the statement or answers the question.

1. What discovery did Becquerel make to contribute to the understanding of radioactivity?
   a. He identified three different types of radiation.
   b. He recognized that uranium emitted invisible rays of energy.
   c. He developed a gas-filled tube for detecting radiation.
   d. He invented an apparatus in which radioactive particles could be tracked.

2. Which elements did Pierre and Marie Curie succeed in isolating?
   a. polonium and radium
   b. radium and uranium
   c. polonium and uranium
   d. radium and plutonium

3. Isotopes of an element have different
   a. atomic numbers
   b. numbers of electrons
   c. positions in the periodic table
   d. numbers of neutrons

4. When a radioactive element releases radiation and changes to a different element, it is said to undergo
   a. a physical change
   b. transmutation
   c. a chemical change
   d. atomic fusion

5. An alpha particle is a
   a. helium nucleus
   b. hydrogen nucleus
   c. helium atom
   d. hydrogen atom

6. High-speed electrons emitted from the nuclei of atoms are called
   a. beta particles   c. alpha particles
   b. gamma rays   d. ions

7. Which form(s) of radiation can be stopped by a sheet of aluminum?
   a. gamma rays
   b. gamma rays and alpha particles
   c. alpha particles and beta particles
   d. beta particles and gamma rays

8. When an atom is subjected to radiation, the atom is
   a. destroyed   c. ionized
   b. disintegrated   d. split

9. Scientists who work with radioactive materials determine the amount of radiation to which they have been exposed by using a device called
   a. a film badge
   b. an electroscope
   c. a Geiger counter
   d. an ammeter

10. Why does the Large Hadron Collider have a long track?
    a. It establishes an electric current.
    b. It provides space for a chain reaction.
    c. It is filled with millions of particles.
    d. It is used to accelerate particles to great speeds.

11. When a uranium-238 atom decays, it emits an alpha particle. The atomic mass of the new atom formed is
    a. decreased by 2
    b. increased by 4
    c. decreased by 4
    d. increased by 2

12. Which application is most directly related to the half-lives of radioactive elements such as carbon-14?
    a. energy production
    b. radioactive dating
    c. tracing fluids in pipes
    d. medical tracers

13. If an original sample of carbon-14 weighs 10 grams and the half-life of carbon14 is 5700 years, at the end of 5700 years what amount of carbon-14 would remain?
    a. 2.5 grams   c. 8 grams
    b. 5 grams   d. 10 grams

14. What phenomenon is described by the equation $E = mc^2$?
    a. Matter decays at different rates.
    b. Matter cannot travel faster than the speed of light.
    c. Matter is conserved in ordinary reactions.
    d. Matter can be converted into energy.

15. When an atom of uranium undergoes fission, the noble gas produced is
    a. argon   c. krypton
    b. neon   d. xenon

16. What is the role of the moderator in a nuclear reactor?
    a. to slow the neutrons
    b. to undergo fission
    c. to circulate a coolant
    d. to prevent radiation from leaking

17. In nuclear fusion, when 4 atoms of hydrogen fuse,
    a. one atom of nitrogen is formed
    b. one atom of helium is formed
    c. a chemical change takes place
    d. a physical change takes place

18. Radioisotopes that are used to track a chemical pathway are called
    a. ions   c. atomic cocktails
    b. tracers   d. radiators

19. Of the following, the radioisotope commonly used to treat a diseased thyroid gland is
    a. cobalt-60
    b. carbon-14
    c. iodine-131
    d. phosphorus-32

20. What are changes in heredity that may be produced by radiation called?
    a. transformations
    b. chemical changes
    c. mutations
    d. physical changes

Modified True-False Questions

In some of the following statements, the italicized term makes the statement incorrect. For each incorrect statement, in your notebook, write the term that must be substituted for the italicized term to make the statement correct. For each correct statement, write the word "true."

1. An element that emits rays is said to be *contaminated.* _____

2. Unstable isotopes of elements are called *radioisotopes.* _____

3. The symbol ^3_1H represents *tritium.* _____

4. *Alpha* rays are the only type of radiation that does not involve particles. _____

5. A clicking device used to detect radiation is a *cyclotron.* _____

6. A device used to observe the tracks of particles that move too rapidly for a cloud chamber is a *bubble chamber.* _____

7. The change of an atom into a new element is called a *chemical change.*

8. The first artificial transmutation was performed by *Albert Einstein.* _____

9. The rate at which a radioactive element decays is known as the *half-life.* _____

10. Devices used in smashing atoms are called *particle accelerators.* _____

11. The *electroscope* is a device being used to investigate the origin of the universe. _____

12. The splitting of an atom into two fragments of approximately equal size is called *nuclear fusion.* _____

13. The self-continuation of nuclear fission is called a *chain reaction.* _____

14. A device used to control a nuclear chain reaction is a *bubble chamber.* _____

15. The sun produces its energy by *thermonuclear reactions.* _____

TEST-TAKING TIP Prefixes often give you clues to figure out the meanings of words you do not know or have forgotten. As you review each chapter, make a list of important prefixes. Being familiar with them may help you to answer questions on an exam. For example, the prefix *radio-* relates to radiation.

Check Your Knowledge
Write the answer to each question in your notebook.

1. Define each of the following terms:
   a. radioactivity
   b. isotope
   c. alpha particle
   d. transmutation
   e. half-life

2. Describe each of the following types of radiation:
    a. alpha particles
    b. beta particles
    c. gamma rays

3. List five devices that can be used to detect radiation.

Think Critically

Write the answer to each of the following questions in your notebook.

1. Determine the age of each of the following specimens:
    a. Scientists have discovered that only 2.5 grams of carbon-14 remain in a sample that originally contained 10 grams.
    b. From 10 grams of radium-226, 5 grams remain. The rest of the radium has changed to lead.

2. Complete each of the following equations:
    a. $^{14}_{7}N + ^{4}_{2}He \rightarrow ^{1}_{1}H +$ _____
    b. $^{234}_{90}Th \rightarrow ^{0}_{-1}e +$ _____
    c. $4\,^{1}_{1}H \xrightarrow{\text{fusion}} 2\,^{0}_{+1}e +$ _____

3. Complete the table, entering the function of each of the parts of a nuclear reactor.

Part	Function
Fuel element	
Moderator	
Control rod	
Shielding	
Pump	

Take It Further

1. Research one accident at a nuclear power plant, such as the one that occurred at Three Mile Island, Chernobyl, or Fukushima Daiichi. Find out what caused the accident and how it affected the region. Present your findings to the class.

2. The scientists who made major contributions to the study of radioactivity were greatly affected by the political and social attitudes of the time during which they worked. Choose one scientist, such as Marie Curie, and research the scientist's life, work, and accomplishments. Share your findings.

3. Early scientists did not yet know the health dangers posed by working with radioactive materials. In fact, radioactive materials were even used in some products, such as watches. Investigate how the health of these scientists and workers was affected by their work. Choose an example and write a brief report summarizing your findings.

CAREER

4. A nuclear medicine technologist uses an understanding of radioactive elements to help doctors diagnose and treat diseases. Research the educational requirements of a nuclear medicine technologist along with opportunities available to them. You may wish to begin your research at the following site: *http://www.bls.gov/oco/ocos104.htm*.

Investigating Issues in Science, Engineering, Technology, and Society

Radioactive Waste: What Should Happen to It?

Would you store dangerous garbage in your basement for as long as you or anyone else lived in your house? In a very real sense, that's a question for which scientists and politicians seek an answer.

The "garbage" in this case is nuclear waste produced by the nuclear-weapons industry and by nuclear power plants. The difference between nuclear garbage and household garbage is that nuclear garbage produces deadly radiation for millions of years. At worst, the household garbage produces an unpleasant smell for a few days. So it's important to put nuclear wastes where they will be contained safely for a very long time.

For a number of years government officials and scientists have searched for a way to get rid of nuclear wastes safely. Among other ideas, suggestions were made to dump canisters of the wastes on the ocean floor or to bury them far below Earth's surface.

The trick was to find a relatively inexpensive burial place that would not leak. The ocean floor was ruled out, partly because of volcanic activity that might crack the canisters of nuclear waste and let radioactive elements escape into the sea. So scientists focused on rock formations under the land. After considerable research, the United States Department of Energy (DOE), which is responsible for nuclear waste disposal, turned its attention to burying the waste underground. That means that the waste has to be transported from where it is produced and to a place where it will be dumped. Who wants the radioactive waste nearby? After all, there is no guarantee that the containers will not leak or be damaged in some way.

Figure 23-9. As nuclear fuel is used to produce electricity, radioactive waste is produced. The waste can remain hazardous for thousands of years to come.

There may be another solution. The fuel used in a nuclear reactor must contain a certain percentage of "burnable" uranium. Once the percentage falls below a certain level, the fuel must be replaced. The used fuel, which is referred to as spent fuel, still contains about 95 percent of the uranium it had at the beginning of the process. Rather than disposing of this fuel, the uranium might be able to be recycled.

The technology to recycle the uranium was developed many years ago. However, the United States passed a law in 1977 preventing the recycling of uranium in this way. The concern was that the process produces plutonium, which can be used to make weapons if it falls into the wrong hands. In other countries, uranium recycling technology is being used with mixed results. In France, for example, nuclear fuel has been recycled for several decades. Similar recycling methods are being used to some extent in countries such as Japan, China, and Russia. Even with recycling, there is still radioactive waste. The difference is that the amount of waste that must be buried is reduced. The technology and the process still need to be improved to the point that the most long-lived elements remaining in nuclear waste can be broken down. All of this needs to be accomplished in a way that makes it affordable to build and maintain a disposal site.

Should the United States reconsider nuclear waste recycling or continue to wait until more reliable technologies are developed? What do you think?

Organize It!

Use a method that your instructor describes to organize the information in this article.

Explain It!

1. Nuclear wastes from weapons factories and from nuclear power plants remain radioactive for
   a. a few days
   b. a few weeks
   c. a few years
   d. millions of years

2. Why isn't the ocean floor a reasonable place to dump nuclear waste?
   a. The waste cannot be transported to the ocean floor.
   b. Volcanic activity might crack the canisters.
   c. Cold temperatures at the ocean floor increase the rate of radioactive decay.
   d. The ocean floor is too soft to maintain canisters of waste.

3. Which radioactive product is formed during the recycling of spent nuclear fuel?
   a. uranium
   b. water
   c. plutonium
   d. cesium

Extend It!

4. Research radioactive uranium and plutonium. Describe the properties of the atoms of each element. Find out why plutonium poses a tremendous risk of terrorist activities. Present your findings.

5. The current burial site selected for nuclear waste in the United States is Yucca Mountain, Nevada. Research the history of the selection of this site. Identify arguments for and against the site, and share your findings with the class.

CAREER

6. Nuclear engineers are people who use the energy released by nuclear reactions to do useful work, such as powering ships, treating disease, and producing electricity. Find out what other responsibilities a nuclear engineer might have and what training is required. You may wish to begin your research at the following site: *http://www.ans.org/pi/edu/students/careers/*.

CHAPTER

24 What Do Forces Do?

It is natural to see a ball streaming down the field at a soccer game, yet the ball would never move without being kicked. What is even more difficult to believe is that the ball would move forever if something did not stop it. That something is a force, and forces can change the motion of objects.

After reading this chapter, you should be able to answer the following questions:

What are forces?

How are forces measured?

How are forces represented?

How do forces combine?

What is the center of gravity?

How are parallel forces described?

Gravity attracts different masses with varying force. As you change the masses loaded on a spring, the spring stretches to different lengths. If you know how much stretch a given mass produces, you can determine the value of an unknown mass by measuring the stretch it produces. In this inquiry investigation, your problem is to find the mass of an unmarked piece of metal.

Materials:

✔ safety goggles
✔ ring stand
✔ clamp
✔ meterstick
✔ set of marked masses
✔ spring
✔ unknown mass
✔ graph paper
✔ pointer

Part A Using Figure 24-1 as a guide, adjust the clamp as high as it will go on the ring stand, attach the pointer to one end of the spring, suspend the spring from the clamp, and position the meterstick alongside the pointer.

Part B Hang the smallest mass from the end of the spring. Keeping your eye level with the pointer, note the marking on the meterstick that is opposite the pointer. Record this reading.

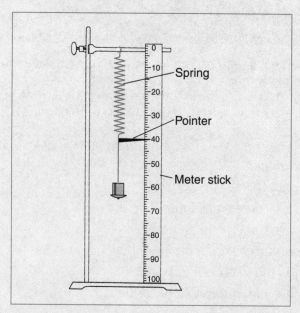

Figure 24-1.

Part C Hang the next largest mass from the end of the spring. Again, keeping your eye level with the pointer, note the marking on the meterstick that is opposite the pointer. Record this reading also.

1. *What effect do the masses have on the spring?*

2. *Is there a limit to the mass that can be hung on a given spring? Explain.*

3. *Before proceeding further with the investigation, outline the plan you intend to follow to determine the force with which gravity attracts the unmarked piece of metal.*

Part D After your teacher has approved it, carry out your plan. Record your results in a table.

Part E Create a graph using the results you obtained.

4. *What relation exists between the marked masses and the amounts they stretch the spring?*

5. *Based on this relation, what is the force with which gravity attracts the unmarked piece of metal?*

What Are Forces?

Every day you exert or experience different kinds of pushes and pulls. You might pull open a door or push a shopping cart. You might pull your backpack toward you or push a ball away from you. Any push or pull exerted upon some object is a **force**. The force of gravity pulls objects toward Earth's center. The force of magnetism between two unlike poles produces attraction that pulls the poles closer together. The force of magnetism between two like poles repels the poles, or pushes them farther apart. In the same manner, electrostatic attraction is the force that attracts or pulls a positively charged object to one that is negatively charged. Electrostatic repulsion pushes two similarly charged objects farther apart.

When you push against the pedal of a bicycle, you contract certain leg muscles and the bicycle moves.

More than one force may act on an object at the same time. The object may not move, however, because the forces on it are *balanced*—that is, the forces counteract each other. The book on your desk is not in motion because the downward pull of gravity on the book is counterbalanced by the equal upward push of the desk on the book. Should you pull the desk out from under the book, the book would fall because you have upset the balance of forces. If two people push a sled with the same force but in opposite directions, the sled does not move. However, if one person exerts less force than the other, the two forces become *unbalanced.* In such a situation, the sled begins to move in the direction in which the greater force is acting.

How Are Forces Measured?

It is easy to see that gravity is one of the major forces acting on matter all the time. The force exerted on a mass by gravity is weight. Therefore, the units of weight are units of force. In the English system of measurement, the **pound** is the standard unit of force. In the SI system, the unit of force is the **newton**. One pound (English system) is approximately equal to 4.5 newtons (SI system). Therefore, a force of 10 pounds exerted on an object would be equal to a force of about 45 newtons.

Scientists use SI units almost exclusively. On the other hand, industry in this country still relies on English units. In this chapter and in the chapters that follow, both systems will be used.

Your inquiry investigation used a simple way of measuring the force exerted by gravity. By suspending known masses on the spring, you determined the relation between the weight (force due to gravity) and the distance the spring stretched.

A spring may be used to weigh objects because it is **elastic**. That is, when the weight (force) is removed, the spring returns to its original position. In all such investigations, the spring should be stretched only up to the point where it can return to its original position. This largest stretch is called the *elastic limit* of the spring. If you exceed the elastic limit by attempting to weigh an extremely heavy object, the spring will be permanently deformed.

The size or amount of a force is called the **magnitude**. A device commonly used to measure the magnitude of a force is the **spring scale**, which is a convenient form of the apparatus used in your inquiry investigation. As shown in Figure 24-2, the spring scale might measure force in ounces (Eng-

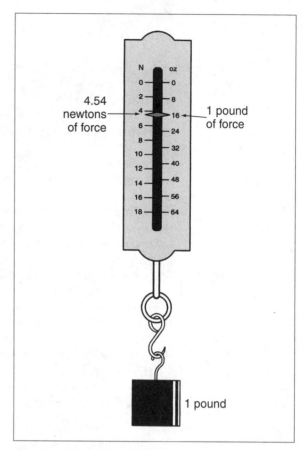

Figure 24-2. A spring scale is commonly used to measure force.

lish system) or in newtons (SI system). Values in newtons can be converted to grams. (A mass of 1 kilogram weighs 9.8 newtons.)

How Are Forces Represented?

An amount of water may be measured in units such as quarts or liters. The measurement tells the volume, that is, how much space the water occupies. A plank of wood may be measured in units such as yards or cubic meters. Such measurements tell how long the plank is (linear units) or how much space the plank occupies (cubic units). Quantities that measure amount or magnitude only are called **scalar quantities**. Examples of scalar quantities include length, volume, and weight.

Forces always have some magnitude. At the same time, forces are always operating in a specific direction. Quantities that have both magnitude and direction are called **vector quantities**. Thus, to describe the force used when Mr. Jones exerts 450 newtons (N) of force to push his stalled car to a service station, it is not sufficient to say that the force is 450 newtons. Instead, you must say that the force is 450 newtons in a given direction (see Figure 24-3a). For example, "Mr. Jones applied a *force* of 450 newtons in an *easterly* direction."

To represent forces on a sheet of paper, scientists use vector diagrams in which the forces are represented by **vectors**. A vector is drawn as an arrow with the head pointing in the direction of the force and with the tail indicating the point at which the force is applied. The length of the arrow represents the magnitude of the force. To show magnitude, you must decide on a scale, such as that found on any map. To determine the distance between two points on a map, you measure the length between the points with a ruler and then compare this length to the map's scale. The first step in drawing a vector diagram is to select a convenient scale. Suppose you let 1.0 centimeter represent 45 newtons of force. Accordingly, the 450-newton force applied by Mr. Jones to his stalled car is represented by a 10-centimeter line, shown in Figure 24-3b.

To indicate direction, it is convenient to follow the usual map convention: the top of the paper is north, the bottom is south, the right edge is east, and the left edge is west. As shown in the figure, you make a dot on your paper to represent the point of application of the force. Because the force is applied in an easterly direction, draw a horizontal 10-centimeter line representing the 450-newton force and attach an arrowhead to the line pointing to the right (to the east). In this example, the vector indicates three things: (1) point of application, (2) magnitude, and (3) direction.

▶ How Do Forces Combine?

When two or more forces act on the same object at the same time, the forces act together as though a single force were present. For example, suppose two people push a large rock in the same direction, each person exerting 250 newtons of force. The overall force is then the sum of the individual forces, or 500 newtons.

A single force that results from a combination of forces is called a *resultant force* or simply the **resultant**. Thus, the resultant of two 250-newton forces acting in the *same direction* is 500 newtons. The forces that produce

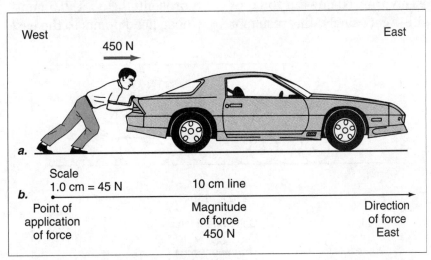

Figure 24-3. (*a*) A force is applied in a given direction. (*b*) The application of the force can be represented by vectors.

a resultant force are called **component forces**. The components of the 500-newton force are the two 250-newton forces. Whether the resultant force is greater than, less than, or equal to the component forces depends on the directions in which the component forces act. Component forces may act on an object in the same direction (as in the example), in opposite directions, or at angles to each other.

Forces Acting in the Same Direction. When two forces act on an object in the same direction, the angle between the forces is 0°. The resultant force produced is equal to the sum of the two forces. The direction in which the resultant force acts is the same as that of the component forces. For example, assume that two girls are pulling on a rope connected to a loaded cart, as shown in Figure 24-4a. One girl pulls with a force of 270 newtons as the other girl pulls in the same direction with a force of 360 newtons. The resultant force is equal to the sum of the combined forces, 270 newtons + 360 newtons, or 630 newtons, acting in the direction in which the pull is exerted.

Figure 24-4b shows this situation in a vector diagram. In this case, the scale is 0.3 centimeter = 90 newtons. Thus, a line 0.9 centimeter in length represents the 270-newton force of the first girl, and a 1.2-centimeter line represents the 360-newton force of the second girl. Accordingly, the resultant force is represented by a line 2.1 centimeters in length. Because all the forces here act in the same direction, the arrowhead of the resultant force points in the same direction as that of the components.

Forces Acting in Opposite Directions. When two forces act on an object in opposite directions, the angle between the forces is 180°. The resultant force produced is equal to the difference between the two forces. The resultant force then acts in the same direction as that of the *greater* component force. For example, assume that two boys are pulling on a loaded cart in opposite directions, as shown in Figure 24-5a. The first boy pulls to the east with a force of 360 newtons, while the second boy pulls to the west with a force of 270 newtons. The resultant force is then equal to the difference between the two component forces: 360 newtons − 270 newtons, or 90 newtons. The resultant force moves the cart toward the east, the direction of the greater component force.

As shown in Figure 24-5b, this case can also be represented by vectors. Using a scale of 0.3 centimeter = 90 newtons, a 1.2-centimeter line pointing to the east represents the 360-newton force and a 0.9-centimeter line pointing to the west represents the 270-newton force. The resultant (90 newtons) is represented by a 0.3-centimeter arrow whose head points to the east.

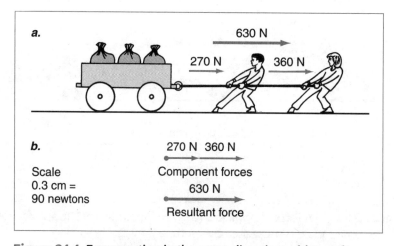

Figure 24-4. Forces acting in the same direction add together.

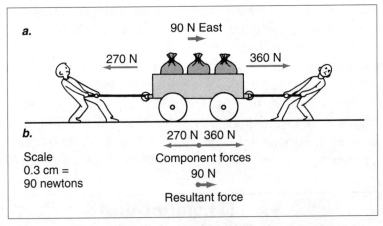

Figure 24-5. Forces acting in opposite directions subtract.

Forces Acting at an Angle. When two forces act on an object at an angle less than 180° to each other, the resultant force produced is not in the direction of either of the component forces. It lies somewhere between the sum and difference between the forces. For example, when two people pull on separate ropes attached to a cart, as shown in Figure 24-6a, the cart moves in a direction somewhere between the two ropes.

Using vectors to represent the component forces, you can determine the magnitude and the direction of the resultant force in this case (see Figure 24-6b). The resultant is the diagonal of a **parallelogram of force** constructed as follows (a parallelogram is a 4-sided figure with opposite sides both equal and parallel):

1. Select an appropriate scale for the vectors. For example, suppose the angle between the two ropes is 90° and one person pulls with a force of 270 newtons, while the other pulls with a force of 360 newtons. You can select a scale of 0.3 centimeter = 90 newtons.
2. Choose a point on the paper to represent the cart. Draw two lines for vectors at right angles to each other. Mark off the lines according to the scale (Figure 24-6b). Insert the arrowheads. Thus, a 0.9-centimeter vector represents the force of 270 newtons and a 1.2-centimeter vector represents the 360-newton force.
3. Use these vectors as the two sides of a parallelogram. Complete the other two

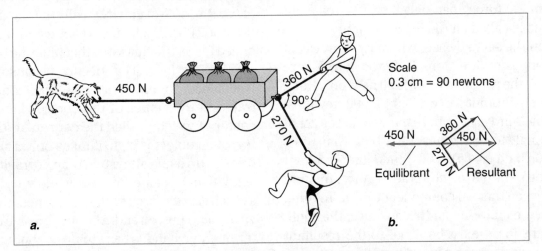

Figure 24-6. Forces acting at an angle produce a resultant force that acts in a direction between the component forces.

sides of the parallelogram by drawing and connecting lines equal to and parallel to each of the vectors. From the point representing the cart, draw the diagonal of the parallelogram as a solid line and place an arrowhead at the end of it. This line represents the resultant force produced by the component forces. The arrowhead shows the direc-tion of the resultant force and the direction in which the cart will move.

To determine the magnitude of the resultant force, measure the length of the diagonal and compare it to your scale. In this problem, the diagonal is 1.5 centimeters long. Since your scale is 0.3 centimeter = 90 newtons, the resultant force is 450 newtons.

What Is Equilibrium?

In the three cases studied so far involving a cart pulled by two people, the cart moved in some direction because the forces acting upon it were unbalanced. An unbalanced force always produces motion. This means that the resultant force was strong enough to move the cart in some direction. If the combinations of forces acting on the cart had been balanced somehow, the cart would not have moved. When a set of balanced forces acts on an object but does not move it, the object is said to be in a state of **equilibrium**.

In the first case, where two forces act in the same direction, you found the resultant force of the two component forces to be 630 newtons (refer back to Figure 24-4). It is easy to see that a 630-newton force acting in the opposite direction to that of the resultant force would put the cart in a state of equilibrium. A force that balances the resultant force is called an *equilibrant* force.

In the second case, where two forces act in opposite directions (refer back to Figure 24-5), the resultant force is 90 newtons. Here, the equilibrant force would be 90 newtons. In the third case, where the two forces act at an angle to each other (refer back to Figures 24-6a and 24-6b), you found the resultant force to be 450 newtons acting in a direction between the two component forces. To bring about equilibrium in this instance, the equilibrant force must be equal to the resultant force and must act in a direction exactly opposite to that of the resultant force as also shown in the figure. In the figure, the equilibrant force is provided by the dog.

▶ What Is the Center of Gravity?

Some objects in equilibrium are easily upset when even a small unbalanced force acts on them. For example, a book standing on its end on a table does not move because it is in equilibrium. When the book is tipped slightly and released, it moves, falls on its face, and stops moving. The book reaches a state of equilibrium again but in a new position. When standing on an end, the book is said to be in **unstable equilibrium**. A book lying on its face is very difficult to upset. When the book is pushed, it moves but does not tip over. In this condition, the book is said to be in **stable equilibrium**.

Tipping the book results in its falling because the force of gravity (really the weight of the book) has a chance to act as an unbalanced force. It is this force that pulls the book over on its face. This occurs because the weight of the book acts as though it is concentrated in the center of the book. When the center of weight, called the **center of gravity**, of an object is high, it takes only a slight force to tip it and allow the force of gravity to act. When the center of gravity is low, it takes a much greater force to change the position of an object. Thus, on end, a book has a high center of gravity and is easy to upset, but on its face, it has a low center of gravity and is difficult to upset. Similarly, a tall truck rounding a curve at high speed may overturn because its center of gravity is high and is unstable. On the other hand, a sports or race car, having a low center of gravity, hugs the road. Such cars are less likely to overturn on sharp curves because they are more stable than tall trucks.

Because the weight of an object is concentrated in its center of gravity, it is possible to balance any object on a point or pivot if the point is placed directly in line with the center of gravity of the object. Balanced in this way, the object is in a state of equilibrium. If you use your finger as a pivot under the 50-centimeter mark of a meterstick, the stick is in balance. If you try to balance the stick at any other point—the 40-centimeter mark, for example—you will find that you cannot do it successfully. The reason is that the weight of the meter stick, concentrated at the midpoint of the stick, pulls one end of the stick downward and unbalances the forces acting on the stick. After determining the center of gravity of an object with either a regular or irregular shape, you can then balance the object on a point or pivot.

Finding the Center of Gravity of Regular Objects. You can find the center of gravity of a regular object such as a square or rectangular board by locating the center point of the object. As shown in Figure 24-7, you can find this point by drawing diagonal lines on the object. The point at which the two lines cross is the center point of the object. To test this point as the location of the center of gravity, try to balance the object at this point on a fingertip or any other suitable pivot.

Finding the Center of Gravity of Irregular Objects. You can find the center of gravity of a flat, irregular object as follows:

1. Attach a mass, such as a heavy washer or nut, to a string. When the mass is freely suspended on the string, it points to Earth's center. The line with a mass attached to it in this way is called a **plumb line**, shown in Figure 24-8a.

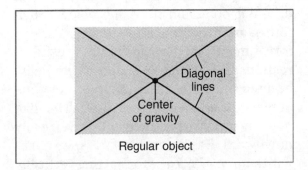

Figure 24-7. The center of gravity of a regular object can be found by drawing diagonal lines.

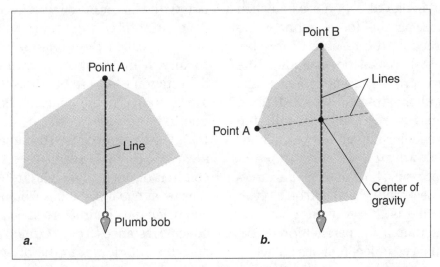

Figure 24-8. The center of gravity of an irregular object can be found by suspending a mass.

2. As shown in Figure 24-8b, select any point A on the object and drive a small nail into this point. Tie a string to the nail and allow the object to swing freely. When the object comes to rest, suspend the weighted string from point A. With a pencil, draw a line from point A along the string to the other side of the object.

3. As shown in Figure 24-8b, repeat this procedure from point B (any other point on the object). When you draw the line from point B along the string, the two lines intersect, or cross, at the center of gravity.

4. Test this point as the location of the center of gravity by balancing the object at this point.

How Are Parallel Forces Described?

The combinations of forces you studied so far in this chapter have dealt with forces acting together on a single point. They were applied to the point from the same direction, from opposite directions, or at an angle to each other. In many instances, forces act together along parallel lines at different points on the same object. Such forces are called **parallel forces**. Parallel forces may act in the same or in opposite directions. For example, suppose two deliverymen carry a load of 450 newtons between them (see Figure 24-9). The 450-newton weight is a force acting vertically downward. Each man supports the weight with a force of 225 newtons acting vertically upward. Here, all three forces are parallel to one another, but one acts in a direction opposite to the other two. Whenever parallel forces acting in one direction are balanced by one or more parallel forces acting in the opposite direction, the resultant force becomes zero. In this case, the resultant of the total upward forces (225 newtons + 225 newtons) and the total downward force (450 newtons) is zero. As a result, the weight is in equilibrium and moves neither upward nor downward.

Parallel forces may act in the same direction on an object that is balanced on a pivot, or **fulcrum**, and is free to turn, or rotate, about the fulcrum. If the parallel forces are equal, the balanced object remains balanced and does not move. Such a situation is com-

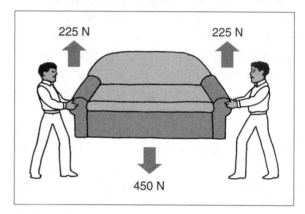

Figure 24-9. Parallel forces act on the same object at different points.

mon when two children of equal weight are placed on opposite sides of a seesaw at equal distances from the fulcrum. (See Figure 24-10a.) If the forces are unequal, the object is unbalanced and begins rotating in the direction of the larger of the two forces. The tendency of a force to produce rotation of an object is called the **moment of force**, or **torque**. If the rotation is toward the right, the rotation is said to be *clockwise* (see Figure 24-10b); if in the opposite direction, it is said to be *counterclockwise* (see Figure 24-10c). The rotation caused by unbalanced moments of force is readily seen when two children of unequal weight are placed on a seesaw at equal distances from the fulcrum and when the children are of equal weight at unequal distances from the fulcrum. In either case the rotation is in the direction of the greater moment of force.

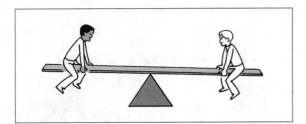

Figure 24-10a. Parallel forces are equal.

Figure 24-10b. Unequal parallel forces can have a clockwise moment.

Figure 24-10c. Unequal parallel forces can have a counterclockwise moment.

How Are Moments of Force Determined?

The moment of a force depends not only on the magnitude of the force but also on the distance of the force from the fulcrum. The moment is calculated by multiplying the force by this distance, thus:

$$\text{moment of force} = \text{force} \times \text{distance from fulcrum}$$

$$\text{moment} = F \times D$$

For example, to find the moment of force of a 5-newton force acting 3 meters from a

fulcrum, substitute these values in the formula, thus:

$$\text{moment} = F \times D$$

$$\text{moment} = 5 \text{ newtons} \times 3 \text{ meters}$$

$$\text{moment} = 15 \text{ newton-meters}$$

Note that the moment of force is expressed in "newton-meters," a unit that includes both the units of weight and distance.

Unequal Moments of Force

Follow along with the calculation of the moments when a 50-pound child sits on the left side of a seesaw and a 60-pound child sits on the right side, and the fulcrum is 5 feet from each child. The moment of force for the left side is:

$$\text{left-side moment} = F \times D$$

$$\text{left-side moment} = 50 \text{ pounds} \times 5 \text{ feet}$$

$$\text{left-side moment} = 250 \text{ pound-feet}$$

The moment of force for the right side is:

$$\text{right-side moment} = F \times D$$

$$\text{right-side moment} = 60 \text{ pounds} \times 5 \text{ feet}$$

$$\text{right-side moment} = 300 \text{ pound-feet}$$

In this case, the moment of force on the right side is greater, and the seesaw will rotate in a clockwise direction.

Using the same children, you can calculate the moments when the child on the left is 7 feet from the fulcrum and the one on the right is 3 feet from the fulcrum. The left-side moment is 50 pounds × 7 feet, or 350 pound-feet. The right-side moment is 60 pounds × 3 feet, or 180 pound-feet. Now the left-side moment is greater, and the seesaw will rotate in a counterclockwise direction.

Equal Moments of Force

When the clockwise and counterclockwise moments of force are equal, an object balanced on a fulcrum does not rotate—that is, the object is in equilibrium. This has been found to be true for a seesaw or any rod or plank in a similar situation. These facts are expressed as the **law of moments**. This law states that when a pivoted body is in equilibrium, the sum of the clockwise moments is equal to the sum of the counterclockwise moments. Expressed as a formula:

$$\text{clockwise moments} =$$
$$\text{counterclockwise moments}$$

$$F_1 \times D_1 = F_2 \times D_2$$

Observe how the law of moments operates. Suppose a 2-newton weight is hung on a steel rod 4 meters from a fulcrum and a 4-newton weight is hung on the other side of the fulcrum, but 2 meters away from it (see Figure 24-11). According to the law of moments,

$$F_1 \times D_1 = F_2 \times D_2$$

Substituting,

$$2 \text{ newtons} \times 4 \text{ meters} =$$
$$4 \text{ newtons} \times 2 \text{ meters}$$

$$8 \text{ newton-meters} = 8 \text{ newton-meters}$$

The relationship expressed in the law of moments enables you to find the weight of an unknown object when its distance from the fulcrum is known if you have another known weight whose distance from the fulcrum is also known. For example, a boy on a seesaw at equilibrium weighs 120 pounds. He is seated 3 feet from the fulcrum. A girl is

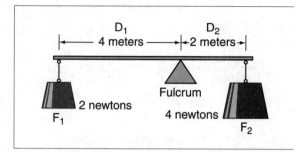

Figure 24-11. According to the law of moments, the sums of the clockwise and counterclockwise moments are equal.

seated 6 feet from the fulcrum. How much does the girl weigh?

$$\text{clockwise moments} =$$
$$\text{counterclockwise moments}$$

$$F_1 \times D_1 = F_2 \times D_2$$
$$120 \text{ pounds} \times 3 \text{ feet} = F_2 \times 6 \text{ feet}$$
$$360 \text{ pound-feet} = F_2 \times 6 \text{ feet}$$
$$F_2 = \frac{360 \text{ pound-feet}}{6 \text{ feet}} = 60 \text{ pounds}$$

The girl weighs 60 pounds.

Using the same formula, you can find one unknown distance when the other three values are known. For example, how far away from a fulcrum must a 225-newton child sit in order to balance her father, who weighs 675 newtons and who sits 1 meter from the fulcrum?

$$F_1 \times D_1 = F_2 \times D_2$$
$$225 \text{ newtons} \times D_1 = 675 \text{ newtons} \times 1 \text{ meter}$$
$$225 \text{ newtons} \times D_1 = 675 \text{ newton-meters}$$

$$D_1 = \frac{675 \text{ newton-meters}}{225 \text{ newtons}} = 3 \text{ meters}$$

Chapter Review

Science Terms

The following list contains all the boldfaced words found in this chapter and the page on which each appears.

center of gravity (p. 402)
component forces (p. 400)
elastic (p. 398)
equilibrium (p. 402)
force (p. 397)
fulcrum (p. 404)
law of moments (p. 406)
magnitude (p. 398)
moment of force (p. 404)
newton (p. 398)
parallel forces (p. 404)

parallelogram of force (p. 401)
plumb line (p. 403)
pound (p. 398)
resultant (p. 399)
scalar quantities (p. 398)
spring scale (p. 398)
stable equilibrium (p. 402)
torque (p. 404)
unstable equilibrium (p. 402)
vector quantities (p. 399)
vectors (p. 399)

Matching Questions

In your notebook, write the letter of the item in column B that is most closely related to the item in column A.

Column A
_____ 1. equilibrium
_____ 2. resultant
_____ 3. scalar quantity
_____ 4. magnitude
_____ 5. fulcrum
_____ 6. elastic
_____ 7. torque
_____ 8. newton
_____ 9. vector quantity
_____ 10. force

Column B
a. unit of force
b. capable of being stretched
c. a push or a pull
d. quantity that expresses both magnitude and direction
e. tendency of a force to produce rotation
f. state in which balanced forces on an object
g. pivot
h. size or amount
i. quantity that measures an amount or magnitude only
j. single force produced by a combination of forces

Multiple-Choice Questions

In your notebook, write the letter preceding the word or expression
that best completes the statement or answers the question.

1. How is a force best defined?
   a. the amount of matter in an object
   b. a push or pull on an object
   c. the ability to return to normal after
      being disturbed
   d. the center of an object's weight

2. Which of the following does not create a
   force?
   a. magnetism   c. electrical charges
   b. gravity   d. scalar

3. When several forces act on an object and
   the object does not move, the forces are
   said to be
   a. balanced   c. stable
   b. unbalanced   d. unstable

4. The force exerted by gravity on a mass is
   known as
   a. density   c. weight
   b. volume   d. specific gravity

5. Which of the following is *not* a scalar
   quantity?
   a. density   c. velocity
   b. volume   d. mass

6. When a vector represents a force, what
   does the length of the vector indicate?
   a. magnitude
   b. direction
   c. magnitude and direction
   d. force

7. A single force that results from a combination of several forces is called
   a. a component   c. an equilibrant
   b. a vector   d. a resultant

8. Two forces that act on an object in the
   same direction
   a. subtract from one another
   b. add together

   c. multiply together
   d. cancel out

9. Using a scale of 0.6 cm = 90 N, the
   number of newtons represented by a
   vector 3 cm long is
   a. 45   c. 225
   b. 180   d. 450

10. When two forces act on an object in oppo-
    site directions, the resultant force is equal
    to the
    a. sum of the forces
    b. product of the forces
    c. difference between the forces
    d. ratio of the forces

11. When two forces, A and B, act on an
    object at an acute angle, the resultant
    force
    a. acts in the direction of A
    b. acts in the direction of B
    c. acts opposite to A
    d. lies between A and B

12. When balanced forces act on an object
    and do not move it, the object is said to
    be in a state of
    a. equilibrium   c. instability
    b. stability   d. torque

13. An equilibrant force is
    a. of the same magnitude and direction as
       the resultant
    b. of different magnitude but the same
       direction as the resultant
    c. of the same magnitude but opposite
       direction as the resultant
    d. of different magnitude and direction as
       the resultant

14. A force of 200 N is exerted to the left on an object. A force of 170 N is exerted to the right on the object. What is the resultant force?
    a. 30 N to the right
    b. 30 N to the left
    c. 370 N to the right
    d. 370 N to the left

15. The point at which the weight of an object seems to be concentrated is the
    a. fulcrum
    b. center of gravity
    c. equilibrium point
    d. moment

16. The center of gravity of a regular object can be found by
    a. measuring the length of a plumb line
    b. determining where the diagonals intersect
    c. comparing distances to the fulcrum
    d. adding all forces acting on the object

17. A point around which an object can rotate is known as the
    a. stability point
    b. center
    c. pivot
    d. center of gravity

18. If equal but opposite parallel forces act on an object, the object
    a. rotates clockwise
    b. does not move
    c. rotates counterclockwise
    d. rotates clockwise and counterclockwise

19. The moment of a force represents its tendency to
    a. remain stationary
    b. move in a straight line
    c. rotate
    d. accelerate

20. When the clockwise moment of force is greater than the counterclockwise moment of force on an object, what happens to the object?
    a. It rotates in a clockwise direction.
    b. It rotates in a counterclockwise direction.
    c. It does not move.
    d. It rotates clockwise and counterclockwise.

Modified True-False Questions

In some of the following statements, the italicized term makes the statement incorrect. For each incorrect statement, in your notebook, write the term that must be substituted for the italicized term to make the statement correct. For each correct statement, write the word "true."

1. When two forces acting on an object are unequal, the forces are said to be *unbalanced.* _____

2. In the SI system, the standard unit of force is the *pound.* _____

3. A device that can be used to measure the magnitude of a force is a *meterstick.* _____

4. Quantities that describe both magnitude and direction are called *scalar quantities.* _____

5. An arrow that is often used to represent a force is known as a *vector.* _____

6. The forces on an object that produce a resultant force are called *component forces.* _____

7. To determine the exact magnitude and direction of a resultant force, you can construct a *triangle.* _____

8. A force that is equal to a resultant force in magnitude but is opposite in direction is called a *moment*. _____

9. The moment of force depends on the magnitude of the force and its *direction*. _____

10. Forces acting in the same direction but at different points on an object are called *vertical forces*. _____

TEST-TAKING TIP Draw any vector diagrams neatly so you can quickly identify the magnitude and direction of each arrow.

Check Your Knowledge
Write the answer to each question in your notebook.

1. Define a force in your own words. Give an example of a force, and indicate the units in which forces are measured in both the English and SI systems.

2. Differentiate between a scalar quantity and a vector quantity, and give an example of each.

3. Relate the terms equilibrium, stable equilibrium, and unstable equilibrium.

4. Explain how to find the center of gravity of an irregular object.

Think Critically
Write the answer to each of the following questions in your notebook.

1. Solve each of the following problems involving combinations of forces:
   a. Two people pull on an object in the same direction, one with a force of 180

newtons and the other with a force of 225 newtons. Find the resultant force.
   b. A girl (*A*) pulls on an object with a force of 270 newtons. A second girl (*B*) pulls on an object with a force of 180 newtons in the opposite direction. Find the resultant force and direction.

2. Two boys pull on an object using ropes fixed at the same point. One boy pulls with a force of 60 newtons (north); the second with a force of 80 newtons (east). The angle between the ropes is 90°. Find the resultant force and direction using the parallelogram method.

3. a. Find the moment of force created when a force of 30 newtons is exerted at a distance of 4 meters from the fulcrum.
   b. Find the moment of force created when a force of 600 pounds is exerted at a distance of 8 feet from the fulcrum.

4. Using the law of moments, solve each of the following problems:
   a. A 100-pound bag is placed on a seesaw at a distance of 8 feet from the fulcrum. How far on the other side of the fulcrum must a 200-pound man sit to balance the seesaw?
   b. A 20-newton weight is hung 4 meters from the fulcrum. A second weight balances the first when it is placed at a distance of 5 meters on the other side of the fulcrum. How heavy is the second weight?

Take It Further

1. One way to add vectors is to place them head-to-tail. Find out what this method is and create a presentation showing how to add vectors in this way.

2. Research additional information about the center of gravity of objects. Prepare a demonstration to show the center of gravity for a specific object and then compare how the center of gravity can change as the size or shape of the object changes.

3. Many scientists, including Albert Einstein, spend their entire careers trying to describe all the forces in the universe as simply as possible. In other words, they have tried to unify all forces into a single force. Research the fundamental forces that have been so far described. Write a brief report describing the forces.

CAREER

4. Athletes use forces all the time to move, or prevent the motion of, various objects. One athlete that needs a thorough understanding of forces is a golfer. Research how an athlete might become a professional golfer. Find out what experience might be required and what organizations such an athlete can join.

25

How Is Work Related to Machines?

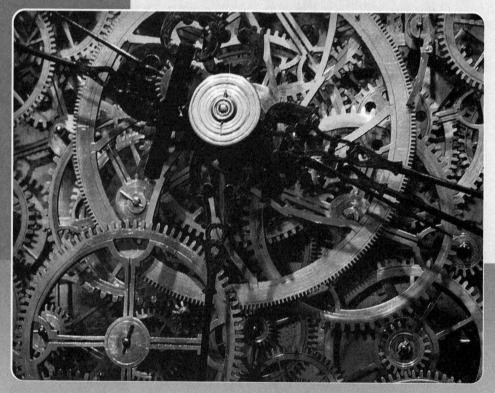

As the one clock gear turns, it makes the others turn as well. Clock gears are a type of simple machine that makes work easier to do.

After reading this chapter, you should be able to answer the following questions:

What is work?

How can you make work easier?

What is the law of machines?

What is mechanical advantage?

What is efficiency?

What is power?

What are the six simple machines?

There is always plenty of work to be done. Simple machines can make the job easier to do. In this inquiry investigation, you will find out just what simple machines do.

Materials:
- ✔ safety goggles
- ✔ 1-kilogram mass
- ✔ spring scale
- ✔ meterstick
- ✔ 2 pulleys
- ✔ rope
- ✔ Hall's carriage
- ✔ inclined plane
- ✔ ring stand with clamp

Part A Place a 1-kilogram mass on your desk. Attach a spring scale to the mass. Lift the mass to a height of 30 centimeters above the table. Observe the reading on the spring scale.

1. What force did you use to lift the mass?

Part B Assemble the rope and pulleys as shown in Figure 25-1. The upper pulley should be at least 1 meter above the table. Attach the 1-kilogram mass to the lower pulley. Attach the spring scale to the free end of the rope. Pull straight down on the spring scale until you have raised the mass 30 centimeters above the table. Observe the reading on the spring scale.

2. What force did you use to lift the mass 30 centimeters?

3. What is the purpose of a pulley system in lifting masses?

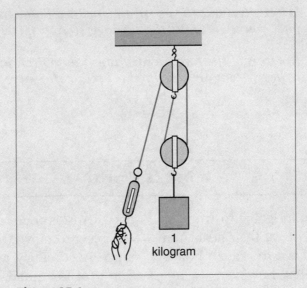

1 kilogram

Figure 25-1.

Part C Attach the small cart (Hall's carriage) to the end of the spring scale and lift it 30 centimeters above the table. Observe the reading on the spring scale.

4. What force did you use to lift the cart?

Part D As shown in Figure 25-2, set up an inclined plane to which a pulley is attached, so that the pulley end of the plane is 30 centimeters above the table. Attach one end of a string to the Hall's carriage and attach the other end of the string to the spring scale. Lay the string over the wheel of the inclined plane.

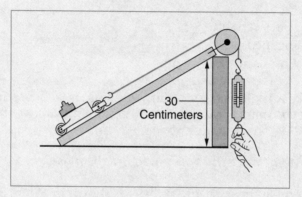

Figure 25-2.

Slowly pull straight down on the spring scale with enough force to pull the Hall's carriage to the top of the inclined plane. Pull on the scale with a steady, constant force. Observe the reading on the spring scale as you pull.

5. What force did you use to lift the carriage to the top of the inclined plane?

6. What effect did the use of the inclined plane have on the amount of force you used to lift the carriage 30 centimeters?

7. In terms of the force needed to lift an object, in what way are the pulley system and the inclined plane the same?

What Is Work?

People may say they are going to work or that they are doing work at their desk. You might feel that you have too much homework. These examples, however, do not qualify as work in a scientific sense. In science, **work** is done only when a force causes an object to move through a particular distance. Accordingly, work involves (1) the action of a force and (2) a specific distance through which the force acts.

Mathematically, work can be defined as the product of the force and the distance through which this force acts in moving the object. As an equation,

$$\text{work} = \text{force} \times \text{distance}$$

or

$$W = F \times D$$

When force is measured in newtons and the distance is measured in meters, the unit of work is the **newton-meter**, also called the *joule*. One newton-meter is the amount of work performed when a force of 1 newton is exerted through a distance of 1 meter. For example, a student does 1 newton-meter of work when he lifts a 1-newton weight from a table to a height of 1 meter above the table.

Now suppose a girl pushes a sled with a force of 180 newtons across a distance of 3 meters. How much work has she done? Substitute the given values into the formula,

$$W = F \times D$$

$$W = 180 \text{ newtons} \times 3 \text{ meters}$$

$$= 540 \text{ newton-meters}$$

The girl does 540 newton-meters of work.

In the English system, the unit of work is the **foot-pound**. Suppose, for example, a man lifts a 100-pound weight to a height of 6 feet. The amount of work performed by the man is

$$W = F \times D$$

$$W = 100 \text{ pounds} \times 6 \text{ feet}$$

$$= 600 \text{ foot-pounds}$$

▶ How Can You Make Work Easier?

When you do work to move an object, you exert a force called the **effort force**. The force the effort force overcomes in moving the object is called the **resistance force**. A **machine** is a device that makes it easier to do work by changing the direction of the effort force, decreasing the effort force required, or decreasing the distance over which the effort force is exerted. Notice that a machine does not change the amount of work you do. It changes the way you do work.

When discussing work, it is common practice to replace the terms *effort force* and *resistance force* with *effort* and *resistance*. This practice will be followed for the remainder of the chapter.

A machine that consists of just a single part, or a combination of a few parts, is called a simple machine. In the inquiry investigation, you studied how some simple machines reduced effort force. You compared the effort required with and without pulleys and inclined planes. Consider the following example to see mathematically how a simple machine can decrease the effort required. To lift a 2000-newton piano to a height of 10 meters, a piano mover may use a set of pulleys arranged in a certain way. When he pulls on the pulley rope, he raises the piano by exerting a force of 500 newtons, which is much less than the weight of the piano. Because the piano is raised 10 meters, you know that 2000 newtons × 10 meters, or 20,000 newton-meters, of work is done. Although the man's effort is only 500 newtons, he still does 20,000 newton-meters of work. To accomplish this, he must pull the rope a distance of 40 meters:

$$W = F \times D$$

$$W = 500 \text{ newtons} \times 40 \text{ meters}$$

$$= 20,000 \text{ newton-meters}$$

The amount of work done in raising the piano to a particular height is the same whether the work is done by the piano mover's unaided muscles or by the mover and his pulleys and rope. However, the set of pulleys decreases the effort needed by increasing the distance over which the effort is applied.

What Is the Law of Machines?

Now you know that, although machines may decrease effort, they do not decrease work. You cannot get more work out of a machine than you put into it. The actual work put into a machine is called the **work input**. The actual work accomplished by using a machine is called the **work output**. In an ideal machine, the work input equals the output.

The work output is the product of the resistance multiplied by the distance through which the resistance is moved. Work input is the product of the effort multiplied by the distance through which the effort moves. Accordingly, the **law of machines** can be expressed as either of the following relationships:

$$\text{work output} = \text{work input}$$

$$\text{resistance} \times \text{resistance distance} =$$
$$\text{effort} \times \text{effort distance}$$

Using the symbols R for resistance, D_R for resistance distance, E for effort, and D_E for effort distance, the relationship may be written as

$$R \times D_R = E \times D_E$$

Looking at this relationship, you can quickly see that the products of force and distance must be equal. If force is magnified, distance must be reduced. If distance is magnified, force must be reduced. If only direction is changed, force and distance must stay the same.

What Is Mechanical Advantage?

The benefit of using a machine is called **mechanical advantage**. The mechanical advantage of a machine is the number of times that it multiplies the effort. Thus, a mechanical advantage of 3 indicates that a machine multiplies the applied force, or effort, three-fold. An effort of 30 pounds can therefore overcome a resistance of 90 pounds.

For some machines, the mechanical advantage is a fraction, such as $\frac{1}{2}$. What would be the advantage of using a machine that actually reduces the effort force? These machines multiply distance. For example, if you have ever used a rake you know that you move the handle a short distance while the other end of the rake moves a longer distance. In this way, the rake makes cleaning up leaves easier.

What does it mean if a machine has a mechanical advantage of 1? It means that the machine does not change the amount of effort force. Instead, it changes the direction in which the effort force is exerted. For example, pulling down on the rope of a pulley is often easier than pulling up.

Ideal Mechanical Advantage. In any real machine, some of the effort applied is lost (wasted) in overcoming friction. In a system of pulleys, for example, the rope rubs against the pulley wheels and the wheels themselves create friction as they turn on their axles. Overcoming friction uses up some of the energy of motion and transforms it into heat energy. This loss of energy due to friction can never be completely reversed in a practical machine. In theory, a machine that is completely frictionless is called an **ideal machine**. While such a machine does not exist, the concept is useful in calculating the theoretical mechanical advantage of various simple machines. The mechanical advantage of an ideal machine is called the **ideal mechanical advantage**. You can find the ideal mechanical advantage (IMA) by dividing the distance the effort moves (D_E) by the distance the resistance moves (D_R):

$$\text{ideal mechanical advantage} = \frac{\text{effort distance}}{\text{resistance distance}}$$

$$IMA = \frac{D_E}{D_R}$$

Actual Mechanical Advantage. The mechanical advantage of a real machine is called the **actual mechanical advantage** (*AMA*). The actual mechanical advantage of a machine, which can be found only experimentally, is determined by dividing the resistance by the actual effort used:

$$\text{actual mechanical advantage} = \frac{\text{resistance}}{\text{effort (actual)}}$$

$$AMA = \frac{R}{E_{actual}}$$

Suppose a woman uses a pulley system to lift a 300-pound safe to a height of 10 feet. Her effort is 120 pounds, and 30 feet of rope pass through her hands. In the absence of friction, you can find the ideal mechanical advantage from the equation

$$IMA = \frac{D_E}{D_R}$$

Because the effort distance is 30 feet and the resistance distance is 10 feet,

$$IMA = \frac{30 \text{ feet}}{10 \text{ feet}} = 3$$

To find the effort the woman *should* use (the ideal effort), use the formula

$$IMA = \frac{R}{E}$$

The resistance (*R*) is 300 pounds and the *IMA* is 3. Thus,

$$3 = \frac{300 \text{ pounds}}{E}$$

$$E = 100 \text{ pounds}$$

In theory, the woman should use 100 pounds of effort to lift the 300-pound safe. In reality, however, the pulley system is not frictionless

and some effort is wasted. Therefore, the actual effort used by the woman is 120 pounds. To calculate the actual mechanical advantage, use the equation

$$AMA = \frac{R}{E_{actual}}$$

$$AMA = \frac{300 \text{ pounds}}{120 \text{ pounds}} = 2.5$$

In the preceding example, note that the *IMA* is 3 and the *AMA* is 2.5. In the rest of this chapter, you will be concerned mainly with the ideal mechanical advantage. Keep in mind that the ideal mechanical advantage is always somewhat greater than the actual mechanical advantage due to friction.

▶ **What Is Efficiency?**

The effectiveness of a machine is expressed as a percentage called **efficiency**. The efficiency of a machine is calculated by dividing its actual mechanical advantage by its ideal mechanical advantage. Because the efficiency of a machine is expressed as a percent, you must multiply this ratio by 100%. Thus,

$$\text{efficiency} = \frac{AMA}{IMA} \times 100\%$$

The efficiency of any ideal machine is 100% because the *AMA* and *IMA* are equal. This means that no effort is wasted in overcoming friction. If, for example, the actual and ideal mechanical advantages were each 3, then

$$\text{efficiency} = \frac{AMA}{IMA} = \frac{3}{3} \times 100\%$$
$$= 1 \times 100 = 100\%$$

Because friction cannot be completely eliminated in any known machine, the actual mechanical advantage is always less than the ideal mechanical advantage and the resulting efficiency is always less than 100%. In the pulley system of the last example, you find the efficiency thus:

$$\text{efficiency} = \frac{AMA}{IMA} \times 100\%$$

$$\text{efficiency} = \frac{2.5}{3} \times 100 = 0.833 \times 100\%$$
$$= 83.3\%$$

What Is Power?

Like the term *work*, the term *power* has both an everyday meaning and a scientific meaning. When people speak about power in everyday life, they generally refer to great strength or authority. The scientific meaning of **power**, however, is the speed, or rate, of doing work. In other words, power is the amount of work (*W*) performed in a given time period (*T*). Expressed as an equation,

$$\text{power} = \text{work per time} = \frac{\text{work}}{\text{time}}$$

$$P = \frac{W}{T}$$

Because work may be expressed as force multiplied by distance,

$$\text{power} = \frac{\text{force} \times \text{distance}}{\text{time}}$$

$$P = \frac{F \times D}{T}$$

In the English system of measurement, power is expressed in foot-pounds per second or horsepower. One **horsepower** is equal to 550 foot-pounds of work done in 1 second. In the SI system, power is expressed in **watts** or kilowatts (1000 watts). One newton-meter per second is equal to one watt. One horsepower equals 746 watts.

Follow along to find the power of a machine that exerts a force of 1100 newtons in lifting an object to a height of 10 meters in 2 seconds.

$$P = \frac{F \times D}{T}$$

Substituting *F* = 1100 newtons, *D* = 10 meters, and *T* = 2 seconds,

$$P = \frac{1100 \text{ newtons} \times 10 \text{ meters}}{2 \text{ seconds}}$$
$$= \frac{11,000 \text{ newtons-meters}}{2 \text{ seconds}}$$
$$P = 5500 \frac{\text{newtons-meters}}{\text{second}}$$

or 5500 newton-meters per second or 5500 watts (or 5.5 kilowatts)

What Are the Six Simple Machines?

Even the most complex machines used in industry are based on six simple machines, used either individually or in combination. You have already been introduced to some of them. The six basic simple machines are the inclined plane, the lever, the pulley, the wheel-and-axle, the wedge, and the screw.

The Inclined Plane. Imagine having to lift a heavy box up into a moving truck. If you were to lift the box, you would have to exert an effort equal to the weight of the box over a distance equal to the height of the truck. It would be easier to slide the box up a ramp. A ramp is an example of an **inclined plane**.

As shown in Figure 25-3, the distance through which the resistance moves (D_R) is the height of the inclined plane (*h*) above its lowest point. The distance through which the effort moves (D_E) is the length of the inclined plane (*l*). Recall that the ideal mechanical advantage of a machine is found by dividing resistance distance into effort distance:

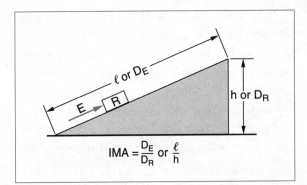

Figure 25-3. An inclined plane magnifies force by exerting the effort over a longer distance.

$$IMA = \frac{D_E}{D_R}$$

Accordingly, the ideal mechanical advantage of the inclined plane is found by dividing the length of the plane by the height to which the object is raised. Thus,

$$IMA \text{ (inclined plane)} = \frac{\text{length of plane}}{\text{height of plane}}$$

$$IMA = \frac{l}{h}$$

As applied to the inclined plane, the law of machines can be expressed as follows:

work output = work input

$$R \times h = E \times l$$

By means of the formulas for ideal mechanical advantage and the law of machines, you can find the effort needed to push heavy objects up a frictionless inclined plane. Suppose two people expect to push a 500-pound steel safe up a 10-foot inclined plane to a height of 2 feet. What effort would they exert if there were no friction?

By substituting the given information into the formula for the law of machines, you can find the ideal effort required to push the safe up the plane:

$$R \times h = E \times l$$

$$500 \text{ pounds} \times 2 \text{ feet} = E \times 10 \text{ feet}$$

$$1000 \text{ foot-pounds} = E \times 10 \text{ feet}$$

$$E = \frac{1000 \text{ foot-pounds}}{10 \text{ feet}} = 100 \text{ pounds}$$

Because some effort will be wasted in overcoming friction, the actual effort will be somewhat greater than 100 pounds.

In a case like this, you can determine the effort needed in another way. The mechanical advantage of inclined plane indicates by how much the machine multiplies effort.

First, find the ideal mechanical advantage of this inclined plane by dividing its length by its height:

$$IMA = \frac{l}{h}$$

$$IMA = \frac{10 \text{ feet}}{2 \text{ feet}} = 5$$

Therefore, you can find the effort by dividing the resistance (500 pounds) by the mechanical advantage (5):

$$E = \frac{500 \text{ pounds}}{5} = 100 \text{ pounds}$$

▶ **The Lever**

A **lever** consists of a rigid bar that can turn about a fixed point called a fulcrum. When effort is applied to one end of the bar, it causes the bar to rotate and move a resistance that is located at some other part of the bar. Examples of the lever and fulcrum were considered in the discussion of moments of force in Chapter 24. Levers are perhaps the oldest of the simple machines. They were used by ancient people to move large objects, such as boulders.

There are three kinds, or classes, of levers, depending on the location of the effort, the fulcrum, and the resistance (see Figure 25-4).

In a **first-class lever**, the fulcrum lies between the effort and the resistance. In this type of lever, both the effort and the resistance act in the same direction (see Figure 25-4a). Examples of first-class levers are a seesaw, a balance scale, and a pair of pliers.

In a **second-class lever**, the resistance lies somewhere between the effort and the fulcrum. In this case, the effort and resistance act in opposite directions (see Figure 25-4b). A wheelbarrow and a nutcracker are examples of second-class levers.

In a **third-class lever**, the effort lies somewhere between the resistance and the fulcrum (see Figure 25-4c). Third-class levers

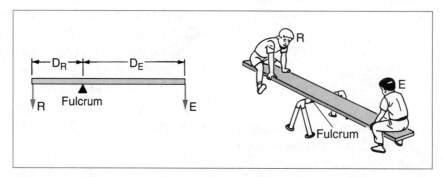

Figure 25-4a. A first-class lever has the fulcrum between the effort and the resistance.

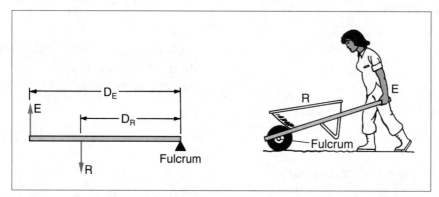

Figure 25-4b. A second-class lever has the fulcrum at the end with the resistance in the middle.

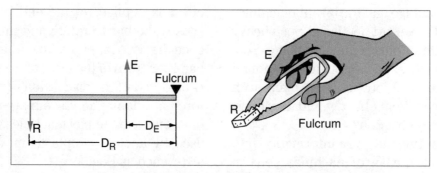

Figure 25-4c. A third-class lever multiplies distance rather than force.

require an effort that is greater than the resistance. However, they are useful because they allow you to increase the distance over which the resistance is moved. Some levers of this type allow you to grasp objects conveniently. The attachment of muscles in the human arm, a fishing pole, and sugar tongs are examples of third-class levers.

The ideal mechanical advantage of levers is found by applying the formula

$$IMA = \frac{D_E}{D_R}$$

$$IMA \text{ (lever)} = \frac{\text{effort distance from fulcrum}}{\text{resistance distance from fulcrum}}$$

$$IMA = \frac{l_E}{l_R}$$

Suppose the distance from the fulcrum to a resistance is 1 meter and the distance from the fulcrum to the effort is 2 meters. Substitute these figures in the formula:

$$IMA = \frac{l_E}{l_R}$$

$$IMA = \frac{2 \text{ meters}}{1 \text{ meter}} = 2$$

The *IMA* of this lever is 2.

The law of machines can be applied to problems concerning levers. For example, find the effort that should be exerted on a first-class lever to lift a 12-newton weight that is located 2 meters from the fulcrum. The effort is applied at a point 4 meters from the fulcrum (see Figure 25-5). Substituting in the formula for the law of machines:

$$R \times D_R = E \times D_E$$

$$12 \text{ newtons} \times 2 \text{ meters} = E \times 4 \text{ meters}$$

$$24 \text{ newton-meters} = E \times 4 \text{ meters}$$

$$E = \frac{24 \text{ newton-meters}}{4 \text{ meters}} = 6 \text{ newtons}$$

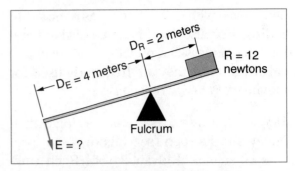

Figure 25-5. A lever problem involves comparing the distances between the forces and the fulcrum.

You can also calculate the effort by using the formula

$$IMA = \frac{l_E}{l_R}$$

In this case, l_E is 4 meters and l_R is 2 meters. Thus,

$$IMA = \frac{4 \text{ meter}}{2 \text{ meter}} = 2$$

Now, knowing the *IMA*, you can find the effort from the formula

$$IMA = \frac{R}{E}$$

$$2 = \frac{12 \text{ newtons}}{E}$$

$$2 \times E = 12 \text{ newtons}$$

$$E = 6 \text{ newtons}$$

This value of E agrees with the value found by using the law of machines.

▶ **Pulleys**

The simplest form of **pulley**, a single pulley, consists of a grooved wheel that can turn within a frame. Such a pulley can be used in two ways. When the pulley is attached to a fixed point, it is known as a **fixed pulley**. When the pulley is attached to the resistance and moves with it, it is known as a **movable pulley**. Because combinations of fixed and movable pulleys can provide large mechanical advantages, they are frequently used for moving very heavy objects.

Single Fixed Pulley. Used alone, a single fixed pulley and its rope (see Figure 25-6a) provide a mechanical advantage of 1. Such a machine makes it possible to apply an effort force in a convenient direction because pulling downward is easier than pulling upward. In this case, the resistance is supported by one strand of rope. In order to raise a weight of 100 pounds, a person must exert an effort of 100 pounds. As the weight rises 1 foot, 1 foot of rope passes through the person's hands. In effect, a single fixed pulley behaves like an equal arm lever. Single pulleys are often used to raise a flag up a pole or lift window blinds.

Single Movable Pulley. Although it may be uncomfortable to use, a single movable pulley (see Figure 25-6b) provides twice the mechanical advantage of the fixed pulley, or 2.

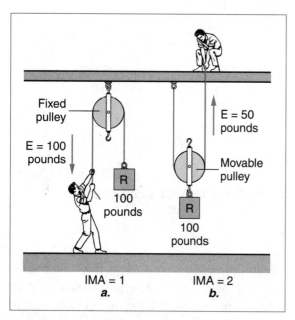

Figure 25-6. Single fixed pulleys change the direction of the effort force but do not multiply force or distance.

As the figure shows, one strand of rope is attached to a support and the other strand is pulled by the man. In this case, each strand of rope supports one-half the weight of the resistance. In order to raise the 100-pound weight 1 foot, the man need use an effort of only 50 pounds, but he must pull 2 feet of rope toward himself.

Combinations of Pulleys. To use the good points of both the fixed pulley and the movable pulley, the two are often used together. For example, several fixed and several movable pulleys may be threaded with one rope and used as a system or single unit. A block and tackle is an example of a combination of pulleys.

The mechanical advantage of any pulley system is found in one of two ways.

1. Because the resistance is supported by several strands of rope, counting the number of strands tells the ideal mechanical advantage. For example, suppose you need to find the mechanical advantage of a set of pulleys consisting of three fixed and two movable pulleys (Figure 25-7a). The effort is directed downward. You count five strands of rope supporting the resistance. (The sixth strand, along which the effort is directed, does *not* support the resistance.) The ideal mechanical advantage, therefore, is 5.

    The same mechanical advantage can be obtained using two fixed and two movable pulleys, shown in Figure 25-7b, providing the effort is directed upward. In this case, five strands support the resistance. In either case, the effort needed to lift a 400-pound object would be 400 pounds ÷ 5 = 80 pounds.
2. You can also use the formula

$$IMA = \frac{D_E}{D_R}$$

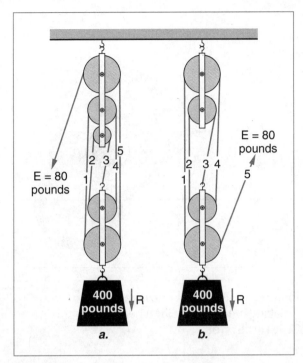

Figure 25-7. Combinations of pulleys take advantage of the best features of fixed and movable pulleys.

In either system of pulleys shown in the figures, you would pull 5 feet of rope in order to raise the resistance 1 foot.

Wheel-and-Axle

A **wheel-and-axle** consists of a large wheel and a smaller wheel, or axle, both firmly connected so that they turn together around the same center point (axis). The wheel-and-axle is used in an automobile steering wheel, a bicycle, a winch, and a doorknob. The effort can be applied to either the larger wheel or the smaller axle in this type of simple machine.

When a small force is applied to the wheel, the axle can exert a force greater than that applied to the wheel. When used in this way, the wheel-and-axle multiplies effort.

Because the effort distance is determined by the radius of the wheel, and the resistance distance is determined by the radius of the axle, the ideal mechanical advantage of the

wheel-and-axle is the radius of the larger wheel (R_{wheel}) divided by the radius of the axle (r_{axle}). Thus,

$$IMA \text{ (wheel-and-axle)} = \frac{\text{radius of wheel}}{\text{radius of axle}}$$

$$IMA = \frac{R_{wheel}}{r_{axle}}$$

A winch is a device that uses ropes to lift objects. Figure 25-8 shows a winch being used to lift a 75-newton pail of water from a well. The crank of this machine is really a rimless wheel consisting of only one spoke to which a horizontal handle has been attached. The radius of this wheel is 21 centimeters. The axle, or drum, on which the rope is wound, has a radius of 7 centimeters. To determine the ideal mechanical advantage,

$$IMA = \frac{R_{wheel}}{r_{axle}}$$

$$IMA = \frac{21 \text{ cm}}{7 \text{ cm}} = 3$$

Because the winch has an ideal mechanical advantage of 3, an effort of 25 newtons is required to lift the 75-newton weight.

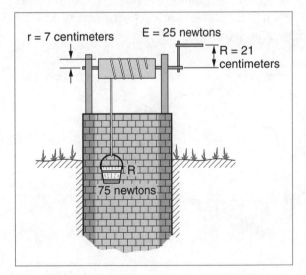

Figure 25-8. A winch uses a wheel-and-axle to magnify force.

When an effort is applied to an axle instead of to its wheel, the rim of the wheel turns a greater circular distance than the rim of the axle. As a result, distance is magnified. This form of a wheel-and-axle is useful in turning such objects as the blades of a ceiling fan or helicopter.

The Wedge

Perhaps you have seen a slanted object used to hold open a door. The device is a **wedge**, which is a double inclined plane. In using a wedge, you usually move the wedge rather than the resistance. For example, you pushed the wedge against the bottom of a door to hold it open. Other examples of wedges include axe heads, knife blades, chisels, and carpenter's nails. (See Figure 25-9.) The mechanical advantage of the wedge is found by dividing the length of the slope by the width of the wedge.

The Screw

Look closely at the end of a light bulb or the lid of a jar. They are screws, much like wood screws or metal screws. A **screw** can be thought of as an inclined plane that is wrapped around a cylinder or center rod. Figure 25-10 shows a type of screw known as a jackscrew.

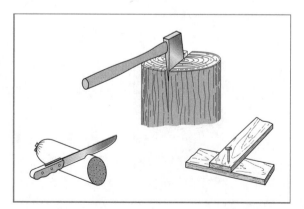

Figure 25-9. Wedges are thick at one end and taper off to a thinner end.

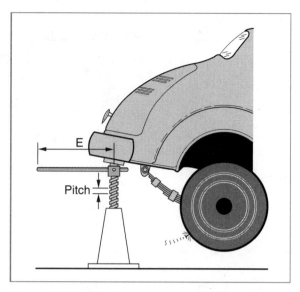

Figure 25-10. A jackscrew magnifies effort, making it possible to lift a heavy automobile with little effort.

The distance between two successive ridges, or threads, of a screw is called the **pitch** of the screw. When a screw is turned through one complete revolution, the screw advances a distance equal to its pitch. This is the distance through which the resistance moves. The effort E is applied to the jack through a long handle. Thus, a small effort moving through a large distance can move a large resistance through a small distance. In this manner, a jack multiplies effort.

Compound Machines

Many devices are made up of combinations of two or more simple machines. These types of machines, known as compound machines, make work easier by combining the advantages of individual simple machines. For example, a bicycle is an example of a compound machine. Each pedal is part of a wheel-and-axle. The hand brakes are levers. Screws are used to hold the parts together. A blender, a watch, and many tools are other examples of compound machines.

Chapter Review

Science Terms

The following list contains all the boldfaced words found in this chapter and the page on which each appears.

actual mechanical advantage (p. 417)

efficiency (p. 417)

effort force (p. 415)

first-class lever (p. 420)

fixed pulley (p. 422)

foot-pound (p. 415)

horsepower (p. 418)

ideal machine (p. 416)

ideal mechanical advantage (p. 416)

inclined plane (p. 418)

law of machines (p. 416)

lever (p. 419)

machine (p. 415)

mechanical advantage (p. 416)

movable pulley (p. 422)

newton-meter (p. 415)

pitch (p. 424)

power (p. 418)

pulley (p. 421)

resistance force (p. 415)

screw (p. 424)

second-class lever (p. 420)

third-class lever (p. 420)

watt (p. 418)

wedge (p. 424)

wheel-and-axle (p. 423)

work (p. 414)

work input (p. 416)

work output (p. 416)

Matching Questions

In your notebook, write the letter of the item in column B that is most closely related to the item in column A.

Column A

_____ 1. first-class lever

_____ 2. description of AMA

_____ 3. example of a wedge

_____ 4. third-class lever

_____ 5. example of an inclined plane

_____ 6. efficiency

_____ 7. ideal machine

_____ 8. watt

_____ 9. second-class lever

_____ 10. example of a wheel-and-axle

Column B

a. frictionless machine

b. ratio of the AMA to the IMA

c. doorknob

d. lever in which the fulcrum is between the effort and resistance

e. lever in which the effort is between the resistance and the fulcrum

f. ramp

g. lever in which the resistance is between the effort and fulcrum

h. axe head

i. always less than IMA

j. metric unit of power

Multiple-Choice Questions

*In your notebook, write the letter preceding the word or expression
that best completes the statement or answers the question.*

1. Work can be calculated by multiplying
   a. force by weight
   b. energy by height
   c. force by energy
   d. force by distance

2. How are simple machines helpful?
   a. They change the way work is done.
   b. They reduce the amount of work that is done.
   c. They eliminate friction from opposing work.
   d. They provide an effort force for doing work.

3. Which unit of measurement is the same as the newton-meter?
   a. foot-pound   c. watt
   b. degree   d. joule

4. How does a single fixed pulley make work easier to do?
   a. It changes the direction of the effort.
   b. It reduces the weight of the object being lifted.
   c. It decreases the effort required to lift an object.
   d. It reduces the distance over which the effort is exerted.

5. When doing work, if the effort required is reduced,
   a. there is no change in the distance moved
   b. the amount of work done decreases
   c. the distance over which it is exerted increases
   d. the distance over which it is exerted decreases

6. What is the ideal mechanical advantage of a single fixed pulley?
   a. –1   c. 1
   b. 0   d. 2

7. In an ideal machine, the work input is
   a. greater than the work output
   b. less than the work output
   c. equal to the work output
   d. always the same

8. The product of the resistance and the distance through which the resistance is moved is called the
   a. law of machines
   b. work input
   c. work output
   d. effort

9. When 30 pounds of effort are applied to a machine with a mechanical advantage of 3, the machine produces an effort of
   a. 10 pounds   c. 30 pounds
   b. 15 pounds   d. 90 pounds

10. Why is the actual mechanical advantage of a simple machine always lower than the ideal mechanical advantage?
    a. Some energy is wasted overcoming friction.
    b. Work is never performed as fast as it can be.
    c. Some parts are always missing.
    d. Simple machines never exist individually.

11. The actual mechanical advantage is found by dividing the resistance by the
    a. effort
    b. friction
    c. resistance distance
    d. effort distance

12. In a frictionless machine, the *IMA*
    a. is greater than the *AMA*
    b. is equal to the *AMA*
    c. is less than the *AMA*
    d. is greater than 0

13. What is the efficiency in a frictionless machine?
a. 0%   c. 50%
b. 25%   d. 100%

14. What is the efficiency of a machine for which the AMA is 3 and the IMA is 5?
a. 30%   c. 60%
b. 40%   d. 80%

15. What is power?
a. the rate of doing work
b. the amount of energy in an object
c. the product of force and distance
d. the ratio of effort to resistance

16. Which of the following is a measurement of power?
a. 30 joules   c. 550 watts
b. 90%   d. 600 foot-pounds

17. In an inclined plane, the distance through which the resistance moves
a. is the same as the length of the plane
b. is greater than the length of the plane
c. is the height of the plane
d. is less than the height of the plane

18. The effort needed to move an object on an inclined plane is found from the formula
a. D_R/IMA   c. E/AMA
b. D_E/IMA   d. R/IMA

19. Which is an example of a first-class lever?
a. seesaw
b. wheelbarrow
c. nutcracker
d. pair of sugar tongs

20. A lever in which the resistance lies somewhere between the effort and the fulcrum is
a. a first-class lever
b. a second-class lever
c. a third-class lever
d. none of these

21. Which is an example of a third-class lever?
a. wheelbarrow
b. pair of sugar tongs
c. pliers
d. nutcracker

22. Which statement is always true about the IMA of a third-class lever?
a. It is always less than 0.
b. It is always equal to 0.
c. It is always less than 1.
d. It is always equal to 1.

23. The ideal mechanical advantage of a pulley system can be found from the formula
a. D_R/D_E c. R/D_E
b. E/R   d. D_E/D_R

24. A simple machine used to steer a car is a
a. lever   c. pulley
b. wedge   d. wheel-and-axle

25. The ideal mechanical advantage of a wheel-and-axle equals
a. the radius of the larger wheel divided by the radius of the axle
b. the radius of the axle divided by the radius of the wheel
c. the effort divided by the resistance
d. the effort distance multiplied by the resistance distance

Modified True-False Questions

In some of the following statements, the italicized term makes the statement incorrect. For each incorrect statement, in your notebook, write the term that must be substituted for the italicized term to make the statement correct. For each correct statement, write the word "true."

1. The work input is the effort times the *resistance* distance._____

2. The actual work accomplished by a machine is called *work output*. _____

3. The equal nature of work input and work output of a machine is expressed in the *law of power*. _____

4. The effectiveness of a machine to reduce effort is expressed as a percentage called *efficiency*. _____

5. *Efficiency* is the rate at which work is done. _____

6. Both the effort and resistance act in the same direction in a *second*-class lever. _____

7. When a pulley is attached to the resistance and moves with it, the pulley is known as a *movable pulley*. _____

8. A modified double inclined plane describes a simple machine known as a *screw*. _____

9. An inclined plane that is wrapped around a cylinder is called a *wedge*. _____

10. The distance between two successive ridges of a screw is called the *pitch*. _____

TEST-TAKING TIP Draw out formulas on index cards as you study. Memorize formulas that you use often, and practice applying them to different situations. Make sure you are familiar with variables used to represent each quantity in a formula.

Check Your Knowledge

Write the answer to each question in your notebook.

1. A boy pushes against a wall with all his might, but the wall does not move. After several minutes, the boy is exhausted but no work was done. Why didn't he do any work even though he exerted a strong force?

2. How are machines helpful if they do not reduce the amount of work that is done?

3. How does the law of machines relate force and distance?

4. Why is the actual mechanical advantage always lower than the ideal mechanical advantage?

5. Complete the chart summarizing the types of simple machines.

Simple machine	IMA	Example
Inclined plane		
Lever		
Pulley		
Wheel-and-axle		

Think Critically

Write the answer to each of the following questions in your notebook.

1. a. Compute the work performed by a man who exerts 600 newtons of force on a sled and moves it 6 meters.
   b. 1000 foot-pounds of work are performed by a force of 50 pounds. Over what distance did the object move?

2. Calculate the effort needed to raise a resistance of 150 pounds using a winch. The radius of the wheel is 15 inches while the radius of the axle is 3 inches.

3. a. A 200-newton object is moved by a lever whose fulcrum is 1 meter from the object. The effort needed to move the object is exerted 2 meters on the

Chapter 25 • How Is Work Related to Machines? 429

other side of the fulcrum. What effort force was needed to move the object?

b. Find the ideal mechanical advantage of the lever used in question 3a.

4. Find the power developed when a force of 1100 newtons moves an object a distance of 20 meters in 2 seconds.

5. a. Find the effort necessary to move a 100-pound object up an inclined plane 20 feet long to a height of 4 feet.

   b. What is the *IMA* of the inclined plane?

Take It Further

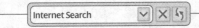

1. The metric unit of power is named after James Watt, who was a Scottish inventor and engineer. Research the life and work of James Watt and identify his contributions to society. Write an essay that begins, "James Watt changed history by . . ."

2. The human body consists of bones and muscles that form levers. Conduct research to find examples of each of the three types of levers in the human body. Prepare a diagram or computer presentation showing an example of each. Be able to describe how each lever operates to do work in the body.

CAREER

3. You may think that a career in fishing is far removed from the world of physical science, but it isn't. Combinations of pulleys known as a block-and-tackle are just one of the many tools used in recreational and commercial fishing. Research a career in fishing to find out what might be involved and what opportunities exist. You may wish to begin your research at the following sites: *http://fishingindustryjobs.com/* and *http://www.college-grad.com/careers/farmi.shtml.*

Robots: Is Bigger Better?

You can hold some simple machines in your hand. Imagine a machine so small that you could not even see it. Unlike a wheel-and-axle or a pulley, this tiny machine would be no bigger than a molecule and it would do work by moving atoms. You might even swallow this machine so that it could do work inside your body!

This amazing machine would be the product of a field generally known as nanotechnology. It involves building machines that are no more than a few nanometers wide—that's only 1×10^{-9} m! This technology might produce motors, robots, or even computers that are much smaller than a human cell.

Although tiny, these devices, often called nanorobots, could do work on a large scale. Groups of nanorobots could work together to assemble objects beginning with atoms and molecules. They could use basic ingredients to construct proteins, foods, and other materials essential to living things. They could carry medicines to the cells where they are needed. They might rebuild the ozone layer or remove contaminants from drinking water supplies.

Sound too good to be true? It just might be. Despite worldwide research, practical nanorobots are still years away, if they will ever become a reality. Part of the problem is that elements behave differently on a nanoscale than they do ordinarily. Researchers are still learning how the scale affects the result. For example, a particle might be toxic when reduced to the tiny scale. If used in medicine, the particle might do more harm than good. In addition, the technology is not yet developed to manufacture nanorobots on any large scale. Only primitive prototypes have been built and tested thus far.

Beyond scientific and technical challenges, nanotechnology poses social challenges as well. The use of nanorobots may lead to the construction of more powerful weapons that would need to be controlled. It will also have a tremendous impact on the world's economy. The idea of building anything people need with the click of a button may eliminate the manufacturing industry. It might even eliminate the need for money.

Opponents of the technology further argue that nanorobots pose a danger sometimes called the grey-goo scenario. They suggest that a swarm of nanorobots may get out of control and make endless copies of themselves. The robots will wind up replacing all living matter on Earth.

Other versions of the scenario describe the possibility that nanorobots either designed to act like living organisms or used to

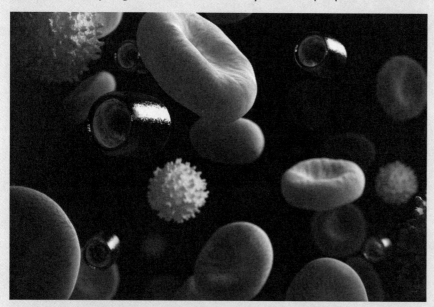

Figure 25-11. Alone, you can't even see them without a powerful microscope. Together, however, tiny robots in the blood such as these pictured by an artist can do amazing work.

change living organisms will replicate uncontrollably. They eliminate natural populations of organisms. This possibility is known as the green-goo scenario.

Proponents of nanotechnology assert that the doomsday concerns are pure science fiction. They counter that controls can be designed to prevent nanorobots from replicating out of control and from assuming lethal applications. Some suggest that the positive applications of nanotechnology far outweigh the risks. For now, all of this debate is purely hypothetical. Once the first actual nanorobot is constructed, however, many questions will need immediate answers. What do you think about it?

Organize It!

Use a method that your instructor describes to organize the information in this article.

Explain It!

1. Nanotechnology mainly involves building machines that
   a. are completely recyclable
   b. do not require energy sources
   c. are smaller than human cells
   d. can become organic

2. How might nanorobots be used in the medical field?
   a. They will replace doctors.
   b. They will carry medicine.
   c. They will be used as payment.
   d. They will become diseases.

3. Nanorobots might most immediately affect the world economy by
   a. replicating to form new robots
   b. developing toxic properties
   c. forming a new type of currency
   d. eliminating manufacturing jobs

Extend It!

4. The term nanotechnology was introduced in the 1980s by K. Eric Drexler. Do research to find out who Drexler is and what contributions he has made to the field of nanotechnology.

Internet Search

5. The National Nanotechnology Initiative has been developed to ensure responsible research into nanotechnology applications. Research the initiative to find out when it was established and what it entails. You may wish to begin your research at the following sites: *http://nano.gov/* and *http://www.nsf.gov/crssprgm/nano/*.

CAREER

6. Nanotechnology combines several fields, including computer science and artificial intelligence. Find out what training computer scientists have and how their expertise might be applied to the field of nanotechnology.

26

How Are Forces Related to Fluids?

A modern jet can soar through the sky because of its shape. Jets and other aircraft are designed so that air lifts them as they move.

After reading this chapter, you should be able to answer the following questions:

How are fluids described by density?

What is pressure?

What are the characteristics of liquid and gas pressure?

How is air pressure measured and used?

How is pressure affected by the motion of a fluid?

Why do some objects float and others sink?

A huge ship can float in water, yet a penny sinks to the bottom of a fountain. The properties of the object and the water determine whether an object will float or sink. In this inquiry investigation, you will compare what happens to two different objects when you place them in water.

Materials:
- ✔ safety goggles
- ✔ string
- ✔ small stone
- ✔ spring scale
- ✔ platform scale
- ✔ catch bucket
- ✔ overflow can
- ✔ water
- ✔ block of wood

Part A Tie a loop in one end of a piece of string. Tie the other end of the string around a small stone. Place the loop on the hook of a spring scale and weigh the stone (See Figure 26-1).

1. Record the weight of the stone.

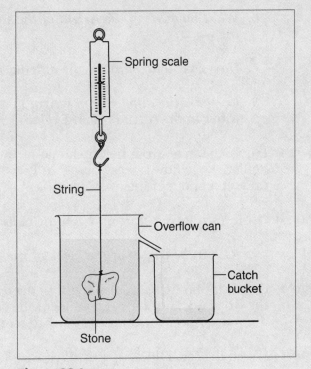

Figure 26-1.

Part B Using a platform scale, weigh an empty catch bucket.

> **2. Record the weight of the bucket.**

Part C Cover the spout of an overflow can with your finger. Fill the can with water up to the spout, remove your finger from the spout, and allow the excess water to drain into the catch bucket. Pour out the excess water and dry the catch bucket. Place the catch bucket under the spout of the overflow can.

Part D Suspend the small stone you weighed in Part A from the spring scale again. Gently lower the stone into the overflow can, taking care that the stone does not touch the sides or bottom of the can. Allow the overflow water to remain in the catch bucket.

> **3. Record the weight of the stone while it is submerged in the water.**

Part E Using the platform scale, weigh the catch bucket partly filled with water.

> **4. Record the weight of the catch bucket and water.**

Part F Find the weight of the water in the catch bucket by subtracting the weight of the empty bucket found in Part B from the weight found in Part E.

> **5. Record the weight of the water.**

> **6. What happens to the weight of the stone when it is submerged in the water?**

> **7. How do you account for the difference in weight?**

> **8. Compare the difference in weight of the stone with the weight of the water in the catch bucket. Explain your findings.**

Part G Empty the water from the catch bucket and dry the bucket thoroughly. Refill the overflow can as you did in Part C and place the catch bucket under the spout of the overflow can.

Part H Using a string as in Part A, weigh the block of wood.

> **9. Record the weight of the block of wood.**

Part I Gently lower the block of wood into the overflow can, taking care that the wood does not touch the sides of the can. Allow the wood to float on the water. Allow the overflow water to remain in the catch bucket.

Part J Weigh the catch bucket partly filled with water.

> **10. Record the weight of the catch bucket and water.**

Part K Find the weight of the water in the catch bucket by subtracting the weight found in Part B from the weight found in Part J.

11. *Record the weight of the water.*

12. *How does the weight of the displaced water compare with the weight of the block of wood?*

13. *Why do certain substances float in water but others sink?*

How Are Fluids Described by Density?

A solid, resting on a surface, presses down on the surface with a force equal to its own weight. Liquids and gases also have weight. Any substance that can flow, such as liquids and gases, is called a **fluid**. Like solids, fluids exert forces on other objects by pressing on them. Furthermore, fluids vary in the amount of force they can exert because of differences in their density.

Density is the mass of a substance per unit of volume.

$$\text{density} = \frac{\text{mass}}{\text{volume}}$$

If you use D to represent density, m to represent mass, and V to represent volume, the formula for density is

$$D = \frac{m}{V}$$

In the English system, density can be measured in pounds per cubic foot; in the SI system, density is often measured in grams per cubic centimeter. To find the density of a substance, you must know its mass and the volume it occupies. For example, suppose that a mass of 15 grams of a substance has a volume of 10 cubic centimeters. To find the density of this substance, you would substitute $m = 15$ grams and $V = 10$ cubic centimeters into the formula:

$$D = \frac{m}{V}$$

$$D = \frac{15 \text{ grams}}{10 \text{ cubic centimeters}}$$

$$D = 1.5 \frac{\text{grams}}{\text{cubic centimeter}}$$

or 1.5 grams per cubic centimeter.

Recall that changes in temperature affect the volume of a liquid and a gas. The density of a liquid or a gas therefore depends on temperature. In the following discussions of density, room temperature will be assumed unless otherwise noted.

In the study of the density of liquids, the density of water is generally used as the standard. The density of water is 1 gram per cubic centimeter in the SI system, and 62.4 pounds per cubic foot in the English system.

Fluids of greater density exert more force on a particular surface than those of lesser density. For example, mercury has a density of 13.6 grams per cubic centimeter compared to the same volume of water, which has a density of 1 gram per cubic centimeter.

Table 26-1.
What Is the Density of
Some Common Fluids?
(At Room Temperature)

Liquid	Density (grams per cubic centimeter)
Water	1.00
Seawater	1.025
Gasoline	0.68
Mercury	13.6
Ethyl alcohol	0.79

As a result, mercury exerts 13.6 times as much force on a given surface as the same volume of water. Table 26-1 gives the density of other common liquids.

What Is Pressure?

You might sometimes say that you feel the *pressure* or that you are under *pressure*. In science, pressure has a very specific meaning that is different from its everyday meaning. The **pressure** exerted by any substance—solid, liquid, or gas—is the amount of force exerted by that substance on a given unit of area. For example, consider a 10-pound rectangular block of metal with the following dimensions: length 10 inches, width 5 inches, thickness 1 inch (Figure 26-2a). When the block lies flat on a table, the area of the table supporting the block is 50 square inches (area of a rectangle is the product of the length and the width: 10 inches × 5 inches = 50 square inches). Because the block weighs 10 pounds, each square inch of the table covered by the block supports 1/5 of a pound:

$$\text{pressure} = \frac{10 \text{ pounds}}{50 \text{ square inches}}$$
$$= \frac{1}{5} \frac{\text{pound}}{\text{square inch}}$$
$$= 0.20 \text{ pound per square inch.}$$

Pressure is the amount of force on a given area, so you can also say that the block ex-

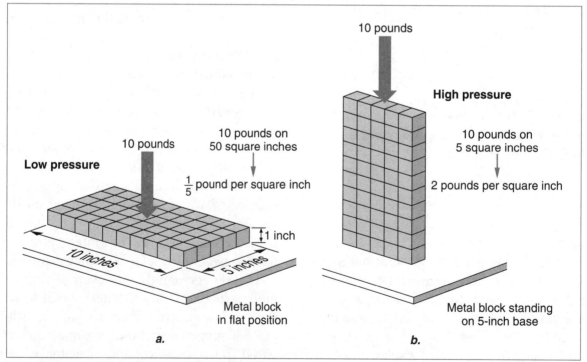

Figure 26-2. The pressure exerted by an object depends on force and area.

erts a pressure of $\frac{1}{5}$ pound on every square inch of the table.

When you stand the block on its 5-inch width, as shown in Figure 26-2b, it covers an area of only 5 square inches. Accordingly, because the weight of the block is still 10 pounds, each square inch of table covered by the block now supports 2 pounds:

$$pressure = \frac{10 \text{ pounds}}{5 \text{ square inches}} = 2 \frac{\text{pounds}}{\text{square inch}}$$
$$= 2 \text{ pounds per square inch.}$$

Thus, the pressure of the block in this position has increased to 2 pounds per square inch. Although the weight of the block of metal remains the same, the pressure it exerts has changed because its weight is now concentrated on a smaller area than before.

From this discussion you can see that pressure is equal to force divided by the area over which the force is spread. Thus,

$$pressure = \frac{\text{force}}{\text{area}}$$

When P represents pressure, F represents force, and A represents area,

$$P = \frac{F}{A}$$

In the English system, pressure is expressed in pounds per square foot or in pounds per square inch. In the SI system, pressure is expressed in grams per square centimeter or in newtons per square meter.

You may be surprised when you compare the pressure exerted on the ground by a woman wearing high heels with that exerted by a truck. If the woman weighs 100 pounds and balances herself on one heel, the area of which is 1 square inch, then the pressure on the ground will be

$$P = \frac{F}{A}$$

$$P = \frac{100 \text{ pounds}}{1 \text{ square inch}}$$

$$P = 100 \text{ pounds per square inch}$$

If the truck weighs 5 tons (10,000 pounds) and has four wheels, its weight will be distributed over the four tires, each of which may have a ground contact area of about 50 square inches. Together, the contact area of the four tires would be 4×50 square inches, or 200 square inches. Then, the pressure of the truck on the ground would be

$$P = \frac{F}{A}$$

$$P = \frac{10,000 \text{ pounds}}{200 \text{ square inches}}$$

$$P = 50 \text{ pounds per square inch}$$

A 100-pound woman can exert twice the pressure of a 5-ton truck!

How Is the Pressure of Liquids Described?

Liquids have weight. Thus, like solids, they exert pressure. You are probably familiar with water pressure because of its effect on your ears when you swim under water. As you go deeper in the water, the pressure increases and may cause discomfort to your eardrums. The pressure of water at great depths is so enormous that submarines and bathyscaphes are specially constructed to withstand it.

Experimentation has shown that, at different depths, the pressure of a liquid depends on two factors: the height of the liquid and its density. Consequently, the pressure exerted by a liquid is expressed by the equation

$$pressure = height \times density$$

When P is pressure, h is height, and D is density,

$$P = h \times D$$

As shown in Figure 26-3, an open cylinder contains a column of water 100 centimeters high. To find the pressure of the water on the bottom of the cylinder, recall that the density of water is 1 gram per cubic centimeter. By substituting this value for density,

$$P = h \times D$$

$$P = 100 \text{ centimeters} \times 1 \frac{\text{gram}}{\text{cubic centimeter}}$$

$$P = 100 \text{ grams per square centimeter}$$

Note: To calculate the units, write cubic centimeter as centimeter × centimeter × centimeter. (When you cube a number, you multiply it by itself three times.) Thus,

$$P = 100 \text{ cm} \times 1 \frac{\text{gram}}{\text{cm} \times \text{cm} \times \text{cm}}$$

$$= 100 \frac{\text{grams}}{\text{cm} \times \text{cm}}$$

$$= 100 \frac{\text{grams}}{\text{square centimeter}}$$

▶ What Are the Characteristics of Liquid Pressure?

A few simple experiments show the important characteristics of the pressure exerted by liquids.

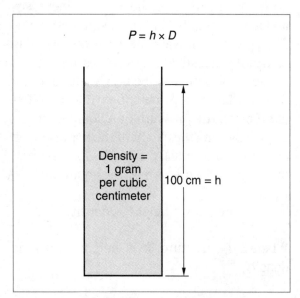

Figure 26-3. The pressure exerted by a column of liquid depends on its height and density.

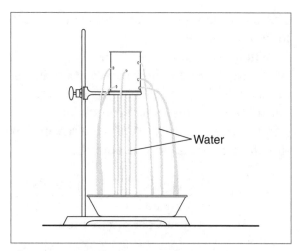

Figure 26-4. Liquid pressure is exerted equally in all directions and depends upon depth.

1. *The pressure exerted by a liquid acts equally in all directions and depends on depth.* The can in Figure 26-4 has holes drilled into the bottom and a series of holes drilled into the side, one above the other. When the can is filled with water, the water runs out of the side holes as well as the bottom holes. This indicates that water exerts pressure in all directions. Notice that water from the lowest side hole travels outward the farthest distance. This shows that the pressure exerted by a liquid depends on its depth; the greater the depth, the greater is the pressure.

   The apparatus in Figure 26-5 further confirms this fact. The apparatus consists of a thistle tube covered by a rubber membrane and connected to a pressure indicator. The indicator shows that, at any one depth, the pressure is equal, regardless of the direction in which the membrane faces. When the membrane is lowered, the pressure at the new depth is again equal regardless of the direction the membrane faces. However, the pressure at the lower level is greater than before.

2. *Liquids seek their own level.* Figure 26-6 shows a long rubber tube connecting a funnel to a long, straight glass tube. Water is poured into the funnel until the

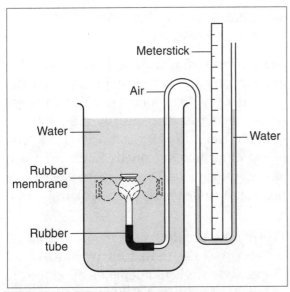

Figure 26-5. An apparatus that measures liquid pressure shows that the pressure is equal in all directions at any given depth.

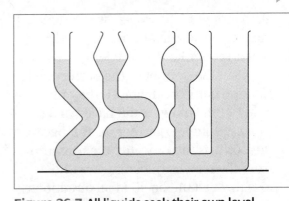

Figure 26-7. All liquids seek their own level.

glass tube is about one-third full of water. As the funnel is raised or lowered, the level of water in the glass tube always matches the level in the funnel. When a system of glass tubes of different shapes and diameters is connected as shown in Figure 26-7 and water is poured into one tube, the level of water in all the tubes reaches the same height. Because the height (depth) of a liquid column determines its pressure, the liquid flows into each tube until the levels, and therefore the pressures, are equal.

3. *The pressure of a liquid is independent of the shape of its container.* The

devices shown in Figure 26-8 are called Pascal's vases. The dimension of the bottom of each vase is the same, but their other dimensions differ. When the vases are filled to the same height with the same liquid, the dials indicate that the pressure at the bottom of all the vases is the same. Thus the pressure of a liquid column depends on its *height* rather than on the *shape* of its container.

4. *Pressure can be transferred throughout a liquid.* In a closed container filled with a liquid, any additional pressure applied to the liquid is transmitted without loss to all other parts of the liquid. Here too, the pressure acts equally in all directions. This statement, known as **Pascal's law**, can be demonstrated as follows: Fill a tall bottle *completely* to the top with water and insert a

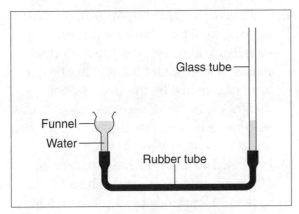

Figure 26-6. Water seeks its own level.

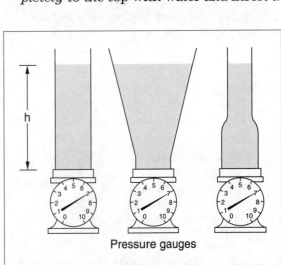
Pressure gauges

Figure 26-8. Pascal's vases show that pressure depends on height rather than shape.

glass stopper. The excess water flows out and no air remains in the bottle. When you strike the stopper gently with a mallet, the bottom of the bottle cracks. Had the bottle been empty, the only result of the blow would have been to force the stopper farther in. Yet, because the bottle is full of water, the pressure from the blow is transmitted without loss through the liquid in all directions. Because the area of the bottom of the bottle is larger than the area of the stopper, the *total force* on the bottom of the bottle increases considerably and, as a result, the bottle breaks.

A hydraulic press, such as the one shown in Figure 26-9, operates according to Pascal's law. Suppose 10 newtons per square centimeter of pressure are exerted on the small piston (*A*). This increase in pressure is transmitted to every square centimeter of the large piston (*B*). Because the area of the large piston is 100 times that of the small piston, 10 newtons of effort on the small piston can move a resistance of 1000 newtons on the large piston. (10 newtons per square centimeter = 1000 newtons per 100 square centimeters.) As in all machines, the work done on both sides is the same. To move the 1000-newton resistance upward 1 centimeter, the small piston must move down 100 centimeters.

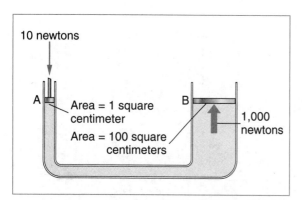

10 newtons

A — Area = 1 square centimeter

B

Area = 100 square centimeters

1,000 newtons

Figure 26-9. A hydraulic press uses the transfer of pressure throughout a liquid to do work.

What Are the Characteristics of Gas Pressure?

Gases are also fluids. Although their weights are very small, gases exert pressure for the same reasons that liquids do. You can best understand gas pressure by studying the common mixture of gases called air. The ocean of air that surrounds Earth is known as the atmosphere. The characteristics of air pressure (atmospheric pressure) are:

1. *Air pressure decreases as the altitude increases.* Recall that the pressure exerted by a liquid depends upon the height of the liquid. This is also true for air pressure. Air pressure is greatest at the bottom of the atmosphere, which is at the altitude of sea level. As you rise in the atmosphere by climbing a mountain or flying in an airplane, the height of the column of air above you becomes smaller. As a result, the air pressure at any altitude above sea level is less than at sea level. At sea level, air pressure is 14.7 pounds per square inch, or 10.13 newtons per square centimeter. This pressure is also known as *one atmosphere.*

   Just as changes in water pressure may cause discomfort to your ears when swimming, changes in air pressure often have the same effect. This may occur when you travel rapidly up or down in an elevator or take off or land in an airplane.

2. *Air exerts pressure equally in all directions.* Like liquids, gases exert pressure equally in all directions. The fact that plants, animals, and inanimate objects are not crushed by the tremendous weight of the air gives evidence that this statement is true. For example, consider a leaf attached by a thin stalk to a branch. The leaf may have an area of 10 square inches. Because the air pressure is 14.7 pounds per square inch at

sea level, the total weight of air on this leaf is 147 pounds (14.7 pounds per square inch × 10 square inches = 147 pounds). Ordinarily, such a great weight would snap the stalk and crush the leaf. However, air exerts pressure equally in all directions, so the same force (147 pounds) is acting upward from the underside of the leaf. The upward force balances the downward force and the leaf remains undamaged.

3. *An increase in pressure reduces the volume of gases.* Unlike liquids and solids, gases can be compressed. *Robert Boyle*, in 1660, showed that when pressure is applied to a gas in a closed container (the temperature remaining constant), the volume of the gas decreases. As the pressure becomes greater, the volume occupied by the gas becomes smaller. Stated in another way, the volume of a gas varies inversely as the pressure on it. This statement is part of **Boyle's law**. For example, when the pressure exerted on a gas is doubled, the volume of the gas is reduced to one-half its original volume. On the other hand, when the pressure on the gas is reduced by half, the volume of the gas doubles (see Figure 26-10). Remember

that, in all of these cases, the temperature must remain unchanged.

How Is Air Pressure Measured?

Air pressure is measured with an instrument called a **barometer**. There are two major types of barometers: the mercury barometer and the aneroid barometer.

The Mercury Barometer. The mercury barometer was first constructed in 1643 by the Italian scientist *Evangelista Torricelli*. This device, which is still in use today, consists of a 32-inch length of glass tubing that is closed at one end. The glass tube is first filled with mercury and then inverted into a dish of mercury. (See Figure 26-11.) The mercury column falls but normally stops when its height reaches 30 inches (at sea level). This is the maximum amount of mercury that the air pressing down on the dish can support. (If the mercury column were 1 square inch in diameter, the mercury in the tube would weigh 14.7 pounds—normal

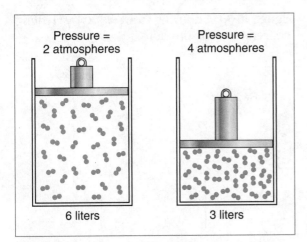

Figure 26-10. According to Boyle's law, as the pressure on the gas is doubled from 2 atmospheres to 4 atmospheres, the volume is halved from 6 liters to 3 liters at constant temperature.

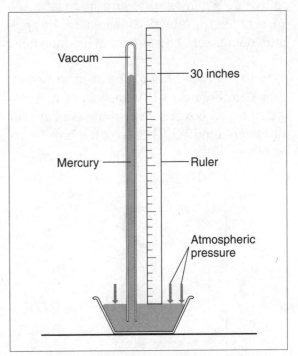

Figure 26-11. A mercury barometer uses the height of a column of mercury to measure air pressure.

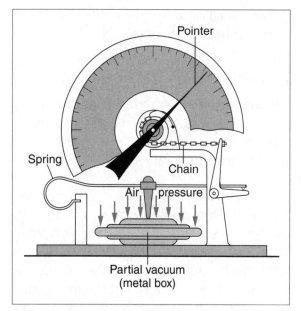

Figure 26-12. An aneroid barometer uses a system of levers and a pointer to measure air pressure.

atmospheric pressure. If the mercury column were 1 square centimeter in diameter, the mercury would weigh 10 newtons.) As the mercury in the tube moves downward, a partial vacuum forms in the 2 inches of space above it. When air pressure increases, the mercury in the tube rises. When the air pressure decreases, the mercury in the tube falls.

The Aneroid Barometer. The aneroid barometer (see Figure 26-12) consists of a corrugated metal box from which most of the air has been removed. The top of the box is sup-

ported by a spring and is connected by chains and levers to a pointer on a scale. When the air pressure increases, it pushes the top of the box downward and causes the pointer to move in one direction. When air pressure decreases, the top of the box moves upward, causing the pointer to move in the opposite direction.

How Is Air Pressure Used Every Day?

Aside from being surrounded by air pressure all the time, many common devices take advantage of differences in air pressure. Drinking straws (see Figure 26-13), medicine droppers (see Figure 26-14), and vacuum

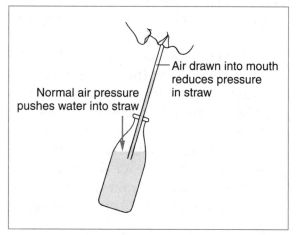

Figure 26-13. A drinking straw works by creating a difference in air pressure.

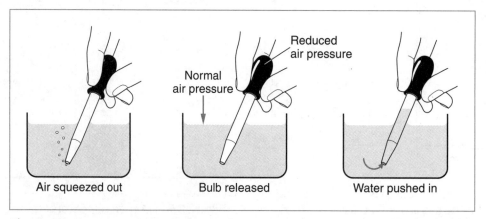

Figure 26-14. Squeezing the bulb of a medicine dropper creates a difference in air pressure.

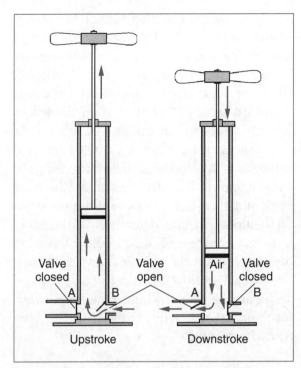

Figure 26-15. A bicycle pump works by increasing the air pressure within a chamber.

cleaners operate by reducing the air pressure inside them and allowing the outside air, under its own pressure, to push something into the device.

Some devices, such as bicycle tire pumps, sprayers, and leaf blowers, operate by increasing the air pressure within a closed space. In these cases, pistons are usually used to force air into the closed space and then compress it. Take a look at the bicycle pump in Figure 26-15. On the upstroke of the piston, the volume of the pump chamber in-

creases. According to Boyle's law, the pressure of the air in the chamber decreases. Air from the outside rushes into the chamber to balance the pressure in the chamber. On the downstroke, the volume of the pump chamber decreases, increasing the pressure of the air. This forces air out of the pump.

▶ How Is Pressure Affected by the Motion of a Fluid?

In the eighteenth century, *Daniel Bernoulli*, a Swiss scientist, observed that the pressure exerted by a fluid in motion is less than that exerted by the same fluid at rest. This observation is now called **Bernoulli's principle**. Figure 26-16 demonstrates this principle. When a fluid is in motion, the pressure of the fluid on the sides of its container is high when its velocity is low. On the other hand, the pressure is low when the velocity is higher. In the figure, water flows through a tube that varies in diameter. In section *A*, a wide part of the tube, the velocity of the water is low and the gauge shows the pressure on the tube to be high. In section *B*, the diameter of the tube decreases. Here, the velocity of the water increases because the same amount of water passes through this section in the same time as in *A*. In section *B*, the gauge shows the pressure to be lower than in *A*. When the water enters section *C*, whose diameter is the same as that of *A*, the water again slows and its pressure increases again.

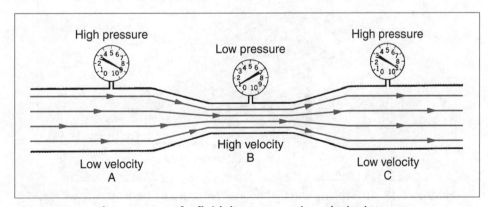

Figure 26-16. The pressure of a fluid decreases as its velocity increases.

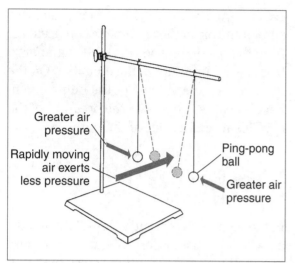

Figure 26-17. Bernoulli's principle explains why ping-pong balls are pushed together when air is forced between them.

Bernoulli's principle, which applies to gases as well as liquids, can be demonstrated by suspending two ping-pong balls on strings about 5 centimeters apart. (See Figure 26-17.) When you blow air between the two ping-pong balls, they move toward each other. This occurs because the rapidly moving air between the balls exerts less pressure than the air on the outer sides of the balls. As a result, the ping-pong balls are pushed together by the pressure of the air that is not in motion.

The motion of ping-pong balls may not be all that important to everyday life, but Ber-

noulli's principle can also explain the ability of an airplane to fly. The forward motion of the airplane forces air to flow over and under the wings of the plane. As shown in Figure 26-18, the upper surface of a wing is curved and therefore somewhat longer than the lower surface, which is almost flat. The moving air above the wing must cover a greater distance in the same time as the air below the wing. As a result, the velocity of the air above the wing is greater than that below and the pressure on the upper surface decreases. At the same time, the pressure of the air below the wing becomes relatively greater than that above the wing. This difference in the air pressure above and below the wing creates an upward force called **lift**, which raises the airplane from the ground.

▶ Why Do Some Objects Float and Others Sink?

You have learned that a liquid that is not in motion exerts pressure in all directions because of its weight. This helps you to understand why objects appear to lose weight when they are immersed in water, as you observed in the inquiry investigation at the beginning of the chapter. For any object to lose weight, the downward force exerted by gravity must be opposed by an upward force.

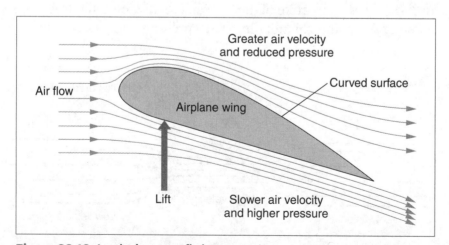

Figure 26-18. An airplane can fly because air pressure beneath the wing is greater than air pressure above the wing.

Because water exerts pressure in all directions, its upward pressure produces a force that is called **buoyant force**. This force opposes the weight of an object and makes it appear to lose weight.

You have taken advantage of the buoyant force of water if you have ever lifted a friend while in water. You would have found that it was much easier to lift your friend in water than on land. That is because the buoyant force of water pushes up on your friend. Your force and the buoyant force add together to lift your friend. It is this same buoyant force that supports ships in water and balloons in air. To find the buoyant force of water on an object, you need only find the difference between the weight of an object in air and its weight in water.

Archimedes' Principle. When you place an object in water, the object pushes aside, or displaces, some water. The volume of water that is displaced is equal to the volume that the object itself occupies. Thus, the buoyant force on the object is the upward pressure of the remaining water on the object. This pressure is equal to the weight of the displaced water. In turn, this weight is equal to the weight the object appears to lose. Observations like these were first described by the ancient Greek mathematician *Archimedes*. These observations, which you made in the inquiry investigation, are summarized in what is now called **Archimedes' principle**.

Archimedes' principle states that an object immersed in a liquid seems to lose the same amount of weight as the weight of the liquid that the object displaces. You verified this principle in your inquiry investigation.

Archimedes' principle applies not only to objects that sink in water, but also to objects that float. When you repeated the investigation using a block of wood instead of a stone, you found that the block sinks a little until the weight of the displaced water equals the weight of the wood in air. This observation, known as the **law of flotation**, states that a floating object displaces a weight of liquid equal to its own weight. Thus, a 100-gram block of wood floats in water with enough of its surface under water to displace 100 grams of water.

If a flat sheet of metal were dropped into a pail of water, the metal would sink. The sheet displaces a volume of water equal to its own volume. However, the displaced water would weigh less than the sheet. (By Archimedes' principle, you know that the weight of the displaced water equals the loss of weight of the metal.) When the same sheet of metal is shaped into a box or a boat and is dropped into water, the metal will float. The little boat now has a greater volume than when the metal was in the form of a flat sheet because it now encloses a volume of air. In this form, the metal displaces an additional volume of water. The total volume of water displaced now equals the weight of the metal and, therefore, the object floats. This idea is applied in the construction of ships. In order for a 10,000-ton ship to float, it must be constructed so that it displaces 10,000 tons of water. Similarly, if a balloon is to float in air, it must be large enough to displace an amount of air whose weight is equal to the weight of the balloon.

▶ What Is Specific Gravity?

You can determine whether an object will sink or float by determining its specific gravity. The specific gravity of a substance is the ratio of the density of the substance to the density of water. Thus, specific gravity can be found according to the formula

$$\text{specific gravity} = \frac{\text{density of substance}}{\text{density of water}}$$

You know that the density of mercury is 13.6 grams per cubic centimeter, whereas the density of water is 1 gram per cubic centimeter. Accordingly, the specific gravity of mercury is 13.6:

specific gravity

$$= \frac{\text{density of mercury}}{\text{density of water}}$$

$$= \frac{13.6 \text{ grams per cubic centimeter}}{1 \text{ gram per cubic centimeter}}$$

$$= 13.6$$

Note that specific gravity has no units. If the specific gravity of a substance, such as mercury, is greater than 1, the substance will sink in water. However, if the specific gravity of a substance is less than 1 (wood, for example, has a specific gravity of about 0.6), the substance will float in the water.

Chapter Review

Science Terms

The following list contains all the boldfaced words found in this chapter and the page on which each appears.

Archimedes' principle (p. 445)

barometer (p. 441)

Bernoulli's principle (p. 443)

Boyle's law (p. 441)

buoyant force (p. 445)

density (p. 435)

fluid (p. 435)

law of flotation (p. 445)

lift (p. 444)

Pascal's law (p. 439)

pressure (p. 436)

Matching Questions

In your notebook, write the letter of the item in column B that is most closely related to the item in column A.

Column A

_____ 1. barometer

_____ 2. Bernoulli's principle

_____ 3. Archimedes' principle

_____ 4. pressure

_____ 5. Pascal's law

_____ 6. pounds per cubic foot

_____ 7. lift

_____ 8. density

_____ 9. result of an increase in pressure

_____ 10. Boyle's law

Column B

a. mass of a substance per unit volume

b. observation that pressure can be transferred throughout a liquid

c. observation that an increase in pressure reduces the volume of a gas

d. upward force

e. observation that the buoyant force on an object equals the weight of the displaced water

f. decrease in volume

g. unit of density

h. a device that measures air pressure

i. observation that pressure decreases as the speed of a fluid increases

j. force per unit area

Multiple-Choice Questions

In your notebook, write the letter preceding the word or expression
that best completes the statement or answers the question.

1. To which of the following would the term *fluid* apply?
   a. a pencil
   b. a gold bar
   c. a sheet of paper
   d. a volume of air

2. Which formula is used to determine density?
   a. m/V   c. m × V
   b. V/m   d. m + V

3. An object with a mass of 20 grams and a volume of 4 cubic centimeters has a density of
   a. 16 grams per cubic centimeter
   b. 5 grams per cubic centimeter
   c. 10 pounds per cubic foot
   d. 10 grams per cubic centimeter

4. The ratio of force per unit area describes
   a. density
   b. specific gravity
   c. power
   d. pressure

5. Liquid pressure depends on the product of the density of the liquid and the
   a. volume
   b. mass
   c. height
   d. specific gravity

6. When glass tubes of different diameters are connected, and a liquid is poured into one tube, the liquid levels are
   a. higher in the thin tubes and lower in the thick tubes
   b. at the same height in all tubes
   c. lower in the thin tubes than the thick tubes
   d. unrelated

7. Which statement about the pressure of a liquid is true?
   a. Pressure cannot be transferred throughout a liquid.
   b. Pressure does not depend on the shape of the container.
   c. Pressure is independent of depth.
   d. Pressure is exerted downward but not upward.

8. Pascal's law is applied in a
   a. hydraulic press
   b. lever
   c. wheel-and-axle
   d. Pascal's vase

9. As the altitude increases, air pressure
   a. increases
   b. increases, then decreases
   c. decreases
   d. remains the same

10. When the pressure on a gas is increased at constant temperature, the volume of the gas
    a. increases
    b. decreases
    c. decreases, then increases
    d. remains the same

11. Air pressure can be measured with an instrument called
    a. an anemometer
    b. an ammeter
    c. a barometer
    d. a thermometer

12. Which of the following devices does *not* use air pressure to function?
    a. hydraulic press
    b. medicine dropper
    c. soda straw
    d. vacuum cleaner

13. When the velocity of a moving fluid increases, what happens to the pressure of the fluid?
    a. increases
    b. decreases
    c. increases, then decreases
    d. remains the same

14. When air is blown between two ping-pong balls that are suspended next to each other, the balls
    a. move together   c. are unaffected
    b. move apart   d. rotate in space

15. When a metallic object attached to a spring scale is lowered into water, the object appears to
    a. gain volume   c. gain weight
    b. lose volume   d. lose weight

16. How do you find the buoyant force of water on an object?
    a. Multiply the weight of the object in air by its weight in water.
    b. Find the difference between the object's weight in air and water.
    c. Add the weights in air and water.
    d. Multiply the weight of the object by its density.

17. When a metallic object is submerged in water, the water displaced
    a. is equal in volume to that of the object
    b. is equal in weight to that of the object
    c. has a greater volume than the object
    d. has a greater weight than the object

18. A floating object in water displaces
    a. a weight of water greater than its own
    b. no water
    c. a weight of water equal to its own weight
    d. a weight of water smaller than its own

19. For a 15,000-ton ship to float, it must displace an amount of water equal to
    a. 10,000 tons   c. 30,000 tons
    b. 20,000 tons   d. 15,000 tons

20. A floating object generally has a specific gravity that is
    a. greater than 1   c. less than 1
    b. equal to 1   d. equal to 2

Modified True-False Questions

In some of the following statements, the italicized term makes the statement incorrect. For each incorrect statement, in your notebook, write the term that must be substituted for the italicized term to make the statement correct. For each correct statement, write the word "true."

1. Density is determined by dividing mass by *weight*. _____

2. The force per unit area exerted by a substance is called *pressure*. _____

3. The pressure of a column of liquid equals the density of the water times its *width*. _____

4. The pressure exerted by a *liquid* acts equally in all directions. _____

5. That pressure can be transferred throughout a liquid is stated in *Boyle's law*. _____

6. The popping of ears as a person travels up and down in an elevator results from changes in *force*. _____

7. Air exerts pressure *equally* in all directions. _____

8. As the pressure on a gas increases, the volume of the gas *increases*. _____

9. The fact that the volume of a gas at constant temperature varies inversely as the pressure on it is known as *Newton's law*. _____

10. The mercury barometer was first constructed by the scientist *Torricelli*. _____

11. The pressure of a liquid is *dependent on* the shape of its container. _____

12. That the pressure exerted by a fluid in motion is less than that exerted by the same fluid at rest is stated in *Pascal's law.* _____

13. An upward force created by the differences in air pressure above and below an airplane wing is known as *lift.* _____

14. The upward force of water against an object placed into it is called the *buoyant force.* _____

15. An object will float if it displaces a weight of liquid *equal to* its own weight. _____

TEST-TAKING TIP Try making a flip-book or journal to associate laws with the scientists who developed them. On one page write the name of the law and on the back write any details, equations, or diagrams that will help you remember the law.

Check Your Knowledge
Write the answer to each question in your notebook.

1. Define each of the following terms:
   a. density
   b. pressure
   c. buoyant force
   d. specific gravity
   e. Pascal's law

2. List four characteristics of liquid pressure.

3. List three characteristics of air pressure.

4. Explain how Bernoulli's principle shows why an airplane can fly.

5. a. Why do objects appear to lose weight in water?
   b. Explain how a steel ship must be constructed if it is to float on water.

6. How is the density of an object related to its specific gravity?

Think Critically
Write the answer to each of the following questions in your notebook.

1. a. Find the density of a substance whose mass is 28 grams and whose volume is 4 cubic centimeters.
   b. Find the density of a substance whose mass is 40 pounds and whose volume is 10 cubic feet.

2. a. Find the pressure exerted by an object that exerts a force of 180 newtons on an area of 10 square centimeters.
   b. Find the pressure exerted by a column of water 20 feet high.

3. An object has a specific gravity less than water. If the specific gravity of mercury is 13.6, will the object float higher or lower in mercury than it does in water? Explain.

Take It Further

Internet Search

1. The story goes that Archimedes reached his famous conclusion about density while trying to prove the authenticity of a gold crown for the king. Research this story to find out how it relates to density. Then devise a modern version and explain to the class how it could be used to determine the identity of an element.

2. Atmospheric pressure is closely related to weather conditions. Conduct research to understand how regions of high pressure are different from regions of low pressure. Find out how differences in air pressure are created and how they are related to winds and storm systems. Share your findings with the class.

3. Differences in pressure make it possible for people to breathe. Muscles in the chest change the size of the chest cavity during breathing. Research the process of breathing and find out how pressure is involved. Create a diagram to present your findings to the class.

4. Several scientists were mentioned in this chapter. Choose one of the scientists and find out information about the person's life and contributions to science. Write a brief report summarizing what you learn.

CAREER

5. Aerodynamics engineers analyze designs of objects that move through fluids, including rockets, airplanes, and even racecars. Research job opportunities for aerodynamics engineers along with the training they require. Share your findings with the class.

27 How Are Forces Related to Moving Objects?

Jumping, spinning, and sliding are just a few of the many types of motion this graceful skater displays. She speeds up, slows down, and changes direction because of the forces acting on her.

After reading this chapter, you should be able to answer the following questions:

What is motion?

How is motion described in terms of speed and velocity?

What is acceleration?

How do forces cause accelerated motion?

What are Newton's laws of motion?

How is circular motion described?

You set objects in motion all the time. You throw a ball, lift a backpack, or pull a door open. Forces are required to change an object's motion. In this inquiry investigation, you will examine the relationship between force and motion.

Materials:
- ✔ safety goggles
- ✔ meterstick
- ✔ Hall's carriage
- ✔ mass balance
- ✔ box of marked masses
- ✔ inclined-plane board with pulley
- ✔ stopwatch
- ✔ string

Part A Find the mass of a Hall's carriage.

1. Record the mass of the carriage.

Part B Place an inclined-plane board and the Hall's carriage on a table as shown in Figure 27-1. Put masses totaling 500 grams in the carriage.

2. Record the total mass of the carriage and its contents.

Part C Slowly raise one end of the board just enough to overcome the friction that keeps the carriage stationary; that is, raise the carriage until it begins to move *slowly*. Wedge a book or some other object under the board to maintain the incline.

Part D Hang a 100-gram mass on the end of the string that passes from the carriage and over the pulley on the end of the inclined plane. Move the carriage to the raised end of the inclined plane. Release the carriage and, using a stopwatch, measure the time it takes for the carriage to reach the pulley. Record the time.

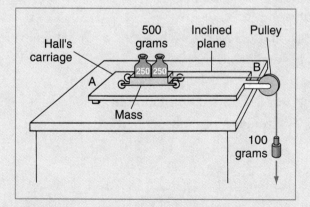

Figure 27-1.

Part E Add another 100-gram mass to the string and repeat Part D. Record the time.

Part F Add a third 100-gram mass to the string and repeat Part D again. Record the time.

3. *In each step of Parts D, E, and F, which factor was kept constant?*

4. *Which factor was changed?*

5. *What effect did the change have on the speed of the carriage?*

Part G Remove all the masses from the string and remove the 500-gram mass from the carriage. Place a 100-gram mass in the carriage and a 100-gram mass on the end of the string. Move the carriage to the raised end of the inclined-plane board. Release the carriage and, using a stopwatch, measure the time it takes for the carriage to reach the pulley. Record the time.

Part H Add another 100-gram mass to the mass already in the carriage and repeat Part G. Record the time.

Part I Add a third 100-gram mass to the carriage and repeat Part G again. Record the time.

6. *In each step of Parts G, H, and I, which factor was kept constant?*

7. *Which factor was changed?*

8. *What effect did the change have on the speed of the carriage?*

9. *Summarize the observations you recorded.*

What Is Motion?

Are you in motion as you read these words? You may be surprised to find out that there is more than one correct answer to this question. The term *motion* generally describes the movement of an object from one point to another. A school bus obviously moves as it takes you to school, but is your school moving? As you look out of a window, you see no evidence of this movement. Yet Earth is turning on its axis at a speed of about 1600 kilometers per hour (1000 miles per hour), and is also revolving around the sun at a speed of over 96,500 kilometers per hour, or 60,000 miles per hour. Because the school is on Earth, it must also be moving. If you are in school right now, you are also in motion. You are not aware of this motion because, relative to what you see around you, the building does not appear to move.

The scientific definition of **motion** is a change in position relative to an object assumed to be at rest. When you are sitting at your desk, you are not moving relative to the floor beneath you, to your chair, and to your desk. Relative to the sun, however, you are moving quite rapidly. Similarly, a passenger seated on a bus driving down the street appears to be moving relative to a person on the street, but not relative to another passenger seated on the bus.

How Is Motion Described in Terms of Speed and Velocity?

You might describe a racecar as moving very fast or a turtle as moving very slowly. The rate at which an object changes position is commonly referred to as speed. More specifically, **speed** is the distance traveled by an object in a unit of time. For example, when a car travels a distance of 80 kilometers in 1 hour, the speed of the car is 80 kilometers per hour. Notice that this statement says nothing about the *direction* in which the car is traveling. Because no direction is involved, speed is a scalar quantity.

If you start a trip in New York City and travel at a speed of 80 kilometers per hour, at the end of 1 hour you could be in New Jersey, Connecticut, or Long Island, depending on the direction in which you traveled. For that reason, you need to know the direction in which you traveled to better describe motion. The speed in a given direction is called **velocity**. Unlike speed, velocity is a vector quantity because it has both magnitude and direction. Thus, if you travel 80 kilometers per hour northeastward from New York City, in 1 hour you might be somewhere in Connecticut. If you travel in an easterly direction, you might be on Long Island. (See Figure 27-2.)

For most examples of motion, velocity is not constant. When you take a trip by bus, car, or train, for example, the velocity constantly changes because of traffic, pedestrians, stop signs, and traffic lights. Rather than knowing

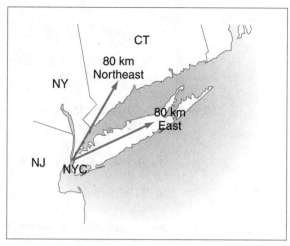

Figure 27-2. Velocity is speed in a given direction.

the instantaneous velocity, which is the velocity at any given instant, you can determine the **average velocity** for the trip if you know the total distance traveled and the total time the trip took.. The average velocity is determined by dividing the distance traveled by the time taken to travel that distance. Thus,

$$\text{average velocity} = \frac{\text{distance}}{\text{time}}$$

When average velocity is represented by $\bar{v}$ (called "v-bar"), distance by d, and time by t, this equation is written

$$\bar{v} = \frac{d}{t}$$

For example, suppose you complete a 250-mile trip from Washington, D.C., to New York City in 5 hours. To determine the average velocity for your trip, you divide the distance (250 miles) by the time (5 hours) and find that the average velocity for the trip is 50 miles per hour:

$$\bar{v} = \frac{d}{t}$$

$$\bar{v} = \frac{250 \text{ miles}}{5 \text{ hours}} = 50 \frac{\text{miles}}{\text{hour}}$$
$$= 50 \text{ miles per hour}$$

This does not mean that you traveled at a steady 50 miles per hour toward New York City for the entire 5-hour trip. You may have slowed when traffic built up or you may have stopped completely to refill the gas tank or eat lunch. Because your speed during these times was considerably less than 50 miles per hour, you would have had to increase your speed during other times to maintain the average speed of 50 miles per hour.

You can rearrange the velocity equation to solve for time or distance if you know the other two values.

$$t = \frac{d}{\bar{v}} \quad \text{and} \quad d = \bar{v}t$$

▶ **What is Acceleration?**

A moving object can speed up, slow down, or change direction. Any of these changes affects velocity. Changes in velocity are called **acceleration**. In scientific terms, acceleration is the rate of change of velocity. Thus, acceleration is the change in velocity divided by the time it takes to make this change. If an object either speeds or slows at a constant rate, it is said to be accelerating uniformly. A decrease in velocity is considered negative acceleration, which is often called **deceleration**.

To find the acceleration of an object, divide the change in its velocity by the time it takes to make the change. The change in velocity is found by subtracting the velocity at the beginning of the acceleration from the velocity at the end of the acceleration. Thus,

$$\text{acceleration} = \frac{\text{final velocity-starting velocity}}{\text{time}}$$

If acceleration is represented as a, final velocity as v_f, and starting velocity as v_s, then the equation is written as:

$$a = \frac{v_f - v_s}{t}$$

The units of acceleration are units of velocity per unit of time. Acceleration can be described in such units as miles per hour per second (mi/h/s), kilometers per hour per minute (km/h/min). The units of time are often written as a square unit; for example, feet per second per second (ft/s²), and centimeters per second per second (cm/s²).

As an example, suppose a driver accelerates a car from a velocity of 20 kilometers per hour (km/h) to 50 kilometers per hour in 5 seconds. To find the acceleration of this car, subtract the starting velocity (20 kilometers per hour) from the final velocity (50 kilometers per hour) and divide this change in velocity by 5 seconds:

$$a = \frac{v_f - v_s}{t}$$

$$a = \frac{50\ \text{km/h} - 20\ \text{km/h}}{5\ \text{seconds}} = \frac{30\ \text{km/h}}{5\ \text{seconds}}$$
$$= 6\ \text{km/h/second}$$
$$= 6\ \text{kilometers per hour per second}$$
$$= 6\ \text{km/h/s}$$

The car accelerates 6 kilometers per hour every second. This means that at the end of each second of acceleration the velocity of the car increases by 6 kilometers per hour. Thus, at the end of 1 second of acceleration, the car traveling at 20 kilometers per hour would travel at a velocity of 26 kilometers per hour. At the end of 2 seconds, the car's velocity would be 32 kilometers per hour, and so on, until, after 5 seconds, it reaches 50 kilometers per hour.

If you know that an object is accelerating uniformly and the length of time during which the acceleration takes place, you can readily compute the final velocity:

$$\text{final velocity} = \text{acceleration} \times \text{time}$$

$$v_f = a \times t$$

From this equation you can determine the final velocity for any object that starts from rest and accelerates. For example, suppose an object starting from rest is accelerated 10 miles per hour per second for 7 seconds. To find the final velocity of the object at the end of 7 seconds, you need only multiply the acceleration (10 miles per hour per second) by the time (7 seconds). The final velocity is 70 miles per hour:

$$v_{f} = a \times t$$

$v_f = 10$ miles per hour per second $\times 7$ seconds

$= 70 \dfrac{\text{miles per hour}}{\text{second}} \times \text{second}$

$= 70$ miles per hour

If the object were not at rest but was traveling at some velocity before it started to accelerate, you must account for this starting velocity when calculating final velocity. For example, if the object in the problem were traveling at 15 miles per hour before it started to accelerate, then the final velocity is the sum of the starting velocity (v_s) and the product of $a \times t$. Thus, the final velocity of a uniformly accelerating body having a starting velocity is found from the equation

$$v_f = v_s + (a \times t)$$

In the problem, the final velocity is 85 miles per hour:

$$v_f = v_s + (a \times t)$$

$v_f = 15$ mph

$\quad + (10$ mph per second $\times 7$ seconds$)$

$= 15$ mph $+ \left(10 \dfrac{\text{mph}}{\text{second}} \times 7 \text{ seconds} \right)$

$= 15$ mph $+ 70$ mph $= 85$ mph

How Do Forces Cause Accelerated Motion?

In 1590, *Galileo* studied the effects of acceleration on objects. He performed experiments to determine how distance, velocity, time, and acceleration are related. One of his experiments, represented in Figure 27-3, concerned the motion of a metal ball rolling down an inclined plane. Galileo found that the distance covered by the ball was related to the square of the time during which the ball accelerated uniformly. (He neglected friction in all his calculations.) If the conditions were such that the ball rolled 1 foot in the first second, he found that it rolled 4 feet by the end of the next second ($2^2 = 4$), and 9 feet by the end of the third second ($3^2 = 9$).

The relationship between distance and acceleration can be stated as follows: The distance covered by an object that starts from rest and is uniformly accelerated depends on the average acceleration and on the square of the time period during which the accelerating force acts. (It is necessary to use the average acceleration here because at the starting point the acceleration is zero and at the end of the time period the acceleration is greatest.) As an equation, this relationship is expressed as

$$\text{distance} = \frac{1}{2} \text{acceleration} \times \text{time}^2$$

$$d = \frac{1}{2} a \times t^2$$

At times the various formulas for objects in motion can be confusing. To help de-

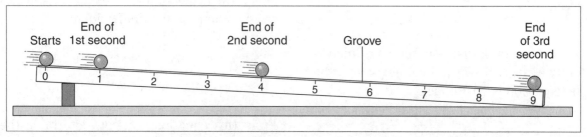

Figure 27-3. Galileo performed an experiment similar to the one shown to investigate the motion of a uniformly accelerated object.

Table 27-1.
What Are the Motion Formulas?

Unknown Quantity	Known Quantities	Formula
Average velocity	Distance, time	$\bar{v} = \dfrac{d}{t}$
Distance	Average velocity, time	$d = \bar{v} \times t$
Time	Distance, average velocity	$t = \dfrac{d}{\bar{v}}$
Acceleration	Final velocity, starting velocity, time	$a = \dfrac{v_f - v_s}{t}$
Final velocity (object initially at rest)	Acceleration, time	$v_f = a \times t$
Final velocity (some initial velocity)	Acceleration, time, starting velocity	$v_f = v_s + (a \times t)$
Distance	Acceleration, time	$d = \dfrac{1}{2} a \times t^2$

termine which formula to use in a given situation, Table 27-1 displays the known quantities, the unknown quantity, and the appropriate formula.

The force that caused the ball to roll down the inclined plane in Galileo's experiment was gravity, which pulls the ball down the incline. The motion was opposed by the force of friction, which opposes the motion of the ball. It seems reasonable to conclude that the force due to gravity will be greatest—and the force of friction will be least—when the ball falls freely to the ground. This would be the situation when an inclined plane is in a vertical position.

By carefully measuring the acceleration imparted to a freely falling object by the force due to gravity, scientists have found that this acceleration is about 9.8 meters per second every second (or 32 feet per second every second). Galileo hypothesized that the acceleration produced by gravity is the same for all objects regardless of their mass. However, when he tested this hypothesis, he found that objects of greater mass often fell faster than some objects of lesser mass. Galileo reasoned that the exceptions to his hypothesis must be related to the effect of air resistance on the objects. Therefore, in a vacuum, all objects should fall at the same rate.

Galileo's idea was proven to be true by scientists using a "coin and feather" tube as shown in Figure 27-4 on page 458. When air is present in the tube and you allow the coin and feather to fall at the same time, the coin accelerates more than the feather and reaches the bottom of the tube first. The feather flutters down more slowly because of the resistance of the air to its motion. However, when the air is removed from the tube, leaving a vacuum in it, the coin and the feather reach the bottom of the tube at the same time.

To calculate the velocity, distance, or time with regard to falling objects, use the appropriate formula in Table 27-1. Because the acceleration due to gravity, g, is uniform ($g = 32$ feet per second per second, or 9.8 meters per second per second), you can substitute this value for acceleration in the formula.

For example, find the final velocity of an object, initially at rest that falls freely for 3 seconds. Referring to Table 27-1,

$$v_f = a \times t$$

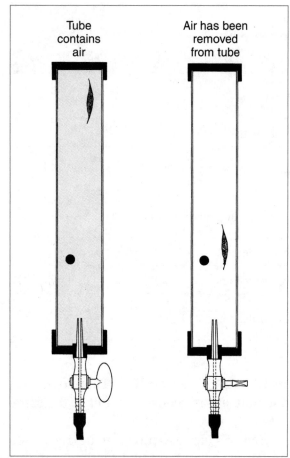

Figure 27-4. The "coin and feather" experiment proves that all objects fall at the same rate in a vacuum.

Replacing a with g,

$$v_f = g \times t$$

$$v_f = 32 \text{ feet per second per second}$$
$$\times 3 \text{ seconds}$$
$$= 96 \frac{\text{feet per second}}{\text{second}} \times \text{second}$$
$$= 96 \text{ feet per second}$$

Knowing the value of g enables you to find the height of a building if you know how long it takes for an object dropped from its top to strike the ground. For example, find the height in meters of a tower if an object dropped from the top reaches the ground in 10 seconds. Since the unknown quantity is the distance traveled by the freely falling ob-

ject, and you know the acceleration and the time, you use the formula

$$d = \frac{1}{2} a \times t^2$$

Replacing a with g,

$$d = \frac{1}{2} g \times t^2$$

$$d = \frac{1}{2} \times 9.8 \text{ meters per second per second}$$
$$\times (10 \text{ seconds})^2$$
$$= 4.9 \frac{\text{meters}}{\text{second} \times \text{second}}$$
$$\times 10 \text{ seconds} \times 10 \text{ seconds}$$
$$= 4.9 \text{ meters} \times 100 = 490 \text{ meters}$$

The building is 490 meters tall.

▶ What Are Newton's Laws of Motion?

In the seventeenth century, Sir Isaac Newton carefully investigated motion. From his observations, Newton formulated three fundamental laws that have contributed tremendously to the current understanding of moving objects. These laws deal with inertia, acceleration, and action and reaction.

Law of Inertia. Newton's first law of motion, also known as the **law of inertia**, states that an object at rest will remain at rest, and an object in motion will remain in motion in a straight line, unless the object is acted on by an unbalanced force. You can demonstrate this law by performing the simple experiment shown in Figure 27-5. Place a card on a drinking glass and a heavy coin on the card. In this position, both the card and the coin are at rest. When you exert a force on the card by sharply flicking it with a finger, the card begins to move outward in a straight line as a result of the one-sided (unbalanced) force that acted on it. Then, as gravity acts on the card, it falls downward in a curved path.

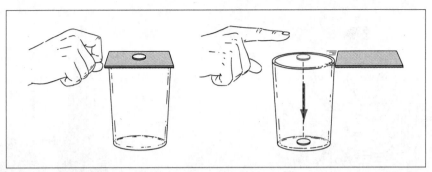

Figure 27-5. As explained by the law of inertia, the coin falls into the glass when the card is removed quickly.

Meanwhile, the coin drops straight downward into the glass. Originally the coin was at rest and remains that way until the flicking force is exerted on the card. The coin tends to remain in its original position because the horizontal flicking force is exerted on the card and not on the coin. As soon as the card moves outward and the supporting force that keeps the coin in its position disappears, the coin keeps its horizontal position and moves only vertically.

Inertia is experienced daily by passengers in vehicles. When standing in a bus or train, people often lurch forward as the vehicle stops. As the brakes are applied to the vehicle, it slows. However, by the law of inertia, the people continue to move forward in a straight line.

Law of Acceleration. The relationship of force and mass to acceleration is expressed in Newton's second law, **the law of acceleration**. This law states that the acceleration of an object depends on the ratio of the acting force to the mass of the body. The law is represented as

$$acceleration = \frac{force}{mass}$$

$$a = \frac{f}{m}$$

An example of the relationship expressed in Newton's second law is a bus that starts and stops. When starting his bus, the driver presses on the gas pedal, causing the engine to exert force on the mass of the bus. This causes the bus to accelerate. When 20 additional people board the bus, thereby increasing its mass, and the driver gives the engine as much gas as before, the bus accelerates more slowly than before. To accelerate a loaded bus as rapidly as an empty one, the engine requires more gas in order to increase the force acting on the mass of the bus. In other words, as the mass increases, the force must also increase if the acceleration is to remain the same. You verified these findings in the inquiry investigation.

Law of Action and Reaction. You have learned that when a force acts on an object, it moves unless another force, acting in the opposite direction balances the first force. When a man sits in a chair, he no longer moves even though he exerts a downward force called weight. That is because the chair exerts an upward force equal to his weight. (See Figure 27-6 on page 460.) The force exerted by one object is balanced by a force exerted by the other. Newton stated his observations of similar situations in his third law, the **law of action and reaction**. This law states that whenever an object exerts a force (action) on a second object, the second object exerts an equal and opposite force (reaction) on the first object.

The same law holds true for objects that are free to move. For example, when a girl

Figure 27-6. The man exerts a downward force on the chair as the chair exerts an equal but opposite force on the man.

steps from an untied rowboat to the dock, she exerts a force against the boat and she moves forward onto the dock. At the same time, the boat exerts an equal force against the girl but in the opposite direction, and the boat moves away from the dock. (See Figure 27-7.) Likewise, when a rifle is fired, the explosive force of the gunpowder causes the bullet to move out of the barrel. At the same time, the bullet exerts an opposite force and the rifle recoils against the shoulder.

The law of action and reaction also operates in jet and rocket engines. When a jet engine is started and when a rocket is launched, rapidly expanding gases exert a

Figure 27-7. The girl pushes against the boat and the boat pushes back against the girl.

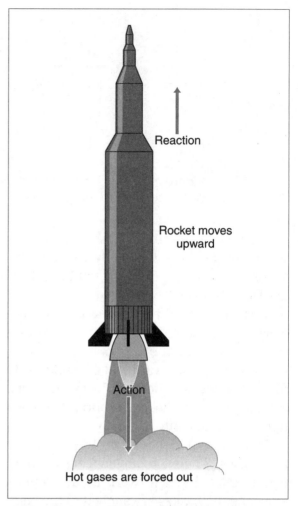

Figure 27-8. Newton's third law of motion explains how rockets liftoff into space.

force on them while they exert equal but opposite forces on the gases. The gases move backward and the jet or rocket moves forward or upward. (See Figure 27-8.)

How Is Circular Motion Described?

The previous discussion of motion concerned itself with the objects moving in a straight line. Orbiting space vehicles, revolving wheels, or the clothes in a washing machine during its "spin" cycle exhibit motion in a curved or circular path. When these objects move at a constant speed along a curved path of constant radius, the motion is called **uniform circular motion**.

Suppose you tie a string to a small stone and then twirl the stone. The stone moves in a circular path because of the force the string exerts on the stone. This force, called **centripetal** (center-seeking) force, pulls the moving stone toward the center of its curved path. At the same time, the stone also exerts a force on the string. This is the reaction to the center seeking force and is called the **centrifugal** (center-fleeing) reaction. If the string were to snap, the stone would fly out in a straight line. Since no centripetal force exists when the string breaks, there is no centrifugal reaction. According to Newton's first law, the object in motion continues in motion in a straight line.

What Is Momentum?

Momentum is closely associated with the acceleration, mass, and speed of moving objects. **Momentum** is the product of the mass of an object and its velocity.

$$\text{momentum} = \text{mass} \times \text{velocity}$$

$$\text{momentum} = m \times v$$

For example, a rifle bullet weighing 25 grams is fired, leaving the rifle barrel at a velocity of 30,000 centimeters per second. What is the momentum of the bullet at the moment it leaves the rifle?

$$\text{momentum} = m \times v$$

$$\text{momentum} = 25 \text{ grams} \times 30,000 \frac{\text{centimeters}}{\text{second}}$$

$$= 750,000 \frac{\text{grams} \times \text{centimeters}}{\text{second}}$$

The unit (grams × centimeters)/second is usually expressed as gram-centimeters/second, so momentum

$$= 750,000 \text{ gram-centimeters/second}$$

An object weighing 30,000 grams and moving at a velocity of 25 centimeters per second would have the same momentum. Thus, momentum can be increased by increasing the mass or the velocity of the moving body (or by increasing both).

Conservation of Momentum. A rolling bowling ball acquires momentum because it has mass and rolls with a specific velocity. When a moving bowling ball strikes a line of five other identical bowling balls, the momentum that it transfers causes only the last bowling ball in the line to move. (See Figure 27-9.) Careful measurements of the velocity of the incoming ball and the outgoing ball show that these velocities are equal. Because the two balls also have the same mass, the momentum of the outgoing ball is the same as that of the incoming ball. In

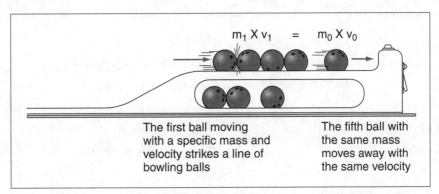

The first ball moving with a specific mass and velocity strikes a line of bowling balls

The fifth ball with the same mass moves away with the same velocity

Figure 27-9. A bowling ball colliding with a line of bowling balls is an example of the conservation of momentum.

general, when two objects collide, the momentum of one object is completely transferred to the second and illustrates **conservation of momentum**. In other words, the conservation of momentum means that the total momentum entering a system is equal to the total momentum leaving the system.

Conservation of momentum can be expressed as

$$\frac{\text{momentum}}{\text{(incoming)}} = \frac{\text{momentum}}{\text{(outgoing)}}$$

Momentum is the product of mass and velocity, so

$$\frac{\text{mass}}{\text{(incoming)}} \times \frac{\text{velocity}}{\text{(incoming)}} = \frac{\text{mass}}{\text{(outgoing)}} \times \frac{\text{velocity}}{\text{(outgoing)}}$$

$$m_i \times v_i = m_o \times v_o$$

Suppose a 10-gram bullet is fired from a 2000-gram rifle with a velocity of 50,000 centimeters per second. At what velocity does the rifle recoil against the rifleman's shoul-

der? To solve this problem, we substitute these values in the equation:

$$m_i \times v_i = m_o \times v_o$$

$$2000 \text{ grams} \times v_i =$$
$$10 \text{ grams} \times 50,000 \text{ centimeters per second}$$

$$v_i = \frac{10 \text{ grams} \times 50,000 \text{ centimeters per second}}{2000 \text{ grams}}$$

$$= 250 \text{ centimeters per second}$$

Accordingly, the rifle recoils at a velocity of 250 centimeters per second.

Essentially, the conservation of momentum is similar to Newton's law of action and reaction. A common example of conservation takes place during the game of billiards. Recall that when one object exerts a force on a second object, the second object exerts an equal but opposite force on the first. Thus, when one billiard ball collides squarely with another, the first ball exerts a force on the second ball. As a result, the second ball moves forward at the same velocity as the first. Also, the second ball exerts an equal but opposite force on the first ball, causing it to stop.

Chapter Review

Science Terms

The following list contains all the boldfaced words found in this chapter and the page on which each appears.

acceleration (p. 455)

average velocity (p. 454)

centrifugal (p. 461)

centripetal (p. 461)

conservation of momentum (p. 462)

deceleration (p. 455)

law of acceleration (p. 459)

law of action and reaction (p. 459)

law of inertia (p. 458)

momentum (p. 461)

motion (p. 454)

speed (p. 454)

uniform circular motion (p. 460)

velocity (p. 454)

Matching Questions

*In your notebook, write the letter of the item in column B that is
most closely related to the item in column A.*

Column A

_____ 1. speed

_____ 2. momentum

_____ 3. velocity

_____ 4. meaning of centripetal

_____ 5. uniform circular motion

_____ 6. acceleration

_____ 7. g

_____ 8. meaning of centrifugal

_____ 9. deceleration

_____ 10. law of inertia

Column B

a. a change in velocity over time

b. 9.8 meters per second per second

c. away from the center

d. negative acceleration

e. distance traveled per unit time in a specific direction

f. resistance to a change in motion

g. product of mass and velocity

h. toward the center

i. rate of change of position

j. motion of clothes in a clothes dryer

Multiple-Choice Questions

*In your notebook, write the letter preceding the word or expression
that best completes the statement or answers the question.*

1. A change in position relative to an object assumed to be at rest is called
a. motion
b. momentum
c. inertia
d. acceleration

2. How is velocity different from speed?
a. Velocity is an average.
b. Velocity describes objects in space only.
c. Velocity describes objects that move extremely fast.
d. Velocity has direction associated with it.

3. Which of the following is a vector quantity?
a. 22 km
b. 19 m/s
c. 38 km/h north
d. west

4. The average velocity can be determined from the formula
a. time/distance
b. time/acceleration
c. distance/time
d. distance × time

5. How much distance is covered by a car traveling at an average velocity of 50 mph for 5 hours?
a. 10 miles
b. 250 miles
c. 55 miles
d. 45 miles

6. The rate of change of velocity is called
a. acceleration
b. motion
c. momentum
d. inertia

7. Final velocity is equal to
a. $\dfrac{\bar{v}}{t}$
b. $\dfrac{t}{a}$
c. $\dfrac{a}{t}$
d. $a \times t$

8. The distance traveled by a falling object can be found by
a. gt
b. $\dfrac{v}{t}$
c. $\dfrac{1}{2}gt^2$
d. 2gt

9. By how much does the speed of a freely falling object increase each second?
a. 4.9 m/s
b. 9.8 m/s
c. 24 m/s
d. 32 m/s

10. Which scientist hypothesized that the acceleration produced by gravity is the same for all objects?
    a. Galileo   c. Copernicus
    b. Newton   d. Archimedes

11. In a "coin and feather" tube, the feather falls at a slower rate than the coin because of
    a. inertia   c. momentum
    b. buoyant force   d. air resistance

12. What is the height of a bridge if a stone dropped from it reaches the water below in 5 seconds?
    a. 49 m   c. 122.5 m
    b. 61.3 m   d. 245 m

13. That an object at rest tends to remain at rest and an object in motion tends to remain in motion in a straight line unless acted on by an unbalanced force is stated in the law of
    a. motion
    b. inertia
    c. momentum
    d. action and reaction

14. A moving bus comes to a sudden stop and the passengers lurch forward. This resistance of the passengers to a change in their motion is
    a. inertia   c. acceleration
    b. momentum   d. deceleration

15. As the unbalanced force acting on an object decreases, the acceleration of the object
    a. increase
    b. decreases
    c. remains the same
    d. increases, then decreases

16. For a constant force, mass is inversely proportional to
    a. speed   c. weight
    b. acceleration   d. volume

17. A rocket lifts off as it expels gases produced by burning fuel. What causes the rocket to move?
    a. The gases exert an equal and opposite force on the rocket.
    b. The rocket floats as its mass decreases from burning the fuel.
    c. Moving air around the rocket pulls it forward.
    d. The gravitational pull of the moon acts on the rocket.

18. An inward force created by uniform circular motion is called
    a. buoyant force
    b. centrifugal reaction
    c. centripetal force
    d. gravity

19. The momentum of an object is the product of the mass of the object and its
    a. acceleration   c. speed
    b. distance   d. velocity

20. What happens when two bowling balls simultaneously roll into a row of bowling balls that are at rest?
    a. The last ball moves out of the row.
    b. Two balls move out of the row.
    c. No change is observed.
    d. All the balls are set in motion.

Modified True-False Questions

In some of the following statements, the italicized term makes the statement incorrect. For each incorrect statement, in your notebook, write the term that must be substituted for the italicized term to make the statement correct. For each correct statement, write the word "true."

1. The distance traveled by an object in a unit of time is called *speed*. _____

2. The slowing of a car in a given time is called *velocity*. _____

3. Acceleration is the rate of change in *position*. _____

4. *Einstein* studied the motion of a metal ball down a ramp to learn about acceleration. _____

5. An object's resistance to a change in its motion is known as *inertia*. _____

6. The gravitational constant for acceleration *varies* for every object studied. _____

7. An object's *deceleration* is the product of its mass and velocity. _____

8. Newton's third law is also known as the law of *acceleration*. _____

9. Velocity is an example of a *scalar* quantity. _____

10. In a *vacuum*, all objects fall at the same rate. _____

TEST-TAKING TIP Be sure to include units of measurement in all answers involving quantities such as speed, velocity, and acceleration. Work through the calculations to make sure you obtain the correct units in your answer. If not, you may have arranged values incorrectly in your calculation.

Check Your Knowledge
Write the answer to each question in your notebook.

1. Define each of the following terms:
   a. motion   d. inertia
   b. velocity   e. momentum
   c. acceleration

2. Summarize Newton's three laws of motion.

3. Explain how a rocket engine lifts the vehicle.

4. Complete the chart to describe the motion of an object that falls from rest.

Time (s)	0	1	2	3	4	5	6
Acceleration (m/s^2)							
Velocity (m/s)							
Distance (m)							

Think Critically
Write the answer to each of the following questions in your notebook.

1. Compute the acceleration of a car that starts from rest and reaches a velocity of 60 kilometers per hour in 10 seconds.

2. A car, starting from rest, accelerates at 8 miles per hour per second. What is the velocity of the car at the end of 4 seconds?

3. a. A stone dropped from the top of a building strikes the ground in 10 seconds. Compute the height of the building in feet.
   b. What is the velocity of the stone at the end of the 7th second?

4. Find the acceleration of an object with a mass of 50 kilograms that is being acted on by an unbalanced force of 200 newtons.

5. A 10-gram bullet is fired from a 3000-gram rifle with a velocity of 60,000 centimeters per second. With what velocity does the rifle recoil?

Take It Further

1. You might be tempted to conclude that the acceleration of a falling object depends on mass, according to Newton's second law of motion. Because acceleration depends on both force and mass, however, the change in the force on a more massive object is offset by the change in mass. Learn more about this relationship and present your findings in the form of a poster or computerized presentation. You may wish to begin your research at the following sites: *http://www.physicsclassroom.com/ Class/newtlaws/U2L3e.cfm* and *http://www.vias.org/physics/bk1_ 05_01.html*.

2. Galileo and Newton concentrated on trying to describe events in the natural world mathematically. This differed substantially from Aristotle's attempts to explain why things happen in ways that could not be tested. Investigate each of these three thinkers, how they went about investigating the natural world, and what contributions they made to science. Write a brief summary of your findings.

CAREER

3. One career that uses a knowledge of forces and moving objects on a daily basis is an athletic trainer. Find out what an athletic trainer might do and what education would be required. You may wish to begin your search at the following sites: *http://www.mshealthcareers.com/ careers/athletictrainer.htm* and *http:// www.physicsdaily.com/physics/ Athletic_trainer*.

Glossary

A

absolute zero the temperature at which all molecular motion would cease; −273°C or 0 K

absorption spectrum a spectrum containing dark areas where particular wavelengths of light have been absorbed; each element has a characteristic absorption spectrum

acceleration the change in the velocity of an object divided by the time during which the change occurs

acid a substance whose water solution contains hydrogen ions

acid rain rainwater with a pH that is less than 7, often because the water contains the pollutant sulfuric acid, a result of burning coal

activation energy the energy required for a chemical reaction to begin

actual mechanical advantage the mechanical advantage of a real machine

adsorption a) the process by which solute molecules stick to a solid surface; b) the accumulation of different substances on the surface of the particles of a colloid

alcohol a hydrocarbon in which a hydrogen atom bonded to a carbon atom is replaced by a hydroxyl group (—OH)

alkane a saturated hydrocarbon

alkene an unsaturated hydrocarbon that contains at least one double bond between carbon atoms

alkyne an unsaturated hydrocarbon that contains at least one triple bond between carbon atoms

alnico magnet a powerful, artificial magnet made of aluminum, nickel, cobalt, and iron

alpha particle a helium nucleus, which consists of 2 protons and 2 neutrons

alternating current an electric current that reverses its direction at regular intervals

amino acid an organic acid in which an amino group (—NH$_2$) replaces an atom of hydrogen in the hydrocarbon molecule

ammeter a device that measures the rate of flow of electrons, or amperage, of an electric current

amperage the rate of flow of electrons

ampere the a rate of flow of one coulomb of electrons per second

amplitude the energy carried by a wave; represented by the distance between rest and the crest or trough of a wave; determines the loudness of a sound

analysis see *decomposition reaction*

angle of dip the angle between the magnetic field of Earth and the horizontal, measured by a dipping needle

angle of incidence the angle between the incident ray and the normal

angle of reflection the angle between the reflected ray and the normal

anode the positive electrode when electrons are put into a system; the negative electrode in a voltaic cell

Archimedes' principle the rule that explains that an object immersed in a liquid seems to lose the same amount of weight as the weight of the liquid that the object displaces

armature a bar that is free to move when an electromagnet is turned on and off

aromatic hydrocarbon an unsaturated hydrocarbon that has a ring structure

artificial light manufactured light, usually associated with electricity or burning fuel

artificial magnet a magnetic substance that does not occur naturally

atom the basic unit of matter

atomic energy energy derived from changes to the nucleus of atoms *atomic mass* the mass of a specific isotope of an element; the total mass of the protons and neutrons in the nucleus of an atom of an element

atomic number the number of protons in the nucleus of an atom of an element

atomic radius the distance between the outermost shell and the nucleus of an atom

average atomic mass average of the masses of the isotopes of an element

average velocity the total distance traveled by an object divided by the total time for the trip

B

barometer an instrument that measures air pressure

base a substance containing metal ions and hydroxide ions; releases hydroxide ions in solution

beam light composed of many parallel rays

beat a throbbing effect produced when sound waves of slightly differing frequencies alternately interfere and reinforce one another

Bernoulli's principle the idea that pressure exerted by a fluid in motion is less than that exerted by the same fluid at rest

beta particle a high-speed electron emitted from the nucleus during beta decay

betatron a particle accelerator that accelerates electrons

bimetallic strip a strip made up of two different metals fastened together

binary compound a compound that contains only two elements

blast furnace a chamber specially designed to remove iron from its ores and remove any impurities at the same time

boiling point the temperature at which a liquid begins to boil at sea level

Boyle's law the rule that describes that the volume of a gas varies inversely as the pressure on it, at a constant temperature

branching circuit a parallel circuit

bright-line spectrum a spectrum composed of several brightly colored, narrow lines separated by large dark spaces

British thermal unit the amount of heat needed to raise the temperature of one pound of water by 1°F

Brownian motion the zigzag movement of particles of a colloidal suspension observed through the high power of a microscope

brush metallic strip mounted so that each brush is always in contact with one of the commutator segments in an electric motor

buoyant force a force produced by the upward pressure of water that opposes the weight of an object and makes the object appear to lose weight

C

calorie the amount of heat needed to raise the temperature of 1 gram of liquid water by 1°C

Calorie a unit of caloric content of food, equal to 1000 calories

calorimeter a device that measures the quantity of heat gained or lost by a substance

carboxyl group—COOH

carrying medium a form of matter through which sound can travel

cast iron pig iron that has been melted and recooled

catalyst a substance that speeds the rate of a chemical reaction without itself being used up

cathode the negative electrode when electrons are put into a system; the positive electrode in a voltaic cell

caustic the description of a substance that is harmful to the skin

cellulose an organic substance that is the main component of wood

Celsius the temperature scale of the SI system on which water freezes at 0 degrees and boils at 100 degrees

center of gravity the point at which all the weight of an object appears to be concentrated; the point on which an object will balance

centrifugal center-fleeing

centrifugation the process of separating the particles of a suspension by spinning the suspension rapidly

centrifuge a device that separates particles from a suspension by spinning the suspension *centripetal* center-seeking

chain reaction a self-continuing nuclear reaction

chemical change a change that results in the formation of substances with properties that are different from the original substances; chemical reaction

chemical energy potential energy stored in the bonds that hold matter together

chemical equation a symbolic representation of a chemical reaction

chemical formula a shorthand notation that indicates the elements in a unit of a compound and the number of atoms of each element

chemical property property that relates to the way in which a substance reacts with other substances

chemical reaction a change that results in the formation of substances with properties that are different from the original substances; chemical change

chemical symbol a one or two-letter notation to represent a chemical element

chromatography a process for separating a mixture of solutes from a small quantity of solution

closed pipe a cylinder open at only one end

cloud chamber an apparatus designed to track and study radioactive particles

coagulation the addition of certain substances to a suspension to hasten sedimentation

coefficient a multiplier used in front of a chemical formula when balancing a chemical equation

collision theory the theory that explains that the more collisions that occur between reactant particles, the more likely a reaction is to occur

colloidal suspension a mixture of very finely divided solids in a liquid that do not settle on standing

combustibility the ability to burn

commutator metal ring, split into two halves, that is located on the shaft of the armature of an electric motor

component force a force that combines with one or more other forces to produce a resultant force

compound a substance composed of two or more elements united chemically

compound bar a bimetallic strip

compression the region where molecules of an elastic medium are crowded together

concave lens a lens that is thicker at the edges than in the middle

concave mirror a mirror that curves inward

concentrated the description of a solution containing a relatively large amount of solute in a given amount of solvent

concentration the amount of solute in a given quantity of solvent

conclusion a statement indicating whether or not a hypothesis was correct based on the data collected during an investigation

conductor a substance that allows heat or electricity to flow through it easily

conservation of momentum the law that states that the total momentum entering a system equals the total momentum leaving the system

continuous spectrum a spectrum in which the colors blend into each other without separations

control the part of an experiment that does not change

convection the transfer of heat in a fluid due to the motion of the liquid or gas itself

convection current a movement of fluid initiated as the warmer part rises and the cooler part sinks

converging lens a convex lens, so named because it converges parallel rays of light

convex lens a lens that is thicker in the middle than at the edges

convex mirror a mirror that curves outward

core in an electromagnet, a magnetic substance surrounded by a coil of wire

corrosion the weathering of metals that weakens and eventually destroys them

coulomb measure of the number of electrons flowing past a given point in a unit of time; 6.3×10^{18} electrons

covalent bonding the attraction between two atoms that takes place when the atoms share one or more electrons

crest the high point of a transverse wave

critical angle the angle of incidence at which a refracted light ray does not leave the original denser medium but, rather, travels along the boundary of the medium

current electricity a flow of electrical charges

cycle a) a complete trip by electrons back and forth in a circuit; b) a complete sound vibration consisting of a compression and rarefaction

cyclotron a particle accelerator that usually speeds up positively charged particles

D

Dalton's Atomic Theory an early theory of matter that suggested matter is composed of tiny particles called atoms, that atoms of elements differ from atoms of other elements, that atoms combine during chemical changes, and that atoms themselves do not change during chemical changes

data observations made during an experiment

deceleration a decrease in the velocity of a moving object

decomposition reaction a reaction in which a compound is broken down into two or more simpler substances

density the mass of a substance per unit of volume

dependent variable the variable that changes in response to changes in the independent, or manipulated variable.

desalinization distillation of seawater

deuterium an isotope of hydrogen that has one proton and one neutron in its nucleus

dial thermometer a bimetallic thermometer often used as an oven thermometer

difference of potential the condition that exists between a point of excess of electrons and a point of deficiency of electrons

diffracted spread out

diffraction grating a flat piece of transparent material on which thousands of parallel lines have been ruled for every square inch of surface

diffuse to move randomly in all directions

diffuse reflection reflection from a rough surface

dilute description of a solution containing relatively little solute in a given amount of solvent

dipping needle a device used to locate Earth's north and south magnetic poles

direct combination reaction a reaction in which two or more elements join to form a compound; also known as synthesis reaction

direct current a flow of electrons traveling in one direction in a circuit

direct-current generator a generator that produces a flow of electrons in one direction only

dispersion the splitting of light into a series of colors as it passes in and out of a medium

dissociation the formation of freely moving ions from ions that are bound in an ionic compound (as in salt, for example)

distillation the process of heating a liquid, collecting the vapor and cooling the vapor; solids remain behind

distilled water chemically pure water prepared by distillation

diverging lens a concave lens

domain a region within a material in which the magnetic fields of individual atoms are aligned

double bond the sharing of two pairs of electrons

double replacement reaction a reaction in which the metals present in two compounds change places to form two new compounds

dry cell a voltaic cell that does not contain liquid

ductility the ability of a metal, when heated, to be drawn into thin wires

E

echo a reflected sound

efficiency the effectiveness of a machine in multiplying effort, expressed as a percentage; efficiency = AMA/IMA × 100%

effort force the force exerted to move an object

elastic able to be stretched and then return to its original size

elasticity the property of matter that allows particles to return to their original positions after being moved apart by force *electrical circuit* a complete path of conductors through which electrons can flow

electrical energy energy of moving electrons

electricity a flow of electrons; electric current

electric motor a device that converts electrical energy into mechanical energy that can be used to do work

electrochemical cell a device that produces a steady flow of electric current by chemical means

electrode a charged piece of metal

electrolyte a compound whose water solution conducts electricity

electromagnet a temporary magnet created by inserting a magnetic substance into a coil of wire carrying current; can be turned on and off

electromagnetic energy energy carried by electromagnetic waves, which consist of electric and magnetic fields vibrating at right angles to one another

electromagnetic induction the production of an electric current by moving a magnet through a coil of wire, or by moving the coil back and forth between the poles of a magnet

electromagnetic spectrum the range of electromagnetic waves as ordered by wavelength and frequency

electromotive force the force created by a difference in potential that pushes electrons through a conductor

electron a negatively charged particle in an atom

electroscope a device used to detect the presence of a static electric charge

electrovalent bonding see *ionic bonding*

element a pure substance that cannot be broken down by ordinary means to any simpler substance

emulsifying agent a substance that, when added to an emulsion, causes the emulsion to become permanent

emulsion a suspension of two immiscible liquids

endothermic a process that absorbs energy

energy the ability to do work or cause change

energy level the energy associated with a given energy level, or orbit, in an atom

energy transformation a change from one form of energy to another

English system a system of measurement that uses the foot as the unit of length, the pound as the unit of weight, and the second as the unit of time

enzyme a catalyst that increases rates of reactions in living things

equilibrium the condition that exists when a set of balanced forces acts on an object but does not move it

ester a substance formed when an organic acid reacts chemically with an alcohol; most have a pleasant odor

excitation subjection of matter to heat or electrical energy

exothermic a process that releases energy

evaporation the process in which molecules in the liquid phase escape into the gas phase

F

Fahrenheit the temperature scale of the English system of measurement on which water freezes at 32 degrees and boils at 212 degrees

ferromagnetic description of a material attracted to a magnet

field magnet a permanent horseshoe magnet or a horseshoe electromagnet found in an electric motor

filtrate the liquid that passes through a filter during filtration

filtration the separation of the components of a suspension by passing the suspension through a porous solid

first-class lever a lever whose fulcrum is between the effort and the resistance

fixed pulley a pulley attached to a fixed point

fluid liquid or gas

focal length the distance between the center of a lens and the principal focus

foot-pound unit of work when force is measured in pounds and distance is measured in feet

force a push or a pull

forced vibration a vibration that is not at an elastic body's natural frequency *formula* a representation of the atoms present in a molecule of a compound and how many of each there are

formula mass the sum of all the atomic masses in a formula

fractional distillation the separation of the components of a liquid mixture by boiling and removal of distilled substances at a variety of boiling points

Fraunhofer lines the dark lines observed in the absorption spectrum of the sun

freezing point the temperature at which a liquid changes to a solid

frequency the number of vibrations that pass a given point in a unit of time

fulcrum a pivot

fundamental tone the main tone produced by all musical instruments when they play the same note

G

galvanized iron iron that has been coated with a thin layer of zinc

galvanometer an electric meter that measures tiny electric currents

gamma radiation high-frequency electromagnetic waves

gamma rays see *gamma radiation*

generator a device that produces electric current by means of electromagnetic induction

group a vertical column on the Periodic Table; also known as a family

half-life the time required for one-half of a given amount of radioactive element to change into another element

H

heat energy thermal energy transferred from one substance to another

heat of fusion the amount of heat that must be removed to change one gram of a liquid (at its freezing point) to a solid

heat of vaporization the amount of heat needed to change one gram of a liquid (at its boiling point) to a gas

hertz the SI unit of frequency equal to one cycle per second, Hz

heterogeneous nonuniform, not the same throughout

homogeneous uniform; the same throughout

horsepower a unit of power; 1 horsepower is equal to 550 foot-pounds of work done in one second

hydrocarbon organic compounds that contain only atoms of hydrogen and carbon

hydrolysis reaction a reaction of a salt and water to form an acid and a base

hydroxide a chemical compound that contains a hydroxyl group–OH; see *base*

hypothesis a possible answer to a question or a suggested solution to a problem

I

ideal machine a theoretical machine that is completely frictionless

ideal mechanical advantage the mechanical advantage of an ideal machine

illuminated lit by reflected light

immiscible unable to be mixed

incident ray the light ray that strikes a surface

inclined plane a machine used to slide an object from one level to a higher level without actually lifting the object; a ramp

independent variable the variable that is changed in order to observe what happens to the dependent variable; also known as manipulated variable

indicator a substance that changes color in the presence of an acid or a base

induction a method of magnetizing a substance by bringing a magnet near a magnetic substance but not allowing the two substances to touch; see also *electromagnetic induction*

inert description of an element that does not react with other elements

inference a statement based on a series of observations

infrared ray electromagnetic wave with a wavelength that is just longer than that of red light

insulator a material that resists the passage of electrons or heat through it

interference the weakening of sound as the frequencies of the two vibrating bodies cancel each other

ion the structure formed when an atom gains or loses electrons

ion exchange reaction see *double replacement reaction*

ionic bonding force of attraction between two atoms that takes place when electrons are transferred from one atom to the other

ionization the formation of freely moving ions

ionizing ray alpha particle, beta particle, or gamma ray

irregular solid an object whose sides are not uniform; examples include a rock and a crown

isomer a form of an organic compound that has the same molecular formula as one or more other forms of the compound, but a different structural formula; the properties of isomers usually differ from one another

isotope a form of an element that has the same atomic number as other forms of the element but a different atomic mass due to a different number of neutrons

K

Kelvin scale a temperature scale based on absolute temperatures; 0 K is absolute zero

kinetic energy the energy possessed by a body in motion

kinetic-molecular theory the idea that molecules of matter are in constant motion

L

larynx the organ in the neck, sometimes known as the Adam's apple, through which air passes and sounds are made

laser a concentrated light beam that consists of one specific wavelength

law of acceleration the law that states that the acceleration of an object depends on the ratio of the acting force to the mass of the body

law of action and reaction the law that states that whenever an object exerts a force on a second object, the second object exerts an equal and opposite force on the first

law of conservation of energy the law that states that energy can neither be created nor destroyed, but can be transformed from one form to another

law of conservation of mass the law that states that although matter may change form, it cannot be created or destroyed so the total amount of mass stays the same

law of conservation of matter and energy the law that states that matter and energy are interchangeable, and therefore the total amount of matter and energy in the universe remains constant

law of definite proportions the law that states that elements always combine with one another in definite proportions by mass

law of electrical attraction and repulsion the law that states that opposite electric charges attract each other; like electric charges repel each other

law of flotation the law that states that a floating object displaces a weight of liquid equal to its own weight

law of inertia the law that states that a body at rest tends to remain at rest, and a body in motion tends to remain in motion in a straight line, unless the body is acted on by an unbalanced force

law of machines the law that states that the work output equals the work input for any simple machine

law of magnetic poles the law that states that like poles of magnets repel each other, whereas unlike poles of magnets attract each other

law of moments the law that states that when the clockwise and counter-clockwise moments of force are equal, an object on a fulcrum does not rotate

law of reflection the law that states that when light strikes a mirror at an angle, the angle of incidence is equal to the angle of reflection

law of refraction the law that states that a light ray passing at an oblique angle from a less dense medium into a more dense medium bends toward the normal; a light ray passing at an oblique angle from a more dense medium into a less dense medium bends away from the normal

left-hand rule a method of determining the north pole of an electromagnet by wrapping the four fingers of your left hand around a coil of wire so that the fingers are pointing in the direction of electron flow, your extended left thumb will point to the north pole

length the distance between two points

lens a thin disk of transparent material whose opposite sides are smooth, curved surfaces

lever a rigid bar that can turn about a fulcrum

lift the upward force created by the difference in air pressure above and below an airplane wing that raises the airplane from the ground

light energy a visible form of electromagnetic energy

lightning a tremendous static electric discharge between clouds, or between clouds and the ground

limewater a water solution of calcium hydroxide

lines of force imaginary lines that form closed arcs around a magnet and that indicate the strength of the magnetic field

load an appliance connected to an electrical circuit

lodestone a naturally magnetic rock that contains the ore magnetite

longitudinal wave a wave in which vibrating particles move parallel to the path taken by the wave

luminous lit by its own light

luster shininess; a property commonly associated with metals

M

machine a device that makes it easier to do work by magnifying force or distance, or changing direction of the effort force

magnetic description of a material that creates a magnetic field

magnetic declination the angle made by lines drawn from an observer to the magnetic and geographic north poles

magnetic field the force exerted in the region around a magnet

magnetic permeability the effect of placing magnetic objects within the lines of force of a magnet

magnetic pole parts of a magnet where the magnetic effects are strongest

magnetism the ability of a substance to attract certain materials, such as iron

magnetite a natural, magnetic iron ore

magnitude size or amount

malleability the ability of a metal to be flattened into thin sheets without shattering or crumbling

mass the amount of matter in an object; a measure of an object's inertia

mass number the total number of protons and neutrons in an atom

matter anything that has mass and volume

mechanical advantage the number of times a machine multiplies an effort

mechanical energy the potential and kinetic energy of an object

melting point the temperature at which a solid starts to melt; same temperature as the freezing point

metal an element that has the properties of luster, ductility, and malleability

metalloid an element with properties sometimes resembling metals and sometimes resembling nonmetals

metallurgy the process of extracting metals from their ores

metric system a system of measurement that uses the meter as the unit of length, the kilogram as the unit of mass, and the second as the unit of time; a subset of the SI system of measurement

microwaves electromagnetic waves with long wavelengths and frequencies between 10^9 and 10^{12} hertz

mineral acid an acid that can be prepared from naturally occurring compounds called minerals

minerals chemical compounds found in rocks

mixture two or more substances (elements, compounds, or both) that are combined but not chemically joined

molecule two or more atoms combined chemically

moment of force the tendency of a force to produce rotation of an object

momentum the product of an object's mass and velocity

motion a change in position of an object relative to a body assumed to be at rest

movable pulley a pulley attached to a resistance and able to move with the resistance

musical tones sounds produced by regular vibrations of an object

mutation a change in the heredity information of a cell

N

natural light light formed in nature, such as the light that comes from the sun or other stars

natural magnet a magnetic substance that occurs naturally, like lodestone

negative terminal the terminal (or prong in a plug) that has an excess of electrons

neutral a) neither acid nor base; b) having no net electrical charge

neutralization reaction a reaction between an acid and a base to form a salt and water

neutron atomic particle with the same mass as a proton but with no electrical charge

newton standard unit of force in the SI system

newton-meter unit of work when force is measured in newtons and distance is measured in meters

noble gas an element that has its outermost shell filled to capacity and is therefore unlikely to react with other elements

noise sounds produced by irregular vibrations of an object

nonelectrolyte a compound whose water solution does not conduct electricity

nonmagnetic description of a material that is not attracted to a magnet

nonmetal an element that does not have the properties of luster, ductility, and malleability, but is instead dull and brittle

nonuniform a heterogeneous mixture; not the same throughout

normal a line drawn at a right angle to a surface

north pole one of two regions of a magnet where the magnetic effect is strongest

nuclear energy energy released by the fission or fusion of atomic nuclei

nuclear equation a chemical equation that shows changes in the atomic number and atomic mass of the atoms involved

nuclear fission the splitting of a nucleus with the release of nuclear energy

nuclear fusion the combination of the nuclei of two light atoms to produce a nucleus of a heavier atom with the release of nuclear energy

nuclear reactor a device designed for controlled nuclear chain reactions

nucleon any particle found in an atom's nucleus

nucleus the small region at the center of an atom where protons and neutrons are found

neutron a neutral particle located in the center, or nucleus, of an atom

O

observation information gathered by using the senses

ohm unit of electrical resistance, Ω

ohmmeter a device that measures electrical resistance

Ohm's law law that states that current is directly related to voltage and inversely related to resistance; current $= \dfrac{\text{voltage}}{\text{resistance}}$

opaque description of a material that does not allow light to pass through

open-hearth process a common method of making steel

open pipe a cylinder open at both ends

optical density a measure of the closeness of molecules in a medium

optical disk a device used to demonstrate the law of reflection

orbit the path of an electron

ore a mineral containing enough metal to be extracted profitably

ore concentration the removal of some of the impurities from an ore

organic acid a hydrocarbon in which a hydrogen atom bonded to a carbon atom is replaced by a carboxyl group (—COOH)

organic chemistry the study of carbon compounds

organic compound originally, chemicals that came from living things; now, simply carbon compounds

overtone complex vibration, produced because of the material an instrument is made of, that gives the instrument its particular quality

oxygen top-blowing process a common method of making steel

P

paper chromatography a separation technique based on the ability of some solutes to stick to molecules on the surface of a piece of porous paper

parallel circuit a circuit in which electrons flow through more than one path or branch

parallel forces forces that act together along parallel lines at different points on the same object

parallelogram of force a method for finding the resultant when two forces act at an angle less than 180° to each other

particle accelerator a device designed to shoot particles at great speed toward atoms; the atoms break apart and release subatomic particles

Pascal's law the law that states that pressure acts equally in all directions

penumbra the lighter part of a shadow that surrounds the umbra

period a horizontal row on the Periodic Table

periodicity the repeating pattern of properties among elements when arranged in order of atomic number in the Periodic Table

permanent magnet a magnetized substance that remains a magnet for a long time

pH scale method of measuring the pH of substances on a scale from 0 to 14; 0 is very acidic, 7 is neutral, 14 is very basic

phase form, or state, of matter; the three main phases of matter are solid, liquid, and gas

phenolphthalein a common indicator used to detect the presence of a base

photon packet of energy

photosynthesis a complex chemical process in plants that requires light and produces oxygen and sugars

physical change a change in which the identity of a substance is not altered

physical property characteristics of matter that can be observed without changing the chemical nature of the substance

pickling the use of sulfuric acid to remove surface oxide layers on metals before the metals are coated with materials that prevent rusting

pig iron iron obtained from a blast furnace

pitch a) the highness or lowness of a musical note; b) the distance between two successive ridges, or threads, of a screw

pitchblende a uranium ore

plasma a fourth phase of matter in which atoms break apart

plumb line the line formed when a mass attached to a string is used to determine the center of mass of an object

polarized light light waves that vibrate in a single plane (direction)

polarizer a crystal that produces polarized light

Polaroid an artificial material that acts as a polarizer

pole one end of a magnet

polyatomic ion a group of atoms that behaves as if it were one charged atom

positive terminal the terminal (or prong in a plug) that has a deficiency of electrons

potential energy stored energy as a result of position or condition

pound standard unit of force in the English system

power the speed, or rate, of doing work

precipitate an insoluble substance formed as a product of a reaction

pressure the amount of force exerted by a substance on a given unit of area

primary coil that part of a transformer that becomes an alternating electromagnet because the original voltage flows through the coil

principal axis a line, normal to the curved surface, that passes through the center of a lens

principal energy level one of the energy levels in which electrons orbit the nucleus of an atom

principal focus the point behind a convex lens where light rays converge

procedure the steps followed during a scientific investigation

product a substance that is produced during a chemical reaction

protein a complex organic molecule made up of amino acids

protium common hydrogen, having one proton but no neutrons in its nucleus

proton a positively-charged particle found in the nucleus of an atom

pulley a grooved wheel that can turn within a frame

Q

quality the property of an instrument that identifies it as different from another instrument playing the same note

quanta packets of energy

quantum theory a theory that explains the nature and behavior of light in terms of the movement of electrons within atoms

R

radiation the transfer of energy by means of waves

radioactive description of a substance that emits particles or energy from the nucleus in order to become stable

radioactive dating the use of radioisotopes with long half-lives to determine the age of ancient objects

radioactive decay the change in an unstable isotope as it emits radiation and becomes another element that has a lower atomic mass, different atomic number, or both

radioisotopes unstable radioactive isotopes

rarefaction the region of an elastic medium where molecules are spread apart

rate of reaction the speed at which a chemical reaction takes place

reactant a substance that enters into in a chemical reaction

reactive description of an atom that combines readily with other atoms

Reactivity Series of the Metals a list of metals in decreasing order of reactivity

real image an image formed by actual rays of light

receiver the earphone of the telephone

rectangular solid an object that consists of six faces that meet one another at right angles; examples include a book and an ice cube

reduction reaction a type of reaction in which oxygen is removed from a compound

reducing agent a substance that can remove oxygen from an oxide ore (or reduce the ore)

reflected ray the light ray that bounces off a surface

refraction the bending of light rays as they pass from one medium to another at an oblique angle

regular reflection reflection from a smooth, flat surface

replacement reaction a reaction in which a more reactive metal replaces a less reactive metal in a compound

resistance any part of an electrical circuit that opposes the flow of electrons

resistance force the force that the effort force overcomes in moving an object

resistance thermometer an instrument based on the principle that the resistance of a wire changes with temperature; resistance thermometers are used to measure high temperatures

resonance the property by which a vibrating object, near or touching an elastic body, can cause the elastic body to vibrate

resonant cavities openings formed by the base and roof of the mouth, by the larynx, or by the nose that affect the production of sound

resultant a single force that results from a combination of forces

roasting the conversion of a compound to an oxide by heating it in air

rust the product of a reaction between iron and oxygen in the presence of moisture

S

salt a compound composed of one or more metals and one or more nonmetals

saturated compound an organic compound in which the carbon atoms form only single bonds with each other

saturated solution one in which the solvent has dissolved as much solute as it can hold at a given temperature

scalar quantity a measurement of an amount or a magnitude only

science a body of knowledge about the natural world as well as the process through which that knowledge is obtained

scientific inquiry the process through which scientists ask questions about the natural world and seek answers to those questions

scientific knowledge knowledge based on observation and reasoning

scientific method a logical and systematic approach to problem solving

screw an inclined plane wrapped around a cylinder or center rod

secondary coil that part of a transformer where a voltage is induced

second-class lever a lever whose resistance is between the effort and the fulcrum

sedimentation the settling of solid particles from a suspension

series circuit a circuit in which the electrons flow along a single path

shadow the dark space formed behind an opaque object when illuminated

shell in Bohr model, a location surrounding the nucleus and at a fixed distance from it where a specific maximum number of electrons can exist

shunt a bar of metal offering low resistance to the flow of electrons that is used in an ammeter

single replacement reaction a reaction in which one element reacts with one compound to form another element and another compound

slip ring one of two metal rings mounted on the same shaft as the armature in a generator

solubility curve a graph showing how much of a given solute dissolves in water at different temperatures

solute the substance that is dissolved in a solution

solution a mixture in which one substance dissolves in another to form a uniform system

solvent the substance that does the dissolving in a solution

sonar a device that detects underwater objects by timing the echo of a sound wave

sound barrier a giant compression formed as sound waves from a moving airplane pile up and reinforce themselves

south pole one of two regions of a magnet where the magnetic effect is strongest

specific heat the quantity of heat needed to raise the temperature of 1 gram of a substance by 1°C

spectroscope a device containing a prism or a diffraction grating that disperses light and forms a spectrum

spectrum the rainbowlike band of color observed when white light is dispersed

speed a scalar quantity that indicates the distance traveled by an object in a unit of time

spring scale a device used to measure force by stretching a spring

stable description of an atom that is less reactive than others

stable equilibrium an equilibrium that is not easily upset

static electricity the buildup of electric charges that do not flow in a current

step-down transformer a transformer in which the secondary coil has fewer turns of wire and, therefore, will have a lower induced voltage than the primary coil

step-up transformer a. transformer in which the secondary coil has more turns of wire and, therefore, will have a greater induced voltage than the primary coil

structural formula a representation of a molecule that shows the number of atoms as well as the way they are arranged

subatomic the description of a particle located within an atom

subscript a number written below and to the right of chemical symbols in a formula to indicate how many atoms of the element are present in a molecule of the compound

substance any sample of matter that is homogeneous and has a unique set of properties

supersaturated solution one in which the solvent holds more solute than it normally can at a given temperature

suspension a nonuniform (heterogeneous) mixture of solid particles in a liquid

synchrotron similar to a cyclotron, this particle accelerator controls the path of accelerated particles better and imparts greater energy to them

synthesis see *direct combination reaction*

T

telephone a device that utilizes an electromagnet to communicate by voice

temporary magnet a magnetized substance that does not remain magnetic for very long

temperature a measure of how hot or cold something is; the average kinetic energy of the particles in a sample of matter

ternary compound a compound that contains three elements

theory of electrolytic dissociation the theory that states that charged particles are formed when certain compounds are dissolved in water

thermal energy the total kinetic energy of the particles of a substance

thermometer an instrument used to measure temperature

thermostat a device containing a bimetallic strip that regulates a heating and cooling system

third-class lever a lever whose effort is between the resistance and the fulcrum

theory a detailed explanation of large bodies of information

thunder a loud sound produced by the sudden expansion of air heated by a lightning bolt

tincture a solution in which alcohol is the solvent

torque see *moment of force*

total internal reflection the reflection of a light ray by the surface of the medium it is in that occurs when the angle of incidence of the ray is greater than the critical angle

tracer a radioisotope whose chemical pathway in the body can be followed with a radioactivity detector

transformer a device designed to change the voltage produced by a power company for use in the home and in industry

translucent description of a material that partially lets light pass through

transmitter the mouthpiece of a telephone

transmutation the transformation of one element into another through radioactive decay

transparent description of a substance that readily lets light pass through

transverse wave a wave in which the vibrating particles move at right angles to the path taken by the wave

triple bond the sharing of three pairs of electrons

tritium an isotope of hydrogen that has one proton and two neutrons in its nucleus

trough the low point of a transverse wave

Tyndall effect the reflection of a beam of light as it passes through a suspension

U

ultrasonic longitudinal vibrations above 20,000 per second

ultraviolet rays electromagnetic waves somewhat shorter than those of violet light

umbra the darker central portion of a shadow

uniform circular motion the motion exhibited by an object moving at a constant speed along a curved path of constant radius

universal solvent water (because it dissolves so many substances)

unpolarized vibrating in all directions

unsaturated compound an organic compound in which the carbon atoms form one or more double or triple bonds

unsaturated solution a solution in which the solvent can dissolve more solute at the same temperature

unstable equilibrium an equilibrium that is easily upset

V

vacuum the absence of matter

valence electron an electron in the outermost shell of an atom, which can be gained, lost, or shared with another atom

valence number the number of electrons an atom may lose, gain, or share

valence shell the outermost shell of a neutral atom

variable a part of an experiment that is changed in some way

vector quantity a measurement of an amount or magnitude that also has a direction

vector arrow used to represent the magnitude and direction of a force

velocity a vector quantity that indicates the speed and direction of an object

verify to confirm or support a hypothesis

vibration a back-and-forth movement

virtual focus the principal focus of a concave lens

virtual image an imaginary image formed by the extension of rays of light

vocal cords vibrating membranes that help produce human speech

volt unit of electromotive force, V

voltage the electromotive force

voltaic cell an electrochemical cell

voltmeter a device that measures the voltage in an electrical circuit

volume the amount of space an object takes up

W

watt unit of power equal to one newton-meter of work done in one second

wave a disturbance spreading out in all directions

wavelength the distance between two successive compressions or rarefactions

wedge a modified, or double, inclined plane

wet cell a type of voltaic cell containing liquid

wheel-and-axle a large and small wheel (axle) firmly connected so that they turn together about the same center point (axis)

word equation a representation of a chemical reaction using the names of the reactants and products

work the force exerted on an object times the distance by which the object moves as a result of the force

work input the actual work put into a machine

work output the actual work accomplished by using a machine

wrought iron cast iron with carbon and sulfur impurities removed

Index

Photo Credits

Chapter 1: Scientist performing an experiment © Rudyanto Wijaya; **Figure 1-11:** Prototype electric car © B.S.P.I./Corbis; **Chapter 2:** Spools of copper wire © syagci; **Figure 2-5:** Compact florescent lightbulb © Alan Chao; **Chapter 3:** Fruits and vegetables © Denis Pepin; **Chapter 4:** Atom © Mike Agliolo/Corbis; **Chapter 5:** Fireworks © Ruslan Gilmanshin; **Chapter 6:** Sugar collection © Ingrid Heczko; **Figure 6-3:** Chef adding ingredients © Willard Culver/National Geographic Society/Corbis; **Chapter 7:** DNA double helix © Denis Scott/Corbis; **Figure 7-11:** Footprints in sand © moodboard/Corbis; **Chapter 8:** Icicle melting, rotofrank; **Chapter 9:** Flaming propane bubble demonstration, Boomer Jerritt; **Chapter 10:** Bronze bull, EIGHTFISH; **Figure 10-7:** Gold mining scar © Martin Harvey/Corbis; **Chapter 11:** Limestone cave, Jami Tarris Max; **Chapter 12:** Ray of light in forest, Picavet; **Chapter 13:** Salt truck © Geórge Disario/Corbis; **Figure 13-9:** Oil spill © Cheryl Gerber/Corbis; **Chapter 14:** Mono Lake tufa formations © Chris Cheadle/All Canada Photos/Corbis; **Figure 14-8:** Acid rain damaged trees, David Woodfall; **Chapter 15:** Rollercoaster © Scott Stuart; **Figure 15-11:** Nuclear power station ©John_Woodcock; **Chapter 16:** Lightning © Adrian Jan Haeringer; **Chapter 17:** Old compasses © José Luis Gutiérrez; **Chapter 18:** Electromagnetic Crane © Malcolm Lubliner/Corbis; **Chapter 19:** Thermogram of a hand © Scientifica/Visuals Unlimited/Corbis; **Chapter 20:** High school orchestra © Hill Street Studios/Blend Images/Corbis; **Chapter 21:** Sunrise, Piero Camiani; **Figure 21-17:** Woman talking on cell phone © WIN-Images/Corbis; **Chapter 22:** Fiber optics © Mayumi Terao; **Figure 22-27:** Sunscreen © Denise Bush; **Chapter 23:** Nuclear fuel rods © Maria Arkhipova; **Figure 23-9:** Spent nuclear fuel storage tank © Roger Ressmeyer/Corbis; **Chapter 24:** Woman kicking soccer ball, Erik Isakson; **Chapter 25:** Gears in a clock © Anton Marinescu; **Figure 25-11:** Nanobots in the blood, Science Picture Co.; **Chapter 26:** Jet in flight, Tim Kiusalaas; **Chapter 27:** Stages of a figure-skating jump, Robert Decelis, Ltd.